FORECASTING
ON YOUR
MICROCOMPUTER

BY DANIEL B. NICKELL

TAB BOOKS Inc.
BLUE RIDGE SUMMIT, PA 17214

To Daniel I. Elder

FIRST EDITION
FIRST PRINTING

Copyright © 1983 by TAB BOOKS Inc.
Printed in the United States of America

Library of Congress Cataloging in Publication Data

Nickell, Daniel B.
Forecasting on your microcomputer.

Bibliography: p.
Includes index.
1. Forecasting—Data processing. I. Title.
CB158.N5   1983   303.4'9'0285   83-4899
ISBN 0-8306-0107-4
ISBN 0-8306-0607-6 (pbk.)

Contents

Acknowledgments

I wish to extend a heartfelt thanks to everyone who has assisted me in the preparation of this book, especially Mary Boblitz for the monumental task of typing the various drafts and to Jan Greene for the cover photographic work. "Last, but not least," my gratitude goes to those loving and understanding friends and family who have been so patient with me for the better part of the last year during the writing of this book.

Introduction

A famous mentalist used to open his program by saying: "We are all interested in the future because that is where we are going to spend the rest of our lives." The function of scientific forecasting is to provide a rational and acceptable basis for what we believe the future holds for us.

The purpose of this book is to help a wide range of readers use a microcomputer in the process of formulating forecasts over a fairly broad range of human interests. The definition of the average reader of this book is rather difficult to state meaningfully. I purposefully did not write it specifically for stock brokers, math teachers, child prodigies, business planners, or any other group likely to have a vested interest in forecasting. Rather, I wrote it as a resource book for each of the foregoing, as well as for others that might have an interest in some aspect of the subject. There is a section of particular interest to one tracking the stock market or similar data sets. For the amateur astronomer, there is a section that provides some useful routines for computing planetary positions and related information. The gambler in us will find some satisfaction in the section on random events in which an effort is made to put some order into chaos.

In the book are some 94 programs (all in BASIC), which illustrate or support one aspect of forecasting or another. Although some of them are obviously demonstration routines, many of them are intended mainly as utilities to be embedded in programs of your own making. Finally, there are several long programs that present some rather useful analysis of variance (ANOVA), multiple correlation, and tabular computation routines that stand on their own merits.

While this book doesn't presume to address the interests of the youngest or the most sophisticated of computer programmers, it is hoped to reach and be of use to the general population of computer users.

A LITTLE ABOUT THE BOOK

The material in this book is grouped into four main divisions: fundamentals, techniques, applications, and dispositions. Each division consists of two or more chapters. Each chapter contains a main body of information, including related programs and examples; several exercises or questions on the chapter's material; and suggested reading.

Fundamentals

In this section I attempt to cover the numerical and mathematical foundations for modern forecasting and to describe the nature, applications, and limitations of modern forecasting. This division attempts to convey the notion that forecasts vary considerably in their reliability, depending on a number of factors including the quality of the data base. Reliable forecasting requires rationally chosen, accurate data that are appropriately quantified. The types of data, scales, and measures that are used to quantify data are examined. Also presented are the dichotomous concepts of absolute and relative scales, parametric and nonparametric data, and continuous and discrete distributions. It is in this section that I provide you with the tools with which to do a descriptive analysis of a set of data and to compute the probabilities of a variety of conditions. The division also includes a primer on data base management, with an emphasis on data bases suitable for microcomputers. I conclude with a few words on the prudent choice of techniques with which to do accurate forecasting.

Techniques

This book presents four basic families of forecasting techniques: correlation and regression analysis, time-series analysis, modeling and simulations, and numerical techniques. Correlation and regression analysis attempts to fit a smoothed curve through available data, assuming the future data will continue to follow the smoothed curve. Time series analysis assumes that the data found are functions of the passage of time. Curve-fitting routines, in time-functional data, often lead to rather bizarre unnecessary shapes and equations. Time-series equations, on the other hand, concentrate on the state of the data at given instants. Modeling a problem is frequently the easiest way to forecast the state of a complex system after a number of operations or periods of time. Closely

related to modeling is creating simulations. The distinctions between the terms is so vague that I am likely to use them interchangeably. Conceptually, a model is thought of as a representation of a real or proposed thing or system (such as an oil factory), whereas a simulation may be used to reflect a less specifically organized set of objects (such as a simulation of waterflow through a swamp land) in which arbitrary starting values are assigned. Numerical analysis is sort of a coverall for all the other miscellaneous techniques that can be used in attempts to fit some sort of conceptual model against the real world. For example, we are given the problem of a lost person in the Arctic. We know where he started and that he appears to be moving clockwise in a circular fashion (it is snowing and drifts often block out the trail) except that the radius of revolutions is increasing. None of the first three techniques will lead quickly to a satisfactory solution. However, by simply fitting one of the spirals of Archimedes noted in Chapter 8, the appropriate search pattern can be developed and the current, most likely location forecast.

Applications

Examples from seven basic areas of human interest in which forecasting techniques can be applied are presented. In addition, there is a brief chapter on miscellaneous techniques that were not otherwise classifiable. It was with a great deal of humility that I undertook these chapters and with an even greater sense of humility that I presumed to finish them. While they each come from some area of my personal and professional experiences, the requisite research to prepare the text led me back into broad domains of human knowledge the vastness of which I had forgotten in my haste to keep pace with the present. Behind each chapter stands several thousands of years of specialized scientific inquiry, which has been cataloged, analyzed, digested and disseminated by hundreds of thousands of scholars—better than eighty percent of them alive since the year 1800AD. In translating their concepts into microcomputer BASIC I hope we have been faithful to the true and underlying concepts.

Dispositions

Many forecasts fail to be implemented due to a misconception, often on the part of the forecaster, as to what to do with the "bottom line" data. In this division the different ways scientific data can be displayed effectively to non-scientific people are illustrated. I also offer some techniques, using the microcomputer, or using results from forecasting efforts to reach meaningful decisions.

The Programs

Listings will always include the complete program written in BASIC. There are short routines that you can simply type in to see what it is I am talking about. There are long programs that do a number of functions. The intent of these longer program listings is to provide complete programs, which you can use intact or from which you can borrow subroutines for other applications. In some instances, I use a technique used by a major retail outlet: I offer a good routine, a better routine, and a best routine. With the longer, more complex programs I also include flowcharts of the program and, if needed, additional documentation showing line references and variable names.

Most of the chapters also include exercises. These are intended to be used either to check your programming skills and understanding of the material just presented or to check student progress in a computer applications course in which this book is used as a text or reference source.

The language used in the book is the Radio Shack TRS-80 Level II version of BASIC. With two exceptions, I have used a programming technique and a dialect of BASIC that is as standard as possible so that most of the programs will run as written on the other leading systems. The first exception is the use of the DEF FN command to define a subroutine used frequently. If your computer does not support this command, you can replace it at each occurrence, for example, $X = FNM$, with a GOSUB command in which the subroutine performs the same function.

The second exception is that in programs requiring intensive data base support, I have used the Exatron Stringy Floppy (ESF) command vocabulary. With minor modifications, those of you who have disk drive systems can make the necessary adjustments to get the programs to run under most versions of DOS. These are the most important changes:

Exatron	Disk (TRSDOS)
@ CLOSE	CLOSE
@ CLOSE b	CLOSE b
@ PRINT A$	PRINT#b, A$
@ INPUT A$	INPUT#b, A$
@ OPEN	OPEN"O",b,file spec.
	for output files, or
	OPEN"I",b,file spec.
	for input files.

where b is the designated buffer.

Refer to Appendix A for further information on the Exatron system.

In brief, this book attempts to define what the forecast process is and what the underlying mathematical principles are, to illustrate ways forecasting has been accomplished in the past, and to suggest what to do with a forecast once it's made. By definition, analogy, example, and actual data resources, I attempt to equip the conscientious reader with a basic forecasting toolkit.

NOTE: Most of the programs in this book are written to be used with a printer. If you do not want to print the output of any of these programs, delete all LPRINT statements from them. If there is no printer connected and you do not delete these statements, the programs will not function and no error message will appear.

Chapter 1

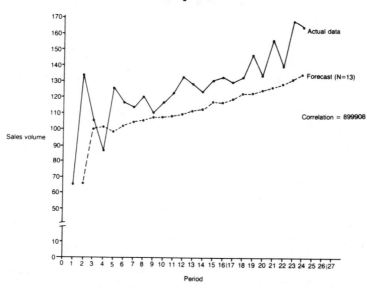

Sales volume

Period

Actual data

Forecast (N=13)

Correlation = 899908

Forecasting Philosophies

Forecasting is an art that exploits science in an effort to identify future events or conditions. Later in this book we will stress the necessity for obtaining as much precise data as possible and emphasize the role of mathematics in forecasting. Nonetheless, forecasting remains an art. For virtually every project, the data available for the solution of the problem exceeds both the memory capacity of our computers and the time allotted to reach a forecast; we must artfully select a sample from the data and forecast from that.

SELECTING DATA SETS

While there are techniques, which will be described herein, that help in the process of selecting the more appropriate data sets, there is no practical way of knowing that the best data and only the best data have been chosen for processing. The quality of the forecast is directly related to the quality of the input data we elect to use. It is very much like the computing maxim: "garbage in—garbage out." If we select relevant data sets and use appropriate

processing techniques, our forecasts will be as responsible as anyone could expect. In preparing a weather forecast, for example, we would probably want to consult historic weather records for the area of coverage, current temperatures, humidity, and wind direction. According to some weather forecasting techniques, we may even want to determine the current sunspot condition. On the other hand, we have no reason to believe any of these data bases would have any utility in the forecasting of future gold prices. The dividing line between the merely good and the truly great forecasters is drawn according to the skill of the forecaster in selecting data bases that will lead consistently to accurate predictions.

Why can't we just crank in all the data bases and pick out the best predictors? In the first place, the volume of data available in the world at any given moment, even in the available, processable form, is tremendous. For one person to attempt to enter even a fraction of some of these data bases into a microcomputer would be an undertaking of several lifetimes. Secondly, assuming we had some sort of device which could handle all of these data for us, the processing needed to determine the most appropriate sets to use quickly becomes unmanageable. Given N sets of data, the number of unique combinations or *permutations* of these sets taken R sets at a time is given by the equation

$$P = \frac{N!}{R! \, (N\text{-}R)!}$$

N! is an expression which means "N factorial" and is computed by N! × 1 × 2 × 3 × 4 . . . . × N. For example, if we have 10 people and 6 chairs, we compute the number of unique permutations of seating 10 people, 6 at a time, as

$$P = \frac{10!}{6!(10-6)!} = \frac{3628800}{720 \times 24} = 210.$$

There are 210 ways to seat 10 people 6 at a time without repeating any possible combination. If we have 10 data bases, there are 252 unique ways we can test the utility of them taking them 4 at a time. But, to check out the utility of the data bases properly, we first need to check them one at a time. This requires 10 evaluations, one at a time, then 45 evaluations doing 2 at a time, 120 evaluations with 3 at a time, and so forth. To check all possible permutations, from 1 to N sets at a time, requires $2^N - 1$ evaluations. In the case of 10 data sets, there must be at least 1023 evaluations. Adding just one data set, making the total, N, 11, doubles the number of evaluations required: $2^{11} - 1 = 2047$. The 1975 *Statistical Abstract of the United States* offers well over 1400 tables of data. To evaluate just these tables, even with very fast microcomputers using optimum programs, would require thousands of years of processing. The working forecaster, of course, rejects such an approach and, by some intuitive process, selects perhaps two or three tables from which to compute a prediction. It is for this reason that forecasting is as much an art as a science.

THE QUALIFICATIONS OF A FORECASTER

The difficulties and complexities just alluded to notwithstanding, it appears that forecasting is a skill or craft a number of so-called laymen can master. A few years ago a study was conducted to determine, among other things, the impact of training and experience on the accuracy of forecasts. The initial hypothesis was that as the experience or training level of a given forecaster increased, there would be a corresponding increase in the accuracy of his or her forecasts. It was anticipated that the graph of the accuracy/experience table would appear very much like that in Fig. 1-1:

Interestingly, however, the data obtained in the study failed to support the hypothesis. Instead, the data suggested that almost anyone with average intelligence and reasonable judgement can become an effective forecaster. The actual relationship between accuracy and training are illustrated in Fig. 1-2:

The implications are clear. You don't necessarily need to have a Ph.D in economics to do financial forecasting, nor do you need advanced degrees in political science to make useful contributions in voter preference studies.

One explanation of the unusual outcome of the study is that the future is really the composite outcome of such a multitude of factors that, beyond a certain level, the precise computations of the highly trained and expensively equipped add little over common sense and a more generalized approach to a problem. With reasonable technical preparation and modest computing gear (such as microcomputers), you can become a very credible forecaster.

The point here is to encourage you to tackle forecasting seriously and not to be intimidated by a shortfall in formal training or professional credentials. The forecaster's best credential is a demonstrated forecasting accuracy.

PRECISION IN FORECASTING

It is best to avoid the lure of the double-precision mathematics capabilities of most of the current microcomputers. There is no point in computing to 16 decimal places data that are meaningful to only three or four. Curve-fitting routines, for example, lead to equations that generate smooth

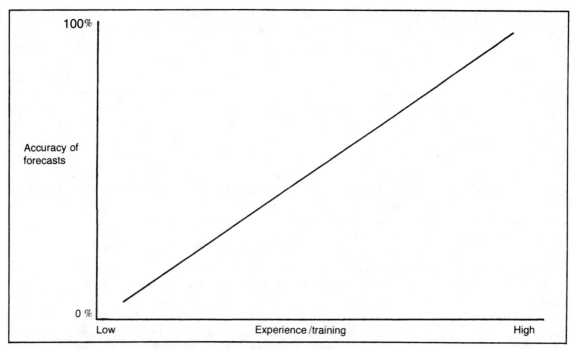

Fig. 1-1. Hypothetical relationship between training and accuracy of forecasts.

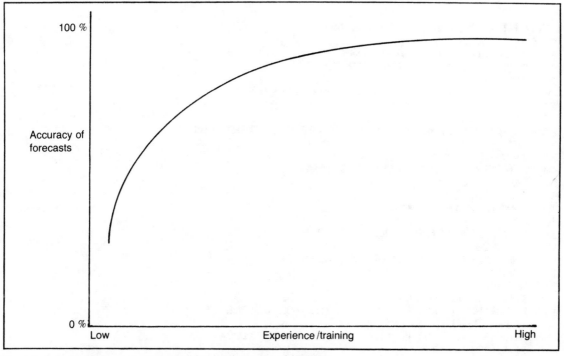

Fig. 1-2. Actual relationship between training and accuracy of forecasts.

continuous curves. People, on the other hand, come in integer units. In the real world we must deal in terms of one person or two, but never in terms of 1.34 persons. It is seldom meaningful to compute fractional human beings, certainly not beyond two or three decimal points in most applications. If the effort is to determine the amount of grain to purchase to feed a million people, it is useful to compute grain consumption only to the degree of precision that will affect the decision to buy one bag of grain more or less. To compute grain requirements to fractions of one grain is meaningless. Be careful to be precise enough so that in adding or multiplying (or subtracting or dividing) the final result is still accurate. Be especially careful when using exponential tools wherein values are raised by powers of numbers. Be precise enough to be accurate, but not tedious. A candidate for political office, for example, looks to the forecaster for an estimate of the number of votes pro and con. In the final analysis, this can and should be an integer value. 501 votes for a candidate are significantly greater than the 499 against: 500.0001, on the other hand, is

effectively equal to 499.9999. Additionally, the double-precision feature dramatically increases computational time. As a demonstration, run Listing 1-1 on your system.

The lesson here is that, except for short programs or programs requiring extremely precise computations, double-precision math can complicate and frustrate your data processing more than it can solve your problems. For example, Chapter 12 contains a simplified program to compute planetary positions (Listing 12-6). The technique used provides an acceptable degree of accuracy for the astronomical hobbyist who can accept a half a degree of arc error here and there.

THE DECISION-MAKING PROCESS

Forecasting involves two philosophies: an internal philosophy that enables the forecaster to remain calm and serene when it appears that the available data bases are either incomplete or inappropriately formatted—thus creating the need for original research before the project can continue—or when it appears the decision-maker is not

Listing 1-1. Double Precision Demonstrator

```
1  '*********************************************
2  'DOUBLE-PRECISION DEMONSTRATOR              *
3  'LISTING 1-1                                *
4  '*********************************************
5  '
10 CLS:GOTO100
20 PRINT"WHEN READY, TOUCH ANY KEY AND START TIM
      ER."
30 Q$=""+INKEY$:IFQ$=""THEN30
40 PRINT"SYSTEM WILL COUNT TO 1000"
50 FOR I=2 TO 10
60   X=3/LOG(I)
70   Y=SIN(X):PRINT@448,I;Y,
80 NEXT I
90 PRINT:PRINT"STOP TIMER, NOW!":RETURN
100 GOSUB20
110 INPUT"ENTER NUMBER OF SECONDS";S1
120 DEFDBL X,Y
130 GOSUB20
140 INPUT"ENTER NUMBER OF SECONDS";S2
150 PRINT:PRINT"BY SIMPLY CALLING FOR DOUBLE PRE
      CISION IN LINE 110, YOUR
COMPUTER'S PROCESSING TIME IS INCREASED";100*((S
      2/S1)-1);" %"
160 END
```

inclined to be rational this month; and an external philosophy that is skeptical and inquiring at its foundation, but includes a reasonable faith in properly collected and processed data as potentially rational indicators of future events or conditions.

Perhaps the dichotomy between the analyst and the decision-maker is created by otherwise useful personality differences. By nature the analyst proceeds in an orderly and frequently plodding manner, working through the various steps of a problem very methodically and conscientiously. By the time the final analysis is done and conclusions are reached, it is often too much of a temptation to lead the decision-maker through the same process one step at a time. The decision-maker, on the other hand, frequently cares about neither the process nor the standard errors and deviations surrounding the bottom line conclusions. Will the widget sell? Yes or no? Will sufficient units be sold to offset all production and sales costs so an acceptable net profit can be realized? Yes or no? All too often, the decision-maker expects the forecaster to simply enter the office, and announce: "Sell (or Don't Sell) the Widget!" and promptly leave. If the original instructions included words and guidance that facilitated such decision-making on the part of the forecaster, the expectation above is valid; otherwise, it is not. The decision could be made if, for example, the Widget marketing task was accompanied by these instructions:

A. If the marketing data can be applied to 95% (or better) of the total market place, with a standard error of plus or minus three,

and

B. if the forecast is for a minimum of 1,000 sales in the first year, 1250 the second year, and, in the third and subsequent years, growth at a rate of 50% per year,

then

C. recommend we sell the Widget; otherwise, recommend we do not sell the Widget.

The point is that the rational way to handle scientific data is through some orderly process. While Chapter 18 goes into some detail concerning decision-making techniques, this concept is introduced now in hope that the forecaster in you will be mindful that at the end of all of the analysis, someone has to make a decision on what to do based on the information. Sometimes it can be precisely expressed as above. These kind of criterion can often be developed independent of any market research. A good plan designer, knowing the function each division and machine will have to perform, and in what sequence, can compute the cost of equipment and operators based on information concerning a nominal number of items under production at that particular time. It is the market analyst who must forecast what the most likely product demand volume will be.

EXERCISES

1. Identify conditions or circumstances that affect the reliability of forecasts.
2. Give examples of areas in which precise forecasts can be made. Give an example of an area in which forecasting is probably a waste of time.
3. Identify an area in your personal life for which you could develop a useful forecasting tool.
4. Select a published forecasting effort (economic, business, or weather, for example) and keep a record of the forecasts and actual performance for a month or two. How well do the forecasters do? Can you explain their successes or failures?
5. Develop a convincing case for conducting and publishing political surveys. Develop a convincing case for not doing political surveys.

SUGGESTED READING

Ayers, R. U. 1969. *Technological Forecasting and Long Range Planning.* New York: McGraw-Hill.

Makridakis, S. and S. C. Wheelwright, 1976. *Forecasting Methods & Applications.* New York: John Wiley & Sons.

Reichard, R. S., 1966. *Practical Techniques of Sales Forecasting.* New York: McGraw-Hill.

Chapter 2

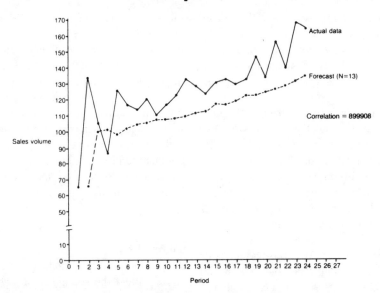

Underlying Mathematical Principles

Related to practically any subject selected for forecasting are all manner of data that may range from the purely subjective ("Yeller was a good ole' dog ...") to the precise and absolute ("Water freezes at 273° Kelvin (K) and boils at 373°K.) I am hard pressed, in this book, to help anyone to do forecasting from the subjective or anecdotal end of the data spectrum. At the same time the data need not all be from absolute scales of measurement. We can frequently (and more often than not, in fact do) make sense and produce effective forecasts from a variety of data types as long as we can count, measure, or by some other means, quantify the data. The key is quantification. If by some rational means or process, you can assign some numerical value to an element under investigation, the data are quantifiable and, more than likely, forecastable to some degree. All that follows, then, deals with numerical or quantified data.

SCALES

Scalar data (those data that describe things in terms of hot to cold, good to bad, little to much, and

so forth) can be categorized into four types of measurement scales: *nominal, ordinal, interval,* and *ratio.* These scales are listed in this order for a purpose. There are a certain number of mathematical operations one may do with nominal data, but only relatively few. With ordinal data, however, one may perform all of those operations, plus a number more. This rule continues through interval and ratio scale data as well. It is important to be sure to use mathematical operations appropriate to the data. Failure to do so results in meaningless forecasts.

Nominal Scales

A nominal scale consists of two or more categories or classifications into which the subjects of the study can be divided. One example of the use of a nominal scale is a census of a population described by nationality. At a particular university there are 3256 Americans, 245 British, 178 French, 89 Italians, 78 Gambians, and 2 Swiss. These categories can be totaled; percentages can be computed, and other similar simple numerical relationships can be established. Assignment to a category is not a value judgement, nor are the numbers that are generated meaningful beyond a limited application. It is entirely proper, however, to use such scales in forecasting. Given a series of university census records taken over a period of time, it is certainly feasible to compute the overall growth (or decline) of the university population and the changing ethnic makeup of the student body, and to draw meaningful conclusions from these data.

Ordinal Scales

An ordinal scale is one in which elements of the population under study are placed in some sort of relative order. Different brands of laundry soap, for example, may be placed on an ordinal scale by a panel of judges. The key feature of the scale is that the ratings or measures tend to be adjectival; that is, the items are rated as good or bad or satisfactory or unsatisfactory according to some criterion (smell, shape, apparent utility). The researcher may even attempt to define a certain precision in all this subjectivity by having the item rated numerically, as "on a scale of 1 to 10, how do you rate the President's foreign policy?" The essential element to remember, though, is that the interval between these scale increments is not constant; rather, it is elastic. In reality, the scale for the responses to the foreign policy question are distributed along a scale that is not measured evenly like this:

```
1   2   3   4   5   6   7   8   9
Poor           Average      Good
```

but one much like this:

```
1 2 3     4      5 6 7      8 9
Poor            Average     Good
```

For this reason, the complexity of the scale will serve to confound rather than aid the analyst, and the recommendation is to reduce the number of increments to three or five. It is even more important to avoid any computations that assume even intervals. It would be irresponsible to imply that a rating of four is just one notch below five, or that a rating of two is to four as four is to six. Such relationships will exist only coincidentally. A very common misuse of ordinal scales occurs in schoolrooms across the nation. Students are frequently given spelling tests, mathematics quizzes, and history exams that consist of a certain number of items or questions. The grade or score is then computed as a percentage of the number of items answered correctly. Unless the test is constructed with extraordinary care and skill, it is most unlikely that a student who scores an 89 is actually 2 percent "smarter" on the topic than a student receiving an 87. The fairest and safest thing we can say is that the first student responded to the test items "better" than the second student. It would be wrong to make much of the quantifiable differences between them.

Testing and grading have demonstratable utility and worth. Tests have been constructed such that, when properly administered, a group of subjects can be reliably divided into those who are likely to succeed at some future effort from those who are likely to fail. One who cannot carry a fifty-pound weight ten paces in a test cannot reliably be expected to carry a hundred and fifty-pound weight from a real burning building. Likewise, one who completes examinations in analytic geometry and algebra well above a responsibly established cutoff score can be expected to do well in calculus. To infer anything of consequence from the fine gradations between scores, however, is quite risky.

Interval Scales

Interval scales are those upon which two or more items can be compared in units of constant measure. An example often given is that of temperature as measured on the centigrade scale. Zero is established as the freezing point of water and one hundred degrees, as the boiling point of water. All other aspects of the scale are derived from this interval. To say that something 20°C is twice as cold as something 10°C is incorrect. At the same time, using ratios of differences is acceptable. It is correct to say there is twice as much change in a score that moves from 3 to 7 as in a score that moves from 3 to 5. The essential element of an interval scale is that it has no absolute zero base or starting point. Only with such a point can we say that twenty of something is twice ten of that thing. Twenty people is twice ten people because there is a condition of absolutely zero people. 10°C is not half 20°C because 0°C is not really the bottom of the scale, but only an arbitrary point on it selected for convenience. (Degrees on the Kelvin scale, however, are measures of absolute temperature because the starting or zero point of the scale is at the point of absolute cold, the point at which nothing, theoretically, can be any colder.)

Ratio Scales

The main distinction between interval and ratio scales is that the ratio scale always has a zero point. Units of weight, time, length, area, volume, angular measure, and the cardinal numbers used to count people, eggs, and money are examples of ratio scales.

All of the mathematical operations that can be applied to the foregoing scales can be used with ratio scales, as well as all the remaining statistical tests and measures, especially those requiring ratio differences from an absolute base.

SUMMATION RULES

Numerical tables are very frequently used in statistical studies and projections. Equally as common is the symbol: ΣX. This means to sum up the values of X, given a set or listing of X values. If there is a set of numbers [1, 4, 8, 2, 4, 8, 3, 7], then $\Sigma X = 1 + 4 + 8 + 2 + 4 + 8 + 3 + 7 = 37$. Consider the matrix below:

i (columns)

		1	2	3	4	Total
	1	X_{11}	X_{21}	X_{31}	X_{41}	X_{i1}
	2	X_{12}	X_{22}	X_{32}	X_{42}	X_{i2}
j (rows)	3	X_{13}	X_{23}	X_{33}	X_{43}	X_{i3}
	4	X_{14}	X_{24}	X_{34}	X_{44}	X_{i4}

Total $\quad \Sigma X_{1j} \quad \Sigma X_{2j} \quad \Sigma X_{3j} \quad \Sigma X_{4j} \quad \overset{4}{\underset{j=1}{\Sigma}} \overset{4}{\underset{i=1}{\Sigma}} X_{ij}$

The notation $\overset{N}{\underset{i=1}{\Sigma}} X_i$ means to sum or add up all of the values from 1 to N. The notation, from the matrix above, $\overset{3}{\underset{j=1}{\Sigma}} \overset{4}{\underset{i=2}{\Sigma}} X_{ij}$ means to add up all of the values in columns 2 to 4 and rows 1 to 3: $X_{21} + X_{31} + X_{41} + X_{22} + X_{32} + X_{42} + X_{23} + X_{33} + X_{43}$. There are three principles in summation that make the task a little easier and less error-prone:

1. Always work from right to left as illustrated above. That is, when two or more summation symbols are given, follow the direction of the symbol on the right first and then move to the left. In the illustration above, the values in columns 2 through 4, row 1, were summed; then all the values in columns 2 through 4, row 2, were summed, and so forth.

2. Complete all work within the parentheses first.

$$\overset{3}{\underset{i=1}{\Sigma}} X_i^2 = X_1^2 + X_2^2 + X_3^2$$

$$\left(\overset{3}{\underset{i=1}{\Sigma}} X_i \right)^2 = (X_1 + X_2 + X_3)^2$$

3. $\overset{N}{\underset{i=1}{\Sigma}} KX_i = K \overset{N}{\underset{i=1}{\Sigma}} X_i$ where K is some constant; e.g.,

$$KX_1 + KX_2 + KX_3 = K(X_1 + X_2 + X_3)$$

The following are examples of the summation principles:

$$\overset{N}{\underset{i=1}{\Sigma}} (X + Y_i) = \overset{N}{\underset{i=1}{\Sigma}} X_i + \overset{N}{\underset{i=1}{\Sigma}} Y_i$$

$$\overset{N}{\underset{i=1}{\Sigma}} (X_i + 2) = \overset{N}{\underset{i=1}{\Sigma}} X_i + 2N$$

$$\overset{N}{\underset{i=1}{\Sigma}} (Y - a)^2 = \overset{N}{\underset{i=1}{\Sigma}} (Y^2 - 2aY + a^2)$$

$$\overset{N}{\underset{i=1}{\Sigma}} Y^2 - 2a \overset{N}{\underset{i=1}{\Sigma}} Y + Na^2$$

STATISTICS

Statistics are numbers that give us information on a given subject. Related to any subject are usually a set of numbers: quantity, size, speed, time values, scale values of attitudes, and whatever else the human imagination can devise to count or measure. Those statistics that *describe* the available data are referred to as *descriptive statistics*. These normally include such things as the frequency, mean, median, mode, range, and skew of a distribution of numbers or values, and the percentages and percentiles derived from them.

Distribution of Data

Data collected on a subject may be described in a number of different types of distributions, but the two we are most concerned with in this book are those describing the magnitude of a characteristic at a given moment (such as voter attitudes, city population, etc.), and those describing the time of the occurrence of an event or a set of related events. The first type is referred to as a frequency distribution, while the second is known as a time series distribution.

Frequency Distribution. Table 2-1 repre-

Table 2-1. Number of Registered Voters by Precinct.

PCT	# VOTERS	PCT	# VOTERS	PCT	# VOTERS	PCT	# VOTERS
1	1607	2	1554	3	846	4	969
5	1408	6	682	7	1739	8	1494
9	2068	10	784	11	2048	12	1905
13	1210	14	2063	15	1832	16	1162
17	2757	18	1419	19	1486	20	1201
21	1586	22	1794	23	1832	24	1417
25	1651	26	1332	27	1434	28	1899
29	1784	30	1093	31	1287	32	1780
33	1616	34	1908	35	1995	36	1576
37	1387	38	1590	39	1948	40	1086
41	1272	42	2203	43	1397	44	1563
45	1480	46	1068	47	1226	48	1346
49	1592	50	1923	51	1578	52	2069
53	1333	54	1584	55	1174	56	1788
57	1369	58	2396	59	1734	60	1952
61	1727	62	1595	63	1404	64	1523
65	1356	66	1484	67	1497	68	430
69	2038	70	1109	71	1271	72	1914
73	1137	74	2022	75	1693	76	2115
77	1832	78	1317	79	1842	80	2372
81	1081	82	1315	83	1327	84	1697
85	1697	86	1532	87	1647	88	768
89	1533	90	868	91	2013	92	1498
93	1323	94	895	95	2167	96	1308
97	2402	98	1856	99	758	100	1166
101	1641	102	1940	103	1884	104	1363
105	1604	106	1651	107	1363	108	1676
109	1658	110	1971	111	1494	112	1515
113	1726	114	1847	115	1346	116	1615
117	1648	118	1730	119	807	120	1842
121	1153	122	1421	123	1452	124	1454
125	1363	126	1972	127	1871	128	1918

sents the results of a survey of the number of registered voters in a political region of a state.

These data are evaluated to determine the range; the largest precinct contains 2757 registered voters, while the smallest contains 430. The range then is 2327. We then divide these data into a number (normally, six to twenty) of subsets called *class intervals*, making an effort to insure the interval is broad enough to include at least five data elements in each division. Initial estimates of the size of the class interval can be obtained from the equation:

$$C = \frac{range}{1 + (3.322 \ Log \ N)}$$

Where C = class interval
N = number of elements or observations

Applying the equation to the data in Table 2-1, we compute C to be:

$$C = \frac{2327}{1 + (3.322 \ Log \ 128)} = \frac{2327}{17,1184} = 135.936$$

The number of class intervals, then, is computed by dividing the largest value (2757) by the interval: 2757/135.936 = 20.2816, or about 21 subsets. The class interval is adjusted by the user so as to specify a size of class interval that

a. Insures that each interval includes a sample of at least five elements.
b. The interval range is an easily computed or comfortable unit of measure. For example, it is easier to handle the interval if it is 5 instead of 3.456: 5-9.9, 10-14.9, and 15-19.9 . . . instead of 3.456-6.911, 6.912-10.367, and 10.368-13.823 . . . .
c. The class intervals do not overlap. If the intervals are stated as 0-5, 5-10, and 10-15, definite ambiguities are created at the point of overlap.
d. All efforts should be taken to insure a constant interval size.

The data then are tallied according to class interval. Figure 2-1 illustrates our data in the tally format. Each class interval is scored. This tally process develops the group frequency data to be used in the subsequent analysis and provides a visual impression of the nature of the data distribution.

Listing 2-1 is a brief routine to input and tally raw data according to the user-defined class intervals. It was used to generate the results in Fig. 2-1, but I would recommend the reader proceed to the program in Listing 2-2 for a more comprehensive evaluation.

Class interval	Tally	Total frequency
0 - 249		0
250 - 499		1
500 - 749		1
750 - 999		8
1000 - 1249		13
1250 - 1499		34
1500 - 1749		32
1750 - 1999		25
2000 - 2249		10
2250 - 2499		3
2500 - 2749		0
2750 - 2999		1
Total		128

Fig. 2-1. Data shown in tally format.

Listing 2-1. Routine to Tally Raw Data

```
1   '*****************************************************
2   'ROUTINE TO TALLY RAW DATA                           *
3   'LISTING 2-1                                         *
4   '*****************************************************
5   '
10  INPUT"CLASS INTERVAL";CI
20  INPUT"NUMBER OF ITEMS";N
30  FORI=1TON
40    PRINT"ENTER VALUE OF ITEM #";I,:INPUTV:T=T+
      V
50    A=INT(V/CI)+1:B(A)=B(A)+1
60  NEXT
70  CLS
80  PRINT"CLASS","","","TOTAL":PRINT"INTERVAL","
      TALLY","","FREQUENCY"
90  LPRINT"":LPRINT"CLASS","","","","","","TOTAL"
      :LPRINT"INTERVAL","","","","    TALLY","","F
      REQUENCY":LPRINT""
100 FORI=1TOC
110   S=0:PRINT((I-1)*CI);"-";(I*CI)-.001,:LPRIN
      T((I-1)*CI);"-";(I*CI)-.001,:IFB(I)=0THEN16
      0
120   FORJ=1TOB(I)
130     PRINT"/";:LPRINT"/";:S=S+1:IFS<5THEN150

140     PRINT" ";:LPRINT" ";:S=0
150   NEXTJ
160   PRINT@120+(I*64),B(I):LPRINTSTRING$(80-B(I
      )+INT(B(I)/5)," ");B(I)
170 NEXTI
180 LPRINTSTRING$(96," ");N
190 END
```

The second phase of this analysis is to compute a variety of statistics which better describe the data. These include the mean, median, mode, skew, kurtosis, and several other related measures.

Mean. This is the preferred term for what we commonly call the average of a set of values. Unless specified as a geometric mean or a harmonic mean or described by some other qualifier, we understand the *MEAN* of a set of numbers to be the sum of those numbers divided by the number of data elements:

$$X = \frac{A_1 + A_2 + A_3 + \ldots + A_n}{n}$$

In the evaluation of a set of data, the mean is the most frequently used value due to the ease with which it can be computed and to its long-standing use. The drawback to the mean is that it is greatly affected by extreme values. Consider the following list of per capita incomes for 6 countries:

Country	Per Capital Income
1	50
2	67
3	78
4	12545
5	17893
6	21378

The mean of this set is 8668.500. Unfortunately, there is no value on the table that is meaningfully close to the mean. We need some other measures.

Geometric Mean. This mean is technically defined as the *n*th root of the product of the n items or values. It is computed according to the expression:

$$G_m = \sqrt[n]{A_1 \cdot A_2 \cdot A_3 \cdots A_n}$$

The following eight numbers were randomly generated from a set zero to one thousand:

N	Value
1	510
2	452
3	631
4	755
5	102
6	452
7	268
8	106

Total 3276   Product $1.438348708238136 \times 10^{20}$
Mean 409.500   Geometric Mean   330.928

The geometric mean has the advantage of not being unduly influenced by extreme values in a distribution and is more typically representative of the distribution than the arithmatic mean. On the other hand, it is more difficult to compute, and if any value in the distribution is zero, the geometric mean becomes zero. In addition, it is not a widely known or understood statistic.

Median. The median value of a distribution is the actual midway point at which one-half of the values lie below it and the other half lie above it. Where there is an odd number of items in a list, the median value is the ((N-1)/2) + 1th item. With an even number of items in the list, it is the ((N/2) + ((N/2) + 1))/2th item; that is, the sum of the two central (N/2 and N/2 + 1) items divided by two. This value is easily computed and is not adversely affected by extreme values. Negatively, it is not as widely understood as the mean, and it requires that the data be sorted by magnitude before it can be identified. Also, it cannot be manipulated algebraically. The data below illustrate the notion of the median.

Odd No. of Items

N	Value	
1	609	
2	748	
3	770	
4	859	←

Odd No. of Items Cont.

N	Value
5	958
6	960
7	994

Total	5898
Mean	842.5714
Median	859

Even No. of Items

N	Value
1	69
2	783
3	849
4	895
5	973
6	984

Total	4553
Mean	758.8333 . . .
Median	(849 + 895)/2 = 1744/2 = 872

Mode. The mode of a set of numbers is the number that occurs most frequently, provided the data set is large enough. Identification of the mode is not especially difficult, particularly if the data have been sorted into an ordered list to find the median. Simply scan the list and find the value that reappears most often. In the event this is too much of a bother, the mode can be estimated from the expression

mode = mean − 3(mean − median)

If the median has not been identified, there are a couple of other ways to compute an estimate of the mode, although they are based on values we have yet to introduce. From the *skew* of the distribution:

mode = mean − (skew • standard deviation)

From the *theory of moments:*

mode = $M_1 - (M_3/\sqrt{M_2^3})$ • standard deviation)

The relationship between these three values, mean, median, and mode, is illustrated in Fig. 2-2.

Skew. You will notice in Fig. 2-2 that the curve is not centered about the mean, but lopsided. The degree of lopsidedness is referred to as *skew*. Unfortunately, generations of mathematicians have established a convention to be used when talking

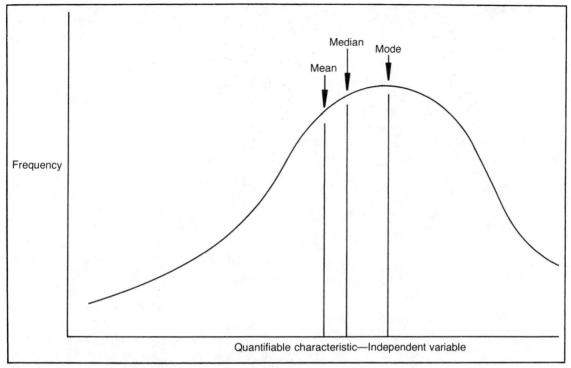

Fig. 2-2. Generalized distribution with mean, mode, and median.

about skew that can be confusing. When the peak of the curve is pushed over to the righthand side of the graph, it is said to be "skewed to the left," and when the peak is closer to the left of the graph, it is "skewed to the right." The equation to determine the degree of skew is:

$$S = \frac{3(\text{mean} - \text{median})}{\text{standard deviation}}$$

(The standard deviation is described below.)

If the value for S is less than zero, the curve is said to be skewed to the left. If it is greater than zero it is skewed to the right. When $S = 0$, the curve is said to be *normal* or symmetrical.

Kurtosis. The pointedness of the curve is defined by the value of its kurtosis. Where the value is a positive figure, the curve is fairly peaked. When it is a negative figure, it is a flat-topped curve. When kurtosis is zero, then it is normally peaked. Theoretically, zero values for both skew and kurtosis should be related to a distribution of data which is normal. Kurtosis is computed from the various *mo-*

ments of the curve, which are discussed below, and is described in the equation:

$$K = (M_4/M_2^2) - 3$$

Standard Deviation. An underlying concept in statistics is the principle of *central tendency*. That is, if we collect *parametric data* about something (height, weight, grades, ages, etc.), we find the data group around the mean, in a hill-shaped curve, in a fashion described by the skew and kurtosis. Few of the data points, however, lie exactly on the mean. Most deviate above or below by some degree. The list below contains ten items. The first step is to sum them and compute the mean.

N	Value
1	123
2	96
3	146
4	45
5	142
6	93
7	66

N	Value
8	95
9	121
10	93
Sum	1020

Mean = 1020/10 = 102.00

The next step is to subtract the mean from each of the input values and sum these. For reasons that will be made clear, you must also square each deviation and sum these.

N	Value	Deviation	Deviation Squared
1	123	21	441
2	96	− 6	36
3	146	44	1936
4	45	− 57	3249
5	142	40	1600
6	93	− 9	81
7	66	− 36	1296
8	95	− 7	49
9	121	19	361
10		− 9	81
Sum	1020	0	9130
Mean	102.00	0	913.00

The mean deviation will always be zero. Since you still need some measure or estimate of the general or normal deviation from the mean, you must use the next available value, the squared deviations. The computed value is called the *standard deviation* and is derived from the equation:

$$\sigma = \sqrt{\frac{\Sigma(x^2)}{N}}$$

where x^2 is the square of each deviation
From our data:

$$\sigma = \sqrt{\frac{9130}{10}} = 30.2159$$

This value is quite handy. If, from the other values computed from the data, we know the data to be in a fairly normal distribution (skew close to zero), we can reasonably assume that about 68 percent of the data are within one standard deviation, plus or minus, from the mean; 95 percent are within two standard deviations, plus or minus, from the mean; and all but a very small fraction of the remainder are within three standard deviations. These relationships are illustrated in Fig. 2-3. From the value of

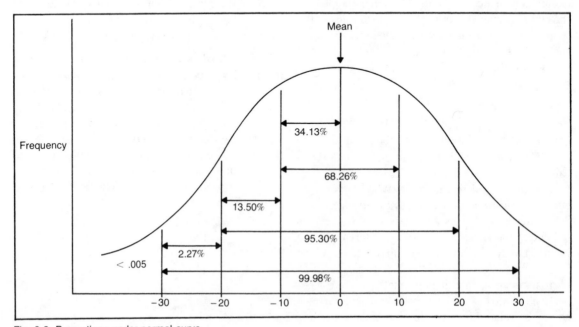

Fig. 2-3. Proportions under normal curve.

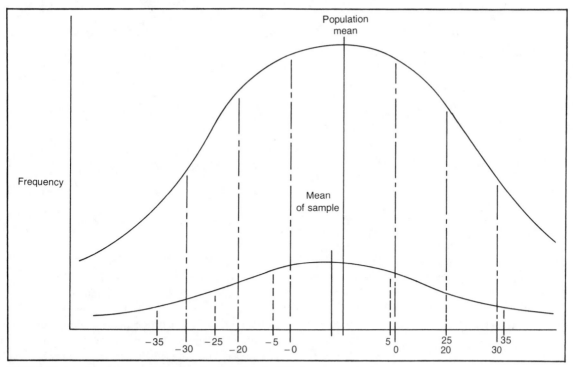

Fig. 2-4. Comparison between sample and population deviations.

the standard deviation, σ, in a normal or even moderately skewed distribution, we can compute the mean deviation as being approximately $.7979\sigma$. Additionally, in a normal distribution, the standard deviation is roughly one-sixth of the range.

The values computed above are based on the assumption that in the entire universe, there are only ten of the items that were measured. Normally, we are not so fortunate to be able to measure each of a given item. Frequently, it is not economical to do so. For example, if we wanted to start a new shoe factory, but needed to know what sizes to make, it would not be practical to go out and measure everyone's feet. Rather, we would measure the feet of a sample of only a few thousand people. If we have properly selected our sample, we can reasonably assume that the mean size and standard deviations computed from the sample are applicable to the whole population. When we sample from a population, however, we must make a minor adjustment in the computations so that the results are more applicable to the whole population. The stan-

dard deviation of a sample is computed from:

$$s = \sqrt{\frac{(x^2)}{N-1}}$$

Applying this equation to the data given above:

$$s = \sqrt{\frac{9130}{6}} = 31.8504$$

The relationship between the distribution of a whole population and the data from a sample is illustrated in Fig. 2-4.

In order to find the standard deviation using a BASIC program, the mean must be computed prior to the computation of the standard deviations. During the collection of the data phase, the program line would read:

XY10   INPUT"ENTER VALUE";V(I):T=T+V(I)

and the processing lines would be:

YZ10   M=T/N
YZ20   FOR I=1 TO N
YZ30   D=V(I)−M:D2+D]2

15

YZ40 NEXT
YZ50 S=SQR(D2/(N−1))

A shorter approach is to use this equation:

$$s = \sqrt{\frac{\Sigma X^2 - \frac{(X)^2}{N}}{N-1}}$$

This permits a much shorter routine and no repetitions of the data:

XY10 INPUT"ENTER VALUE";
      V(I):T=T+V(I):X2=X2+2X]2

. . . .

YZ10 M=T/N:S=SQR((X2−((T]2))/(N−1))

Moments. The *moments* of a distribution are constants that are computed to facilitate analysis of a curve of the distribution. Space does not permit the development of the equations, nor is a more comprehensive explanation necessary for the use of moments in forecasting. We will leave the subject with a listing of the equations used to compute them.

In general

$$M_r = \frac{1}{N} \sum_{i=1}^{N} (X_i - \overline{X})^r$$

Then:

$$M_1 = 0$$

$$M_2 = \frac{1}{N} \sum_{i=1}^{N} (X_i - \overline{X})^2$$

$$M_3 = \frac{1}{N} \sum_{i=1}^{N} (X_i - \overline{X})^3$$

$$M_4 = \frac{1}{N} \sum_{i=1}^{N} (X_i - \overline{X})^4$$

Skew can be computed:

$$S_k = \frac{M_3}{\sqrt{2M_2^3}}$$

Kurtosis, then, is:

$$K = \frac{M_4}{M_2^2}$$

Happily, the microcomputer makes fairly short work of all these computations and tedious summations. Listing 2-2 is a program which implements all of the foregoing data collection and processing routines to compute the descriptive values relative to a distribution. While it is not necessary to key in and run the program as written, it does provide a working example of the ways to implement the different equations.

Listing 2-2. Data Distribution Analysis

```
1  ´******************************************
2  ´DATA DISTRIBUTION ANALYSIS            *
3  ´LISTING 2-2                           *
4  ´******************************************
5  ´
10 ONERRORGOTO1370
20 RANDOM:CLS:SM=1.0E+10:LG=1.0E-10:XG=1
30 PRINT"INITIAL DISTRIBUTION ANALYSIS":PRINT:PR
   INT
40 INPUT"ENTER NUMBER OF DATA ITEMS TO BE ENTERE
   D";N:DIMV(N)
50 ´ROUTINE TO GENERATE N RANDOM NUMBERS TO CHEC
   KOUT/DEMONSTRATE PROGRAM
60 INPUT"ENTER MEAN OF DISTRIBUTION";X:INPUT"ENT
   ER STANDARD DEVIATION";S
70 FORI=1TON
80    A=2*RND(0)-1:B=A[2+(2*RND(0)-1)[2:IFB>=1THE
   N80
90    R=INT(X+(A*SQR((-2*LOG(B))/B))*S):PRINTI;R,
   :LPRINTI;R,:V(I)=R:T=T+R:X2=X2+R[2
100 NEXTI
```

```
110 GOTO140
120 'ACTUAL DATA INPUT ROUTINE
130 FORI=1TON:PRINT"ENTER DATA FOR ITEM #";I,:IN
    PUTV(I):T=T+V(I):X2=X2+V(I)[2:NEXTI
140 A=1:PRINT:IFN>48THENB=48ELSEB=N
150 PRINT:FORI=ATOB:PRINTI;V(I),:NEXT
160 'CORRECTION SUBROUTINE
170 PRINT:PRINT"ARE ALL THESE ITEMS CORRECT?   (Y
    /N)";
180 Q$=""+INKEY$:IFQ$=""THEN180   ELSEIFQ$="Y"THE
    N210
190 PRINT:INPUT"ENTER ITEM NUMBER AND CORRECT VA
    LUE";X,V(X)
200 GOTO150
210 IFB=NTHEN250
220 A=A+48:B=B+48:IFB>NTHENB=N
230 GOTO150
240 'COMPUTATION OF SMALLEST AND LARGEST VALUES
250 PRINT:PRINT"DOING INITIAL COMPUTATIONS":PRIN
    T
260 FORI=1TON
270    PRINT@864,I;
280    IFSM<V(I)THEN300
290    SM=V(I):GOTO320
300    IFV(I)<LGTHEN320
310    LG=V(I)
320 NEXT
330 'COMPUTATION OF RANGE, CLASS INTERVAL, # CLA
    SSES
340 RG=LG-SM:C=RG/(1+(3.322*LOG(N))):NC=INT(RG/C
    )+1
350 PRINT:PRINT"THE COMPUTED CLASS INTERVAL IS "
    ;C:PRINT"THIS IMPLIES";NC;"CLASSES.   DO YOU
    CONCUR?   (Y/N)":SF=127/NC
360 Q$=""+INKEY$:IFQ$=""THEN360
370 IFQ$="Y"THEN430
380 PRINT:PRINT"      A --  NUMBER OF CLASSES
    B  --   CLASS INTERVAL":PRINT:INPUT"ENTER TY
    PE VALUE AND VALUE";V$,V
390 IFV$="A"THEN410
400 C=V:NC=INT(RG/C)+1:GOTO420
410 NC=V:C=RG/NC
420 GOTO350
430 DIMF(NC+1),U(N),E(N)
440 CLS:PRINT"COMPUTING AGAIN";:SF=0
450 'SET UP SORTING LIST (U(I)), CHECK EACH INPU
    T VALUE FOR CLASS INTERVAL
460 FORI=1TON
470    U(I)=V(I):E(I)=1
480    A=INT(V(I)/C)+1
490    F(A)=F(A)+1:SET(A,47-F(A))
500    PRINT@30,I;
510 NEXTI
520 'HEAPSORT SORTING ROUTINE TO PUT INPUT LIST
    IN ORDER
530 PRINT@0,"SORTING                 ";:K=N:L=INT
    (N/2)+1
```

Listing 2-2. Data Distribution Analysis (continued from page 17).

```
540 IFL=1THEN650
550 L=L-1:A=U(L)
560 J=L
570 I=J:J=2*J
580 IFJ=KTHEN620
590 IFJ>KTHEN640
600 IFU(J)>=U(J+1)THEN620
610 J=J+1
620 IFA>U(J)THEN640
630 U(I)=U(J):GOTO570
640 U(I)=A:PRINT@50,K;:GOTO540
650 A=U(K):U(K)=U(1)
660 K=K-1
670 IFK<>1THEN560
680 U(1)=A
690 'PRINT SORTED LIST
700 PRINT:FORI=1TON:PRINTU(I),:NEXTI
710 'COMPLETE COMPUTATIONS OF MEAN, MEDIAN, MODE
    , SKEW, AND KURTOSIS
720 AV=T/N:SD=SQR((X2-((T[2)/N))/(N-1))
730 IFINT(N/2)=N/2THEN750
740 ME=U(((N-1)/2)+1):GOTO760
750 ME=(U(N/2)+U((N/2)+1))/2
760 GM=EXP(XG/N)
770 PRINT@0,"COMPUTING MOMENTS";:FORI=2TO4:FORJ=
    1TON:PRINT@40,I;J;:M(I)=M(I)+(U(J)-AV)[I:NE
    XTJ:M(I)=M(I)/N:NEXTI
780 SK=M(3)/SQR(2*(M(2)[3)):K=(M(4)/(M(2)[2))-3
790 MC=AV-(SK*SD)
800 PRINT:PRINT:PRINT"NUMBER OF ITEMS = ";N
810 PRINT"SMALLEST = ";SM:PRINT"LARGEST = ";LG:P
    RINT"RANGE =";LG-SM:PRINT"TOTAL = ";T,"MEAN
     = ";AV:PRINT"STANDARD DEVIATION = ";SD:PRI
    NT"MEDIAN = ";ME:PRINT"COMPUTED MODE = ";MC
    :PRINT"   (DO YOU WANT TO KNOW THE ACTUAL M
    ODE?  (Y/N)";
820 Q$=""+INKEY$:IFQ$=""THEN820  ELSEIFQ$="N"THE
    N970
830 PRINT:PRINT"     PLEASE BE PATIENT.   THIS WI
    LL TAKE A MOMENT..."
840 'LOCATE ACTUAL MODE
850 FORI=1TON-1
860   FORJ=ITON
870     PRINT@960,I,J;
880     IFU(I)<>U(J)THEN900
890     E(I)=E(I)+1
900   NEXTJ
910 NEXTI
920 FORI=1TON
930   IFE(I)<=MATHEN950
940   MA=E(I):AM=I
950 NEXT
960 PRINT:PRINT"THE ACTUAL MODE IS ";U(AM);"WITH
    ";MA;"REPETITIONS"
970 PRINT:PRINT"SKEW = ";SK
```

```
980  IFSK<0THENPRINT"   (LEFT, PEAK TO THE RIGHT)"
     ELSEIFSK=0THENPRINT"    (NORMAL CURVE)"ELSEP
     RINT"   (RIGHT, PEAK TO THE LEFT)"
990  IFK<0THENK$="FLAT-TOPPED"ELSEIFK=0THENK$="NO
     RMAL"ELSEIFK>0THENK$="POINTED"
1000 PRINT"KURTOSIS = ";K,K$:PRINT"GEOMETRIC MEA
     N = ";GM:PRINT"MOMENTS  --  M1 = ";M(1);"
      M2 = ";M(2);"
               M3 = ";M(3);"   M4 = ";M(4):PRINT
1010 PRINT@960,"(G)RAPHICS    (P)RINT STATISTICS
      (T)ABLE OF DATA   (N)EW";
1020 Q$=""+INKEY$:IFQ$=""THEN1020
1030 IFQ$="P"THEN1050 ELSEIFQ$="T"THEN800   ELSEI
     FQ$="G"THEN1100
1040 RUN
1050 LPRINT"SORTED INPUT DATA  (READ: ITEM NUMBE
     R, VALUE)":LPRINT""
1060 FORI=1TON:LPRINTI;U(I),:NEXT:LPRINT""
1070 LPRINT"NUMBER OF ITEMS =";N,"SMALLEST = ";S
     M,"LARGEST = ";LG,"RANGE = ";R,"SUM OF ALL
      ITEMS = ";T,"MEAN = ";AV,"GEOMETRIC MEAN =
      ";GM,"STANDARD DEVIATION = ";SD,"MEDIAN = "
     ;ME,"MODE(S) =";MC;V(AM),"SKEW = ";SK,"KURT
     OSIS = ";K,
1080 LPRINT"MOMENTS: M1 = ";M(1),"M2 = ";M(2),"M
     3 = ";M(3),"M4 = ";M(4)
1090 GOTO1010
1100 E=2.71828:CLS:FORX=0TO127:SET(X,47):NEXT:FO
     RY=0TO47:SET(0,Y):NEXT
1110 ONERRORGOTO1370
1120 PRINT@0,"ACTUAL DATA";
1130 FORI=1TONC
1140    B=I*C:A=B-C
1150    FORY=47TO47-(63.9191*(F(I)/N))STEP-1
1160      IFY<0THENY=0
1170      FORX=127*(A/RG)TO127*(B/RG)
1180        SET(X,Y)
1190      NEXT
1200    NEXT
1210 NEXT
1220 PRINT@0,"NORMAL CURVE";
1230 RESTORE
1240 FORX=-63TO63
1250    READ Y:Z=X+63
1260    IFPOINT(Z,Y)THENRESET(Z,Y)ELSESET(Z,Y)
1270 NEXT
1280 FORI=1TO1000:NEXT
1290 PRINT@0,"(P)RINT OF GRAPH    (R)ETURN TO TA
     BLES";
1300 Q$=""+INKEY$:IFQ$=""THEN1300 ELSEIFQ$="R"TH
     EN1010
1310 FORR=3TO47
1320    FORC=0TO127
1330      IFPOINT(C,R)THENLPRINT"*";ELSELPRINT" "
     ;
1340    NEXTC
1350 NEXTR
```

Listing 2-2. Data Distribution Analysis (continued from page 19).

```
1360 GOTO1010
1370 RESUMENEXT
1380 DATA43,43,43,43,42,42,42,41,41,41,41,40,40,
     39,39,39,38,38,38,37,37,36,36,35,35,34,34,3
     3,33,32,32,32,31,31,30,30,29,29,28,28,27,27
     ,26,26,26,25,25,24,24,24,23,23,23,23,22,22,
     22,22,22,22,22,22,21,21,21,22,22,22,22,22,2
     2,22,22,23,23,23,23,24,24
1390 DATA24,25,25,26,26,26,27,27,28,28,29,29,30,
     30,31,31,32,32,32,33,33,34,34,35,35,36,36,3
     7,37,38,38,39,39,39,40,40,41,41,41,41,42,42
     ,42,43,43,43,43
```

To describe the data is often only the first of two steps in the statistical process. Frequently, the data are measures of a sample taken from a larger population. We use statistics as a tool to learn useful information about large populations or universes by sampling small portions of the whole. To aid us in the inductive process of generalizing from the data related to the sample to conclusions about the whole, we use *inferential statistics*.

For example, a biologist wants to determine whether the water contained in a larger wooden barrel is suitable for use in a series of experiments. The water within the barrel constitutes the universe understudy. The one-quart ladle of water drawn is the sample. The convention is that the water in the ladle is reliably representative of all of the water. (Whether the one-quart sample is statistically adequate to support the subsequent conclusions is the subject of a later section on sampling theory.) Having drawn the water, the biologist examines the sample microscopically and chemically. It is understood that virtually all samples of water will contain some contaminants, the question is whether the level of contamination exceeds some prescribed level or percentage. One procedure the biologist might use is to place a sample (from the sample) under the microscope to count larger microbes. In the viewing area, the plane is optically divided into a matrix of smaller cells. Each cell is surveyed to determine the number of microbes in it. These are summed to obtain the total population of the sample. This process is repeated a number of times. Since we know the volume of water in each sample drop, as well as the number of

drops and the number of microbes in each drop, we can compute the mean number of microbes in each drop. We can also determine the mode and median values, the standard deviations from these norms, the skew of the distribution, and finally, an estimate of the total number of microbes in the barrel itself. This last step and the subsequent test undertaken to make the inductive leap are the inferential portions of the effort.

PROBABILITY

As a science, the study of probability is often considered a major subset of statistics. As a practical effort, probability and statistical studies had separate origins. The accepted origin of modern probability study is the French mathematician, Pascal, who was employed by a gambler, the Chevalier de Mere, to develop some rational basis for a better gaming strategy in a dice game popular at the time. The broader statistical practices of counting inventories; determining average (mean) crop yield; rainfall, or production rates for hand labor; and using other industrial or agricultural measures, which became systematically organized into statistical science, have their origins much further back, perhaps several thousand years ago. Today, probability theory contributes several powerful tools to inferential statistics, and the systematic procedures of descriptive statistics enhance the preliminary probabilistic analysis.

Set Operations

Any well-defined collection of objects is considered to be a set. A well-defined collection of sets is considered to be a universe. For example, a local high school can be considered a universe containing several sets. These sets can be variously described as: all students, all students who are male, all students who are female, all teachers, all visitors, all administrators, all janitorial staff, everyone within the facility over (or under) a certain age, and on and on.

We normally denote a set with a capital letter (A) and elements of sets with small letters (a). The symbol $\in$ is used as a shorthand to relate an element to a set. Thus, the notation a $\in$ A signifies that a is an element of the set A. "John is a member of the band" could be noted as: j$\in$B. The second symbol often used is the vertical bar: |, and is taken to mean "such that" or "given." Hence, the expression [a | a < 12] is understood to mean that a is a member or element of a set of numbers such that it is less than 12. The symbol $\subset$ means inclusion in the sense of a subset; that is, B$\subset$A is taken to mean "B is a subset of A." The observation that "flutes are among the normal range of band instruments" could be noted: F$\subset$B.

Venn diagrams (named after a leading proponent) are useful tools for graphically describing sets and working out appropriate logical relationships. Figure 2-5 illustrates a standard Venn diagram.

The box around the sets is understood to represent the universe relevant to the sets. It can represent Ohio State University. Set A represents all males present there. Set B represents all graduate students. Given this setting, the following operations can be described: union, intersection, complements, and subtraction.

Figure 2-5 shows a *union* of two sets. The notation used is: A$\cup$B. Any element that is con-

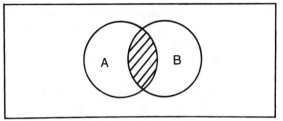
Fig. 2-6. Venn diagram with intersection.

tained in either set A or set B or both is included in the expression A$\cup$B.

Figure 2-6 is the same as Fig. 2-5, except that a portion of it is shaded to highlight that area of overlap or mutual inclusion. This area is the *intersection* of sets and is noted: A$\cap$B.

If A is a set containing the numbers 1, 3, 7, and B is another set containing the numbers, 2, 4, 7 then A$\cap$B = 7 and A$\cup$B = 1, 2, 3, 4, 7.

The *complement* of a set includes all those things which are not elements of that set, and is noted by an overscore, $\overline{A}$. If all graduate students are represented by the notation, G, $\overline{G}$ represents everyone who is not a graduate student.

Subtraction of sets uses the complement of a set for its description: [A] − [B] = A$\cap\overline{B}$. The effect or meaning of the subtraction of set B from set A is described as the intersection of set A with all those elements of the specified universe that are not elements of set B.

Given this notation, we can now summarize the various possible associations, called *distributive rules*.

1. A$\cup$B = B$\cup$A
2. A$\cap$B = B$\cap$A
3. (A$\cup$B)$\cup$C = A$\cup$(B$\cup$C)
4. (A$\cap$B)$\cap$C = A$\cap$(B$\cap$C)
5. A$\cup$(B$\cap$C) = (A$\cup$B)$\cap$(A$\cup$C)
6. A$\cap$(B$\cup$C) = (A$\cap$B)$\cup$(A$\cap$C)

Application of Set Operations Probability

The number of graduate students will be described with the expression n(a), and the total number of people, regardless of sex, occupation, or function, normally found at the university by the value N. The probability, then, of anyone we might

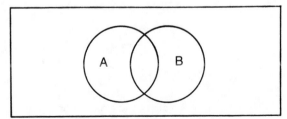
Fig. 2-5. Generalized Venn diagram.

encounter being a graduate student is defined by this relationship: $p(a) = n(a)/N$. If there are 6000 students and 1000 graduate students, the probability of running into a graduate student is 1000/6000 or .166666666 .... Yes, that is the same probability given one six-sided die. The die's universe consists of six sides, one of which at rest, will normally be up.

The complement rule lets us also define the probability as: $p(a) = 1 - p(\overline{a})$. That is, the probability of "a" is one minus the probability of all other related events. At our mythical university, there are 5000 nongraduate students. The value $p(\overline{a})$ is 5000/6000 = .833333 .... Therefore, $p(a) = 1 - .833333... = .166666...$. Elsewhere in probability texts the probability of an event may be noted as P or P_a. Concurrently, the complement of P is given as Q: $\overline{Q} = 1 - P$. The following relationships are also true:

1. $P(a) = n(a)/N$
2. $p(a) = 1 - p(\overline{a})$
3. $p(A - B) = p(A) - p(B)$
4. $p(A \cup B) = p(A) + p(B) - p(A \cap B)$
5. $p(A \cup B \cup C) = p(A) + p(C) - p(A \cap B)$
   $\quad\quad - p(B \cap C) - p(A \cap C) +$
   $\quad\quad p(A \cap B \cap C)$

Two or more events are said to be *independent* of each other if the happening of one does not depend on the happening or nonhappening of the other. A fair die is one which can be relied upon to deliver truly random results when rolled. The outcome of the second roll, therefore, is independent of the outcome of the first roll. This permits the following relationships:

6. $p(a \mid b) = p(a)$ (probability of "a" given "b" happens)
7. $p(b \mid a) = p(b)$
8. $p(A \cap B) = p(A) \times p(B)$

The last relationship asks a slightly different question than rules 6 and 7. Rule 6 says, in effect, the probability of a 5 on the roll of a die, given that a 4 has just been rolled is still simply equal to the normal probability of rolling a 5. Rolling a 4 does not make a 5 any more or less likely to happen. Rule 8, on the other hand, defines the probability of rolling a

4 and then rolling a 5. Such a relationship is called a *conditional probability*. It is useful in computing the probability of flipping four heads in a row ($P_{4\,heads}$ = .0625), dealing four aces in a row ($P_{4\,aces} = 4/52 \times 3/51 \times 2/50 \times 1/49 = .076923 \times .058824 \times .040000 \times .020408 = .00000369379$); or figuring the probability of more serious but equally independent matters. What about those relationships that are not so independent? Time for rule number 9.

9. $(B \mid A) = \dfrac{p(A \cap B)}{p(A)}$

For purpose of illustration, let us assume the following relationships are true:

a. Females (F) are 51% of the population (M = 49%).
b. 11% of the population is left-handed (L).
c. Only 5% of females are left-handed ($p(F \mid L) = .05$).
d. 20% of the males are left-handed ($p(M \mid L) = .20$).

Therefore,

$$p(L \mid M) = \frac{p(M \cap L)}{p(M)} = \frac{.20}{.49} = .408163$$

The probability of being left-handed, provided one is male, is .408163 according to the data.

Likewise,

$$p(L \mid F) = \frac{p(F \cap L)}{p(F)} = \frac{.05}{.51} = .0980392$$

In reality, left-handedness is not nearly so sexist, but the illustration above accurately portrays the hypothetical data.

If the foregoing is true (and it is), rule 10 must be true:

10. $p(A \cap B) = p(A) \times p(B \mid A) = p(B) \times p(A \mid B)$
    $\quad\quad = p(B)/p(a) = p(B \mid A)/p(A \mid B)$

At this point we are ready for a more serious and useful application of some of these rules and their combinations. Such an application is found in Baye's Theorem, the algebraic expression of which is:

$$p(A \mid B) = \frac{p(B \mid A)p(A)}{p(B \mid A)p(A) + p(B \mid \overline{A})p(\overline{A})}$$

Let us assume these variables represent these relationships:

A = Took poison tablets = p(A) = .333
$\overline{A}$ = Took aspirin = p($\overline{A}$) = .667
B = Experiencing stomach/intestinal distress after taking poison = p(B | A) = .8000
$\overline{B}$ = Feeling good after taking aspirin = p($\overline{B}$ | $\overline{A}$) = .95. Experiencing stomach/intestinal distress after taking aspirin = p(B | $\overline{A}$) = .05

The question, then, is: presented with a person complaining of stomach pains, after taking a tablet from one of three unmarked bottles, what is the probability that the person has taken poison? The computed answer is:

$$p(A \mid B) = \frac{.80 \times .333}{(.80 \times .333) + (.05 \times .667)}$$
$$= \frac{.2664}{.2664 + .03335}$$
$$= .888741$$

Listing 2-3 is a short routine which implements and facilitates Baye's theorem in the form we have just presented above.

Listing 2-3. Simple Baye's Theorem

```
  1 ′****************************************
  2 ′SIMPLE BAYE′S THEOREM                  *
  3 ′LISTING 2-3                            *
  4 ′****************************************
  5 ′
 10 CLS
 20 INPUT"NAME OF EVENT # 1";N1$
 30 PRINT"PROBABILITY OF ";N1$," (5%=5)",:INPUT A
     :PA=A/100:QA=1-PA
 40 INPUT"NAME OF RELATED EVENT # 2";N2$
 50 PRINT"PROBABILITY OF ";N2$;" GIVEN ";N1$,"(5%
     =5)",:INPUT B:PB=B/100
 60 PRINT"PROBABILITY OF ";N2$;" GIVEN NOT ";N1$,
     "(5%=5)",:INPUT C:QB=C/100
 70 AB=(PB*PA)/((PB*PA)+(QB*QA)):PRINT
 80 PRINT"THE PROBABILITY OF ";N2$;" GIVEN ";N1$;
     " IS = ";AB
 90 END
```

Very often, however, there are a number of variables related to a given phenomenon. For example, related to winter in northern regions are wind, rain, and snow—among others. There is a modification of Baye's theorem which will facilitate the computation of the appropriate probability. It is:

$$p(B_k \mid A) = \frac{p(B_k) \times p(A \mid B_k)}{\displaystyle\sum_{i=1}^{N} p(B_i) \times p(A \mid B_i)}$$

To illustrate:

p(Wind) = .33333	p(Winter | Wind) = .75
p(Rain = .15000	p(Winter | Rain) = .05
p(Snow) = .25000	p(Winter | Snow) = .90

Using the equation above, the probability of one of those variables happening, given the condition of winter, can be computed to be:

p(Wind | Winter) = .5181320
p(Rain | Winter) = .0155441
p(Snow | Winter) = .4663240

Listing 2-4 is a short program which implements the more complex version of Baye's Theorem.

Listing 2-4. Complex Baye's Theorem

```
1   '*******************************************
2   'COMPLEX BAYE'S THEOREM                    *
3   'LISTING 2-4                               *
4   '*******************************************
5   '
10  CLS
20  INPUT"NAME OF PRIMARY EVENT";A$
30  PRINT"NUMBER OF EVENTS/CONDITIONS RELATED TO
        ";A$,:INPUT N
40  DIM E$(N),E(N),AE(N):PE=0
50  FORI=1TON
60      PRINT"NAME OF EVENT/CONDITION #";I,:INPUTE$
        (I)
70      PRINT"PROBABILITY OF ";E$(I),"(5%=5)",:INPU
        TE:E(I)=E/100
80      PRINT"PROBABILITY OF ";A$;" GIVEN ";E$(I),"
        (5%=5)",:INPUT P
90      AE(I)=P/100:PE=PE+(E(I)*AE(I))
100 NEXTI
110 CLS
120 PRINT"B = ";A$
130 PRINT"ITEM","NAME  (A)","P(A)","P(A GIVEN B)
    "
140 FORI=1TON:PRINTI,E$(I),E(I),(E(I)*AE(I))/PE:
    NEXT:PRINT
150 END
```

Counting Rules

The following principles help define many useful probabilistic characteristics:

K = number of possible outcomes in a single trial (in a normal cube die, K = 6)

N = number of trials

K^N = total possible sequences of outcomes

A coin toss has two outcomes: heads or tails. If we are to toss a coin five times (N = 5), there are 2^5 or 32 possible sequences. Even with just three flips there are 2^3 or 8 possible outcomes, HHH, HHT, HTH, THH, HTT, THT, TTH, TTT. This concept leads us into the notions of *combination* and *permutations*.

If you have three objects, it can be shown there are six ways, or permutations, that these objects can be arranged in a line: ABC, BAC, BCA, CAB, CBA. The general formula to determine the number of permutations given N objects is:

C = N! (read "N factorial")

N! = 1 × 2 × 3 × 4 . . . . × N

This gives us the number of different ways N number of objects can be arranged using all N object. Frequently, however, we are faced with situations in which we want to know the number of combinations possible using only R number of the N objects at a time. For example, a car dealer has ten cars in stock, but only room for three of the cars to be displayed in the showroom. How many different combinations does the salesman have to consider? The notation used to solve this sort of problem is:

$$P(\tfrac{N}{R}) = \frac{N!}{(N - R)!}$$

Therefore:

$$P(\tfrac{10}{3}) = \frac{10!}{(10 - 3)!} = \frac{10!}{7!} = \frac{3628800}{5040} = 720$$

The only problem with this computation is that it includes reflections of combinations. That is, it counts the combination of ABC as different from BAC. In trying to determine the number of arrangements of three cars this is not a meaningful count, unless the dealer is also trying to determine the number of ways each combination could be arranged. There is one more equation to help sort out the combinations:

$$C\left(\begin{smallmatrix} N \\ R \end{smallmatrix}\right) = \frac{N!}{R!(N-R)!}$$

Using this equation:

$$C\left(\begin{smallmatrix} 10 \\ 3 \end{smallmatrix}\right) = \frac{10!}{3!(10-3)!} = \frac{3628800}{6 \times 5040} = \frac{3628800}{30240} = 120$$

That makes the selection process a lot easier—only 120 different combinations have to be evaluated for sales effect. Having made the selection of what three cars to use, there only remains the task of picking which of the six (N!) lineups are the most effective.

From time to time it might be useful or interesting to know what the total number of combinations of objects is possible taking one at a time, two at a time, three at a time, and so on to N at a time. For example:

	N = 4			N = 5	
R	P	C	R	P	C
1	4	4	1	5	5
2	12	6	2	20	10
3	24	4	3	60	10
4	24	1	4	120	5
			5	120	1
Total	64	15		325	31

On examination we find that the sum of all possible permutations (P), given N, is $\Sigma P = \sum_{R=1}^{N} C\left(\begin{smallmatrix} N \\ R \end{smallmatrix}\right)$; and the sum of all possible combinations is $\Sigma C = 2^{N-1}$. Therefore, the car salesman has 1023

unique ways to display the ten cars ($2^{10} - 1 = 1024 - 1 = 1023$).

Listing 2-5 is a short routine used to do the various computations to determine the permutations and combinations of numbers less than 34. A number equal to or greater than 34 will cause most 8-bit systems to overflow. If normal use of such a program would involve numbers of N larger than 33, the basic factorial lines can be amended to use logarithms. For example

```
              N < 34
100   N!=1
110   FOR I=1 TO N
120   N!=N!*I
130   NEXT
140   R!=1
150   FOR I=1 TO(N-R)
160   R!R=R!*I
170   NEXT
180   P=N!/R!
190   PRINT"PERMUTATIONS=";P
200   END
              33 > N
100   N!=0
110   FOR I=1 TO N
120   N!=N!+LOG(I)
130   NEXT
140   R!=0
150   FOR I=1 TO (N-R)
160   R!=R!+LOG(I)
170   NEXT
180   P=N!-R!
190   IF P 87.3366 THEN 210
200   PRINT"LOG OF
      PERMUTATIONS=";P:END
210   PRINT"PERMUTATIONS=";
      ESP(P);END
```

Listing 2-5. Combinations and Permutations

```
1  '*******************************************
2  'COMBINATIONS AND PERMUTATIONS             *
3  'LISTING 2-5                               *
4  '*******************************************
5  '
10 CLS
20 INPUT"ENTER NUMBER OF OBJECTS";N
30 PRINTN;"OBJECTS CAN BE ARRANGED INTO";(2[N)-1
   ;"UNIQUE AND DIFFERENT SETS"
```

```
40 P!=1
50 FORI=1TON
60    P!=P!*I
70 NEXT
80 PRINT:INPUT"HOW MANY OBJECTS ARE TO BE TAKEN
      AT A TIME";R
90 P1=1
100 FORI=1TO(N-R)
110    P1=P1*I
120 NEXTI
130 PR=1
140 FORI=1TOR
150    PR=PR*I
160 NEXTI
170 C1=P!/P1:C2=P!/(PR*P1)
180 PRINT:PRINT"THE NUMBER OF COMBINATIONS WITH
      REFLECTIONS =";C1
190 PRINT"THE NUMBER OF UNIQUE COMBINATIONS =";C
      2
200 PRINT:RUN20
```

Probabilities and Permutations

By combining the various principles just presented, a very useful relationship can be demonstrated. Remember, not too many pages ago we defined the probability of something happening with P and its complement Q where: $Q = 1 - P$. As an illustration consider this information:

P = Probability of a defective item coming off an assembly line = .1 $Q = 1 - .1 = .9$

The supervisor of the assembly line has indicated that a run with forty percent or more defective items will result in a complete shut down and start up. We need to compute the probability that we would find two defective items out of five. The general equation to solve this problem is:

$$P_{R,N} = \frac{N!}{R!(N-R)!}(P^R Q^{(N-R)})$$

Solving:

$$P_{2,5} = \frac{5!}{2!(5-2)!} \quad (.1^2 \times .9^{(5-2)})$$

$$= \frac{120}{2 \times 6} \cdot (.1^2 \times .9^3)$$

$$= \frac{120}{12} (.01 \times .729) = 10 \times .0729 =$$

$$.72900$$

Based on the foregoing, there is a good likelihood that the line will shut down frequently. The recommendation would be to retool the line or otherwise improve their production technique.

The equation above computes the probability of exactly R defective items appearing in N objects. There are two other equations that are also useful:

1. $$\sum_{i=R}^{i=N} \frac{N!}{i!(N-i)!} (p^i \times Q^{N-i})$$

Probability of at least R defective items.

2. $$\sum_{i=0}^{i=R} \frac{N!}{i!(N-i)!} (p^i \times Q^{N-i})$$

Probability of at most R defective items out of N.

Listing 2-6 is a modification of the program in listing 2-5 that includes these computations. It includes a check for numbers larger than 33, which sends the computations into a logarithmic process if N is greater than 33.

Probability and Forecasting

A forecast is an estimate of some future condition. A probability is an estimate of the likelihood of that forecast being true. As we have just observed,

Listing 2-6. Combinations and Permutations Modified

```
1  '*****************************************
2  'COMBINATIONS AND PERMUTATIONS, MODIFIED *
3  'LISTING 2-6                             *
4  '*****************************************
5  '
10 CLS
20 INPUT"ENTER NUMBER OF OBJECTS";N
30 PRINTN;"OBJECTS CAN BE ARRANGED INTO";(2[N)-1
   ;"
UNIQUE AND DIFFERENT SETS"
40 R=0:PRINT:INPUT"HOW MANY OBJECTS ARE TO BE TA
   KEN AT A TIME";R
50 IFR>NTHEN40
60 INPUT"WHAT IS THE PROBABILITY OF 'SUCCESS' (
   5%=.05)";P
70 IFP>1THEN60   ELSEQ=1-P
80 IFN>33THEN250
90 NF=1:FORI=1TON:NF=NF*I:NEXT
100 FORI=0TON
110    X=I:Y=N-I:XF=1:YF=1
120    FORJ=1TOX:XF=XF*J:NEXTJ
130    FORJ=1TOY:YF=YF*J:NEXTJ
140    PI=(P[I)*(Q[(N-I))
150    PX=(NF/(XF*YF))*PI:IFI>RTHEN180
160    P1=P1+PX:IFI<RTHEN190
170    P2=PX
180    P3=P3+PX
190 NEXT
200 PRINT:PRINT"THE PROBABILITY OF....":PRINT
210 PRINT"    EXACTLY  ";R;"SUCCESSES IN";N;"TR
    IALS IS";P2
220 PRINT"    AT LEAST ";R;"SUCCESSES IN";N;"TR
    IALS IS";P3
230 PRINT"    AT MOST  ";R;"SUCCESSES IN";N;"TR
    IALS IS";P1
240 PRINT:PRINT:RUN20
250 NF=0:FORI=1TON:NF=NF+LOG(I):NEXT
260 FORI=0TON
270    X=I:Y=N-I:XF=0:YF=0
280    FORJ=1TOX:XF=XF+LOG(J):NEXTJ
290    FORJ=1TOY:YF=YF+LOG(J):NEXTJ
300    PI=(P[I)*(Q[(N-I))
310    PX=EXP(NF-(XF+YF))*PI:IFI>RTHEN340
320    P1=P1+PX:IFI<RTHEN350
330    P2=PX
340    P3=P3+PX
350 NEXT
360 GOTO200
```

however, there are several ways to view that forecast and probability. Given a forecast, we should ask whether the estimate is "at least," "at most," or "exactly." It is incumbent upon a responsible forecaster to make these aspects clear to the consumer of the information.

EXERCISES

1. Give two examples each of nominal, ordinal, interval, and ratio scales.

2. Given the following data, $X_1 = 23$, $X_2 = 45$, $X_3 = 32$, $X_4 = 123$, $X_5 = 43$, $X_6 = 56$, $X_7 = 98$, $X_8 = 67$, $X_9 = 78$, compute the correct value of $\Sigma\ X\ \Sigma\ X^2$.

3. Collect the ages of thirty to fifty friends or classmates. Tally these data and identify appropriate class intervals.

4. Using the data collected for 3 above, compute the mean and standard deviation of the data. Using the third standard deviation as the limit, define significantly "younger," and "older" ages.

5. Discuss kurtosis and skew and their utility in describing distributions.

SUGGESTED READING

Arkin, H. and R. R. Colton, 1970. *Statistical Methods*. New York: Barnes & Noble, Inc.

Bruning, J. L. and B. L. Kintz, 1968. *Computational Handbook of Statistics*. Glenview, IL: Scott, Foresman Company.

Byrkit, D. R., 1972. *Elements of Statistics*. New York: Van Nostrand Reinhold Company.

Minium, E. W., 1970. *Statistical Reasoning in Psychology and Education*. New York: John Wiley & Sons, Inc.

Chapter 3

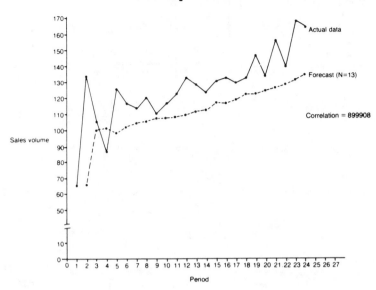

Data Base Management

This chapter has two objectives or levels of interest: how to manage data in the development of a program and how to manage data in the operation of a program. The nature of higher-language operation, especially interpretative languages such as BASIC, make it very easy to program directly on the computer as opposed to the older procedure of coding the program on paper and then keying the program into the computer for compiling and subsequent operation. During this period of program building and debugging, we are more interested in getting the program to work than we are in processing large amounts of data. Accordingly, we only need to enter a minimal amount to get all of the subroutines checked out. Only when the program is completed do we really need to approach the large data base. At the same time, we must develop a clear notion of the types of data processing we are going to require as these will influence the structure of the data base and aspects of the program. The conceptual processing is done in the stages shown in Fig. 3-1.

The task begins when the programmer perceives a need to write or create a program. The first step is to conceptually describe the output of the program and decide what kind of data are required to be input to the program to generate the desired output. Are these the types of data that remain static and well-defined, or do they vary with each use of the program? For example, in Chapter 12, we have an extensive program to compute the positions of the planets in the solar system for any given date. We depend upon a number of numerical constants that can be placed in a data base, as well as the desired data which is user-supplied. Therefore, we create a data base of the unchanging data and supply an input routine for the rest of the data. If we decide the nature of the program is such that no data base is required, we go directly to the building, debugging, and operating of the program. During the building process, however, we may want to create a small data base to help in the debugging. This application is discussed in the section on program building.

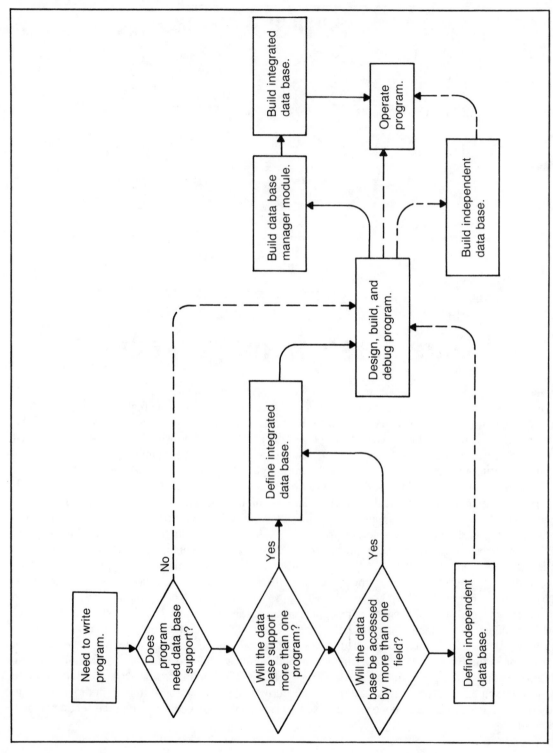

Fig. 3-1. Program development flowchart.

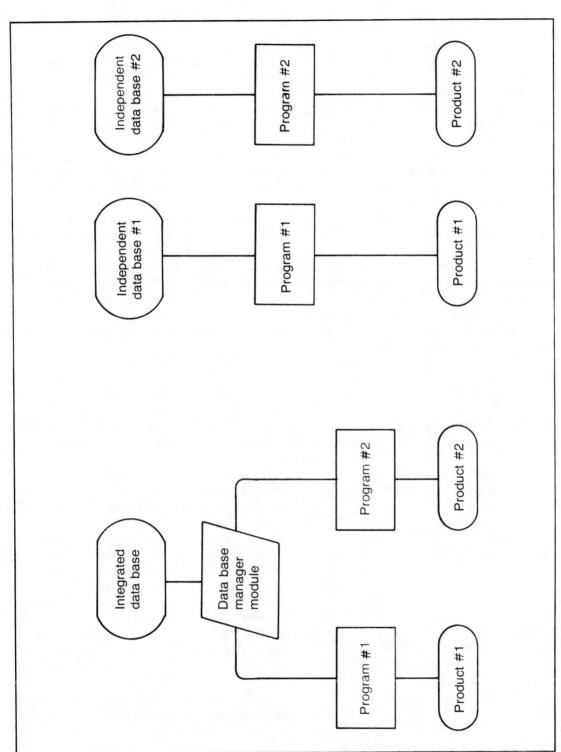

Fig. 3-2. Data base comparison.

If we decide a data base is desirable for the regular operation of the program, we should ask whether we have or will have other programs that can use the same kind of data. We may have only one application for astronomical data, but several applications for stock market data. Even if the decision is that there is only one program in which the data base will be used, we still should ask whether or not the program subroutines would call upon different aspects of the data. If the data base can support two or more programs or if the data base can be accessed by more than one subroutine, each one calling for different aspects of the data, an integrated data base should be defined; otherwise a file-type data base is sufficient. In either event, the data base should be defined adequately so that the program will call the same type of variables (integer, string, double precision, etc.), that are in the data base, and so that the data base will be ready to deliver the types of data required. Definition of the data base at this stage is also useful in determining whether or not to embed the data base in the program itself as data statements or to use external data storage. The number of string variables in the data base will influence the need to use the clear in command in the program.

The next step is to build the program and debug it. Later in this chapter you will find a short section on program building and debugging, which includes several approaches to interim data bases.

Once the program is constructed, the master data base, if required, is built. In the case of a multiple-program, integrated data base, you will also need to build the data-base manager module. Each of these aspects will be covered in greater detail.

DATA BASE TYPES

For our purposes, we will divide data bases into two basic types: *independent* and *integrated*. These two forms are illustrated in Fig. 3-2.

Using the astronomical example, independent data base # 1 could hold all of the ephemeral data related to each planet's motion around the sun, while independent data base # 2 could hold all of the data related to each planet's physical constitution, such as mass, mean temperature, atmospheric chemistry, and so forth, as well as the number of satellites and the physical aspects of them. Given the task of preparing a report on the physical aspects of each planetary system, you would have to go to program # 2 for the physical data and then to program # 1 for orbital computations. Conversely, given the task of doing a very precise computation of a planet's orbit, you must include the influence of the planet's satellites, obtained from data base # 2 and reentered into program # 1. Alternatively, the data concerning the satellites would have to be held in both data bases. A simpler solution might be to create an integrated data base containing all of the relevant data. While larger than either of the independent data bases, it would be smaller than the sum of the two.

Management Module

In larger computing systems, the data base management module is a separate program or computing system that our own terminal would address for assistance in obtaining the required information. In microcomputer systems, we refer to this manager as a module, meaning that it is a subroutine normally built into each program using the common data base. Listing 3-1 is an example of such a module. It standardizes the format in which the data is read from the data base and the procedures used to modify the data base. Every program using the master data file uses this module as written. Knowing this, the user can use a separate data base management program to update the file by adding to, subtracting or deleting from, or changing the entries without having to load and use one of the operating programs. Listing 3-2 is an example of the external data base manager/housecleaning program. In programs in which the data are contained within data statements, the external maintenance routine is inappropriate and would have to be built into the main program.

Listing 3-1 Data File Manager (Construct)

```
1  '******************************************
2  'DATA FILE MANAGER (CONSTRUCT)          *
3  'LISTING 3-1                            *
4  '******************************************
5  '
10 CLS:@CLEAR:CLEAR500:PRINTCHR$(210);"DATA FILE
      MANAGER  (CONSTRUCT)":PRINT:PRINT
20 INPUT"WHAT WILL BE THE FILE NUMBER";F:DIM N$(
      F)
30 INPUT"WHAT WILL BE THE FILE NAME";N$(F)
40 INPUT"ENTER BEGINNING YEAR";Y1:INPUT"ENDING Y
      EAR";Y2
50 PRINT:PRINT"A  --   ANNUAL
B   --   SEMI-ANNUAL
C   --   QUARTERLY
D   --   MONTHLY
E   --   WEEKLY
F   --   DAILY                   SELECT PERIOD   ";
60 GOSUB290  :P$=Q$
70 PRINT:INPUT"NUMBER OF COLUMNS FOR EACH ENTRY"
      ;C:DIM F$(F,C)
80 @OPENF
90 @PRINTN$(F),Y1,Y2,F,C
100 FORI=1TOC
110    PRINT"WHAT IS THE HEADING FOR COLUMN #";I,
       :INPUTF$(F,I):@PRINTF$(F,I)
120 NEXT
130 IFP$="A"THENP=1ELSEIFP$="B"THENP=2ELSEIFP$="
       C"THENP=4ELSEIFP$="D"THENP=12ELSEIFP$="E"TH
       ENP=52ELSEIFP$="F"THENP=365
140 M=C*(P*((Y2-Y1)+1)):@PRINTM
150 DIM M(M)
160 FORI=1TOMSTEPC
170    FORJ=1TOC
180    PRINTF$(F,J)
190       PRINT"ENTER VALUE, PERIOD";INT(I/C)+1;",
       COLUMN ";J,:INPUTM(I+J-1)
200    NEXTJ
210 NEXTI
220 CLS:FORI=1TOM:PRINTI;M(I),:NEXT
230 PRINT:PRINT"ALL DATA CORRECT?  (Y/N)   ";:GOS
       UB290
240 IFQ$="Y"THEN260
250 INPUT"ENTER ITEM NUMBER AND CORRECT VALUE";I
       ,M(I):GOTO220
260 FORI=1TOM:@PRINTM(I):NEXT
270 @CLOSE
280 END
290 Q$=""+INKEY$:IFQ$=""THEN290
300 PRINTQ$:RETURN
```

Listing 3-2 Data File Manager (Examine)

```
LLIST
1  '*********************************************
2  'DATA FILE MANAGER (EXAMINE)              *
3  'LISTING 3-2                              *
4  '*********************************************
5  '
10 CLS:@CLEAR:PRINTCHR$(210);"DATA FILE MANAGER
      (EXAMINE)":PRINT:PRINT
20 INPUT"WHAT WILL BE THE FILE NUMBER";F:DIM N$(
      F)
30 @OPENF
40 @INPUTN$(F),Y1,Y2,F,C
50 PRINTN$(F),"FROM";Y1;"TO";Y2
60 DIM F$(F,C)
70 PRINT"PERIOD",
80 FORI=1TOC
90    @INPUTF$(F,I):PRINTF$(F,I),
100 NEXT
110 PRINT
120 @INPUTM
130 DIM M(M)
140 FORI=1TOMSTEPC
150    PRINTINT(I/C)+1,
160    FORJ=1TOC
170       @INPUTM(I+J-1):PRINTM(I+J-1),
180    NEXTJ
190  PRINT
200 NEXTI
210 @CLOSE
220 PRINT:PRINT"DATA OK?  (Y/N)   ";:GOSUB310
230 IFQ$="Y"THEN330
240 CLS:FORI=1TOM:PRINTI;M(I),:NEXT:PRINT
250 PRINT:INPUT"ENTER ITEM NUMBER AND CORRECT VA
      LUE";X,M(X):GOTO220
260 @OPENF
270 @PRINTN$(F),Y1,Y2,F,C
280 FORI=1TOC:@PRINTF$(F,I):NEXT:@PRINT M
290 FORI=1TOM:@PRINTM(I):NEXT
300 @CLOSE:END
310 Q$=""+INKEY$:IFQ$=""THEN310
320 PRINTQ$:RETURN
330 END
```

Data Arrays

Data may be entered into the file in a free form tied to a primary key only by sequence or may be coded to show a relationship to the primary or secondary keys. For example, we may enter the planetary data in a specified sequence: name, motion 1, motion 2, size, distance, and so on. If we make a mistake or want to process another portion of the data, we have to reenter the data in the same sequence until we find what we are looking for. On the other hand, we can create arrays that are called up by key numbers. We can create a set of single dimension arrays, one for each planet. For example, $N\$(I)$ is the planet's name, $M1(I)$ is the planet's motion 1, $M2(I)$ is motion 2, $S(I)$ is the planet's size, and $D(I)$ is the planet's distance. By arbitrarily numbering each planet, 1 through 9 in any sequence, largest to smallest, nearest to the sun to the farthest from the sun, or whatever, we can call up any of the desired elements. Alternatively, we can create a two-dimensional array, V$(I,J), in which I is the planet's number, as above, and J is the variable identifier. As we obtain knowledge of other planetary systems around other stars, we could create a three-dimensional array, V$(I,J,K), in which K identifies the particular stellar system. The numerical values would be read first as strings and then converted to mathematical properties by using the V = VAL (V$(I,J,K)) command structure.

PROGRAM BUILDING

This book really doesn't presume to be a text on the finer points of computer programming techniques, but a few words on how the programs in this book were developed may be of some use to the less-experienced programmer. The principles noted here were arrived at pragmatically and are recommended on that basis; that is, we recommend them because they work.

Top Down Programming

Programs are solutions to computational or data manipulation problems or tasks. In the old days of computer programming, the first several periods of activity were consumed by conceptual and graphic analysis and flowcharting of the problem and the program. Sections of the program were written to solve subsets of the problem and were painstakingly handcoded and toggleswitched number by number into the computer. The operation of the computer itself was very fast, once the program was written and installed. The time to complete the program, on the other hand, was so time-consuming that it was undertaken for the most serious of purposes.

BASIC, and a number of other higher languages, however, have made light work of many programming tasks. The penalty we pay for the ease of programming is loss of speed of operation. Using interpretive languages forces the computer to take precious computing time to translate each instruction into a form it really understands. Unfortunately, we are easily lulled into inefficient pro-

gramming habits by the friendliness of the language. The nature of BASIC encourages us to use a technique known as *top down* programming. This technique works pretty much like it sounds. We start at the top of the program (line 10) with the beginning of the solution to the problem. As we go from the top of the program down to the end we can trace the flow of the solution to the problem. Some programmers place data statements in the program at the point in the processing where the data is required. To the extent the problem and its solution are straightforward and noniterative, this is as acceptable an approach as any. When we begin to move into complex programs calling for subroutines (using GOSUB commands) and other complex operations, top down programming loses some of its utility. Computers operating in BASIC begin at the first line number and work their way through the program listing as you would read a book: from the top left, to bottom right. Whenever you use a GOTO, the computer goes to the first line number and then counts down until it finds the indicated line number. If we are at line 2350 and use GOTO 2380, the computer will not jump ahead three lines, but will go to line 10 and then read 238 lines until it reaches line 2380. Even though it doesn't execute the instructions, the computer must take time to recognize the line number and check it to see if the destination has been reached. The same process is undertaken with even worse consequences when a GOSUB command is used. Not only does the computer go to the top of the program to start hunting for the indicated line, but it has to remember where it came from. When it completes the subroutine, it has to go to the top of the program and start hunting for the instruction immediately following the GOSUB instruction. To demonstrate this effect, take the longest program you have and load it into your computer. Assuming your program begins at line number 10 and ends before line number 60000, add this routine to your program:

```
1   GOTO 60000
2   PRINT"SUBROUTINE TIME TEST".
3   RETURN

    . . . . .
```

```
60000    GOSUB 2
60010    I=I+1
60020    IF I=1000 THEN 60000
60030    STOP
```

Run your new program. All it is doing are the six instructions you've just added. Time the execution of the 1000 iterations. Now, delete all of the lines of the program except for the six lines above. Run the program and time the execution. Subtract the time of the second run from the time of the first run. Divide the difference by the number of lines in the original program plus one. The result is the time each line of a program adds when the computer is told to go on a GOSUB search. The way to speed up the operation of your computer, then, is to put the subroutine(s) at the head of the program. The first line of the program is to GOTO instruction pointing to the first line of the operational program, bypassing the block of subroutines at the head. If you have a number of complex subroutines, try to determine the one most frequently used and sequence the subroutines according to the frequency with which they are used. Having said all that, I must confess that a number of the programs in this book place subroutines where they logically appear in the process. This is not because I don't believe what I say, but because I have balanced the cost of the time lost in the operation of the program against the desire to present a readable program. The time consumed by GOSUBs becomes most critical in executing graphics-intensive programs in which you want to create or manipulate an image rapidly. It can be very frustrating to watch a program compute a point, search through 200 lines, set the point, search back through 250 lines, compute the next point, and so forth. In this instance, optimum placement of both the computation and the setting components is very desirable.

Whether you use top down or some other approach to programming, I recommend that you decide early on what your data requirements are going to be (Fig. 3-1). Even if your program will ultimately not use data base information, you may want to create a line or two of data statements containing the type of data (and in the proper format) that the program will ask the user for when operational. In the example, you will need to know the user's day, month, and year of birth. You may also want to use the exact time of birth. It is a lot easier to debug the program and tidy up the displays if you don't have to take the time to reenter these data each time you run the program. The way to do this is shown below:

```
 9    RESTORE
10    PRINT"BIORHYTHM PROGRAM"
11    READ M,D,Y: PRINT"DATE = ",
      M,D,Y
12    GOTO 30
20    INPUT"ENTER MONTH, DAY, AND
      YEAR OF BIRTH"M,D,Y
30    . . . . (Compute and display biorhythms
      . . .)
. . . .
10000    DATA 5,29,1942
```

When the program is complete and the displays look just the way you want them delete lines 9, 11, 12, and 10000. In a similar fashion, if the program you are writing involves extensive and time-consuming computations followed by a complicated graphic display, you may want to develop the computational part of the program first and then use the computed data as above, skipping the computations, but reading data statements for the input to the graphics section. Alternatively, it may be expedient to let your computer generate a temporary data base. For example, let's say you've written a program to analyze several year's worth of temperature data. Rather than constructing an extensive table of data, let the computer build the table for you. At the very beginning and end of the program, add these lines:

```
 9      RANDOM: DIM T(60)
20000   FOR I = 1 TO 60
20010   M = 6.28 * (I/12 − INT(I/12))
20020   T (I) = (40 * SIN(M))) + RND(15) +
        20
20030   NEXT
20040   RETURN
```

This routine generates a series of numbers

that range from -35 to $+75$ along a twelve-month sine wave for a five-year period. You can change the values of the data in line 20030 so that the range more resembles the locality in which you are interested. You can change the period by altering the value in lines 9 and 20010. At the point in the program where you would normally enter the actual data or read the data from data statements, use: XXXX GOSUB 20000. These data will be sufficient to develop and debug the operation of the program and the graphic displays. In the process, it may occur to you that you need data of a different sort or that you can successfully use fewer data elements, etc. In the end, you will have a good idea of the volume and type of data you need to properly run the program without having wasted the time typing in actual data at the beginning.

Program Development

In closing this all-too-brief section on programming techniques, we offer several guidelines that may make the task simpler and the program more enjoyable:

1. Define in words and illustrations exactly what it is that you want as an output.
2. Consider the number of times you need to perform this task (generate the output), and decide whether or not computer processing or assistance is the quickest, easiest way to go. If not, cease and desist. Do it the easy way.
3. If the computerized way is the optimum way, examine the output required to determine what process and what sort of equations are required to generate that output.
4. As a function of the processing required, determine what sort of input data items are required. Refer to Fig. 3-1. Do you need to build a data base? Can you access someone else's data base? Follow the program development as recommended in the figure.

DATA BASES FOR MICROCOMPUTERS

Having decided that your program requires

data base support, you have two options: build your own data base or tap existing data bases.

Existing Data Bases

In the suggested reading section of this book are a number of references to existing data bases of quite a wide variety. Many of them are very expensive and are designed mainly for business or commercial applications. The on-line services all require that your system have a modem to facilitate transfer of data, and many require a communications terminal software package and disk drive so that your system can accept the data coming in. The point is that while it may be neither cheap nor easy to access commercial data bases, it is possible nonetheless. Some of the other data bases exist only on wide tape medium, so you have to have some sort of system to transfer the data from the tape into your system. Again, while few home or microcomputer systems include wide (½" to 2") tape format drives, the data bases are available. As an alternative to intensive research, you may find some of these data bases in print format. This approach won't reduce typing time, but will eliminate the need for original data hunting and compiling.

Data Base Construction

Entering data by keyboard is the course of last resort. If there is any way for you to enter data from an electronic source (disk, tape, remote data base), do so. If there is a way to enter the data via light pen or bar code reader, use it. Keyboard entry of data has at least two strikes against it: it is tediously time consuming, and it is prone to human error. In the event that it must be done, as will often be the case, I highly recommend you devise a way to avoid doing the task twice. Develop a fairly standardized format and enter the data in such a way that it can be saved on either disk or tape for subsequent use in other programs. In developing the data base, be sure to allow for expansion and correction of entries.

DATA FILE ORGANIZATION

The computer industry has developed three basic ways to arrange data files for processing:

sequential access method (SAM), indexed sequential access method (ISAM), and direct access method (DAM). The file organizations are pretty well suggested by their names.

Sequential Access Method

Data files using SAM consist of data in some sort of sequence. This can be date of occurrence, identification number, age, etc. Processing of these data is normally done in a sequential fashion. One application would be an accounts receivable package in which the customer files are listed in some order, normally by account number, and processed in that order on some periodic basis. For example, once a month the system would process each of the files, from the first to the last, checking to see if payments have been made, crediting each account for payments and accumulated interest, and noting amounts payable. It might also prepare the billing statements. Used in this fashion, the file can well be in a simple sequential order with new accounts added at the end of the file as new business is generated.

Indexed Sequential Access Method

As data files grow in size, the SAM system may become too slow at best, and the file may outgrow the capacity of any one of the storage media. Using ISAM, the data are separated into more manageable groups by some indexing system. In a mailing list program, for example, one may place the first half of the alphabet on one tape or disk and the second half on a second tape or disk. The data search routine would be a two step process. Ater you input the name of the data file to be retrieved, the computer determines the proper storage medium and prompts you to install it on a cassette system or, in the case of a multiple disk drive system, activates the appropriate drive mechanism. The second step is to search through these data for the desired item. Depending on the length of the specific file, there may be a secondary indexing. Using the mailing file example and the Exatron stringy floppy tape system, let's assume we have the list divided into three parts, A-I, J-R, and S-Z. Each part is contained on one of three tape drives,

0-2. Except for tape 3, each tape contains nine files, 1-9. The file matrix is shown in Fig. 3-3.

To access the system and pull out a specific address, rather than reading the whole file sequentially, the operator would enter the key name, N$. The computer, then, would identify the drive number from:

$$N = ASC(LEFT\$,1) - 65$$
$$D = INT(N/9)$$

The file number would be computed from.

$$F = N - (D * 9) + 1$$

Then, the drive and file are accessed by:

```
XX00  @D OPEN F: READ NF
XX10  FOR I = 1 TO NF
XX20  INPUT X$,A$
XX30  IF XR=N$THENXX60
XX40  NEXT I
XX50  PRINT"DATA REQUESTED NOT
      ON FILE":@D CLOSE: RETURN
XX60  PRINT:PRINT"DATA LOCATED":
      PRINT
XX70  PRINT N$,A$
XX80  RETURN
```

In a similar fashion, indexing based on the first *two* letters would be possible if the files were lengthy and complex enough to warrant the trouble.

Using this approach, updating the files would

	Drive		
File	0	1	2
1	A	J	S
2	B	K	T
3	C	L	U
4	D	M	V
5	E	N	W
6	F	O	X
7	G	P	Y
8	H	Q	Z
9	I	R	

Fig. 3-3. Hypothetical drive allocation.

be a bit more complicated than in the SAM. The process would follow this algorithm:

1. Identify the drive and the file number to be amended (D and F).
2. Open Files 10 through 18-F.
3. Move the data from file F + 1 into file 10 to make room for the expansion. Do the same for files F +2 to 9, into files 11 through 18-F.
4. Load in the data from file F and make the necessary corrections, deletions, etc.
5. Load in the data from files 10 through 18-F into files F + 1 to 9.

A program to implement this sort of file management is given in Listing 3-3.

Direct Access Method

In this approach, the data are called directly by some index or key element within the file. For example, a teacher could maintain student records by student number. To call up a file, the teacher would simply use the command: PRINT G$(SN), where G$( ) is a student's grade average, and SN is the student number. The limiting factor in this process is that all of the data would have to be resident in memory, and the array would have to be defined. Furthermore, if the student numbers were not sequential, some other method would be required to define the array matrix value.

Menu-Based Data Base Systems

Sometimes the easiest approach to accessing

Listing 3-3. Editing

```
1   '***************************************************
2   'FILE EDITING                                      *
3   'LISTING 3-3                                       *
4   '***************************************************
5   '
10  CLS:@CLEAR
20  PRINT"FILE EDITOR":PRINT:PRINT
30  INPUT"ENTER NUMBER OF FILE TO BE UPDATED";F
40  FORI=F+1TO9
50     @OPEN I
60     @INPUT N
70     FORJ=1 TO N:@INPUT A$(J):NEXTJ
80     @CLOSE
90     @OPEN 9+I-F
100    @PRINT N
110    FORJ=1 TO N:@PRINT A$(J):NEXTJ
120    @CLOSE
130 NEXT I
140 PRINT:PRINT"TRANSFER COMPLETE":PRINT
150 PRINT"HOW MANY NEW DATA ITEMS FOR FILE #";F,:INPUT M
160 FORI=1 TO M
170    PRINT"ENTER ITEM #";I,:INPUT A$(I)
180 NEXTI
190 @OPEN F
200 @PRINT N+M
210 FORI=1 TO N+M
220    @PRINT A$(I)
230 NEXT I
240 @CLOSE
250 FORI=10TO10+F
260    @OPEN I
270    @INPUT N
280    FORJ=1 TO N:@INPUT A$(J):NEXTJ
290    @CLOSE
300    @OPENF+I-9
310    @PRINT N
```

Listing 3-3. Editing (continued from page 39).

```
320    FORJ=1 TO N:@PRINT A$(J):NEXTJ
330    @CLOSE
340 NEXT I
350 PRINT:PRINT"READY FOR NEW FILE.":RUN
```

the data bases is to offer the use a menu of each portion of the data base that can be accessed. The commercial data bases, such as the Source, Dow-Jones News Service, or CompuServe, are examples of systems that use a menu to access the subsections. In such systems it is frequently useful to have one or more layers of menus and sub menus. Figure 3-4 illustrates the concept of a tree of menus.

It is not until the lowest level in a menu branch is reached that the actual data base is defined and loaded into the system for reading or processing.

CASSETTE DATA STORAGE

Up to this point, the assumption implicit in the discussion has been that the user will employ either a true disk or a data storage system that resembles a disk system, for example, the Exatron stringy floppy. Those owning simpler systems need not give up hope. Data storage and retrieval using only a cassette-based system is feasible. The main limitations upon such a system are the speed of access and the nondynamic nature of the data base.

The speed of access is limited to 500 to 1500 baud, depending on the type of computer system being used. The optimum file format is the SAM. The data exist on the tape in a sequential form and must be extracted in that fashion. Once in the memory of the computer, virtually any format and access method may be employed, so long as the entire data base can reside in memory at one time. If the data base exceeds memory capacity, the file format option returns to SAM.

Because of these limitations, changes to the data base usually require a total rewrite of the tape. If the data base is too large to be held in memory at one time, the problem becomes even more cumbersome, but not impossible. Data base management of cassette systems varies a little according to whether the user has a single or dual cassette option.

Dual cassette systems are somewhat easier to use for the purpose of upgrading or making changes.

Figure 3-5 illustrates the process of managing a dual cassette system.

The process illustrated is simply a housekeeping program. To add new files, a subroutine to add in the desired number of new files would be inserted just before recording the end marker.

In single cassette systems, the operator has to either keep switching between record and playback functions for each file item or use a system in which only a portion of the data base is processed at a time, depending on the amount of memory available. Figure 3-6 illustrates this process.

In both routines the actual number of files retained on the new data tape is accumulated by the variable J.

File structures in cassette-based systems can either be fixed-length records or variable-length records. The fixed-length record is the easier to input and output, but often consumes greater memory space than necessary. The variable-length record makes optimum use of memory space, but requires a much more involved program routine to isolate the individual records.

In the *fixed-length* record, each byte of a 255-byte file is assigned a particular meaning. The file is read from the tape as a string:

XX20   INPUT#−1, A$

The individual files, then, are extracted using the MID$ function:

XX30   FOR I=1 TO B
XX40   F$(I)=MID$(A$,((I−1)*(255/B))
        +1,INT(255/B))
XX50   NEXT I

As read from the tape, a mailing list file might read:

A$="JOHN A. SMITH   3393 E. FOUNTAZI RD.
BALTIMORE MD 20765 MARY K. JOHNSON   2101
1 WAVERLY   LAUREL MD 20707   HOWARD W.
WANDAKOWSKY   2567 SUNSET DR. WASHINGTON DC
20001"

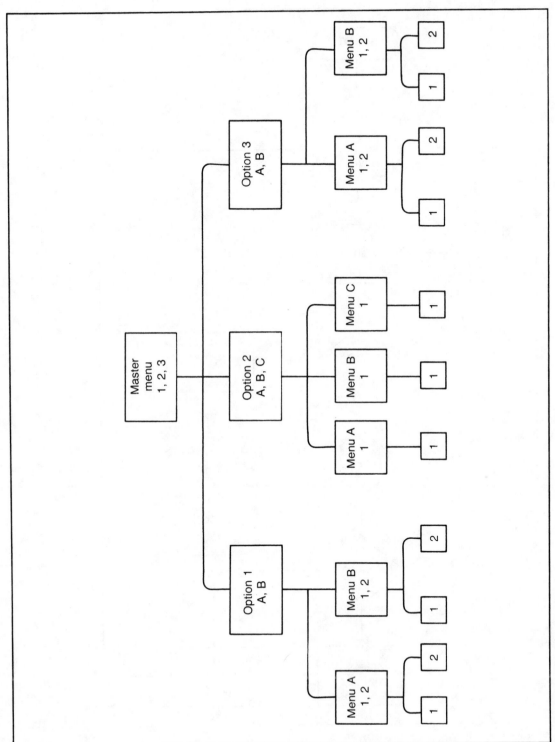

Fig. 3-4. Menu-based data base.

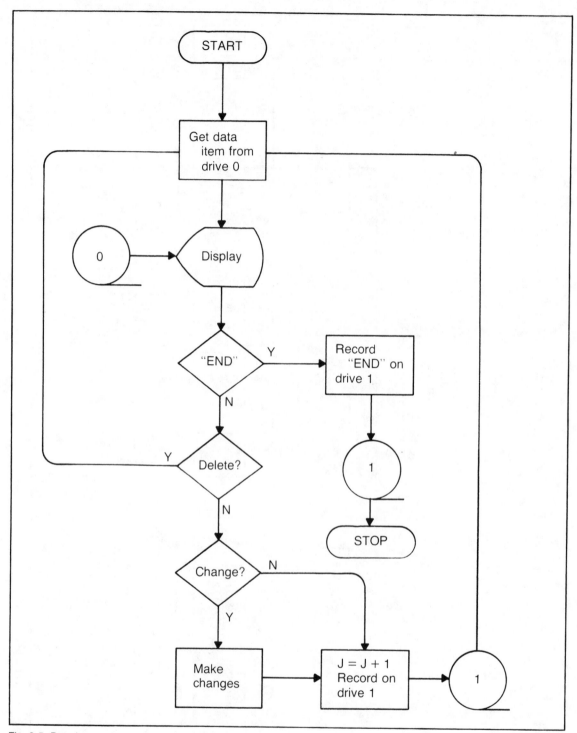

Fig. 3-5. Data base management flowchart, two tapes.

The spaces are required so the extraction routine knows where to look to specified items. By convention, the first 66 bytes (in this program) of each A$ string is the first name and address file. Each A$ would hold room for three names. A subroutine would extract from positions 1-23 the name, from 24-45 the street, and from 46-66 the city, state, and zip code. By reducing the individual file length to 63 bytes, the string could hold data for four names. An examination of the three files shown, however, suggests the average file is about 50 bytes long, implying we should be able to get five files onto a string. We can do this with a variable-length file.

In a *variable-length* file, we mark the beginning or end of each file with a special character, for example, the @ symbol. We can subdivide the individual file using other rarely used characters. Our file from above is converted to read

A$="JOHN A. SMITH/3393 E. FOUNTAZI RD./BALTIMORE MD 20765@MARY K. JOHNSON/21011 WAVERLY/LAUREL MD 20707@HOWARD W. WANDAKOWSKY/ 2567 SUNSET DR./WASHINGTON DC 20001@ . .. ."

Having inputted the string, A$, the process to extract the names and addresses goes something like this:

```
XX00    INPUT#−1,A$
XX10    L=LEN(A$):A=1
XX20    FOR I=A TO L
XX30       B$=MID$(A$,I,1)
XX40       IF B$="/" THEN XX60
XX50    NEXT I
XX60    N$=MID$(A$,A,I−A):A=I+1:'N$=
        NAME
XX70    FOR I=A TO L
XX80       B$=MID$(A,I,1)
XX90       IF B$="/" THEN X110
X100    NEXT I
X110    S$=MID$(A$,A,I−A):A=I+1:'S$=
        STREET
X120    FOR I=A TO L
X130       B$=MID$(A$,I,1)
X140       IF B$="@" THEN X160
X150    NEXT I
X160    C$=MID$(A$,A,I−A):A=I+1:
        'C$=CITY/STATE/ZIP
X170    IF A= >200 THEN XX00
X180    ((Process file data as desired))
XYYY    GOTOXX10
```

Numerical data can also be filed away in compacted strings as above. To extract the data, the routine above is invoked; then the substrings containing the numerical data are converted using the VAL(X$) command. Although all these processing considerations could be overcome simply by creating a data tape on which each separate data piece is recorded by itself, there are several good reasons for attempting to stuff as much data in a string space as possible.

The first reason is that each time the INPUT#−1 (or OUTPUT#−1) command is used, an electro-mechanical relay is "thrown" and a small electrical arc is created between the points of the relay. If done too frequently, the relay can literally weld itself shut. The second reason is that each time the command is given, the tape drive counts off 255 null bytes before reading data. This is done to allow the drive motor time to come up to proper speed for data transfer. The maximum string length is 255 bytes; therefore, at best, half of the time in each input is spent listening to nulls. If each string is only 50 bytes long, nearly 84 percent of the input time is spent in motor speed-up time. The third reason is that it is a waste of string space and memory.

To sum up, data bases are tedious to put together, but once you have completed that task, computer analysis of broad areas of subject matter becomes very easy and quick. The interested reader who has a hobby (other than the microcomputer itself) may wish to build one or more large general purpose data bases. Daily weather and economic data are readily available on various new media. Almanacs and other publications are sources of data base materials. By preestablishing a data base in an area of interest, it is easy and gratifying to follow an inspired thought and use the data base to check out a notion or theory.

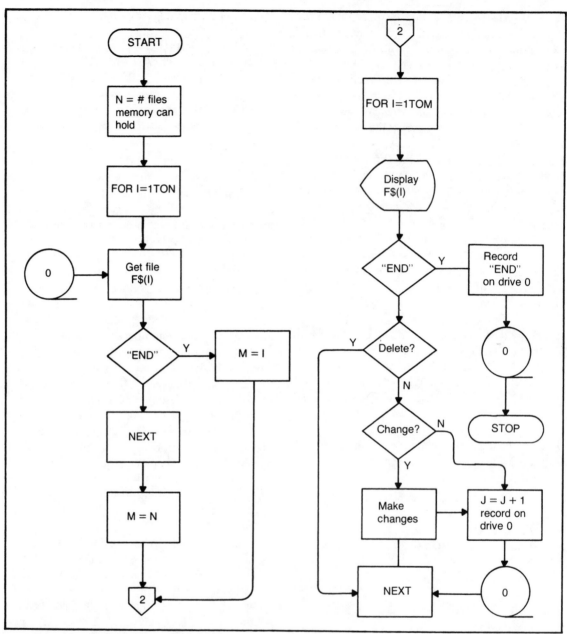

Fig. 3-6. Data base management flowchart, one tape.

EXERCISES

1. Give three examples of data processing tasks in which independent data bases are appropriate.

2. Give three examples of data processing tasks in which integrated data bases are appropriate.

3. Develop a program to manage a mailing list using a sequential access method.

4. Develop a menu-based program to manage

a data base consisting of at least five levels of refinement with at least two alternative options at each level for each superior option (see Fig. 3-4).

SUGGESTED READING

Katzan, H., 1975. *Computer Data Management and Data Base Technology*. New York: Van Nostrand Reinhold Company.

Martin, J., 1975. *Computer Data-Base Organizations*. Englewood Cliffs, NJ: Prentice-Hall.

Sprowles, R. C., 1976. *Management Data Bases*. New York: Wiley/Hamilton.

The National Technical Information Service (NTIS), a division of the U.S. Department of Commerce, 5285 Port Royal Road, Springfield, VA 22161, offers listings of data bases.

Chapter 4

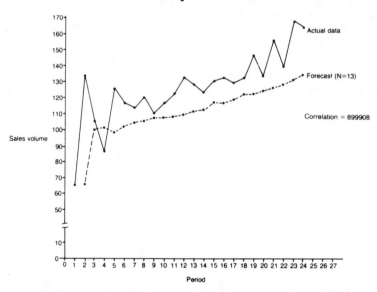

Technique Selections

The basic approach of this book assumes there are four main families of techniques available for use in forecasting efforts: correlation and regression analysis, time-series analysis, modeling and simulations, and numerical techniques. While there are certainly other techniques that have been contrived by mankind over the last several thousand years for looking ahead, some more practical than others, they are not generally suitable for immediate application using microcomputers. Selecting the most appropriate technique for a forecasting effort is at once a simple, straightforward task, and a complex, deceptive effort. Consider Fig. 4-1. This illustrates some hypothetical data generated to cover an extended period of time, say ten to twenty years.

How do we handle this complex curve from a forecasting perspective? The answer, in this instance, depends on how much of the curve you need to handle at one time. The curve section shown in Fig. 4-2 is taken directly from a segment of Fig. 4-1. If this is all we have to work with, however, we might be induced to assume we could do a forecast from a simple linear regression analysis.

This might work if it were the basis for the data. In reality, the data were generated as the sum of the three curves and one linear trend shown in Fig. 4-3.

In the final analysis, the solution to the problem requires a time-series decomposition approach—not readily evident from the initial data curve. The first task in technique selection, then, is to determine, as best you can, just what the available data represent. The second task is to determine what the different components that influence a given data point magnitude are. In the data just illustrated, do the points represent sales data? For how many profit centers? What is the product line? How many different customer types constitute the market? Is it a youth fad item or a staple product? Is the region going through any significant population change? What is the prevailing economic environment? The answers to questions such as these are most useful in establishing the analytic parameters of the forecast.

In general, the selection of techniques can be based on the following guide lines. When the data

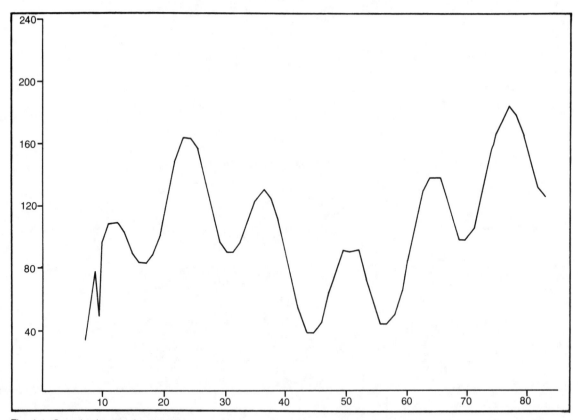

Fig. 4-1. Complex/composite curves.

appear to be functionally related to or a function of the passage of time, the forecaster will be inclined to pursue one or another of the time-series routines. When the data are not clearly time-related, the correlation and regression analysis area, often depending upon multivariate regression analysis should be considered. When the data are too obscure and are derived as the output of a complex process, you may, instead, choose to model or simulate the process itself in an effort to forecast future states by accelerating the flow of information through the model. Alternatively, it might be time and cost effective to exploit standard numerical techniques to build a mathematical model of a process which yields the desired output without duplication of the actual internal process or structure.

The final test of a forecaster's skill is the correlation between the forecast and the outcome, regardless of the method used to produce the forecast. From a scientific point of view, it is most desirable to build a forecast based on a rational basis. That is, if the data are largely a function of time, the technique used should be a time-series approach. If correlation and regression analysis can be used to demonstrate a cause and effect relationship, we probably ought to use one of those techniques.

EXERCISES

1. Give two examples of applications for each of the four basic techniques used in forecasting.

2. Identify the optimum technique for predicting the outcome of a football game.

3. Identify the optimum technique to forecast the outcome of the second half of a season of

47

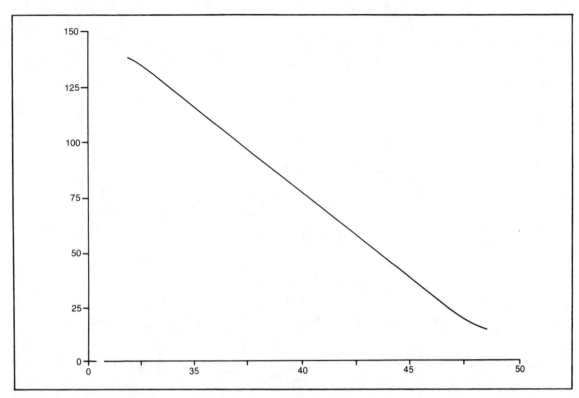

Fig. 4-2. Segment of curve (Fig. 4-1).

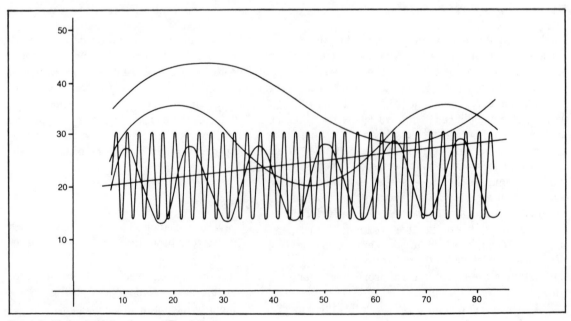

Fig. 4-3. All components of curve (Fig. 4-1).

football games among a league of six or more teams.

4. Define the primary distinction between correlation/regression analysis and time-series forecasting.

5. Research and develop a fifth family or technique for forecasting on a microcomputer.

SUGGESTED READING

Ayers, R. U., 1969. *Technological Forecasting and Long Range Planning.* New York: McGraw-Hill.

Bruning, J. L. and B. L. Kintz, 1968. *Computational Handbook of Statistics.* Glenview, IL: Scott, Foresman Company.

Edwards, A. L., 1976. *An Introduction to Linear Regression and Correlation.* San Francisco: W. H. Freeman and Company.

———, 1979. *Multiple Regression and the Analysis of Variance and Covariance.* San Francisco: W. H. Freeman and Company.

Makridakis, S. and S. C. Wheelwright, 1976. *Forecasting Methods & Applications.* New York: John Wiley & Sons.

Chapter 5

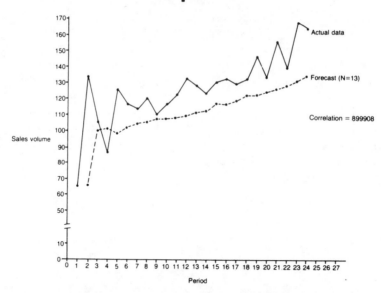

Correlation and Regression Analysis

Forecasting is frequently accomplished with the assistance of two statistical operations: correlation and regression analysis. For example, after some research the administrators of a school system have determined that there is a reliable relationship, or correlation, between the current population of the city and the number of students enrolled. Since the operating costs of the school (salaries, supplies, utilities) are all functions of the number of students, a forecast of the number of students will provide the data necessary for proper funding projections. If the board can project an accurate forecast of the city population far enough in advance, useful budget forecasts are possible. The relationship between total population and the number of students is a correlation. The estimate of the city population as a function of time is derived (in this example) from regression analysis. Correlations can be computed between two variables (normally an independent and a dependent variable). This procedure leads to a simple correlation. A correlation between a dependent variable and two or more independent variables is called a multiple correlation.

Regression analysis normally leads to the development of an equation that predicts the value of the dependent variable as a function of the independent variable(s). The basic form is $Y = A + BX$. That is, the dependent variable, Y, is the function of a constant, A, and the magnitude of the independent variable, X, multiplied by some coefficient, B. While B can take a fairly complex form, the basic principle remains the same. In very broad terms, regression equations, when plotted, can be said to take either linear or curvilinear form. The linear form is simply a straight line as illustrated in Fig. 5-1.

Curvilinear regression equations can produce, on the other hand, a wide variety of curves and shapes. Which form to use is determined by the correlation function. The regression equation gives estimates of the dependent variable as a function of the independent. The regression equation that produces the highest correlation between the known or real data and the estimate is the preferred equation.

This chapter outlines the procedures to com-

50

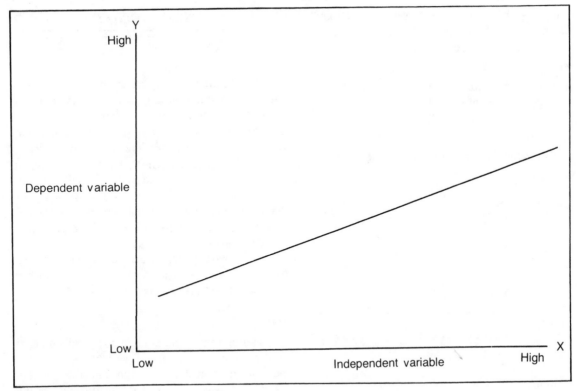

Fig. 5-1. Linear trend form.

pute both simple and multiple correlations and linear and curvilinear equations.

SIMPLE CORRELATION

Table 5-1 lists data in the form of a dependent variable, Y, as a function of the independent variable, X.

The task is to determine the relationship, if any, between the two. An algebraic solution yields the following relationships:

$$Y = A + BX$$

$$B = \frac{\Sigma \ (X - \overline{X}) \ (Y - \overline{Y})}{\Sigma \ (X - \overline{X})^2} \text{ or } B = \frac{XY - N\overline{XY}}{\Sigma X^2 - N\overline{X}^2}$$

$$A = \overline{Y} - \overline{BX}$$

where $\overline{X}$ and $\overline{Y}$ are the arithmetic means of X and Y.

The simple computation uses the sum of the product of X and Y, XY. Therefore

$$B = \frac{\Sigma \ XY - N\overline{XY}}{\Sigma \ X^2 - N\overline{X}^2} = \frac{1295 - 10 \dot{} 5.5 \dot{} 19.1}{385 - 10 - 3.25}$$

$$= \frac{244.50}{82.5} = 2.96364$$

Table 5-1. Sample Data.

	X	Y
	1	6
	2	10
	3	10
	4	13
	5	19
	6	22
	7	23
	8	26
	9	29
	10	33
Sum	55	191
Mean	5.5	19.1

$A = \overline{Y} - \overline{BX} = 19.1 - 5.5 \cdot 2.96364 \times 2.79998$

Hence, for any specified value of X:

$Y = 2.79998 + 2.96364\ X$

The formal process to derive these values is:

1. Collect the data related to the dependent and independent variables. These pairs are identified as: $X_1, Y_1\ ;\ X_2, Y_2\ ;\ X_3, Y_3\ ;\ \ldots;\ X_N, Y_N$.

2. Table the data according to this scheme:

Item	X_i	X_i^2	Y_i	Y_i^2	$X_i Y_i$
1	X_1	X_1^2	Y_1	Y_1^2	$X_1 \times Y_1$
2	X_2	X_2^2	Y_2	Y_2^2	$X_2 \times Y_2$
3	X_3	X_3^2	Y_3	Y_3^2	$X_3 \times Y_3$
. . .					
N	X_N	X_N^2	Y_N	Y_N^2	$X_N \times Y_N$
Totals	$\sum\limits_{i=1}^{N} X_i$	$\sum\limits_{i=1}^{N} X_i^2$	$\sum\limits_{i=1}^{N} Y_i$	$\sum\limits_{i=1}^{N} Y_i^2$	$\sum\limits_{i=1}^{N} X_i Y_i$

3. Compute the Beta coefficient from

$$B = \frac{XY_i - NX_i Y_i}{X_i^2 - NX_i^2}$$

4. Compute the Alpha residual from

$$A = Y_i/N - B\ X_i/N$$

5. Compute the coefficient of correlation (r) from

$$r = \frac{\sum\limits_{i=1}^{N} X_i Y_i - (\sum\limits_{i=1}^{N} X_i)(\sum\limits_{i=1}^{N} Y_i)}{\sqrt{[N \sum\limits_{i=1}^{N} X_i^2 - (\sum\limits_{i=1}^{N} X_i)^2][N \sum\limits_{i=1}^{N} Y_i^2 - (\sum\limits_{i=1}^{N} Y)^2]}}$$

The last value computed, r, is formally known as the Pearson Product-Moment Correlation, and is one of the most widely known and used coefficients of correlation. Without all the subscripts the equation looks a little tidier

$$r = \frac{N\Sigma XY - (\Sigma X)(\Sigma Y)}{\sqrt{[N\Sigma X^2 - (\Sigma X)^2][N\Sigma Y^2 - (\Sigma Y)^2]}}$$

and works just as well.

The coefficient of correlation, properly computed, will fall in the range $-1 < = r < = +1$. A correlation of either -1 or $+1$ means that the regression equation perfectly predicts the dependent variable from the independent. A positive correlation, $\emptyset < r < = +1$, means that as the independent variable increases, the dependent will also increase. A negative correlation, $-1 < = r\ \emptyset$, means that as the independent variable increases, the dependent variable decreases. A zero correlation, $r = \emptyset$, means there is no apparent relationship between the two variables. But, how confident can we be about the regression analysis? The standard error and the "t-Test" answer the question.

Standard Error

During the computation of a regression equation we obtain several useful variables such as the mean and median of the data, the standard deviation about the mean, as well as the coefficients of the equation. In practice, the expression $Y' = A + BX$ means that for a specific value of X, we will compute an estimate of Y. Given the mean and standard deviation of a distribution, we assume that we know how all of the data will be grouped around the mean, but how does each estimated value of Y, or Y', relate to the corresponding points in reality? Consider the figure below.

As the figure illustrates, virtually none of the points actually lie on the computed line of regression. On closer examination, however, we see that they do group about the line of regression in a manner very similar to data grouping about a mean. What we want to compute is a value very similar to the standard deviation that will give us some measure of the accuracy of the estimates. Such a value can be computed and is the "standard error of the estimate." It gives us the capability not only to forecast an estimate, but to specify with some reliability the range within which the estimate will fall. For regression equations, the standard error is computed from the equation:

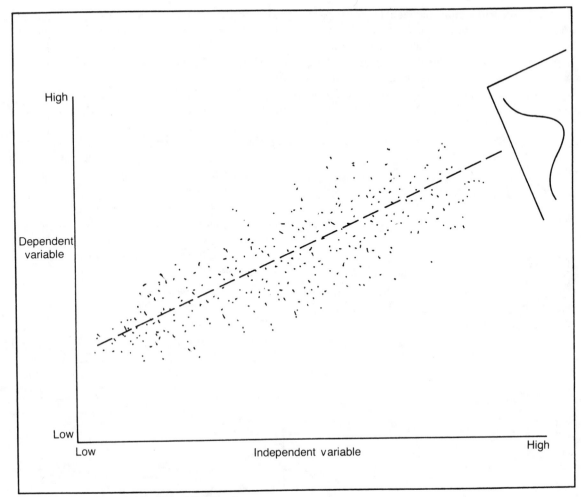

Fig. 5-2. Scattergram of data along linear trend.

$$S_{yx} = \sqrt{\Sigma (Y - Y')^2/N}$$

in which there is an estimate, Y', for each of N points for which there is a known value, Y. This is algebraically equal to the expression: $S_{yx} = S_y \sqrt{1 - R_{xy}^2}$ in which S_y is the standard deviation of Y and R_{xy} is the coefficient correlation between X and Y, a factor easily derived from the computation of the regression equation data. The basic regression program developed in this chapter contains a section to compute the standard error of the estimate.

t-TEST FOR SIGNIFICANCE

Two sets of data can be found to have the same coefficient of correlation, yet one is more meaningful than the other. How can this be? The difference is a function of sample size. The theory is that a coefficient computed from a sample of a thousand items is more meaningful than that computed from a sample of twenty. The *t-Test* is a measure of the confidence level of a correlation. The value of t is computed from:

$$t = \frac{r \sqrt{N - 2}}{\sqrt{1 - r^2}}$$

where N is the number of items in the sample.

The value of t can be any real number from nearly negative infinity to positive infinity. As r approaches zero, t approaches zero. As r approaches unity, plus or minus, the N grows larger, t approaches infinity, plus or minus. The value thus computed, however, has little immediate meaning, but is used to compute the probability that the coefficient of correlation is significantly free from chance error. Using calculus, the value of t is computed from the integral:

$$I(x,v) = \int_{-x}^{x} \frac{\dfrac{v+1}{2} \left(1 + \dfrac{y^2}{v}\right)^{-\frac{v+1}{2}}}{\sqrt{\pi v}\ \dfrac{v}{2}}\ dy$$

where x > Ø
and v is the degrees of freedom.

The integral, I(x,v) is represented by the shaded area in Fig. 5-3. The part we are interested in is the unshaded part. If the area under the curve is equal to one, then the tail end area is found using 1 − I(x,v). And here we come up against a fact of statistical life. Knowing that few things are certain, we have to decide at what point to accept or reject the conclusions of our analysis as being meaningful. In the social sciences, we are generally confident of our data and its implications if we can be 95% sure of the output. This is the same as I(x,v) = .95000. That is, we know the data are contaminated to some degree by random deviations and clerical error. Nonetheless, we will accept the findings if we are fairly sure the degree of contamination is 5% or less. In the more precise engineering sciences, where elements of an experiment can be much more tightly controlled, we frequently require the data to be at least 99% or even 99.99% pure. Whatever we select as the cutoff, that is the point against which we compare our data and the computations of r and t. Fortunately, we don't have to wade into integral calculus for help. Given a value of t, we can approximate the remaining values from

$$p = .5(1 + .196854X + .115194X^2 + .000344X^3 + 1.019527X^4)^{-4} + \Sigma$$
where $\Sigma < 2.5 \times 10^{-4}$ and D = v,

To return to the initial task: given a table of data, such as Table 5-1, the problem is to compute the alpha and beta coefficients for the linear trend,

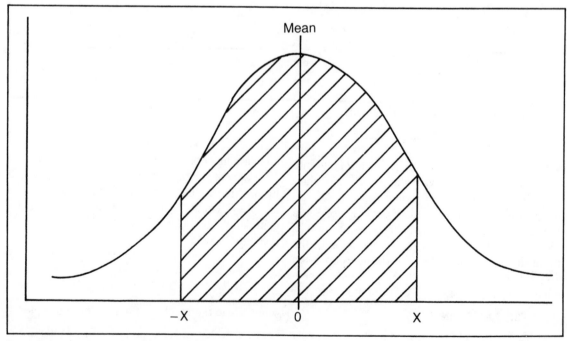

Fig. 5-3. Area under normal curve between +/− X standard deviations.

the coefficient of correlation, the corresponding value of t, and the tail values from the t-distribution—not to mention the standard statistics: the mean and the standard deviation. Using the routine in Listing 5-1, all of these variable are quickly computed.

CURVILINEAR ANALYSIS

In real life, unfortunately, a researcher seldom gets a set of data that distribute themselves neatly about a linear regression line such as in Fig. 5-2. Consider, instead, the data in Table 5-2.

When we run these data through Program 5-1,

Listing 5-1. Routine to Compute Linear Trend

```
1  '***********************************************
2  'ROUTINE TO COMPUTE LINEAR TREND               *
3  'LISTING 5-1                                    *
4  '***********************************************
5  '
10 CLS
20 INPUT"HOW MANY DATA PAIRS ARE THERE";N
30 FORI=1TON
40    PRINT"ENTER PAIR #";I,:INPUTX,Y
50    TX=TX+X:TY=TY+Y:X2=X2+(X[2):Y2=Y2+(Y[2):XY=
      XY+(X*Y)
60 NEXT
70 MX=TX/N:MY=TY/N
80 SX=SQR((X2-((TX/N)[2))/(N-1)):SY=SQR((Y2-((TY
   /N)[2))/(N-1))
90 R=((N*XY)-(TX*TY))/SQR(((N*X2)-(TX[2))*((N*Y2
   )-(TY[2)))
100 XE=SX/SQR(N):YE=SY/SQR(N):RE=SY*SQR(1-(R[2))

110 B=(XY-(N*MX*MY))/(X2-(N*(MX[2))):A=MY-(B*MX)

120 PRINT:PRINT"ITEM     SUM           MEAN           S.
    D.      S.E."
130         A$="  %%    #####.##   #####.##   #####.
    ##   #####.##"
140 PRINTUSINGA$;"X";TX;MX;SX;XE:PRINTUSINGA$;"Y
    ";TY;MY;SY;YE
150 PRINT"COEFFICIENT OF CORRELATION = ";R
160 PRINT"REGRESSION EQUATION:   Y' = ";
170 IFA<0THEN210
180 PRINTA;:IFB<0THEN200
190 PRINT"+";
200 PRINTB;"X":GOTO220
210 PRINTB;"X";A
220 T=(R*SQR(N-2))/SQR(1-(R[2))
230 PRINT"STANDARD ERROR OF REGRESSION = ";RE
240 PRINT"STUDENT'S T OF THIS DISTRIBUTION = ";T
250 U=N-1:X=1:Y=1:T=T[2:D=U:IFT<1THEN270
260 S=Y:R=D:Z=T:GOTO280
270 S=D:R=Y:Z=1/T
280 J=S*.22222:K=R*.22222:L=ABS((1-K)*Z[(1/3)-1+
    J)/SQR(K*Z[(2/3)+J):IFR<4THEN300
290 X=.5/(1+L*(.196854+L*(.115194+L*(.000344+L*.
    019527)))[4:GOTO310
300 L=L*(1+.08*L[4/R[3):GOTO290
310 IFT>=1THEN330
```

Listing 5-1. Routine to Compute Linear Trend (continued from page 55)

```
320 X=1-X
330 PRINT"TAIL VALUE = ";X
340 PRINT"PERCENT WITHIN CURVE =";100*(1-X)
350 PRINT:RUN20
```

the correlation is a discouraging .648776. It is time to follow the first rule in statistical analysis: plot the data—draw a picture. Figure 5-4 is a picture of the data from Table 5-2.

How can such a neat little line have such a horrible coefficient of correlation? Easy, we used the wrong process. We need a nonlinear process.

Simple, Nonlinear Regression Analysis

Figure 5-5 illustrates standard nonlinear curve functions that can be computed from the routine to compute a linear equation, with only a few additions.

The equations of the curves in the figure are listed below. To the right of each equation is the linear form of the same equation.

Power $\quad\quad Y = A X^B$

Exponential $\quad Y = A e^{BX}$

Logarithmic $\quad Y = A + B \log X$

$\log Y = B \log X + \log A$

$\log_e Y = B X + \log_e A$

same

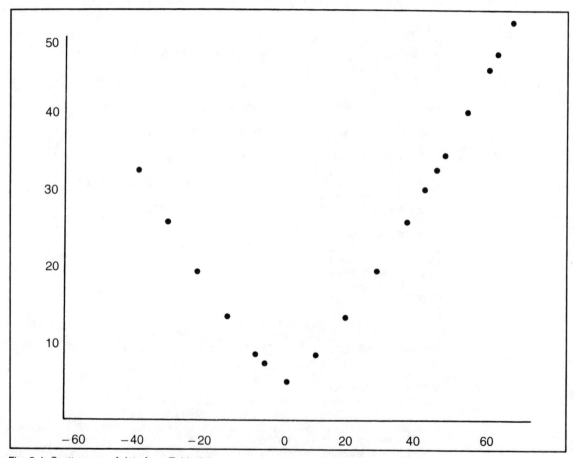

Fig. 5-4. Scattergram of data from Table 5-2.

Table 5-2. Sample Data.

X	Y	X	Y	X	Y	X	Y
− 40	32.980	− 32	26.035	− 24	29.560	− 16	13.669
− 8	8.572	0	5.000	8	8.572	16	12.669
24	19.560	32	26.035	40	32.983	48	40.331
56	48.031	60	52.000	42	34.784	− 6	7.473
54	46.075	37	30.327				

The regression equations for each of these are:

Power:

$$B = \frac{\Sigma (LogX)(Log\, Y) - \dfrac{(\Sigma LogX)(\Sigma LogY)}{N}}{\Sigma (LogX)^2 - \dfrac{(\Sigma LogX)^2}{N}}$$

$$A = \exp\left[\frac{\Sigma LogY}{N} - B\frac{\Sigma LogX}{N}\right]$$

$$r^2 = \frac{\left[\Sigma(LogX)(LogY) - \dfrac{(\Sigma Log\, X)(\Sigma LogY)}{N}\right]^2}{\left[\Sigma (Log\, X)^2 - \dfrac{(\Sigma LogX)^2}{N}\right]\left[\Sigma (Log\, Y)^2 - \dfrac{(\Sigma\, Log\, Y)^2}{N}\right]}$$

$$r = \sqrt{r^2}$$

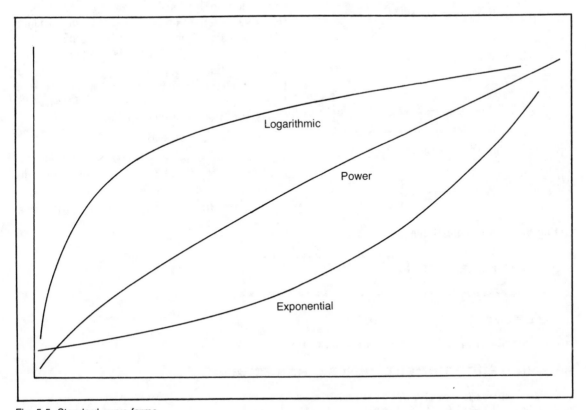

Fig. 5-5. Standard curve forms.

Exponential:

$$B = \frac{\Sigma\,X\,\mathrm{Log}\,Y - \dfrac{1}{N}\,(\Sigma X)\,(\Sigma\,\mathrm{Log}\,Y)}{\Sigma\,X^2 - \dfrac{1}{N}\,(\Sigma X)^2}$$

$$A = \exp\left[\frac{\Sigma\,\mathrm{Log}\,Y}{N} - B\,\frac{\Sigma X}{N}\right]$$

$$r^2 = \frac{\left[\Sigma\,X\,\mathrm{Log}\,Y - \dfrac{1}{N}\,\Sigma X \Sigma\,\mathrm{Log}\,Y\right]^2}{\left[\Sigma X^2 = \dfrac{(X)^2}{N}\right]\left[\Sigma\,(\mathrm{Log}\,Y)^2 - \dfrac{(\Sigma\,\mathrm{Log}\,Y)^2}{N}\right]}$$

Logarithmic:

$$B = \frac{\Sigma Y\,\mathrm{Log}\,X = \dfrac{1}{N}\mathrm{Log}\,X\,\Sigma\,Y}{\Sigma\,(\mathrm{Log}\,X)^2 - \dfrac{1}{N}(\Sigma\,\mathrm{Log}X)^2}$$

$$A = \frac{1}{N}\,(\Sigma\,Y - B\,\Sigma\,\mathrm{Log}\,X)$$

$$r^2 = \frac{\left[\Sigma\,Y\,\mathrm{Log}\,X - \dfrac{1}{N}\,\Sigma\,\mathrm{Log}\,X\,\Sigma\,Y\,^2\right]}{\left[\Sigma\,(\mathrm{Log}\,X)^2 - \dfrac{1}{N}\,(\Sigma\,\mathrm{Log}\,X)^2\right]\left[\Sigma\,Y^2 - \dfrac{1}{N}\,(\Sigma Y)^2\right]}$$

Listing 5-2 provides a combination of routines to compute all of the functions in this chapter to this point. After an input routine, the data are verified for accuracy. The program then computes the coefficients for each of the three curvilinear forms above, as well as the coefficients for a standard linear regression. For each equation a coefficient of correlation is computed. The program displays each of the resulting equations and then selects the one for which the correlation is the best. At this point the user is offered the option of computing interpolated points or proceeding to the graphic display of the input data. The graphic display can be directed to a printer if desired.

Although the lines generated by the power, exponential, and logarithmic equations are frequently anything but straight and linear, they are referred to as linear because they are computed from the basic form of the least-squares linear regression equation. They are referred to as simple regressions in that the dependent variable is a function (we assume) of one independent variable. While the data in Table 5-2, which is graphed in Fig. 5-4, were derived from a single independent variable generating the dependent variable, the computation of the trend line is not based on the foregoing linear regression, but on a form called a *parabolic regression*. The basic equation for this type is

$$Y = A + B\,X + C\,X^2$$

Using the routine shown in Listing 5-3, the coefficient of correlation becomes a healthy .984398, and the specific equation reads

$$Y' = 10.0401 - .0194275X + .0121101X^2$$

Listing 5-2. Linear Curve Fitting

```
1  '***********************************************
2  'LINEAR CURVE FITTING                          *
3  'LISTING 5-2                                   *
4  '***********************************************
5  '
10 CLEAR500
20 CLS
30 PRINT"******    LINEAR CURVE FITTING    ******"

40 PRINT:PRINT:PRINT"WILL THE LINE PRINTER BE US
      ED?  (Y/N)"
50 Q$=INKEY$:IFQ$=""THEN50
60 IFQ$="Y"THENLP=1ELSELP=0:Q$="":PRINT
```

```
70 PRINT:PRINT"THIS ROUTINE ACCEPTS THE DATA IN
      PAIRED X,Y FORMAT AND ATTEMPTS TO  IDENTIFY
      THE BEST LINEAR OR CURVE FIT."
80 CLS:PRINT:INPUT"ENTER NUMBER OF PAIRS:";P:DIM
      XY(30),XX(P),YY(P):PRINT
90 FORI=1TOP:INPUT"ENTER NEW X & Y VALUES:";XX(I
      ),YY(I):NEXTI
100 CLS:PRINT"# ";"X ";"Y ","# ";"X ";"Y ","# ";
      "X ";"Y ","# ";"X ";"Y":FORI=1TOP:PRINTI;XX
      (I);YY(I),:NEXTI:PRINT
110 PRINT:PRINT"ARE THESE VALUES CORRECT?   (Y/N)
      "
120 QQ$=INKEY$:IFQQ$=""THEN120
130 IFQQ$="Y"THEN150
140 INPUT"ENTER ITEM NUMBER, NEW X VALUE, NEW Y
      VALUE:";I,XX(I),YY(I):GOTO110
150 CLS:PRINT@512,"PLEASE BE PATIENT, COMPUTING"

160 FORI=1TOP
170     ONERRORGOTO880
180     X=XX(I):Y=(YY(I)):E(1)=E(1)+(X*Y):E(2)=
    E(2)+(X*LOG(Y))
190     IFXX(I)>LXTHENLX=XX(I)
200     E(3)=E(3)+(Y*LOG(X)):E(4)=E(4)+(LOG(X)*L
    OG(Y))
210     IFXX(I)<SXTHENSX=XX(I)
220     F(1)=F(1)+X:F(2)=F(1):F(3)=F(3)+LOG(X):F
    (4)=F(3)
230     IFYY(I)>LYTHENLY=YY(I)
240     G(1)=G(1)+Y:G(3)=G(1):G(2)=G(2)+LOG(Y):G
    (4)=G(2)
250     IFYY(I)<SYTHENSY=YY(I)
260     H(1)=H(1)+X[2:H(2)=H(1):H(3)=H(3)+LOG(X)
    [2:H(4)=H(3)
270     I(1)=F(1)[2:I(2)=I(1):I(3)=F(3)[2:I(4)=I
    (3)
280     J(1)=J(1)+Y[2:J(3)=J(1):J(2)=J(2)+LOG(Y)
    [2:J(4)=J(2)
290     K(1)=G(1)[2:K(3)=K(1):K(2)=G(2)[2:K(4)=K
    (2)
300     PRINT@640,"I =";I;
310 NEXTI
320 FORM=1TO4
330     B(M)=(E(M)-(F(M)*G(M))/P)/(H(M)-I(M)/P)
340     A(M)=(G(M)-B(M)*F(M))/P
350     R(M)=SQR((E(M)-F(M)*G(M)/P)[2/((H(M)-I(M
    )/P)*(J(M)-K(M)/P)))
360     PRINT@704,"M =";M;
370 NEXTM
380 CLS:PRINT"","A","B","R":PRINT"LINEAR:",A(1),
    B(1),R(1):PRINT"EXPONENTIAL:",EXP(A(2)),B(2
    ),R(2):PRINT"LOGARITHMIC:",A(3),B(3),R(3):P
    RINT"POWER:",EXP(A(4)),B(4),R(4):A(4)=EXP(A
    (4)):A(2)=EXP(A(2))
390 FORI=1TO6:R(I)=ABS(R(I)):NEXTI
400 IFR(1)>R(2)THEN440
410 IFR(2)>R(3)THEN460
420 IFR(3)>R(4)THEN490
```

Listing 5-2. Linear Curve Fitting (continued from page 59)

```
430 M=4:GOTO500
440 IFR(1)<R(3)THEN420
450 IFR(1)>R(4)THEN470    ELSE430
460 IFR(2)>R(4)THEN480    ELSE430
470 M=1:GOTO500
480 M=2:GOTO500
490 M=3
500 PRINT
510 F$(1)="LINEAR":F$(2)="EXPONENTIAL":F$(3)="LO
    GARITHMIC":F$(4)="POWER":E$(1)="Y = A + BX"
    :E$(2)="Y = EXP(LOG A + BX)":E$(3)="Y = A +
    B LOG X":E$(4)="Y = EXP(LOG A + B LOG X)"
520 PRINT"THE BEST CURVE FIT IS ";F$(M):PRINT"TH
    E EQUATION IS: ";E$(M):PRINT"A =";A(M);"
    B =";B(M);"   R =";R(M):PRINT:PRINT"DO YOU
    WANT TO COMPUTE A TERM?  (Y/N)"
530 IFSX=>0ANDSY=>0THEN550
540 ZZ=1:PRINT:PRINT"(DATA INCLUDES NEGATIVE VAL
    UES, ONLY THE LINEAR EQUATION IS
VALID.  IF
    ANOTHER FORM IS RECOMMENDED, PROGRAM WILL D
    ISREGARD
AND COMPUTE LINEAR.)"
550 QZ$=INKEY$:IFQZ$=""THEN550
560 CLS
570 IFQZ$="N"THEN860
580 PRINT@960,"ENTER '@' TO STOP:";
590 PRINT@512,"WHICH VALUE (X OR Y) WILL BE ENTE
    RED?";:PRINT@576,"                         ";
600 QX$=INKEY$:IFQX$=""THEN600
610 IFQX$="Y"THEN660
620 IFQX$="@"THEN860
630 PRINT:INPUT"ENTER X-VALUE";X
640 ONMGOSUB690  ,740  ,780  ,820
650 GOTO680
660 PRINT:INPUT"ENTER Y-VALUE";Y
670 ONMGOSUB710  ,760  ,800  ,840
680 CLS:PRINT@384,"X =";X;"      Y =";Y:PRINT:GOT
    O570
690 Y=A(1)+B(1)*X
700 RETURN
710 X=(Y-(A(1)))/B(1)
720 RETURN
730 RETURN
740 Y=EXP(LOG(A(2))+B(2)*X)
750 RETURN
760 X=(LOG(Y)-LOG(A(2)))/B(2)
770 RETURN
780 Y=A(3)+B(3)*LOG(X)
790 RETURN
800 X=EXP((Y-A(3))/B(3)
810 RETURN
820 Y=A(4)*(X[B(4))
830 RETURN
840 X=(Y/A(4))[(1/B(4))
850 RETURN
```

```
860 GOSUB1090
870 GOTO930
880 RESUMENEXT
890 P=N:GOSUB1090
900 GOTO930
910 END
920 PRINT:PRINT"THANKS FOR USING CURVE FITTING!!
    "
930 IFLP<>1RUN10
940 LPRINTSTRING$(2,10)
950 LPRINT" ":LPRINT"TABLE OF INPUT/OUTPUT VALUE
    S":LPRINT" "
960 LPRINT"INPUT":LPRINT"X","Y","X","Y","X","Y",
    "X","Y"
970 FORI=1TOP:LPRINTXX(I),YY(I),:NEXTI
980 IFRR=2THEN1070
990 LPRINT" ":LPRINT"INTERMEDIATE VALUES":LPRINT
    "I","E(I)","F(I)","G(I)","H(I)","I(I)","J(I
    )","K(I)"
1000 FORI=1TO4:LPRINTI,E(I),F(I),G(I),H(I),I(I),
    J(I),K(I):TT(I)=(R(I)*SQR(P-2)/SQR(1-(R(I)
    [2)):NEXTI
1010 LPRINT" ":LPRINT"OUTPUT":LPRINT" ","A","B",
    "R","t-TEST","EQUATIONS"
1020 LPRINT"LINEAR",A(1),B(1),R(1),TT(1),E$(1)
1030 LPRINT"EXPONENTIAL",A(2),B(2),R(2),TT(2),E$
    (2)
1040 LPRINT"LOGARITHMIC",A(3),B(3),R(3),TT(3),E$
    (3)
1050 LPRINT"POWER",A(4),B(4),R(4),TT(4),E$(4)
1060 LPRINTSTRING$(5,10):CLS:RUN10
1070 LPRINTSTRING$(3,10)
1080 END
1090 FX=(LX-SX)/127:FY=(LY-SY)/47
1100 ZX=127*(ABS(SX)/(LX-SX)):ZY=47-(47*(ABS(SY)
    /(LY-SY)))
1110 CLS
1120 FORI=1TOP
1130    SET((XX(I)-SX)/FX,47-((YY(I)-SY)/FY))
1140 NEXTI
1150 X=ZX:FORY=0TO47:SET(X,Y):NEXTY
1160 Y=ZY:FORX=0TO127:SET(X,Y):NEXTX
1170 PRINT@960+INT(ZX/2),0;:PRINT@1017,LX;:PRINT
    @64*INT(ZY/3),0;:PRINT@0,LY;
1180 IFRR=2THEN1210
1190 GOSUB1360
1200 IFLP=1THEN1230
1210 PRINT@34,"ENTER TO CONTINUE";:INPUTZQ
1220 RETURN
1230 LPRINT" "
1240 FORY=0TO47
1250    FORX=0TO127
1260        IFPOINT(X,Y)=-1THENLPRINT"*";
1270        IFPOINT(X,Y)=0THENLPRINT" ";
1280    NEXTX
1290    LPRINT" "
1300 NEXTY
```

Listing 5-2. Linear Curve Fitting (continued from page 61)

```
1310 LPRINT" "
1320 LPRINT"X-AXIS: MINIMUM =";SX;"  MAXIMUM =";
     LX;"  SCALE INTERVAL VALUE =";(LX-SX)/128
1330 LPRINT"Y-AXIS: MINIMUM =";SY;"  MAXIMUM =";
     LY;"  SCALE INTERVAL VALUE =";(LY-SY)/48
1340 LPRINTSTRING$(3,10)
1350 RETURN
1360 FORI=SXTOLXSTEP(LX/100)
1370    ONERRORGOTO880
1380    X=I:IFRR=1THEN1430
1390    ONMGOSUB690 ,740 ,780 ,820
1400    SET((X-SX)/FX,47-((Y-SY)/FY))
1410 NEXTI
1420 RETURN
1430 X$=STR$(X):GOSUB1470
1440 GOTO1400
1450 END
1460 RESUMENEXT
1470 X=VAL(X$):P=0:FORJ=1TOD:P=P+R(J+1,D+1)*X[J:
     Y=P:NEXTJ:RETURN
```

Listing 5-3. Least Squares Parabolic Fit

```
1  '***********************************************
2  'LEAST SQUARES PARABOLIC FIT             *
3  'LISTING 5-3                             *
4  '***********************************************
5  '
10 CLS:INPUT"NUMBER OF DATA POINTS";N
20 IFN<3THEN10
30 DIM X(N),Y(N),YY(N)
40 PRINT
50 FORI=1TON:PRINTI,"X, Y DATA";:INPUTX(I),Y(I):
   NEXTI
60 FORI=1TON:PRINTI;X(I);Y(I),:NEXTI:PRINT
70 PRINT"ARE ALL DATA CORRECT  (Y/N)";
80 Q$=""+INKEY$:IFQ$=""THEN80
90 IFQ$="Y"THEN110
100 PRINT:INPUT"ENTER ITEM NUMBER AND CORRECT VA
    LUES";I,X(I),Y(I):GOTO60
110 PRINT:PRINT"COMPUTING ...":PRINT
120 FORI=1TON
130    A1=A1+X(I):A2=A2+(X(I)[2):A3=A3+(X(I)[3):A
    4=A4+(X(I)[4):B0=B0+Y(I):B1=B1+(Y(I)*X(I)):
    B2=B2+(Y(I)*(X(I)[2))
140 NEXTI
150 A1=A1/N:A2=A2/N:A3=A3/N:A4=A4/N:B0=B0/N:B1=B
    1/N:B2=B2/N
160 D=(A2*A4-A3[2)-A1*(A1*A4-A3*A2)+A2*(A1*A3-A2
    [2)
170 U=(B0*(A2*A4-A3[2)+B1*(A3*A2-A1*A4)+B2*(A1*A
    3-A2[2))/D
180 V=(B0*(A3*A2-A1*A4)+B1*(A4-A2[2)+B2*(A2*A1-A
    3))/D
190 W=(B0*(A1*A3-A2*A2)+B1*(A1*A2-A3)+B2*(1*A2-A
    1*A1))/D
200 PRINT:PRINT"    Y' = ";U;:IFV<0THEN220
```

```
210 PRINT"+";
220 PRINTU;"X ";:IFW<0THEN240
230 PRINT"+";
240 PRINTW;"X[2 ":PRINT
250 PRINT"COMPUTING .... AGAIN ..."
260 FORI=1TON
270    TX=TX+X(I):Y=U+(V*X(I))+(W*(X(I)[2)):YY(I)
       =Y:TY=TY+Y
280    X2=X2+(X(I)[2):Y2=Y2+(Y[2):XY=XY+(X(I)*Y)
290    IFX(I)<=LXTHEN310
300    LX=X(I)
310    IFY>Y(I)THEN340
320    IFY(I)<=LYTHEN360
330    LY=Y(I):GOTO360
340    IFY<=LYTHEN360
350    LY=Y
360    IFX(I)>SXTHEN380
370    SX=X(I)
380    IFY<Y(I)THEN410
390    IFY(I)>SYTHEN430
400    SY=Y(I):GOTO430
410    IFY>SYTHEN430
420    SY=Y
430 NEXTI
440 R=((N*XY)-(TX*TY))/SQR(((N*X2)-(TX[2))*((N*Y
    2)-(TY[2)))
450 PRINT"COEFFICIENT OF CORRELATION = ";R:PRINT

460 PRINT"(N)EW DATA   (G)RAPH   (I)NTERPOLATION"
    ;
470 Q$=""+INKEY$:IFQ$=""THEN470   ELSEIFQ$="G"THE
    N490   ELSEIFQ$="I"THEN750   ELSEIFQ$<>"N"THE
    N470
480 RUN
490 CLS
500 ONERRORGOTO740
510 IFSY<0THEN530
520 Y=47:DY=LY:GOTO540
530 DY=LY-SY:Y=INT((LY/DY)*47)
540 IFSX<0THEN560
550 X=0:DX=LX:GOTO570
560 DX=LX-SX:X=127*(LX/DX)
570 FORI=0TO127:SET(I,Y):NEXT
580 FORI=0TO47:SET(X,I):NEXT
590 PRINT@(INT(Y/3)*64)+58,LX;
600 PRINT@INT(X/2)+65,LY;
610 FORI=1TON
620    IFX(I)<=0THEN640
630    XI=X+(X*(X(I)/LX)):GOTO650
640    XI=X-(X*X(I)/SX)
650    IFY<=0THEN670
660    Y1=47-(47*(YY(I)/LY)):GOTO680
670    Y1=47*(YY(I)/SY)
680    IFY(I)<=0THEN700
690    Y2=47-(47*(Y(I)/LY)):GOTO710
700    Y2=47*(Y(I)/SY)
710    SET(XI,Y1):SET(XI,Y2)
```

Listing 5-3. Least Squares Parabolic Fit (continued from page 63)

```
720 NEXTI
730 PRINT@10,"";:GOTO460
740 RESUMENEXT
750 PRINT:INPUT"ENTER X COORDINATE";X
760 Y=U+(V*X)+(W*(X[2)):PRINT"Y = ";Y:PRINT:GOTO
    460
```

This program collects a number of variables not used in Listing 5-2, so the programs have not been merged. Depending on the available memory in your system, this routine could be incorporated, at some loss of processing speed, into the previous program.

An interesting variation on the foregoing regression form is a more generalized approach called an *nth order regression*. This regression takes the generic form:

$$Y = A + BX + CX^2 + DX^3 + \ldots + NX^n$$

The coefficient of correlation will vary according to the degree of the equation specified by the user, which will depend on the input and the number of items. The program in Listing 5-4 computes the various coefficients and related statistics, depending only on the degree of the equation specified by the user. The only real limitation, other than the memory capacity of the computer, is that the number of data points must be at least two more than the degree of the equation. After the first pass, the program gives the user the option of a step-wise check to verify which degree provides the best correlation. Again, as with the program in Listing 5-3, the variables collected are in a different format from those in Listing 5-2, making inclusion in that program cumbersome. Nonetheless, provided that memory capacity is not strained, it would be useful to embed this program in one similar to the one in Listing 5-2.

Listing 5-4. Nth Order Regression

```
1   '*****************************************
2   'N-TH ORDER REGRESSION                   *
3   'LISTING 5-4                             *
4   '*****************************************
5   '
10 CLS:INPUT"DEGREE OF EQUATION";D
20 INPUT"NUMBER OF KNOWN POINTS";N
30 IFN>(D+1)THEN50
40 PRINT"SORRY--WE NEED AT LEAST";D+2;"POINTS":G
    OTO20
50 DIM XX(N),YY(N),A((2*(N))+1),R(N,N),T(N):A(1)
    =N
60 FORI=1TON:PRINT"X, Y OF POINT #";I;:INPUTXX(I
    ),YY(I):NEXT
70 FORI=1TON:PRINTI;XX(I);YY(I),:NEXTI
80 PRINT:PRINT"ARE THESE CORRECT?  (Y/N)"
90 Q$=""+INKEY$:IFQ$=""THEN90    ELSEIFQ$="Y"THEN
    110
100 PRINT:INPUT"ITEM #, X, Y";I,XX(I),YY(I):GOTO
    70
110 CLS:PRINT"COMPUTING...":PRINT
120 FORI=1TON
130    X=XX(I):Y=YY(I)
140    FORJ=2TO((2*D)+1):A(J)=A(J)+(X[(J-1)):NEXT

150    FORK=1TOD+1:R(K,D+2)=T(K)+(Y*(X[(K-1))):T(
    K)=T(K)+(Y*(X[(K-1))):NEXTK
160    T(D+2)=T(D+2)+(Y[2)
```

```
170 NEXTI
180 FORJ=1TOD+1:FORK=1TOD+1:R(J,K)=A(J+K-1):NEXT
    K:NEXTJ
190 FORJ=1TOD+1
200    FORK=JTOD+1
210      IFR(K,J)<>0THEN240
220    NEXTK
230    PRINT"NO UNIQUE SOLUTION":GOTO510
240    FORI=1TOD+2:S=R(J,I):R(J,I)=R(K,I):R(K,I)=
    S:NEXTI
250    Z=1/R(J,J):FORI=1TOD+2:R(J,I)=Z*R(J,I):NEX
    TI
260    FORK=1TOD+1
270      IFK=JTHEN300
280      Z=-R(K,J)
290      FORI=1TOD+2:R(K,I)=R(K,I)+(Z*R(J,I)):NEX
    TI
300    NEXTK
310 NEXTJ
320 IFQ$="C"THEN350
330 PRINT"           CONSTANT = ";R(1,D+2)
340 FORJ=1TOD:PRINTJ;"DEGREE COEFFICIENT = ";R(J
    +1,D+2):NEXTJ:PRINT
350 P=0
360 FORJ=2TOD+1:P=P+(R(J,D+2)*(T(J)-(A(J)*(T(1)/
    N)))):NEXTJ
370 Q=T(D+2)-((T(1)[2]/N):Z=Q-P:I=N-D-1:J=P/Q:PR
    INT
380 IFQ$="C"THEN400
390 PRINT"COEFFICIENT OF DETERMINATION (R[2) = "
    ;J
400 IFJ=>0THEN420
410 PRINT"COEFFICIENT OF CORRELATION        = "
    ;-1*SQR(ABS(J)):GOTO430
420 PRINT"COEFFICIENT OF CORRELATION        = "
    ;SQR(J)
430 IFQ$="C"THEN580   ELSEIFZ=>0THEN450
440 PRINT"STANDARD ERROR OF ESTIMATE         =";
    -1*SQR(ABS(Z/I)):GOTO460
450 PRINT"STANDARD ERROR OF ESTIMATE         = "
    ;SQR(Z/I)
460 PRINT:PRINT"(I)NTERPOLATION   (C)ORRELATION
    ANALYSIS   (N)EW
470 Q$=""+INKEY$:IFQ$=""THEN470   ELSEIFQ$="N"THE
    N510   ELSEIFQ$="C"THEN530   ELSEIFQ$<>"I"THE
    N470
480 PRINT:P=R(1,D+2):INPUT"ENTER X VALUE";X
490 FORJ=1TOD:P=P+(R(J+1,D+2)*(X[J)):NEXTJ
500 PRINT"Y = ";P:GOTO460
510 RUN10
520 END
530 PRINT:PRINT"COMPUTING";N-2;"REGRESSION CORRE
    LATION COMPARISONS"
540 FORD=1TON-2
550    FORI=2TO((2*N)+1):A(I)=0:NEXTI
560    FORI=1TON:FORJ=1TON:R(I,J)=0:NEXTJ:T(I)=0:
    NEXTI
570    PRINT"D =";D,:GOTO120
```

65

Listing 5-4. Nth Order Regression (continued from page 65)

```
580 NEXTD
590 PRINT:INPUT"COMPLETE STATISTICS FOR WHAT DEG
    REE";D:Q$="":GOTO120
600 GOTO460
```

To this point we have presented some routines to process data in a basic two-variable (independent and dependent variables) format. To the extent the dependent variable is a direct function of the independent variable, we should usually be able to predict the dependent variable by using one of the equations below:

$$Y = A + BX \qquad \text{normal}$$
$$Y = AX^B \qquad \text{power}$$
$$Y = Ae^{BX} \qquad \text{exponential}$$
$$Y = A + B \log X \qquad \text{logarithmic}$$
$$Y = A + BX + CX^2 +$$
$$\ldots + NX^N \qquad \text{Nth Order}$$
$$Y = A + BX + CX^2 \qquad \text{parabolic (special case of Nth Order)}$$

Seldom, however, are things quite so neat and tidy. Dependent variables have a disagreeable habit of being related to two or more otherwise independent variables. How tall are you? Is that a function of age, sex, family genetics, or diet? Probably a little bit of each of those and others. To compute height as a function of just one variable would produce results of only limited value. Never fear, however, we have techniques to handle multiple variables, and we refer to these as multiple regression techniques.

MULTIPLE REGRESSION

The generalized form of a multiple regression equation is:

$$Y = A + BX_1 + CX_2 + \ldots + NX_N$$

where X_k are different variables, such as X_1 = age, X_2 = weight, X_3 = reading level, X_4 = number of sisters, $\ldots X_n$ = number of pets (or any other kinds of variables)

Listing 5-5 provides a technique for evaluation of the effect of a set of multiple variables upon a dependent. Provided you have the patience and your computer has the memory capacity, any number of variables can be entered into this program and processed against some specified dependent variable. The program outputs the appropriate coefficients for each variable and the residual for the equation. In addition, it computes the coefficient of correlation. At the end of the first run, the program offers the options of using a trial value (an interpolation subroutine), entering new data, or computing a *best fit*. This last subroutine redefines the parameters of the task and recomputes the various coefficients and correlations to determine which set of variables, taken singly or in combination, produce the best predictor of the dependent variable. Of course, the program does not concern itself with logical relationships, but simply identifies those variables that seem to relate best to the dependent variable. If the number of goldfish in your tank at home relates best to your SAT score, so be it.

The data in Table 5-3 were processed using the following program and the results are given.

Listing 5-5. Multiple Linear Regressions

```
1  '*****************************************
2  'MULTIPLE LINEAR REGRESSIONS             *
3  'LISTING 5-5                             *
4  '*****************************************
5  '
10 DEFDBL A,P
20 CLS:INPUT"NUMBER OF KNOWN POINTS";N
30 DIM X(N+1),S(N+1),T(N+1),A(N+1,N+2)
40 INPUT"NUMBER OF INDEPENDANT VARIABLES";V:DIM
     Y(N,V+1),YY(N,V+1)
```

```
50 FORI=1TON:PRINT"POINT #";I:FORJ=1TOV:PRINT"
        INDEPENDENT VARIABLE #";J,:INPUTYY(I,J):
    NEXTJ:INPUT"            DEPENDENT VARIABLE";Y
    Y(I,J):NEXTI:UU=U
60 LPRINT"":LPRINT"INPUT VARIABLES"
70 FORI=1TON
80    PRINT"POINT ";I:FORJ=1TOV:PRINT"",J,YY(I,J)
      :Y(I,J)=YY(I,J):NEXTJ:PRINT"",J;"DEPENDENT
      = ";YY(I,J):Y(I,J)=YY(I,J)
90    PRINT"ARE THESE DATA CORRECT?  (Y/N)";
100   Q$=""+INKEY$:IFQ$=""THEN100  ELSEIFQ$="Y"T
      HEN120
110    PRINT:INPUT"ENTER VARIABLE NUMBER AND CORR
      ECT VALUE";J,Y(I,J):GOTO80
120    PRINT:LPRINT"POINT ";I:FORJ=1TOV:LPRINT"
      VARIABLE",J,YY(I,J):NEXTJ:LPRINT"","DEPEND
      ENT = ";YY(I,J)
130 NEXTI
140 X(1)=1:PRINT:PRINT"COMPUTING..."
150 FORI=1TON
160    FORJ=1TOV:X(J+1)=Y(I,J):NEXTJ:X(V+2)=Y(I,J
      )
170    FORK=1TOV+1:FORL=1TOV+2:A(K,L)=A(K,L)+(X(K
      )*X(L)):S(K)=A(K,V+2):NEXTL:NEXTK
180    S(V+2)=S(V+2)+(X(V+2)[2)
190 NEXTI
200 FORI=2TOV+1:T(I)=A(1,I):NEXTI
210 FORI=1TOV+1
220    J=I
230    IFA(J,I)<>0THEN260
240    J=J+1:IFJ<=(V+1)THEN230
250    PRINT"NO UNIQUE SOLUTION":GOTO450
260    FORK=1TOV+2:B=A(I,K):A(I,K)=A(J,K):A(J,K)=
      B:NEXTK
270    Z=1/A(I,I)
280    FORK=1TOV+2:A(I,K)=Z*A(I,K):NEXTK
290    FORJ=1TOV+2
300      IFJ=ITHEN330
310      Z=-A(J,I)
320      FORK=1TOV+2:A(J,K)=A(J,K)+(Z*A(I,K)):NEX
      TK
330    NEXTJ
340 NEXTI
350 LPRINT"":LPRINT"EQUATION COEFFICIENTS:"
360 PRINT:PRINT"EQUATION COEFFICIENTS:":PRINT"
        CONSTANT: ";A(1,V+2):LPRINT"       CONSTAN
      T = ";A(1,V+2)
370 FORI=2TOV+1:PRINT"  VARIABLE #";I-1,A(I,V+2)
      :LPRINT"  VARIABLE #";I-1,"=";A(I,V+2):NEXT
      I
380 P=0
390 FORI=2TOV+1:P=P+(A(I,V+2)*(S(I)-(T(I)*S(1)/N
      ))):NEXTI
400 R=S(V+2)-((S(1)[2)/N):Z=R-P:L=N-V-1:I=P/R:PR
      INT
410 PRINT"COEFFICIENT OF DETERMINATION = ";I:LPR
      INT"COEFFICIENT OF DETERMINATION = ";I,:IF
      I<0THEN430
```

Listing 5-5. Multiple Linear Regressions (continued from page 67)

```
420 PRINT"COEFFICIENT OF MULTIPLE CORRELATION =
    ";SQR(I):LPRINT"COEFFICIENT OF MULTIPLE COR
    RELATION = ";SQR(I):GOTO440
430 PRINT"COEFFICIENT OF MULTIPLE CORRELATION =
    ";-1*SQR(ABS(I))
440 IFL<>0  PRINT"STANDARD ERROR OF ESTIMATE = "
    ;SQR(ABS(Z/L)):LPRINT"STANDAR ERROR OF ESTI
    MATE = ";SQR(ABS(Z/L))
450 IFQ$="B"THEN630
460 PRINT:PRINT"(T)RIAL VALUE    (N)EW DATA RUN
     (B)EST FIT";
470 Q$=""+INKEY$:IFQ$=""THEN470   ELSEIFQ$="N"THE
    N510  ELSEIFQ$="B"THEN530  ELSEIFQ$<>"T"THE
    N470
480 PRINT:P=A(1,U+2)
490 FORJ=1TOU:PRINT"INDEPENDANT VARIABLE #";J;:I
    NPUTX:P=P+(A(J+1,U+2)*X):NEXTJ
500 PRINT:PRINT"   DEPENDANT VARIABLE = ";P:GOTO
    460
510 PRINT:RUN20
520 END
530 ZZ=(2[U)-1:PRINT" ",Q$
540 FORII=1TOZZ
550   A=II:PRINT"USING VARIABLE(S) #";;:LPRINT"":
    LPRINT"USING VARIABLE(S) #",
560   FORJ=1TON+1:X(J)=0:S(J)=0:T(J)=0:FORK=1TON
    +2:A(J,K)=0:NEXTK:NEXTJ:K=0
570   FORJ=UUTO1STEP-1
580     IF(2[(J-1))>ATHEN610
590     A=A-(2[(J-1)):PRINTJ;:LPRINTJ,
600     K=K+1:FORL=1TON:Y(L,K)=YY(L,J):NEXTL
610   NEXTJ
620   U=K:GOTO140
630 NEXTII
640 GOTO460
```

Although we began with four variables, it is clear that only three of the variables are of any use in forecasting the magnitude of the dependent variable.

OTHER CORRELATIONS

So far, the coefficient of correlation we have been referring to has been the Pearson Product-Moment Correlation, or the *rho-correlation*. This is not, however, the only coefficient of correlation available, nor even the most appropriate in some instances. What follows, then, is a brief description of a number of alternative coefficients of correlation and their computation.

Point-Biserial Correlation Coefficient

You often have data such that one variable is continuous and the other is dichotomous. For example, the independent variable may be lifting strength (a continuous variable) and the dependent variable may be lifting strength (a continuous variable) and the dependent variable may be the sex of the lifter (a dichotomous variable). Table 5-4 summarizes a hypothetical set of test data. Column A identifies the sex of the lifter (0 = female, 1 = male), and column B gives the maximum weight lifted in four trials.

Two equations for the computation of a biserial correlation are shown on following page.

Table 5-3. Multivariate Sample Input Data.

Item #	Independent Variables 1	2	3	4	Dependent Variable
1	1.9245	2.04412	4.15012	6.43881	1
2	2.54461	5.83935	8.74113	5.59329	4
3	3.60942	7.7939	9.28686	4.99721	6
4	4.31564	9.51458	12.9678	6.70319	8
5	5.24965	11.6141	15.6512	1.465	10
6	6.49682	12.5547	18.2942	1.70637	12
7	7.50094	14.992	21.7468	1.98965	14
8	8.67358	17.6187	26.6055	6.98466	16
9	9.75344	18.5086	29.4656	6.93737	18
10	10.9158	21.9598	30.3651	.638662	20

$$(1) \quad r_b = \frac{N(\Sigma'Y) - \Sigma N_1 Y}{NA \sqrt{N\Sigma Y^2 - (\Sigma Y)^2}}$$

Where:

N = total number of points

N_1 = number of points where the dichotomous variable is "1"

$\Sigma'Y$ = sum of all points (y) where the dichotomous is "1"

ΣY = sum of all continuous variables

A = height of the ordinate of a normal curve at a distance from the mean where the area of the tail is equal to: N_1/N.

An easier equation is:

$$(2) \quad r_b = \frac{\overline{Y}_0 - \overline{Y}_1}{\sigma} \sqrt{pq}$$

Table 5-4. Test Results.

Lifter #	Sex Code	Weight Lifted
1	0	310 lbs
2	1	280
3	1	560
4	0	30
5	1	250
6	0	240
7	0	480
8	0	290
9	1	770

Where:

σ = is the standard deviation of all the points

$\overline{Y}_0$ = mean score of those items in category 0

$\overline{Y}_1$ = mean score in those items in category 1

P = N_1/N

q = $1 - p$

From the data given in Table 5-4, we compute the values:

$\sigma = 215.523 \quad Y_0 = 270 \quad Y_1 = 465$

$p = .444444 \quad q = .555556$

solving for r_b:

$$r_b = \frac{270 - 465}{215.523} \sqrt{.444444 \times .555556}$$

$$= -.449588$$

Spearman's Rank-Order Correlation

The data in Table 5-5 below summarizes the grades one class of students received in two different subjects. The question the teacher has is whether or not there is a relationship between the skills used in the two subjects. That is, if a student is good in one subject, will he or she also be good in the other?

The values in columns two and three are simple enough; they are the grades received on a recent test. In columns four and five are the corresponding ranks each score represents. The equation for computing Spearman's correlation is

$$r_s = 1 - \frac{6 \sum\limits_{i=1}^{n} D_i^2}{n(n^2 - 1)}$$

where: n = number of data pairs

D_i = rank (x_i) − rank (y_i)

With this coefficient there is a test value to measure the degree of reliability of the correlation. It is computed from $z = r_s \sqrt{n - 1}$. The z-score is roughly equal to the standard deviation of the normal curve that includes the data. That is, if z is greater than ± 1.96, the value of r_s is significant at

Table 5-5. Rank-Ordered Grade Data.

Student Number	Math Grade	English Grade	Math Rank	English Rank	Difference D	D²
1	92	86	1	2	1	1
2	47	24	5	8	−3	9
3	48	42	4	5	−1	1
4	61	60	3	4	−1	1
5	7	14	10	10	0	0
6	23	35	7	7	0	0
7	85	38	2	6	−4	16
8	33	23	6	9	−3	9
9	15	92	9	1	8	64
10	20	68	8	3	5	25
					2	126

n = 10

the 5% level or better. There is also another relationship of interest where

$$r = 2 \sin\left(\frac{\pi}{6} r_s\right)$$ where r is Pearson's rho.

From the basic equation

$$r_s = 1 - \frac{6 \times 126}{10 \times (10^2 - 1)} = 1 - \frac{756}{10 \times 99} = 1 - \frac{756}{990}$$

$$= .236364$$

$$r = 2 \sin\left(\frac{\pi}{6} r_s\right) = 2 \sin (.523599 \times .236364)$$

$$= 2 \sin (.12376) = 2 \times .123444 = .246888$$

$$z = r_s \sqrt{n - 1} = .236364 \times 9 = 2.12728$$

Partial and Multiple Coefficients of Correlation

After a long evening of computing correlations

between pairs of data sets you may be in a position to ask: if I know the relationship between A and B, the relationship between A and C, and the relationship between B and C, and if I know that A is a function of both B and C, what is the relationship between A and B without the benefit of C and, likewise, what is the relationship between A and C without the benefit of B? The answer is found in the equation

$$r_{ab.c} = \frac{r_{ab} - r_{ac}\, r_{bc}}{\sqrt{(1 - r_{ac}^{\,2})\,(1 - r_{bc}^{\,2})}}$$

Likewise

$$r_{ac.b} = \frac{r_{ac} - r_{ab}\, r_{bc}}{\sqrt{(1 - r_{ac}^{\,2})\,(1 - r_{bc}^{\,2})}}$$

And

$$r_{bc.a} = \frac{r_{bc} - r_{ab}\, r_{ac}}{\sqrt{(1 - r_{bc}^{\,2})\,(1 - r_{ab}^{\,2})}}$$

The multiple coefficient of correlation from these data is computed from

$$r_{ab.c} = \sqrt{\frac{r_{ab}^{\,2} + r_{ac}^{\,2} - 2\, r_{ab}\, r_{ac}\, r_{bc}}{1 - r_{bc}^{\,2}}}$$

Listing 5-6 implements all of the foregoing equations to compute the biserial and rank-order correlations, as well as the partial and multiple correlations.

Listing 5-6. Miscellaneous Correlations

```
1 '*******************************************
2 'MISCELLANEOUS CORRELATIONS              *
3 'LISTING 5-6                             *
4 '*******************************************
5 '
10 CLS:PRINT"CORRELATIONS":PRINT:PRINT:PRINT"1
     --   POINT-BISERIAL CORRELATION
2  --   SPEARMAN'S RANK-ORDER CORRELATION   (RHO)
3  --   PARTIAL/MULTIPLE CORRELATIONS"
20 PRINT"SELECT ONE";
30 Q$=""+INKEY$:IFQ$=""THEN30   ELSEONVAL(Q$)GOT
     O40  ,230  ,340
40 CLS       'POINT-BISERIAL CORRELATION
50 INPUT"TOTAL NUMBER OF ITEMS TO BE ENTERED";N
```

```
60  FORI=1TON
70     PRINT"ENTER DATA FOR SUBJECT #";I;"
       DICHOTOMOUS CHARACTERISTIC (1 OR 0)     ";
80     Q$=""+INKEY$:IFQ$=""THEN80
90     IFQ$<"0"ORQ$>"1"THEN80
100    PRINTQ$:Q=VAL(Q$):INPUT"        ENTER CONTINU
       OUS VALUE";X
110    IFQ=1THEN130
120    N(0)=N(0)+1:S(0)=S(0)+X:GOTO140
130    N(1)=N(1)+1:S(1)=S(1)+X
140    TX=TX+X:X2=X2+(X[2)
150 NEXTI
160 S=SQR((X2-((TX[2)/N))/(N-1))
170 Y0=S(0)/N(0):Y1=S(1)/N(1):P=N(0)/N:Q=1-P
180 RB=((Y1-Y0)/S)*SQR(P*Q)
190 PRINT:PRINT"SUM OF Y1 = ";S(1);"     MEAN = ";
    Y1;"     PERCENT = ";P
200 PRINT"SUM OF Y0 = ";S(0);"     MEAN = ";Y0;"
       PERCENT = ";Q
210 PRINT"STANDARD DEVIATION = ";S
220 PRINT:PRINT"POINT-BISERIAL CORRELATION = ";R
    B:PRINT:RUN50
230 CLS        'SPEARMAN'S RANK CORRELATION
240 INPUT"NUMBER OF DATA PAIRS";N
250 FORI=1TON
260    PRINT"PAIR #";I
270    INPUT"ENTER RANK, VARIABLE # 1";R1
280    INPUT"ENTER RANK, VARIABLE # 2";R2
290    DI=DI+((R1-R2)[2)
300 NEXTI
310 RS=1-((6*DI)/(N*((N[2)-1))):Z=RS*SQR(N-1)
320 R=2*SIN(.523599*RS)
330 PRINT:PRINT"SPEARMAN'S RANK CORRELATION = ";
    RS:PRINT"PEARSON'S RHO CORRELATION = ";R:PR
    INT"Z-SCORE = ";Z:RUN240
340 CLS        'PARTIAL CORRELATIONS
350 PRINT"A IS THE CRITERION OR DEPENDENT VARIAB
    LE"
360 INPUT"ENTER CORRELATION BETWEEN SET A AND SE
    T B";R(1)
370 INPUT"ENTER CORRELATION BETWEEN SET A AND SE
    T C";R(2)
380 INPUT"ENTER CORRELATION BETWEEN SET B AND SE
    T C";R(3)
390 PR(1)=(R(1)-(R(2)*R(3)))/(SQR(1-(R(2)[2))*SQ
    R(1-(R(3)[2)))
400 PR(2)=(R(2)-(R(1)*R(3)))/(SQR(1-(R(1)[2))*SQ
    R(1-(R(3)[2)))
410 PR(3)=(R(3)-(R(1)*R(2)))/(SQR(1-(R(1)[2))*SQ
    R(1-(R(2)[2)))
420 PR(4)=(((R(1)[2)+(R(2)[2))-(2*R(1)*R(2)*R(3)
    ))/(1-(R(3)[2))
430 IFPR(4)<0THEN450
440 PR(4)=SQR(PR(4)):GOTO460
450 PR(4)=-1*SQR(ABS(PR(4)))
460 PRINT:PRINT"PARTIAL CORRELATIONS:"
470 PRINT"   A WITH B LESS C = ";PR(1)
```

Listing 5-6. Miscellaneous Correlations (continued from page 71)

```
480 PRINT"   A WITH C LESS B = ";PR(2)
490 PRINT"   B WITH C LESS A = ";PR(3)
500 PRINT:PRINT"MULTIPLE CORRELATION OF THE DEPE
    NDENT VARIABLE A AND
THE INDEPENDENT VARIABLES B AND C = ";PR(4)
510 RUN350
```

KENDALL'S COEFFICIENT OF CONCORDANCE

Kendall's coefficient of concordance (W) is a useful tool to evaluate the relationship between the ratings a panel of judges give to individuals in some comparative activity, such as sports events, where part or all of the score is based on a subject evaluation of the event; in the results of a panel of judges rating musicians; or in any other situation in which N individuals are ranked 1 to N according to some characteristic by K judges. The degree to which these judges agree (or their concordance) is given by the equation:

$$W = \frac{12 \sum\limits_{i=1}^{N} \left(\sum\limits_{j=1}^{K} R_{ij} \right)^2}{K^2 N(N^2 - 1)} - \frac{3(N + 1)}{N - 1}$$

Where R_{ij} is the rank given to the ith individual by the jth judge.

Very much like a coefficient of correlation, W ranges from 0 (no agreement between judges) and 1 (total agreement among judges). If the number of judges is greater than seven, the degree of confidence one can place in the coefficient can be estimated from

Table 5-6. Diving Scores, Multiple Judges.

Diver i	1	2	3	Judge 4	5	6	7	Total	Score	Final Rank
1	2	2	3	8	3	1	8	27	1	1
2	6	6	7	5	10	3	5	42	5	5
3	4	10	5	2	6	7	6	40	4	4
4	3	9	2	1	5	9	4	33	2	2
5	10	9	1	7	4	10	1	36	3	3
6	9	5	10	3	1	2	10	40	4	4
7	7	7	6	4	9	5	2	40	4	4
8	1	4	8	9	8	4	9	43	6	6
9	5	1	4	10	7	8	7	42	5	5
10	8	8	9	6	2	6	3	42	5	5

$$\chi^2 = K(N - 1)W$$

which has an approximate relationship with the chi-square distribution (see the next section).

Table 5-6 gives the hypothetical outcome of a diving competition as rated by seven judges.

The computation of the coefficient starts by tabulating the row scores, and then squaring each one.

Item	Score	Score Squared
1	27	729
2	42	1764
3	40	1600
4	33	1089
5	36	1296
6	40	1600
7	40	1600
8	43	1849
9	42	1764
10	42	1764
		Sum = 15055

Then:

$$W = \frac{12 \times 25055}{7^2 \times 10(10^2 - 1)} - \frac{3(10 + 1)}{10 - 1}$$

$$= \frac{180660}{48510} - \frac{33}{9} = 3.72418 - 3.66666$$

$$= .057513$$

The chi-square statistic is:

$$7 \times (10 - 9) \times W \; 3 \; 3.6233.$$

One concludes with a reasonable assurance that there is actually little real agreement among the judges. A protest of the scores would not be out of order. Listing 5-7 implements this process, making the tabulations a little quicker.

Listing 5-7. Kendall's Coefficient of Concordance

```
1   '*********************************************
2   'KENDALL'S COEFFICIENT OF CONCORDANCE    *
3   'LISTING 5-7                             *
4   '*********************************************
5   '
10 CLS
20 INPUT"NUMBER OF INDIVIDUALS";N
30 INPUT"NUMBER OF JUDGES";K
40 DIMS(N,K):PRINT
50 FORI=1TON
60    PRINT"INDIVIDUAL #";I
70    FORJ=1TOK
80       PRINT"   RATING BY JUDGE #";J,:INPUTS(I,J
      )
90       SR=SR+S(I,J)
100   NEXTJ
110   SN=SN+(SR[2):SR=0
120   PRINT
130 NEXTI
140 W=((12*SN)/((K[2)*(N*((N[2)-1))))-((3*(N+1))
      /(N-1))
150 PRINT:PRINT"KENDALL'S COEFFICIENT OF CONCORD
      ANCE = ";W
160 PRINT"CHI-SQUARE = ";K*(N-1)*W;"WITH";N-1;"D
      EGREES OF FREEDOM"
170 PRINT:RUN20
```

CHI-SQUARE DISTRIBUTIONS

By using a number of the techniques given in this book, you can use the microcomputer to develop a mathematical model or algorithm with which future values can be computed as a function of some set of known or estimated values. At a later time, you will be able to evaluate the relationship between the model and the actual outcome by a process known as the chi-square distribution. It is beyond the scope of this book to go into the development of the statistic, but Listing 5-8 facilitates the computation of chi-square with

— Expected values equal
— Expected values unequal
— 2 × K contingency
— 2 × 2 contingency
— Bartlett's chi-square
— Chi-square for difference between correlations
— Distribution and density functions of the chi-square statistic

With these seven routines, virtually all of the common forms of the statistic and an evaluation of the curve can be computed. A brief description of each of the foregoing follows.

Expected Values Equal

In this model the assumption is that a characteristic of each subject will be the same in each sample. For example, one die is tossed N times. If the die is fair, you would expect each number to appear N/6 times, such as:

Number	1	2	3	4	5	6
Frequency	44	27	49	46	46	38

N = 250
Expectation = N/6 = 41.6667

Chi-square is computed from:

$$\chi^2 = \frac{N \; \Sigma \; 0_i^2}{\Sigma \; 0_i} - 0_i$$

In this example

$$\chi^2 = \frac{6 \times 10742}{250} - 250 = 7.80808.$$

Expected Values Unequal

This approach is based on the assumption that the expected value (e) is a function of some variable and will not be constant from sample to sample as the independent variable changes. For example, a market survey suggests that the volume of customers in a store will not be a constant value equal to the average number of weekly customers divided by the number of days the store is open, but will vary according to the day of the week:

Day	Volume
Monday	23
Tuesday	47
Wednesday	49
Thursday	36
Friday	234
Saturday	310

The store owner keeps traffic records for a week, then tables the findings:

	Mon	Tue	Wed	Thu	Fri	Sat
Observed	32	34	56	31	108	452

	Mon	Tue	Wed	Thu	Fri	Sat
Expected	23	47	49	36	234	310
0 - E	9	−13	7	−5	−126	142

The equation for this form is

$$\chi^2 = \sum_{i=1}^{N} \frac{(0_i - E_i)^2}{E_i}$$

Hence

$$\chi^2 = \frac{9^2}{23} + \frac{-13^2}{47} + \frac{7^2}{49} + \frac{-5^2}{36} + \frac{-126^2}{234} + \frac{142^2}{310}$$

$$= 141.703$$

2 × K Contingency Table

Contingency tables are used to evaluate the independence of two sets of variable data. The 2 × k implies there are two variables, each producing k items of data. The chi-square equation used to compute the chi-square is:

$$\chi^2 = \frac{N}{N_a} \sum_{i=1}^{k} \frac{A_i^2}{N_i} + \frac{N}{N_b} \sum_{i=1}^{k} \frac{B_i^2}{N_i} - N$$

where N is the total number of items ($N_a + N_b$) and A_i and B_i are data elements from each set.

Mr. Pearson (of Pearson's Coefficient of Correlation fame) has also developed a coefficient of contingency (C) that gives us an estimate of the degree to which the two variables are associated. It is computed from:

$$C = \sqrt{\frac{\chi^2}{N + \chi^2}}$$

2 × 2 Contingency Table with Yates Correction

This is a delightful little routine used to determine the significance, if any, of the difference between two groups of subjects as measured by some dichotomous variable. For example, let's assume a group of educators and traffic safety experts believe there is a relationship between driver training programs and reduced accident rates. They collect the available data and table as below:

Number of People

	Accident-Free	Have Had Accidents	Total
Trained	1023	214	1237
Untrained	324	968	1292
Total	1237	1182	2529

Casual inspection of the data, in this instance, suggests the hypothesis is true. Indeed, the computed chi-square of these data is $\chi^2 = .840.601$. The probability these data have fallen out this way as the consequence of chance or random error is less than one in a million. The basic equation for this form is

$$\chi^2 = \sum \frac{(0 - E)^2}{N}$$

Unfortunately, the distribution associated with this equation is not quite properly fitted to the chi-square distribution. A statistician named Yates,

74

however, has been kind enough to provide a correction feature which smooths out the curve into a nice and proper form. With the correction, the equation reads

$$\chi^2 = \Sigma \left[\frac{(\mid 0 - E \mid - .5)^2}{N} \right]$$

where the expression $\mid 0 - E \mid$ means the absolute difference between 0 and E.

The computational formula for this contingency table, however, is

$$\chi^2 = \frac{(A = B\ C + D)\ [\ \mid AD - BC \mid - .5\ (A\ B + C + D)]^2}{(A + B)\ (A + C)\ (C + D)\ (B + D)}$$

where A, B, C, and D are taken from the form

	Characteristic	
	1	2
Group A	A	B
Group B	C	D

This formula is numerically equivalent to the basic equation with Yates correction.

Barlett's Chi-Square

This tool is used by statisticians who have collected data on a variable from a number of different sample groups (such as the computed reading level of junior high school students from several different schools). Having computed the mean and standard deviation from each sample, this routine gives an estimate of whether the students in each of the sample groups came from the same general population or from different educational systems. A major feature of this approach calls for the *variance* of the sample data. The variance, assuming an otherwise normal population distribution, is the square of the standard deviation. If s is the standard deviation of a sample, s^2 is the variance. The equation is:

$$\chi^2 = \frac{F\ Log_e\ S^2 - \sum\limits_{i=1}^{k} f_i\ Log_e\ S_i^2}{1 + \frac{1}{3(k-1)} \left[\left(\sum\limits_{i=1}^{k} \frac{1}{f_i} \right) - \frac{1}{F} \right]}$$

where S_i^2 = sample variance of the ith sample,
f_i = degrees of freedom associated with S_i^2,
k = number of samples,

$$f = \sum\limits_{i=1}^{k} f_i, \text{and}$$

$$S^2 = \frac{\sum\limits_{i=1}^{k} f_i S_i^2}{F}$$

If we have these data

	Sample Number				
	1	2	3	4	5
Variance	3.2	4.5	6.7	3.1	7.8
f_i	34	56	87	43	12

the resulting chi-square is: $\chi^2 = 12.77$ with 4 degrees of freedom.

Chi-square for the Difference Between Correlation Coefficients

Given coefficients of correlations derived from two samples, the question is whether or not there is a relationship between the two samples: do the findings represent the profile of one homogenous population or two different populations? The equation is

$$\chi^2 = (N_1 - 3)Z_1^2 + (N_2 - 3)Z_2^2$$
$$- \frac{[\ (N_1 - 3)Z_1 + (N_2 - 3)Z_2\ ]^2}{(N_1 - 3) + (N_2 - 3)}$$

where N_1 and N_2 are the sample sizes for each sample. Z_1 and Z_2 are transformations of the correlation coefficients, and are computed from

$$z_i = .5\ [Log_e(2 + R_i) - Log_e\ (1 - R_i)]$$

Given $N_1 = 104 \qquad N_2 = 98$ and
$\qquad R_1 = .98756 \qquad R_2 = .87693$, then

$Z_1 = .5\ [Log_e\ (1 + .98756) - Log_e$
$\qquad (1 - .98756)] = 2.53687$

$Z_2 = .5\ Log_e\ (1 + .87693) - Log_e$
$\qquad (1 - .87693) = 1.36232$

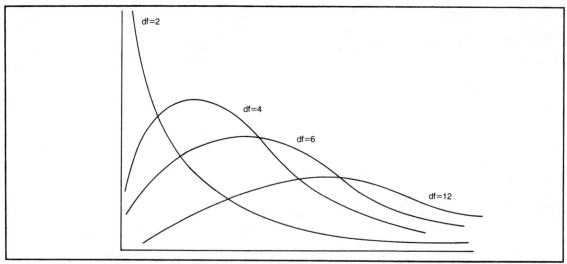

Fig. 5-6. Standard chi-square curves.

$$\chi^2 = 101 \times 2.53687^2 + 95 \times 1.36232^2$$

$$- \frac{[101 \times 2.53687 + 95 \times 1.36232]^2}{101 + 95}$$

$$= 67.5364 \text{ with one degree of freedom.}$$

Distribution and Density Functions

Figure 5-6 illustrates the basic range of forms the chi-square distribution can take as a function of the number of degrees of freedom.

Figure 5-7 illustrates a nominal chi-square distribution and shows the portions of the distribution of particular interest to us.

The cumulative distribution under the curve, $P(x)$, is computed from:

$$P(x) = \frac{2x}{v} f(x) \left[1 + \sum_{k=1}^{00} \frac{X^K}{(v+2)(v+4) \ldots (v+2K)} \right]$$

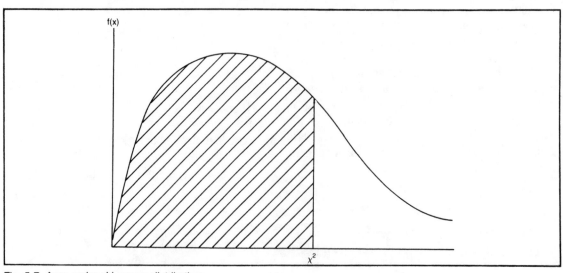

Fig. 5-7. Area under chi-square distribution.

where x > 0, and v is the degrees of freedom. The density function for any value of x is:

$$f(x) = \frac{x^{\frac{v}{2}-1}}{2^{\frac{v}{2}} \Gamma\left(\frac{v}{2}\right) e^{\frac{x}{2}}}$$

1. 1 - P(x) is the tail value behind x. It is equal to the probability that the data being evaluated result from random or chance error. The smaller this value is, the more likely it is that the experimental findings are the result of the influence of the independent variable.

Listing 5-8 implements all of the foregoing equations and relationships.

ANALYSIS OF VARIANCE

Analysis of Variance (also known as one-way or two-way ANOVA) is a statistical technique frequently used by medical researchers to determine the effect of drugs on humans or animals and by

Listing 5-8. Chi-Square Computations

```
1  '*********************************************
2  'CHI-SQUARE COMPUTATIONS                    *
3  'LISTING 5-8                                *
4  '*********************************************
5  '
10 DIMYY(128):CLS:PI=3.1415929:E=2.71828
20 PRINT"          ********* CHI-SQUARE UNLIMI
   TED *********":PRINT:PRINT
30 PRINT:PRINT"          1  --  EXPECTED VALUES
   EQUAL
          2  --  EXPECTED VALUES UNEQUAL
          3  --  2 X K CONTINGENCY
          4  --  2 X 2 CONTINGENCY, WITH YATES C
   ORRECTION
          5  --  BARTLETT'S CHI-SQUARE"
40 PRINT"          6  --  CHI-SQUARE FOR DIFFERE
   NCE BETWEEN CORRELATIONS
          7  --  DISTRIBUTION AND DENSITY FUNCTI
   ONS":PRINT:PRINT
50 PRINT:PRINT"ENTER NUMBER OF DESIRED ROUTINE";
60 R$=INKEY$:IFR$=""THEN60    ELSER=VAL(R$)
70 IFR<1ORR>7THEN50
80 ONRGOTO340 ,380 ,420 ,480 ,620 ,840 ,10
   0
90 RETURN
100 ONERRORGOTO1350 :CLS:PRINT"CHI-SQUARE":PRINT
   :PRINT
110 INPUT"ENTER 'X' VALUE";X
120 INPUT"ENTER DEGREES OF FREEDOM";V:V1=V:GOTO1
   40
130 V=DF:V1=DF
140 A=1:FORI=VTO2STEP-2:A=A*I:NEXTI
150 B=X[(INT((V+1)/2))*EXP(-X/2)/A
160 IFB<1.0E-37THENB=1.0E-37
170 IFINT(V/2)=V/2THEN200
180 C=SQR(2/X/3.1415929)
190 GOTO210
200 C=1
210 D=1:E=1
```

Listing 5-8. Chi-Square Computations (continued from page 77)

```
220 ONERRORGOTO590
230 U=U+2:E=E*X/U:IFE<.0000001THEN250
240 D=D+E:GOTO230
250 CH=INT(X):P=C*B*D:T=1-P:FX=(P/D)/((2*X)/U1)
260 PRINT"CUMULATIVE DISTRIBUTION =";P
270 PRINT"DENSITY FUNCTION =";FX
280 PRINT"TAIL-END VALUE =";T
290 PRINT
300 PRINT:PRINT"WILL THESE DATA BE PRINTED?  (Y
    OR N)";
310 P$=""+INKEY$:IFP$=""THEN310  ELSEIFP$="Y"THE
    N1040
320 PRINT:PRINT"DO YOU WANT A GRAPHIC REPRESENTA
    TION?  (Y/N)":PRINT
330 P$=""+INKEY$:IFP$=""THEN330  ELSEIFP$="Y"THE
    N1110 ELSE1380
340 CLS:PRINT"EXPECTED VALUES EQUAL":PRINT:PRINT

350 INPUT"HOW MANY ITEMS";N
360 FORI=1TON:INPUT"ENTER OBSERVED VALUE";O:O2=O
    2+(O[2):SO=SO+O:NEXTI
370 X2=((N*O2)/SO)-SO:DF=N-1:GOTO560
380 CLS:PRINT"EXPECTED VALUES UNEQUAL":PRINT:PRI
    NT
390 INPUT"HOW MANY ITEM PAIRS";N
400 FORI=1TON:PRINT:INPUT"ENTER EXPECTED VALUE";
    E:INPUT"ENTER OBSEVERED VALUE";O:X2=X2+(((O
    -E)[2)/E):NEXTI:DF=N-1
410 GOTO560
420 CLS:PRINT"2 X K CONTINGENCY TABLE":PRINT:PRI
    NT
430 INPUT"WHAT IS THE VALUE OF K";K
440 FORI=1TOK:PRINT:INPUT"ENTER A VALUE";A:INPUT
    "ENTER B VALUE";B:N=N+A+B:NA=NA+A:NB=NB+B:N
    I=A+B:SA=SA+((A[2)/NI):SB=SB+((B[2)/NI):NEX
    TI
450 X2=((N/NA)*SA)+((N/NB)*SB)-N:C=SQR(X2/(N+X2)
    )
460 X=X2:DF=K-1
470 PRINT:PRINT"PEARSON'S COEFFICIENT OF CONTING
    ENCY =";C:PRINT:GOTO560
480 CLS:PRINT"2 X 2 CONTINGENCY"
490 ONERRORGOTO590
500 PRINT@212,"1              2":PRINT@324,"GROUP  A
        A            B":PRINT@452,"GROUP   B
        C            D":Y=13:FORX=10TO71:SET(X,Y):
    NEXTX:X=30:FORY=9TO26:SET(X,Y):NEXTY
510 PRINT:PRINT:INPUT"ENTER A, B, C, AND D";A,B,
    C,D
520 DF=3:X2=((A+B+C+D)*((ABS((A*D)-(B*C))-((A+B+
    C+D)/2))[2))/((A+B)*(A+C)*(C+D)*(B+D))
530 N=A+B+C+D
540 C=SQR(X2/(N+X2))
550 GOTO470
560 PRINT:PRINT"CHI-SQUARE =";X2;"   WITH";DF;"D
    EGREES OF FREEDOM"
```

```
570 X=X2
580 GOTO130
590 IFERR/2+1=6THEN610
600 END
610 P=.999999:T=1-P:FX=(P/D)/((2*X)/V1):GOTO260

620 CLS:PRINT"BARTLETT'S CHI-SQUARE STATISTIC":P
    RINT:PRINT
630 INPUT"HOW MANY SAMPLES IN STUDY";K
640 DIMSI(K),FI(K),X(K,100):F=0:SX=0
650 PRINT:PRINT"DO YOU ALREADY HAVE THE SAMPLE S
    TATISTICS?  (Y OR N)";
660 S$=INKEY$:IFS$=""THEN660
670 IFS$="Y"THEN760
680 CLS
690 FORI=1TOK
700    PRINT"HOW MANY ITEMS IN SAMPLE #";I;"  (MA
    X 100)";:INPUTSS
710    FORJ=1TOSS:PRINT"ENTER VALUE FOR ITEM #";J
    ;:INPUTX(I,J):SX=SX+X(I,J):XT=XT+(X(I,J)[2)
    :NEXTJ
720    SI(I)=SQR((XT-((SX[2)/SS))/(SS-1)):FI(I)=S
    S-1:F=F+FI(I):X1=X1+(FI(I)*SI(I))
730    SX=0:XT=0
740 NEXTI
750 GOTO770
760 PRINT:PRINT:FORI=1TOK:PRINT"ENTER VARIANCE F
    OR SAMPLE #";I;"AND NUMBER OF ITEMS:";:INPU
    TSI(I),FI(I):F=F+FI(I):X1=X1+(FI(I)*(SI(I))
    ):NEXTI
770 S2=X1/F:DF=K-1
780 FORI=1TOK
790    A=A+(FI(I)*LOG(SI(I))):B=B+(1/FI(I))
800 NEXTI
810 X=(F*LOG(S2)-A)/(1+((1/(3*(K-1)))*(B-(1/F)))
    )
820 PRINT"CHI-SQUARE VALUE =";X;"   WITH";DF;"DE
    GREES OF FREEDOM"
830 GOTO130
840 CLS:PRINT"CHI-SQUARE FOR THE DIFFERENCE BETW
    EEN CORRELATION COEFFICIENTS":PRINT:PRINT
850 PRINT"DO YOU HAVE THE NECESSARY STATISTIC CO
    LLECTED?  (Y OR N)"
860 S$=INKEY$:IFS$=""THEN860  ELSEIFS$="Y"THEN98
    0
870 FORS=1TO2
880    PRINT:PRINT"HOW MANY PAIRS IN SET #";S;"
    (MUST BE >3)";:INPUTN(S)
890    IFN(S)<4THEN880
900    FORI=1TON(S)
910      INPUT"ENTER X,Y DATA";X,Y
920      TX=TX+X:TY=TY+Y:X2=X2+(X[2):Y2=Y2+(Y[2):
    XY=XY+(X*Y)
930    NEXTI
940    R(S)=((N(S)*XY)-(TX*TY))/SQR(((N(S)*X2)-(T
    X[2))*((N(S)*Y2)-(TY[2))):TX=0:TY=0:X2=0:Y2
    =0:XY=0
```

Listing 5-8. Chi-Square Computations (continued from page 79)

```
950   PRINT"CORRELATION SET #";S;"=";R(S)
960 NEXTS
970 GOTO990

980 PRINT:PRINT:FORI=1TO2:PRINT"ENTER CORRELATIO
      N AND NUMBER OF PAIRS IN SET #";I;:INPUTR(I
      ),N(I):NEXTI
990 DF=1
1000 FORI=1TO2:Z(I)=.5*(LOG(1+R(I))-LOG(1-R(I)))
      :NEXTI

1010 X=((N(1)-3)*(Z(1)[2))+((N(2)-3)*(Z(2)[2))-(
      ((((N(1)-3)*Z(1))+((N(2)-3)*Z(2)))[2)/((N(1
      )-3)+(N(2)-3)))
1020 PRINT"CHI-SQUARE =";X;"   WITH 1 DEGREE OF
      FREEDOM"
1030 GOTO130
1040 LPRINT"":LPRINT"CHI-SQUARE =";X;"     WITH";
      U1;"DEGREES OF FREEDOM."
1050 LPRINT"THE DENSITY FUNCTION IS =";FX

1060 LPRINT"THE CUMULATIVE DISTRUTION =";P
1070 LPRINT"THE TAIL-END VALUE IS =";T
1080 LPRINT" "
1090 GOTO320
1100 RUN10

1110 CLS:FORY=0TO47:SET(0,Y):NEXTY:FORX=0TO127:S
      ET(X,47):NEXTX
1120 FORI=1TO120
1130  X=I/10
1140  U=U1
1150  A=1:FORZ=UTO2STEP-2:A=A*Z:NEXTZ

1160  B=X[(INT((U+1)/2))*EXP(-X/2)/A
1170  IFINT(U/2)=U/2THEN1200
1180  C=SQR(2/X/3.1415929)
1190  GOTO1210
1200  C=1

1210  D=1:E=1
1220  U=U+2:E=E*X/U:IFE<.0000001THEN1240
1230  D=D+E:GOTO1220
1240  P=C*B*D:FX=(P/D)/((2*X)/U1):YY(I)=FX
1250  V=47-(47*FX):IFFX>LGTHENLG=FX
1260   SET(10*X,Y)
1270 NEXTI
1280 PRINT@0,LG;
1290 FORX=1TO120:RESET(X,47-(47*YY(X))):SET(X,47
      -(44*(YY(X)/LG))):NEXTX

1300 FORY=47-(44*(YY(10*CH)/LG))TO47STEP2
1310   SET(10*CH,Y)
1320 NEXTY
1330 IFCH<12THENPRINT@959+(5*CH),CH;
1340 GOTO1340
1350 IFERR/2+1=11THEN1370
1360 PRINT:PRINT"BETWEEN THE TWO OF US AN UGLY E
      RROR OF SOME SORT HAS HAPPENED.
LET'S TRY AGAIN.":PRINT:GOTO20
```

psychologists to test the effect of different teaching methods on groups of students, to name just a few applications. Whether the ANOVA is called one-way or two-way (or three-way . . .) depends on the number of variables or treatments involved in the experiment. An experiment in which there is only one stimulus affecting the subjects, such as the amount of a drug given or sleep permitted, would constitute an experiment suitable for a one-way ANOVA, while an experiment where there is a combination of stimuli involved, such as both the amount of drug given and the amount of sleep permitted, would be good for a two-way ANOVA. The program offered below gives the user the option of both a two-way and a one-way ANOVA. The program includes provision for the data to be output to a printer as well as the CRT.

It's not necessary for the user of this program to be a trained statistician or researcher. For those interested, the equations and technical considerations are given. There is, however, one feature all users must understand to make proper use of the routines, the *alpha criterion value*. At the beginning of the program, the user will be asked to provide this value. While the computer will accept any number, the answer should be between .00001 and .10000. In virtually all experiments, the collected data are tainted with some degree of random error. The knowledgeable researcher, however, is ready for this and will (must) provide for a certain margin of error. He will say, in effect, that if he can be reasonably sure that the output data are at least XX% pure or free from error, he will accept the theory or hypothesis being tested. The alpha value is the amount of acceptable error, expressed as a decimal; for example, 10% =.10. Researchers normally use either .05 or .01. Research in more exact and controllable sciences often use more rigorous values of .001 or .0001 as cutoff points. Which value you use depends largely on whether you are a chemist or a sociologist.

The second serious consideration for the reader is that this program and the comments about it are concerned solely with the mathematics of the analysis and not with experimental design. Indeed, whole graduate-level courses are taught just on designing experiments. But don't let this deter you. With proper attention paid to detail and cleanly-designed experiments, the output of this program will give reliable indicators.

The final consideration is that the number of subjects in each group or cell should be equal. The program will compute the necessary statistics regardless of the number of items in a cell, but as the degree of inequality increases, so will the difficulty of producing an accurate analysis. Keep the number of items per cell larger than five and as equal in number as you can. Tables 5-7 and 5-9 are the input data and test results from two different experiments. The numbers could represent the number of correct answers students give after being subjected to different types of teaching methods, or they could be chickens' reaction times, in milliseconds, to a variety of stimuli. The difference between the two sets is that the first involves only one stimulus, applied against two groups, and the second, involves two treatments applied against three groups. Tables 5-8 and 5-10 show the data output from the computer.

Table 5-7. One-Way ANOVA Input Data.

Group 1	Group 2
7	42
33	25
26	8
27	28
21	30
6	22
14	17
19	32
6	28
11	6
11	1
18	15
14	9
18	15
19	2
14	37
9	13
12	2
6	23
24	18
7	1
10	3
1	4
10	6
343	387

Table 5-8. One-Way ANOVA Output.

Source	SS	DF	MS	F	P
Total	4801.68	47			
Between	114.09	1	114.09	1.12	.2958
Within	4687.58	46	101.90		

The Program

Lines		
	10-90	Initial set-up and program selection
	100-700	One-way ANOVA routine
	120-239	Set-up and data input
	240-290	Basic computations
	300-370	Table set-up
	390	Probability computation
	400-460	Output data display
	470-510	Evaluation of probability
	520	Display of input data
	540	End of routine
	550-700	Display subroutine
	710-1580	Two-Way ANOVA routine
	740-850	Set-up and data input
	860-890	Basic computations, probability
	900-1050	Table set-up and output data display
	1060-1090	Evaluation of probability
	1120-1390	Data input subroutine
	2400-1460	Evaluation display
	2470-1580	Display subroutine
	1590-1730	Probability computation subroutine

The tables of output data uses conventional statistical notation: SS = Sum of Squares, DF = Degrees of Freedom, MS = Mean Squares, F = the F-distribution value, and P = the probability function, Q(F).

Table 5-9. Two-Way ANOVA Input Data.

		Group 1	Group 2	Group 3	
Treatment A					
Group 1		7	6	9	
		33	11	12	
		26	11	6	
		27	18	24	
		21	14	7	
		6	18	10	
		14	19	1	
		19	14	10	
		152	111	79	343
Treatment B					
Group 2		42	28	13	
		25	6	2	
		8	1	18	
		28	15	23	
		30	9	1	
		22	15	3	
		17	2	4	
		32	37	6	
		204	113	70	387
		357	224	149	730

Table 5-10. Two-Way ANOVA Output.

Source	SS	DF	MS	F	P
Total	5030.02	47			
Column	1415.38	2	707.69	8.65	.001000
Row	60.77	1	60.77	.74	.601900
Row x Col	115.87	2	57.93	.71	.502800
Error	3438.00	42	81.06		

The equations One-Way ANOVA

$$\text{Total SS} = \sum_{i=1}^{K} \sum_{j=i}^{Ni} V_{ij}^2 - \frac{\left(\sum_{i=1}^{K} \sum_{j=1}^{Ni} V_{ij} \right)^2}{N_i}$$

$$\text{Treatment SS} = \sum_{i=1}^{K} \frac{\left(\sum_{j=1}^{Ni} V_{ij} \right)^2}{N_i} - \frac{\left(\sum_{i=1}^{K} \sum_{j=i}^{Ni} V_{ij} \right)^2}{N_i}$$

Error SS = Total SS − Treatment SS

Treatment DF = K−1

$$\text{Error DF} = \sum_{i=1}^{K} N_i - K$$

$$\text{Treatment MS} = \frac{\text{Treatment SS}}{\text{Treatment DF}}$$

$$\text{Error MS} = \frac{\text{Error SS}}{\text{Error DF}}$$

$$F = \frac{\text{Treatment MS}}{\text{Error MS}}, \text{ with K}-1 \text{ and } \sum_{i=1}^{K} N_i - K \text{ DF.}$$

Two-Way ANOVA

$$\text{Total SS} = \sum_{r} \sum_{c} \sum_{i} V_{irc}^2 - \left(\frac{\sum_{r} \sum_{c} \sum_{i} V_{irc}}{N_t} \right)^2, \text{ DF}$$

$$= N - 1$$

$$\text{Column SS} = \frac{\sum_{c} \left(\sum_{r} \sum_{i} V_{irc} \right)^2}{RN_r} - \frac{\left(\sum_{r} \sum_{c} \sum_{i} V_{irc} \right)^2}{N_t}, \text{ DF}$$

$$= C - 1$$

$$\text{Row SS} = \frac{\sum_{r} \left(\sum_{c} \sum_{i} V_{irc} \right)^2}{CN_c} - \frac{\left(\sum_{r} \sum_{c} \sum_{i} V_{irc} \right)^2}{N_t}, \text{ DF} = R-1$$

$$\text{Within SS} = \sum_{r} \sum_{c} \sum_{i} V_{irc}^2 - \frac{\sum_{r} \sum_{c} \left(\sum_{i} V_{irc} \right)^2}{N_w}, \text{ DF}$$

$$= RC(N -)$$

$$\text{Between SS} = \frac{\sum_{r} \sum_{c} \left(\sum_{i} V_{irc} \right)^2}{N_{rc}} - \frac{\sum_{c} \left(\sum_{r} \sum_{i} V_{irc} \right)^2}{RN_t} -$$

$$\frac{\sum_{r} \left(\sum_{c} \sum_{i} V_{irc} \right)^2}{CN_t} + \frac{\left(\sum_{r} \sum_{c} \sum_{i} V_{irc} \right)^2}{N_t},$$

$$\text{DF} = (R-1)(C-1)$$

$$F_{row} = \frac{\text{Row SS}^2}{\text{Within SS}^2} \quad F_{column} = \frac{\text{Column SS}^2}{\text{Within SS}^2}$$

$$\text{Between F} = \frac{\text{Between SS}^2}{\text{Within SS}^2}$$

The value P, or A(x), is evaluated as the integral of the F-distribution:

$$Q(F) = \int_{F}^{\infty} \frac{\Gamma\left(\frac{D_n + D_m}{2}\right)^{\frac{D_n}{y2}} - 1 \left(\frac{D_n}{D_m}\right)^{D_n/2}}{\Gamma\left(\frac{D_n}{2}\right) \Gamma\left(\frac{D_m}{2}\right) \left(1 + \frac{D_{ny}}{D_m}\right)\left(\frac{D_n + D_m}{2}\right)}$$

dy, D_n = Degrees of freedom, numerator

D_m = Degrees of freedom, demoninator

Where:

N = total number of items or responses = N_t
N_r = number of items in a row
N^c = number of items in a column
N_w = number of items within a cell
R = number of rows
C = number of columns
DF = Degrees of Freedom
V_{irc} = Actual value of the item i at the intersection of row r and column c.

Listing 5-9. Combined Analysis of Variance

```
1   '*********************************************
2   'COMBINED ANALYSIS OF VARIANCE               *
3   'LISTING 5-9                                 *
4   '*********************************************
5   '
10  CLEAR100
20  CLS:PRINT"         ********** ANALYSIS OF
    VARIANCE   **********":PRINT:PRINT:PRINT"
       A -- ONE-WAY ANOVA
       B -- TWO-WAY ANOVA":PRINT:PRINT
30  PRINT"ENTER LETTER OF FORM DESIRED.";
40  Q$=INKEY$:IFQ$=""THEN40
50  Q=ASC(Q$)-64:ONQGOTO60     ,680
60  CLS
70  PRINT"        ******** ONE-WAY ANALYSIS OF
        VARIANCE  ********":PRINT:PRINT:PRINT
80  INPUT"WHAT IS THE CRITCAL ALPHA VALUE
    FOR REJECTING NULL HYPOTHESIS  (0 < X <= 1.00)";
    CV
90  PRINT:INPUT"HOW MANY GROUPS";G
100 DIM GP(G),GS(G):M=INT(MEM/45):DIM V(G,M) 'PR
    ESERVATION OF VALUE 'V' IS FOR SUMMARY AT E
    ND.   CAN BE CHANGED TO SIMPLY 'V'
110 PRINT:PRINT"THE AVERAGE SIZE OF EACH GROUP S
    HOULD BE";INT(M/G);"OR LESS.":PRINT
120 FOR I=1TOG
130     PRINT"HOW MANY SUBJECTS IN GROUP";I;:INP
    UTS:GP(I)=S
140     IF S>LG THEN LG=S
150     FOR J=1TOS
160         PRINT"ENTER VALUE FOR GROUP";I,"SUBJ
    ECT";J;:INPUTV(I,J)
170         GS(I)=GS(I)+V(I,J):TS=TS+V(I,J)
180         TQ=TQ+(V(I,J)[2):N=N+1
190     NEXT J
200 NEXT I
210 CLS:PRINT@512,"PLEASE BE PATIENT, COMPUTING.
    ..."
220 SQ=TS[2:QN=SQ/N:SS=TQ-QN
230 FOR I=1 TO G
240     QQ=QQ+((GS(I)[2)/GP(I))
250 NEXT I
260 SB=QQ-QN:SW=SS-SB:FT=N-1:FB=G-1:FW=FT-FB
270 MT=SS/FT:MB=SB/FB:MW=SW/FW:F=MB/MW
280 CLS
290 LPRINT" "
300 PRINT@323,"SOURCE              SS          DF
         MS         F           P";
310 LPRINT"   SOURCE              SS          DF
         MS        F          P"
320 LPRINTSTRING$(70,"*")
330 Z$="   ########.##     ####    ####.##  ####.##
        #.######"
340 ZZ$="   ########.##     ####"
350 ZY$="   ########.##     ####   ####.##"
```

```
360 DE=FW
370 GOSUB1580
380 PRINT@448,"TOTAL        ";:PRINTUSINGZZ$;SS;FT
390 LPRINT"TOTAL        ";:LPRINTUSINGZZ$;SS;FT
400 PRINT@512,"    BETWEEN";:PRINTUSINGZ$;SB;FB;M
    B;F;P
410 LPRINT"    BETWEEN";:LPRINTUSINGZ$;SB;FB;MB;F
    ;P
420 PRINT@576,"     WITHIN";:PRINTUSINGZY$;SW;FW;
    MW
430 LPRINT"     WITHIN";:LPRINTUSINGZY$;SW;FW;MW
440 LPRINT" "
450 Y=19:FORX=0TO127:SET(X,Y):NEXTX:X=24:FORY=15
    TO31:SET(X,Y):NEXTY
460 PRINT:IFCV>PTHEN480
470 PRINT"THE DATA IS NOT SUFFICIENT TO REJECT T
    HE NULL HYPOTHESIS.";:LPRINT" ":LPRINT"THE
    DATA DO NOT SUPPORT REJECTION OF THE NULL H
    YPOTHESIS":GOTO490
480 PRINT"VARIATIONS NOTED ARE LIKELY TO BE THE
    RESULT OF THE TREATMENT.":LPRINT" ":LPRINT"
    VARIATIONS NOTED ARE LIKELY TO BE THE RESUL
    T OF THE TREATMENT."
490 GOSUB520
500 PRINT:PRINT:INPUT"'ENTER' WHEN READY";ZZ:RUN
    1
510 END
520 LPRINT" "
530 LPRINT"INPUT VALUES":LPRINT" "
540 FORI=1TOG:LPRINT"GROUP";I,:NEXTI
550 LPRINT" "
560 FORI=1 TO LG
570    FOR J=1 TO G
580        IF GP(J)<I THEN 600
590        LPRINTV(J,I),:GOTO610
600        LPRINT" ",
610    NEXT J
620    LPRINT" "
630 NEXT I
640 LPRINT" "
650 FOR I=1 TO G:LPRINTGS(I),:NEXTI:LPRINT"
    SUM"
660 LPRINT" ":FORI=1 TO G:LPRINTGS(I)/GP(I),:NEX
    TI:LPRINT"    AVERAGE"
670 RETURN
680 'START
690 CLS
700 CLEAR 100
710 'ANALYSIS OF VARIANCE ROUTINES
720 PRINT"          ********  TWO-WAY ANALYSIS O
    F VARIANCE  ********":PRINT:PRINT:PRINT
730 INPUT"WHAT IS THE CRITICAL ALPHA VALUE
FOR REJECTING THE NULL HYPOTHESIS.  (0 < X <=1.0
    )";CV
740 N=1
750 PRINT:INPUT"TREATMENT 'A' (COLUMNS) CONSISTS
    OF HOW MANY GROUPS";A
```

Listing 5-9. Combined Analysis of Variance (continued from page 85)

```
760 INPUT"TREATMENT 'B' (ROWS) CONSISTS OF HOW M
    ANY GROUPS";B
770 CC=A:RR=B
780 D=90
790 DIM GN(B,A),GT(B,A),GS(B,A),RN(B),RT(B),R2(B
    ),CN(A),CT(A),C2(A):M=INT(MEM/19):DIMV(M) '
    PRESERVATION OF 'V' IS SIMPLY FOR SUMMARY A
    T END.  CAN BE CHANGED TO 'U'
800 PRINT:PRINT"THE AVERAGE CELL SIZE SHOULD NOT
     EXCEED";INT(M/(A*B)):PRINT
810 Z$="  ########.##     ####   ####.##  ####.##
    #.######"
820 ZZ$="  ########.##     ####"
830 ZY$="  ########.##     ####   ####.##"
840 GOSUB1120
850 F=FC:FB=DC:GOSUB1580
860 PC=P:F=FR:FB=DR:GOSUB1580
870 PR=P:F=FI:FB=DI:GOSUB1580
880 PI=P
890 CLS
900 PRINT@323,"SOURCE               SS          DF
         MS       F           P"
910 LPRINT" ":LPRINT"SOURCE                    SS
         DF        MS        F           P"
920 LPRINTSTRING$(70,"*")
930 PRINT@448,"TOTAL            ";:PRINTUSINGZZ$;ST;
    DT
940 LPRINT"TOTAL            ";:LPRINTUSINGZZ$;ST;DT
950 PRINT@512,"   COLUMN     ";:PRINTUSINGZ$;SC;D
    C;MC;FC;PC
960 LPRINT"   COLUMN     ";:LPRINTUSINGZ$;SC;DC;M
    C;FC;PC
970 PRINT@576,"     ROW      ";:PRINTUSINGZ$;SR;D
    R;MR;FR;PR
980 LPRINT"     ROW      ";:LPRINTUSINGZ$;SR;DR;M
    R;FR;PR
990 PRINT@640," ROW X COL    ";:PRINTUSINGZ$;SI;D
    I;MI;FI;PI
1000 LPRINT" ROW X COL    ";:LPRINTUSINGZ$;SI;DI;
    MI;FI;PI
1010 PRINT@704,"    ERROR     ";:PRINTUSINGZY$;ES
    ;DE;ME
1020 LPRINT"    ERROR     ";:LPRINTUSINGZY$;ES;DE
    ;ME
1030 Y=19:FORX=0TO127:SET(X,Y):NEXTX:X=24:FORY=1
    5TO35:SET(X,Y):NEXTY
1040 PRINT
1050 IF CV>PCTHENPRINT"COLUMN EFFECTS ARE SIGNIF
    ICANT"ELSEPRINT"COLUMN EFFECTS ARE NOT SIGN
    IFICANT"
1060 IF CV>PRTHENPRINT"ROW EFFECTS ARE SIGNIFICA
    NT"ELSEPRINT"ROW EFFECTS ARE NOT SIGNIFICAN
    T"
1070 IFCV>PITHENPRINT"ROW/COLUMN INTERACTION IS
    SIGNIFICANT"ELSEPRINT"ROW/COLUMN EFFECTS AR
    E NOT SIGNIFICANT"
```

```
1080 GOSUB1390
1090 PRINT@0,"'ENTER' WHEN FINISHED";::INPUTZZ
1100 RUN1
1110 END
1120 'DATA INPUT AREA
1130 FOR I=1 TO B
1140     FOR J=1 TO A
1150         PRINT"HOW MANY RESPONSES IN CELL";I;"
    -";J;::INPUTR:GN(I,J)=R
1160         FOR K=1 TO R
1170             PRINT"ENTER VALUE FOR ITEM";K;::INP
    UTV(N)
1180             T=T+V(N):TS=TS+V(N)[2:GT(I,J)=GT(I
    ,J)+V(N)
1190             GS(I,J)=GS(I,J)+V(N)[2:N=N+1
1200         NEXT K
1210         CT(J)=CT(J)+GT(I,J):RN(I)=RN(I)+GN(I,
    J)
1220         CN(J)=CN(J)+GN(I,J):RT(I)=RT(I)+GT(I,
    J)
1230     NEXT J
1240     R2(I)=RT(I)[2
1250 NEXT I
1260 CLS:PRINT@512,"PLEASE BE PATIENT, COMPUTING
    ...."
1270 FOR I=1 TO A:C2(I)=CT(I)[2:NEXT I
1280 N=N-1
1290 T2=(T[2)/N
1300 ST=TS-T2
1310 FORI=1TOA:SC=SC+((CT(I)[2)/CN(I)):NEXTI:SC=
    SC-T2
1320 FORI=1TOB:SR=SR+((RT(I)[2)/RN(I)):NEXTI:SR=
    SR-T2
1330 FORI=1TOB:FORJ=1TOA:SI=SI+((GT(I,J)[2)/GN(I
    ,J)):NEXTJ:NEXTI:SI=SI-T2-SC-SR
1340 ES=ST-SC-SR-SI
1350 DT=N-1:DC=A-1:DR=B-1:DI=DC*DR:DE=DT-DC-DR-D I
1360 MC=SC/DC:MR=SR/DR:MI=SI/DI:ME=ES/DE
1370 FC=MC/ME:FR=MR/ME:FI=MI/ME
1380 RETURN
1390 LPRINT" "
1400 LPRINT"SIGNIFICANT FINDINGS:"
1410 IF CV>PC THEN LPRINT"              COLUMN EFF
    ECTS ARE SIGNFICANT"
1420 IF CV>PR THEN LPRINT"              ROW EFFECT
    S ARE SIGNIFICANT"
1430 IF CV>PI THEN LPRINT"              ROW/COLUMN
     INTERACTION EFFECTS ARE SIGNIFICANT"
1440 IF PC>CV AND PR>CV AND PI>CV THEN LPRINT"
              NONE"
1450 LPRINT" "
1460 LPRINT"INPUT VARIABLES"
1470 N=1
1480 FOR I=1 TO RR
1490     FOR J=1 TO CC
1500     LPRINT" ":LPRINT"CELL GROUP";I;J;":";
1510         FOR K=1 TO GN(I,J)
1520             LPRINT V(N),:N=N+1
```

Listing 5-9. Combined Analysis of Variance (continued from page 87)

```
1530        NEXT K
1540      NEXT J
1550 NEXT I
1560 LPRINT" "
1570 RETURN
1580 X=1
1590 IF F<1 THEN1610
1600 A=FB:B=DE:C=F:GOTO1620
1610 A=DE:B=FB:C=1/F
1620 D=2/9/A:E=2/9/B:YY=ABS((1-E)*C[(1/3)-1+D)/S
     QR(E*C[(2/3)+D)
1630 IF B<4 THEN1670
1640 XX=.5/(1+YY*(.196854+YY*(.115194+YY*(.00034
     4+YY*.019527))))[4
1650 XX=INT(XX*10000+.5)/10000
1660 GOTO1690
1670 YY=YY*(1+.08*YY[4/B[3)
1680 GOTO1640
1690 IF F>=1 THEN1710
1700 P=1-XX:P=1-P:GOTO1720
1710 P=1-XX
1720 P=1-P:RETURN
1730 END
```

ROWS AND COLUMNS

Statistical data are frequently tabulated into a row and column format. Normally, one or more of the other routines that have just been presented in this chapter are used to evaluate the data against some well-defined hypothesis. The routine defined in Listing 5-10, however, is useful when you have a bunch of data, in tabular form, but no real firm notion of what it all means. The data are entered item by item from left to right, starting with row 1, column 1, and going row by row down the table. The program takes over and computes the sum, mean, and standard deviation of each row and then each column. Following this, the program computes the correlation between each of the rows in a pairwise fashion and then between each of the columns the same way. This routine is not meant to replace the other routines, but to provide a tool for preliminary analysis of a set of raw data. For example, we may want to examine a number of characteristics of a set of students as they enter a course of training to identify those characteristics which seem to be related to success (or failure) later in the course. Before investing a lot of time collecting data that may later prove to be irrelevant, we can use this program to evaluate a smaller set of data from a broad range of characteristics to get a rough notion of relevant characteristics. Having run this program, the more meaningful data items can be collected in depth and processed by one or another of the previous (or subsequent) programs.

Listing 5-10. Rows and Columns

```
1  '******************************************
2  'ROWS AND COLUMNS                         *
3  'LISTING 5-10                             *
4  '******************************************
5  '
10 ONERRORGOTO1610 :LPRINTSTRING$(3.10):CLS
20 INPUT"HOW MANY ROWS ARE THERE IN THE MATRIX";
     R
30 PRINT:INPUT"HOW MANY COLUMNS ARE THERE";C
40 IF (R+C)>37THEN50    ELSE60
```

```
50 CLS:PRINT"SUM OF ROW AND COLUMN MUST BE LESS
      THAN 38":PRINT:PRINT:GOTO20
60 DIM CR(R-1,R),YX(R-1,R),Y(R),Y2(R),RC(C-1,C),
      I(R,C),X(C),X2(C),XY(C-1,C)
70 LPRINT" ":LPRINT"NUMBER OF ROWS =";R:LPRINT"N
      UMBER OF COLUMNS =";C
80 LPRINT" "
90 CLS
100 FOR J=1 TO R
110     FOR K=1 TO C
120         PRINT@350,"ROW  COL";
130         PRINT@468,"ITEM:":PRINT@478,J:PRINT@
    483,K
140         INPUT I(J,K)
150     NEXT K
160 NEXT J
170 CLS
180 PRINT@512,"ARE THESE DATA CORRECT?   (Y/N)"
190 Q$=INKEY$:IFQ$=""THEN190
200 IF Q$="Y"THEN230  ELSE210
210 CLS:PRINT@512,"ENTER ROW AND COLUMN OF DATA
      TO BE CORRECTED":INPUTJ,K
220 PRINT:INPUT"ENTER CORRECT DATA";I(J,K):GOTO1
    70
230 CLS:FOR J=1 TO R
240     PRINT@512,"J =";J;"           ";
250     FOR K=1 TO C
260     PRINT@512,"K =";K;"          ";
270         X(K)=X(K)+I(J,K):X2(K)=X2(K)+(I(J,K)
    [2)
280         Y(J)=Y(J)+I(J,K):Y2(J)=Y2(J)+(I(J,K)
    [2)
290     NEXT K
300     FOR K=1 TO C-1
310         FOR L=K+1 TO C
320             XY(K,L)=XY(K,L)+(I(J,K)*I(J,L))
330         NEXT L
340     NEXT K
350 NEXT J
360 FOR M=1TOC
370     PRINT@512,"M=";M;"            ";
380     FOR K=1TO(R-1)
390         PRINT@512,"K =";K;"         ";
400         FOR J=K+1TOR
410             PRINT@512,"J =";J;"        ";
420             YX(K,J)=YX(K,J)+(I(K,M)*I(J,M))
430         NEXT J
440     NEXT K
450 NEXT M
460 CLS
470 FOR K=1 TO C-1
480     PRINT@512,"K =";K;"            ";
490     FOR L=K+1 TO C
500         PRINT@512,"L =";L;"          ";
510         RC(K,L)=((R*XY(K,L))-(X(K)*X(L)))/SQ
    R(((R*X2(K))-(X(K)[2))*((R*X2(L))-(X(L)[2))
    )
```

Listing 5-10. Rows and Columns (continued from page 89)

```
520       NEXT L
530 NEXT K
540 CLS
550 FOR K=1TO(R-1)
560       PRINT@512,"K =";K;"            ";
570       FOR J=K+1TOR
580             PRINT512,"J =";J;"            ";
590             CR(K,J)=((C*YX(K,J))-(Y(K)*Y(J)))/SQ
      R(((C*Y2(K))-(Y(K)[2))*((C*Y2(J))-(Y(J)[2))
      )
600       NEXT J
610 NEXT K
620 CLS
630 GOTO870
640 PRINT"COLUMN A","COLUMN B","CORRELATION";
650 PRINT
660 FOR K=1 TO C-1
670       FOR L=K+1 TO C
680             PRINTK,L,RC(K,L)
690       NEXT L
700 NEXT K
710 LPRINT"                  TABLE OF COLUMN CORRELATION
      S"
720 LPRINT"COLUMN A","COLUMN B","CORRELATION","t
      -TEST"
730 LPRINT" "," ","A WITH B"
740 LPRINT" "
750 FOR K=1 TO C-1
760       FOR L=K+1 TO C
770             LPRINTK,L,RC(K,L),((RC(K,L))*SQR(C-2
      ))/SQR(1-(RC(K,L)[2))
780       NEXT L
790 NEXT K
800 LPRINT" ":LPRINT"                  TABLE OF ROW CORR
      ELATIONS":LPRINT"ROW A","ROW B","CORRELATIO
      N","t-TEST":LPRINT" "," ","A WITH B":LPRINT
      " "
810 FOR M=1 TO R-1
820       FOR N=M+1 TO R
830             LPRINTM,N,CR(M,N),((CR(M,N))*SQR(R-2
      ))/SQR(1-(CR(M,N)[2))
840       NEXT N
850 NEXT M
860 GOTO1150
870 IF C>4THEN1150 ELSE880
880 LPRINT" ":LPRINT"                  TABLE OF INPUT VA
      RIABLES"
890 PRINT" ":PRINT"            INPUT VARIABLES"
900 LPRINT" ",
910 FOR K=1 TO C:LPRINT K,:PRINTK;:NEXT K
920 LPRINT"SUM","AVERAGE","STANDARD DEVIATION"
930 LPRINT" "
940 PRINT" "
950 FOR J=1 TO R
960       LPRINTJ,
970       FOR K=1 TO C
```

```
980          LPRINT I(J,K),
990          PRINTI(J,K);
1000     NEXT K
1010     LPRINT Y(J),Y(J)/C,SQR((Y2(J)-((Y(J)[2)
    /C))/(C-1))
1020     PRINT Y(J);Y(J)/C;SQR((Y2(J)-((Y(J)[2)/C
    ))/(C-1))
1030 NEXT J
1040 LPRINT" "
1050 PRINT" "
1060 LPRINT" ",
1070 FOR K=1 TO C:LPRINT X(K),:PRINT X(K);:NEXT
    K:LPRINT"SUM":PRINT"SUM"
1080 LPRINT" ",:FOR K=1 TO C:LPRINT X(K)/R,:PRIN
    T X(K)/R;:NEXT K:LPRINT"AVERAGE":PRINT"AVER
    AGE"
1090 LPRINT" ",
1100 FOR K=1 TO C
1110     LPRINT SQR((X2(K)-((X(K)[2)/R))/(R-1)),

1120     PRINT SQR((X2(K)-((X(K)[2)/R))/(R-1));
1130 NEXT K:LPRINT"STANDARD DEVIATION":PRINT"STA
    NDARD DEVIATION"
1140 LPRINT" ":GOTO640
1150 IF C>12THEN1490 :LPRINT" ":LPRINT"
    TABLE OF INPUT VARIABLES"
1160 LPRINT" "
1170 LPRINT" ";
1180 FORK=1 TO C:LPRINTK;:NEXT K
1190 LPRINT" ","SUM","AVERAGE","STANDARD DEVIATI
    ON"
1200 FOR J=1 TO R
1210     LPRINTJ;
1220     FOR K=1 TO C
1230          LPRINT I(J,K);
1240          PRINTJ,K,I(J,K)
1250     NEXT K
1260     LPRINT" ",
1270     LPRINT Y(J),Y(J)/C,SQR((Y2(J)-((Y(J)[2)
    /C))/(C-1))
1280 NEXT J
1290 GOTO1390
1300 FOR M=1 TO R-2
1310     FOR N=M+1 TO R-1
1320          FOR O=N+1 TO R
1330               LPRINT"ROW";M;N;".";O;"= ";(CR(
    M,N)-(CR(M,O)*CR(N,O)))/SQR((1-(CR(M,O)[2))
    *(CR(N,O)[2))
1340          NEXT O
1350     NEXT N
1360 NEXT M
1370 LPRINT" "
1380 GOTO1470
1390 LPRINT" ";:FOR K=1TOC:LPRINTX(K);:NEXT K:LP
    RINT" ",:LPRINT" ",:LPRINT"  SUM"
1400 LPRINT" ";:FOR K=1TOC:LPRINTX(K)/R;:NEXT K:
    LPRINT" ",:LPRINT" ",:LPRINT"  AVERAGE"
1410 LPRINT" ";
```

Listing 5-10. Rows and Columns (continued from page 91)

```
1420 FOR K=1TOC
1430     LPRINT SQR((X2(K)-((X(K)[2)/R))/(R-1));

1440 NEXT K
1450 LPRINT" ",:LPRINT" ",:LPRINT"   STANDARD DEV
     IATION"
1460 GOTO1140
1470 LPRINT" "
1480 END
1490 LPRINT"           TABLE OF INPUT VARIABLES"
1500 LPRINT" "
1510 LPRINT"ROW","COLUMN","ROW","COLUMN","ROW","
     COLUMN","ROW","COLUMN"
1520 FOR J=1 TO R
1530    LPRINT"SUM OF ROW";J;"=";Y(J):LPRINT"AVER
     AGE OF ROW";J;"=";Y(J)/C:LPRINT"STANDARD DE
     VIATION OF ROW";J;"=";SQR((Y2(J)-((Y(J)[2))
     /(C-1))
1540     FOR K=1 TO C STEP 2
1550         LPRINT J,K,I(J,K),J,K,I(J,K+1)I(J,K)
     ,
1560         LPRINT"SUM OF COLUMN";K;"=";X(K):LPR
     INT"AVERAGE OF COLUMN";K;"=";X(K)/R:LPRINT"
     STANDARD DEVIATION OF COLUMN";K;"=";SQR((X2
     (K)-((X(K)[2)/R))/(R-1))
1570         LPRINT"SUM OF COLUMN";K+1;"=";X(K+1)
     :LPRINT"AVERAGE OF COLUMN";K+1;"=";X(K+1)/R
     :LPRINT"STANDARD DEVIATION OF COLUMN";K+1;"
     =";SQR((X2(K+1)-((X(K+1)[2)/R))/(R-1))
1580     NEXT K
1590 NEXT J
1600 LPRINT" "
1610 RESUMENEXT
1620 CLS
```

EXERCISES

1. Define the phrase *violent crime*. Review the leading local newspaper daily for two or three months. Record the number of violent crimes committed each day and the daily temperature and precipitation. At the end of the test, compute the correlation between crime and weather. If possible, conduct the test during a transitional weather period; that is, from winter into spring or from fall into winter.

2. Select an economic indicator, such as the Dow-Jones stock index. Conduct the experiment in 1 above, using the economic index instead of weather.

3. Attend a sports event, such as a high diving competition, where there are three or more judges giving subjective ratings on the contestants. Keep your own record of each judge's ratings, then compute a Kendall's Coefficient of Concordance.

4. Using sex as the dichotomous variable, and last year's grades for a selected class as the continuous variable, compute a Point-Biserial correlation to determine if there is a sex-related component to the grades.

5. Using the grades identified in 4 above, compute a rank order correlation between last year's grades and the grades of each student on the last test in this course.

SUGGESTED READING

Bruning, J. L. and B. L. Kintz, 1968. *Computational Handbook of Statistics*. Glenview, IL: Scott,

Foresman and Company.

Edwards, A. L., 1976. *An Introduction to Linear Regression and Correlation*. San Francisco: W. H. Freeman and Company.

— — — 1979. *Multiple Regression and the Analysis of Variance and Covariance*. San Francisco: W. H. Freeman and Company.

Minium, E. W., 1970. *Statistical Reasoning in Psychology and Education*. New York: John Wiley & Sons.

Chapter 6

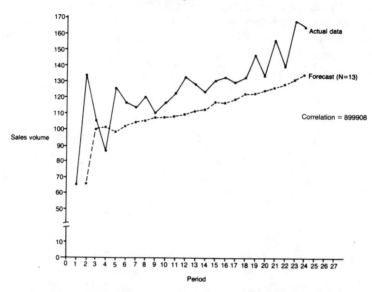

Time-Series Analysis

Perhaps one of the most frequently used techniques in current forecasting are those found under the heading of time-series analysis. The commercial interests in forecasting are very often an effort to determine, as far in advance and as accurately as possible, the future value of a stock, the price of an essential commodity, or the volume of demand for a product—all based on past history, or the preceding time-series. These problems are often complicated by the multitude of factors affecting the magnitude of the desired variable. Other areas suitable for time-series analysis include population studies, weather patterns, sunspot cycles . . . . in short, anything the quantity or magnitude of which is, or appears to be, a function of time.

The simplest form of time-series analysis is the computation of the mean of a set of data. Figure 6-1 presents a set of data points and the computed mean, which is shown as a heavy line running from right to left.

To the extent that the data are more or less linear, and the coefficient of correlation is ap-

proaching zero, the mean is a reliable predictor of future conditions. As the data becomes less and less linear, more sophisticated methods of analysis are necessary.

The methods we will examine for time-series analysis are: smoothing and decomposition methods, autoregressive/moving averages, multivariate time-series, linear and non-linear curve fitting, seasonal and cyclic trend analysis, and indexing techniques.

SMOOTHING AND DECOMPOSITION METHODS

Underlying this approach is the notion that an observed data point is a function of one or more of the preceding points. Although an average or mean of all of the data point leads to meaningless result, an average of some of the data points produces useful results.

There are a number of smoothing techniques available. Among them are: single moving averages, single exponential smoothing, linear moving averages, and linear exponential smoothing.

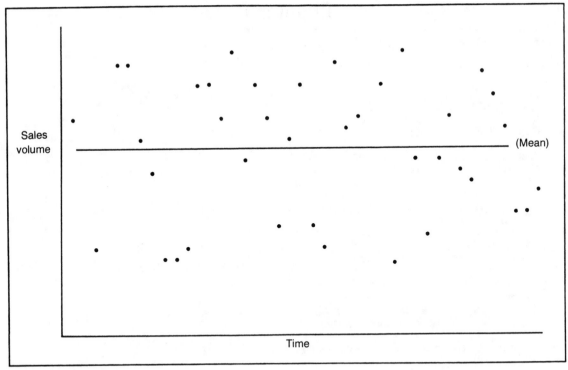

Fig. 6-1. Basic scattergram.

Single Moving Averages

This technique uses the average or mean of N previous periods to compute the next value. An example of this is given in Table 6-1. The resulting graph is shown in Fig. 6-2.

It is possible (and advisable) to evaluate the utility of a given value of N by computing the coefficient of correlation between the actual and predicted values. There is no routine to compute the optimum N, but microcomputers make easy work of selecting this value. Yesterday's statistician had to pick several values of N manually and make the necessary computations, selecting the value that appeared to yield the best results. The microcomputer approach is to compute the moving average for each value of N from two to the number of available data points less one. That is, if there are K data points, the moving average for N = 2 to K − 1 is computed. At the same time, the coefficient of correlation for the predictions for each value of N is computed.

Listing 6-1 is a routine to accept a set of data and evaluate it as described above. The input is simply the value for each data point. The output is the recommended value of N, based on the coefficient of correlation. The user can add features to printout the intermediate data and the coefficients of correlation for the other values of N.

Linear Moving Averages

As you will note in Table 6-1, the moving average lags behind (or underestimates) the actual data on a steady trend upward and overstates the estimate on a downward trend. If we compute the moving average of this moving average, however, we find the difference between the two moving averages is equal to the error between the first average and the actual data. We can exploit this fact by using the following procedure:

1. $E' = \dfrac{X_1 + X_2 + X_3 + \ldots + X_n}{N}$

Listing 6-1. Moving Averages

```
1  '**********************************************
2  'MOVING AVERAGES                              *
3  'LISTING 6-1                                  *
4  '**********************************************
5  '
10 CLS
20 INPUT"HOW MANY DATA POINTS";K
30 DIM V(K),R(K),A(K+1,K),ES(K):BR=0
40 FORI=1TOK:PRINT"ENTER VALUE FOR POINT #";I,:I
   NPUTV(I):NEXT
50 FORI=1TOK:PRINTI;V(I),:NEXT:PRINT
60 PRINT"ARE THESE ALL OK?  (Y/N)   ";
70 Q$=""+INKEY$:IFQ$=""THEN70    ELSEPRINTQ$
80 IFQ$="Y"THEN100
90 INPUT"ENTER NUMBER OF ITEM AND CORRECT VALUE"
   ;J,V(J):GOTO50
100 PRINT"PRINTING INPUT DATA":LPRINT"INPUT DATA
    ":FORI=1TOK:LPRINTI;V(I),:NEXT:LPRINT""
110 PRINT"N","SUM OF F'CAST","CORRELATION","NET
    ERROR"
120 PRINT:LPRINT"N    SUM OF X    SUM OF Y    CORRE
    L.    BEST    N    NET ERROR"
130   N$="##    ####.##    ####.##    #.#####    #
    .#####    ##    ######.##"
140 FORN=2TOK-1
150   T=0:TX=0:TY=0:X2=0:Y2=0:XY=0:A(1,N)=V(1):E
    S(N)=0
160   FORI=1TON-1
170     X=V(I):T=T+X:TX=TX+X:Y=TX/I:TY=TY+Y:X2=X
    2+(X[2):Y2=Y2+(Y[2):XY=XY+(X*Y):A(I+1,N)=TX
    /I:ES(N)=ES(N)+V(I)-A(I,N)
180   NEXTI
190   FORI=NTOK
200     A=A(I,N):T=T+V(I):A(I+1,N)=T/N:TX=TX+V(I
    ):TY=TY+A:X2=X2+(V(I)[2):Y2=Y2+(A[2):XY=XY+
    (A*V(I)):T=T-V(I-N+1):ES(N)=ES(N)+V(I)-A(I,
    N)
210     NEXT
220   R(N)=((K*XY)-(TX*TY))/SQR(((K*X2)-(TX[2))*
    ((K*Y2)-(TY[2)))
230   IFABS(R(N))<ABS(BR)THEN250
240   BR=R(N):RN=N
250   LPRINTUSINGN$;N;TX;TY;R(N);BR;RN;ES(N)
260 PRINTN,TY,R(N),ES(N)
270 NEXT
280 LPRINT"":ES=0:INPUT"AVERAGE FREQUENCY DESIRE
    D";FD
290 LPRINT"PERIOD","ACTUAL","FORECAST","ERROR"
300 FORI=1TOK
310   LPRINTI,V(I),A(I,FD),V(I)-A(I,FD)
320 NEXT
330 LPRINT""
340 LPRINT"EACH SET CONTAINS";RN;"ITEMS,    CORREL
    ATION = ";R(RN);"    NET SUM OF ERROR = ";ES
    (RN)
350 END
```

Table 6-1. Input and Output Data from Moving Average Routine.

```
SINGLE MOVING AVERAGE
PERIOD FOR AVERAGING =  0
```

N	SUM OF X	SUM OF Y	CORREL.	BEST	N	NET ERROR
2	3045.00	2896.00	0.66884	0.66884	2	149.00
3	3045.00	2899.67	0.87197	0.87197	3	179.33
4	3045.00	2873.42	0.85726	0.87197	3	207.92
5	3045.00	2845.33	0.86903	0.87197	3	232.17
6	3045.00	2827.50	0.88758	0.88758	6	255.50
7	3045.00	2809.17	0.88655	0.88758	6	276.00
8	3045.00	2792.07	0.89081	0.89081	8	294.21
9	3045.00	2776.95	0.89334	0.89334	9	311.05
10	3045.00	2761.53	0.89694	0.89694	10	326.69
11	3045.00	2748.24	0.89591	0.89694	10	340.77
12	3045.00	2736.21	0.89319	0.89694	10	353.98
13	3045.00	2725.31	0.89991	0.89991	13	366.70
14	3045.00	2715.01	0.89961	0.89991	13	378.22
15	3045.00	2705.58	0.89465	0.89991	13	388.35
16	3045.00	2698.10	0.89712	0.89991	13	396.90
17	3045.00	2691.39	0.89485	0.89991	13	404.68
18	3045.00	2685.45	0.88976	0.89991	13	411.38
19	3045.00	2680.38	0.88895	0.89991	13	417.28
20	3045.00	2676.27	0.87844	0.89991	13	422.89
21	3045.00	2673.50	0.87976	0.89991	13	426.35
22	3045.00	2672.73	0.87437	0.89991	13	428.79
23	3045.00	2670.83	0.86849	0.89991	13	431.49

PERIOD	ACTUAL	FORECAST	ERROR
1	66	66	0
2	134	66	68
3	107	100	7
4	87	102.333	-15.3333
5	126	98.5	27.5
6	117	104	13
7	114	106.167	7.83334
8	121	107.286	13.7143
9	111	109	2
10	117	109.222	7.77778
11	123	110	13
12	133	111.182	21.8182
13	129	113	16
14	124	114.231	9.76923
15	131	118.692	12.3077
16	133	118.462	14.5385
17	130	120.462	9.53846
18	133	123.769	9.23077
19	147	124.308	22.6923
20	134	126.615	7.38461
21	156	128.154	27.8462
22	140	130.846	9.15384
23	168	133.077	34.9231
24	164	137	27

EACH SET CONTAINS 13 ITEMS, CORRELATION = .899903   NET SUM OF ERROR = 366.695

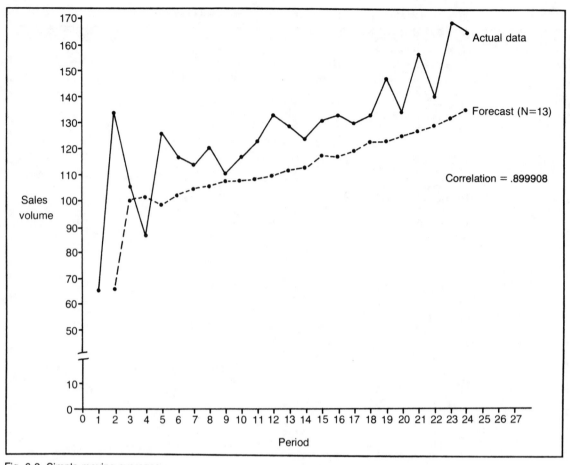

Fig. 6-2. Simple moving averages.

2. $E' = \dfrac{E_1' + E_2' + E_3' \ldots + E_n'}{N}$

3. $A = 2\,E' - E''$

4. $B = (2/(N-1)) \times (E' - E'')$

5. $F = A + B\,M$

Where M is the number of periods ahead to be forecast.

Figure 6-3, based on the data in Table 6-2, illustrates the effect of this approach.

Single Exponential Smoothing

The routine used above requires considerable memory space to store each of the input data points. In addition, each point, regardless of position relative to the present, has equal mathematical weight in the computation of the mean. In reality, recent values may be disproportionately more significantly than older points. In many firms the sales force is constantly changing, and sales volume is a function of the skill level of the team and the interaction of personalities, as well as product-related factors.

The basic component for exponential smoothing is the alpha value, A. If X is the most recent actual value, and LF is the last forecast, the current forecast, CF, is computed from

$$CF = A\,X + (1 - A)\,LF$$

and $LF = CF$

The obvious attraction of this approach is that you need only the most recent data for computation. The difficult part of the technique is assigning the proper value to A. The smaller A becomes, the less responsive the forecast will be to current shifts or trends. One approach to this problem is to begin a series of forecasts with A = .3 or so. After a year or so of experience, the value is adjusted to a smaller value; frequently A = .1.

For example, John opens a small ice-cream cone stand in Miami. Since he has to operate on a very narrow margin, he cannot afford to order more ice-cream from the supplier than he is likely to use prior to spoilage. At the same time, he cannot afford to buy too little product. It doesn't pay to sell out before the end of the day. Having no prior experience, the first year or so will be a speculative period at best. By using A = .3, though, his estimates should be fairly responsive to the local demand and shifts in demand. After a year or two, LF should be reliable and A can become .1.

John can maintain the essential forecast data on a small slip of paper: yesterday's forecast and today's sales. Table 6-3 shows the result of using A = .3 for six months and A = .1 for the remainder.

The computational equation is:

1. $F'' = F' + A (X - F')$
2. $F' = F''$

when F'' is the current forecast and F' is the previous forecast.

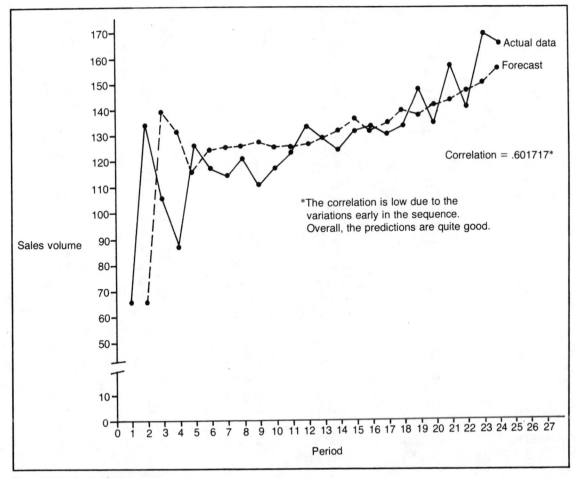

Correlation = .601717*

*The correlation is low due to the variations early in the sequence. Overall, the predictions are quite good.

Fig. 6-3. Linear moving averages.

Linear Exponential Smoothing

Just as we could improve the estimate of the moving average with the linear moving average technique, we can improve the exponential estimate by a similar double averaging of the exponential process. The equations needed for this technique are:

1. $CF' = A X + (1 - A) LF'$
2. $CF'' = A CF' + (1 - A) LF''$
3. $A = 2 CF' - CF''$

4. $B = (A/(1 - A)) (CF' - CF'')$
5. $F = A + B M$

Table 6-4 and Fig. 6-4 illustrate the various estimates derived from the preceding technique. Listing 6-2 is a smoothing program offering all four techniques as options.

Decomposition Methods

Despite its morbid name, decomposition really assists the analyst in identifying underlying pat-

Table 6-2. Linear Moving Average Data.

```
LINEAR MOVING (DOUBLE) AVERAGES
PERIOD FOR AVERAGING =  13
```

PERIOD	ACTUAL	MOVING AVERAGE	ERROR	DOUBLE AVERAGE	ERROR
1	66	66	0	66	0
2	134	66	68	66	68
3	107	100	7	139.667	-32.6667
4	87	102.333	-15.3333	131.5	-44.5
5	126	98.5	27.5	115.903	10.0972
6	117	104	13	124.339	-7.33889
7	114	106.167	7.83334	125.644	-11.6435
8	121	107.286	13.7143	125.286	-4.2857
9	111	109	2	126.75	-15.75
10	117	109.222	7.77778	125.259	-8.25926
11	123	110	13	125.341	-2.34074
12	133	111.182	21.8182	126.507	6.49329
13	129	113	16	129.169	-.169852
14	124	114.231	9.76923	130.592	-6.59193
15	131	118.692	12.3077	135.93	-4.93022
16	133	118.462	14.5385	130.701	2.29857
17	130	120.462	9.53846	133.378	-3.37795
18	133	123.769	9.23077	138.918	-5.91774
19	147	124.308	22.6923	137.817	9.18337
20	134	126.615	7.38461	140.994	-6.99414
21	156	128.154	27.8462	142.492	13.5077
22	140	130.846	9.15384	146.453	-6.45291
23	168	133.077	34.9231	149.326	18.6743
24	164	137	27	155.685	8.31514
SUM	3045	3100.58	366.695	1671.45	-24.6491

```
NEXT FORECAST = 160.095        CORRELATION = .601717
```

Table 6-3. Single Exponential Moving Average Data.

SINGLE EXPONENTIAL SMOOTHING

EXPONENTIALLY SMOOTHED AVERAGES

PERIOD	ACTUAL	A = .1	A = .2	A = .4	A = .8
1	66	66	66	66	66
2	134	66	66	66	66
3	107	72.8	79.6	93.2	120.4
4	87	76.22	85.08	98.72	109.68
5	126	77.298	85.464	94.032	91.536
6	117	82.1682	93.5712	106.819	119.107
7	114	85.6514	98.257	110.892	117.421
8	121	88.4862	101.406	112.135	114.684
9	111	91.7376	105.324	115.681	119.737
10	117	93.6639	106.46	113.809	112.747
11	123	95.9975	108.568	115.085	116.149
12	133	98.6977	111.454	118.251	121.63
13	129	102.128	115.763	124.151	130.726
14	124	104.815	118.411	126.09	129.345
15	131	106.734	119.529	125.254	125.069
16	133	109.16	121.823	127.553	129.814
17	130	111.544	124.058	129.732	132.363
18	133	113.39	125.247	129.839	130.473
19	147	115.351	126.797	131.103	132.495
20	134	118.516	130.838	137.462	144.099
21	156	120.064	131.47	136.077	136.02
22	140	123.658	136.376	144.046	152.004
23	168	125.292	137.101	142.428	142.401
24	164	129.563	143.281	152.657	162.88
SUM	3045	2374.94	2637.88	2817.02	2922.78

Listing 6-2. Composite Moving Averages

```
1  '**************************************************
2  'COMPOSITE MOVING AVERAGES                        *
3  'LISTING 6-2                                      *
4  '**************************************************
5  '
10 CLS
20 INPUT"HOW MANY DATA POINTS";K
30 DIM V(K),R(K),A(K+1,K),ES(K),F(K+1):BR=0
40 FORI=1TOK:PRINT"ENTER VALUE FOR POINT #";I,:I
     NPUTV(I):NEXT
50 FORI=1TOK:PRINTI;V(I),:NEXT:PRINT
60 PRINT"ARE THESE ALL OK?  (Y/N)  ";
70 Q$=""+INKEY$:IFQ$=""THEN70    ELSEPRINTQ$
80 IFQ$="Y"THEN100
90 INPUT"ENTER NUMBER OF ITEM AND CORRECT VALUE"
     ;J,V(J):GOTO50
```

101

Listing 6-2. Composite Moving Averages (continued from page 101)

```
100 PRINT"PRINTING INPUT DATA":LPRINT"INPUT DATA
    ":FORI=1TOK:LPRINTI;V(I),:NEXT:LPRINT""
110 PRINT:PRINT"1  --  SINGLE MOVING AVERAGE
2   --   LINEAR MOVING AVERAGE
3   --   SINGLE EXPONENTIAL SMOOTHING
4   --   LINEAR EXPONENTIAL SMOOTHING":PRINT:PRINT
    "SELECT ROUTINE",
120 T=0:TX=0:TY=0:X2=0:V2=0:XY=0
130 Q$=""+INKEY$:IFQ$=""THEN130   ELSEPRINTQ$
140 ONVAL(Q$)GOTO200  ,480  ,830  ,1150
150 '***********************************************
    ****************
160 '
                      *
170 '           SINGLE MOVING AVERAGES
                      *
180 '
                      *
190 '***********************************************
    ****************
200 LPRINT"SINGLE MOVING AVERAGE"
210 PRINT"N","SUM OF F'CAST","CORRELATION","NET
    ERROR"
220 PRINT:LPRINT"N   SUM OF X   SUM OF Y   CORRE
    L.    BEST    N    NET ERROR"
230   N$="##   ####.##   ####.##   #.#####   #
    .#####   ##   ######.##"
240 FORN=2TOK-1
250   A(1,N)=V(1):ES(N)=0:T=0:TX=0:TY=0:X2=0:V2=
    0:XY=0
260   FORI=1TON-1
270     X=V(I):T=T+X:TX=TX+X:Y=TX/I:TY=TY+Y:X2=X
    2+(X[2):V2=V2+(Y[2):XY=XY+(X*Y):A(I+1,N)=TX
    /I:ES(N)=ES(N)+V(I)-A(I,N)
280   NEXTI
290   FORI=NTOK
300     A=A(I,N):T=T+V(I):A(I+1,N)=T/N:TX=TX+V(I
    ):TY=TY+A:X2=X2+(V(I)[2):V2=V2+(A[2):XY=XY+
    (A*V(I)):T=T-V(I-N+1):ES(N)=ES(N)+V(I)-A(I,
    N)
310   NEXT
320   R(N)=((K*XY)-(TX*TY))/SQR(((K*X2)-(TX[2))*
    ((K*V2)-(TY[2)))
330   IFABS(R(N))<ABS(BR)THEN350
340   BR=R(N):RN=N
350   LPRINTUSINGN$;N;TX;TY;R(N);BR;RN;ES(N)
360   PRINTN,TY,R(N),ES(N)
370 NEXT
380 LPRINT"":ES=0:INPUT"AVERAGE FREQUENCY DESIRE
    D";FD
390 LPRINT"PERIOD","ACTUAL","FORECAST","ERROR"
400 FORI=1TOK
410   LPRINTI,V(I),A(I,FD),V(I)-A(I,FD)
420 NEXT
430 LPRINT""
```

```
440 LPRINT"EACH SET CONTAINS";FD;"ITEMS,    CORREL
    ATION = ";R(RN);"     NET SUM OF ERROR = ";ES
    (RN)
450 GOTO110
460 '*************************************************
    *****************
470 '
                        *
480 '           LINEAR MOVING AVERAGE
                        *
490 '
                        *
500 '*************************************************
    *****************
510 INPUT"NUMBER OF ITEMS TO BE AVERAGED AT A TI
    ME";N:IFN>KTHEN510
520 INPUT"NUMBER OF PERIOD TO BE FORECAST AHEAD"
    ;M
530 SF=0:E1=0:T=0:ES(N)=0:TX=0:TY=0:X2=0:Y2=0:XY
    =0:R(N)=0:A(1,N)=U(1):F(1)=U(1)
540 FORI=1TON-1
550   X=U(I):T=T+X:TX=TX+X:X2=X2+(X[2):A(I+1,N)=
    TX/I
560   T2=0:FORJ=1TOI:T2=T2+A(J,N):NEXT
570   E2=T2/I:A=(2*A(I+1,N))-E2:B=(2/(N-1))*(A(I
    +1,N)-E2):F(I+1)=A+(B*M):Y=F(I):TY=TY+Y:Y2=
    Y2+(Y[2):XY=XY+(X*Y):ES(N)=ES(N)+U(I)-F(I):
    E1=E1+U(I)-A(I,N):SA=SA+F(I)
580 NEXTI
590 FORI=NTOK
600   X=U(I):T=T+X:A(I+1,N)=T/N:Y=A(I+1,N):IFI=>
    (2*N)THEN630
610   T2=0:FORJ=I-N+1TOI:T2=T2+A(J,N):NEXT
620   E2=T2/N:A=(2*A(I+1,N))-E2:B=(2/(N-1))*(A(I
    +1,N)-E2):GOTO650
630   T2=0:FORJ=I-N+1TOI:T2=T2+A(J,N):NEXT
640   E2=T2/N:A=(2*A(I+1,N))-E2:B=(2/(N-1))*(A(I
    +1,N)-E2)
650   F(I+1)=A+(B*M):Y=F(I+1)
660   PRINTI,U(I),F(I),U(I)-F(I)
670   TX=TX+X:TY=TY+Y:X2=X2+(X[2):Y2=Y2+(Y[2):XY
    =XY+(X*Y):ES(N)=ES(N)+U(I)-F(I):T=T-U(I-N+1
    ):E1=E1+U(I)-A(I,N):SF=SF+F(I)
680 NEXT
690 R=((K*XY)-(TX*TY))/SQR(((K*X2)-(TX[2))*((K*Y
    2)-(TY[2)))
700 LPRINT"LINEAR MOVING (DOUBLE) AVERAGES"
710 LPRINT"PERIOD FOR AVERAGING = ";N
720 LPRINT"","","MOVING","","DOUBLE"
730 LPRINT"PERIOD","ACTUAL","AVERAGE","ERROR","A
    VERAGE","ERROR"
740 FORI=1TOK:LPRINTI,U(I),A(I,N),U(I)-A(I,N),F(
    I),U(I)-F(I):NEXT
750 LPRINT"SUM",TX,TY,E1,SF,ES(N)
760 LPRINT"NEXT FORECAST = ";F(K+1),"CORRELATION
     = ";R:LPRINT""
770 GOTO110
```

103

Listing 6-2. Composite Moving Averages (continued from page 103)

```
780  '***************************************************
     *******************
790  '
                        *
800  '              SINGLE EXPONENTIAL SMOOTHING
                        *
810  '
                        *
820  '***************************************************
     *******************
830  LPRINT"":LPRINT"SINGLE EXPONENTIAL SMOOTHING
     "
840  SA=0:FORI=1TO4:F(I)=0:NEXT
850  FORI=1TO4:A(1,I)=U(1):NEXT
860  LPRINT"","","","EXPONENTIALLY SMOOTHED AVERA
     GES"
870  LPRINT"PERIOD","ACTUAL","A = .1","A = .2","A
      = .4","A = .8"
880  FORI=1TOK
890     FORJ=1TO4:A(I+1,J)=A(I,J)+(((2[(J-1))/10)*
        (U(I)-A(I,J))):NEXT
900     SA=SA+U(I):FORJ=1TO4:F(J)=F(J)+A(I,J):NEXT

910     LPRINTI,U(I),A(I,1),A(I,2),A(I,3),A(I,4)
920  NEXT
930  LPRINT"SUM",SA,F(1),F(2),F(3),F(4)
940  PRINT:PRINT"ANOTHER ALPHA VALUE?   (Y/N)",
950  Q$=""+INKEY$:IFQ$=""THEN950   ELSEPRINTQ$
960  IFQ$="N"THEN1090
970  TX=0:TY=0:X2=0:Y2=0:XY=0:SA=0:F(1)=0:E=0
980  INPUT"DESIRED ALPHA VALUE";A
990  LPRINT"":LPRINT"PERIOD","ACTUAL","FORECAST",
     "ERROR","USING A = ";A
1000 FORI=1TOK
1010    X=U(I):A(I+1,1)=A(I,1)+(A*(U(I)-A(I,1))):
        Y=A(I,1)
1020    TX=TX+X:TY=TY+Y:X2=X2+(X[2):Y2=Y2+(Y[2):X
        Y=XY+(X*Y)
1030    SA=SA+U(I):F(1)=F(1)+A(I,1):E=E+U(I)-A(I,
        1)
1040    LPRINTI,U(I),A(I,1),U(I)-A(I,1)
1050 NEXT
1060 LPRINT"SUM",SA,F(1),E
1070 R=((K*XY)-(TX*TY))/SQR(((K*X2)-(TX[2))*((K*
     Y2)-(TY[2)))
1080 LPRINT"CORRELATION = ";R:LPRINT""
1090 GOTO110
1100 '***************************************************
     *******************
1110 '
                        *
1120 '              LINEAR EXPONENTIAL SMOOTHING
                        *
1130 '
                        *
```

```
1140 ´*********************************************
     ******************
1150 LPRINT"":LPRINT"LINEAR EXPONENTIAL SMOOTHIN
     G",
1160 INPUT"ENTER DESIRED ALPHA VALUE";A
1170 M=1:INPUT"NUMBER OF PERIODS FORECAST AHEAD"
     ;M
1180 L1=V(1):L2=V(1)
1190 LPRINT"ALPHA VALUE = ";A,"M = ";M:LPRINT"PE
     RIOD","ACTUAL","SINGLE EST.","LINEAR EST.",
     "FORECAST","ERROR"
1200 FORI=1TOK
1210   C1=(A*V(I))+((1-A)*L1)
1220   C2=(A*C1)+((1-A)*L2)
1230   AA=(2*C1)-C2:B=(A/(1-A))*(C1-C2)
1240   F=AA+(B*M):X=V(I):Y=F:ES(1)=ES(1)+V(I)-F
1250   PRINTI;V(I);AA;B;F
1260   LPRINTI,V(I),C1,C2,F,V(I)-F
1270   TX=TX+X:TY=TY+Y:X2=X2+(X[2):Y2=Y2+(Y[2):X
     Y=XY+(X*Y):L1=C1:L2=C2
1280 NEXT
1290 LPRINT"SUM",TX,"","",TY,ES(1)
1300 R=((K*XY)-(TX*TY))/SQR(((K*X2)-(TX[2))*((K*
     Y2)-(TY[2)))
1310 LPRINT"CORRELATION = ";R:LPRINT"":GOTO110
1320 DATA 66,134,107,87,126,117,114,121,111,117,
     123,133,129,124,131,133,130,133,147,134,156
     ,140,168,164
```

terns influencing numerical data, frequently those from economic and business efforts. In the previous section, the smoothing techniques were generally based on the notion that the data were the result of two main factors: some basic trend up or down and random events or noise. The smoothing techniques attempted to isolate or cancel out the random noise and define the basic trend. Decomposition techniques, on the other hand, accept and accommodate the concepts of trend, season, and business cycle and attempt to specify the contribution each factor makes in the computation of a forecast. Decomposition techniques assume that each piece of data representing a given period is the function of the underlying pattern(s) and that

Data = f(trend, cycle, season) + error.

The basic algorithm for most decomposition methods is

1. Given a series of data points, X, X, X, X . . . ., compute a moving average making N equal to the length of the season. That is, if the data are given in months, then N = 12 (for quarters, N = 4, for days in a week, N = 7, etc.).
2. Separate the result of the moving average from the data. This leaves data affected by the trend and the cycle.
3. Separate the seasonal factors by averaging them for each of the data points for one season.
4. Examine the plotted shape of the data and determine the appropriate shape: linear trend, ogive curve, non-linear curves, etc.
5. Compute: Data − trend − moving average = cyclic + random error.
6. Compute: Data − trend − moving average − cycle = error.

The simplest solutions to this type of problem can be found in a sine wave and an exponential smoothing technique presented.

Seasonal Smoothing

If you have reason to believe that your data are seasonal, or the forecasts derived from the preced-

Table 6-4. Linear Exponential Smoothing Data.

LINEAR EXPONENTIAL SMOOTHING		ALPHA VALUE = .3		M = 1	
PERIOD	ACTUAL	SINGLE EST.	LINEAR EST.	FORECAST	ERROR
1	66	66	66	66	0
2	134	86.4	72.12	106.8	27.2
3	107	92.58	78.258	113.04	-6.04
4	87	90.906	82.0524	103.554	-16.554
5	126	101.434	87.8669	120.816	5.18399
6	117	106.104	93.3381	124.341	-7.34097
7	114	108.473	97.8785	123.608	-9.6075
8	121	112.231	102.184	126.583	-5.58341
9	111	111.862	105.037	121.539	-10.5391
10	117	113.403	107.582	121.719	-4.7189
11	123	116.282	110.192	124.982	-1.98228
12	133	121.298	113.524	132.403	.597061
13	129	123.608	116.549	133.693	-4.6928
14	124	123.726	118.702	130.902	-6.90243
15	131	125.908	120.864	133.114	-2.11398
16	133	128.036	123.015	135.207	-2.20737
17	130	128.625	124.698	134.234	-4.23448
18	133	129.937	126.27	135.177	-2.17664
19	147	135.056	128.906	143.842	3.15759
20	134	134.739	130.656	140.573	-6.57282
21	156	141.118	133.794	151.579	4.42035
22	140	140.782	135.891	147.77	-7.77014
23	168	148.948	139.808	162.004	5.99559
24	164	153.463	143.904	167.119	-3.11881
SUM	3045			3100.6	-55.6006
CORRELATION =	.927893				

ing routines are not satisfying, you may want to consider one of the following procedures.

Sine wave Smoothing. This approach assumes the seasonal variation is continuously and evenly variable over the range of the year, the distribution of data points fall more or less on a sine wave, such as shown in Fig. 6-5.

If the data are more or less horizontal, varying mainly as a function of time of year, the equation to use in this process is

$$F = ((Sin .9856473321\ D) \times (Max - Min) + Max - Min)/2$$

where:

D is the number of days since the beginning of the annual cycle. If J1 is the Julian date of the start of the cycle, and J2 is Julian date of the subject day, $D = J2 - J1 + 1$

Max is the normal maximum volume

Min is the normal minimum volume

Where there is an identifiable trend line in which sales volume is both seasonal and, from year to year, either increasing or decreasing, the forecast equation is modified by adding the regression equation describing the long term trend. Computation of this regression equation will provide the mean of the trend line and the coefficients of the line as a function of time. It is possible that the coefficient of correlation will be fairly low as the deviations resulting from the seasonal influences will be considered as random error or random deviation. By combining the regression equation with the sine wave equation, the resulting forecast equation becomes

$$F = ((\text{Sin } .9856473321 \text{ } D(\text{Max} - \text{Min}) + \text{Max} - \text{Min})/2 + A + BD$$

It is equally possible to use any geometric or trigonometric (see Chapter 8) relationships such as the sine wave as a predictor protocol. As a matter of fact, many business components don't behave neatly along the sine wave throughout the year. There is no mathematical routine available to identify the optimum waveform in this type of approach. The user should review a chart of standard curve shapes and adapt the one that appears to resemble the pattern of the data best.

Linear and Seasonal Exponential Smoothing (after Winters). Compared to the preceding approach this approach gives the impression of greater objectivity and mathematical precision, but it is really as subjective as the sine wave approach. The primary advantage is that it automatically accommodates cyclic periods which may not have an annual basis. Rather, whether the period of the cycle is measured in quarters, days, or decades, the routine accepts the period as the user desires. It has the added feature of smoothing out random noise data—true random deviations as opposed to deviations caused by seasonal influence. The equations used in this process are:

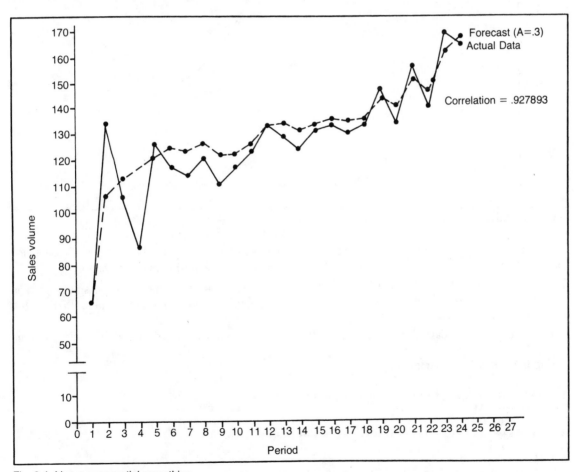

Fig. 6-4. Linear exponential smoothing.

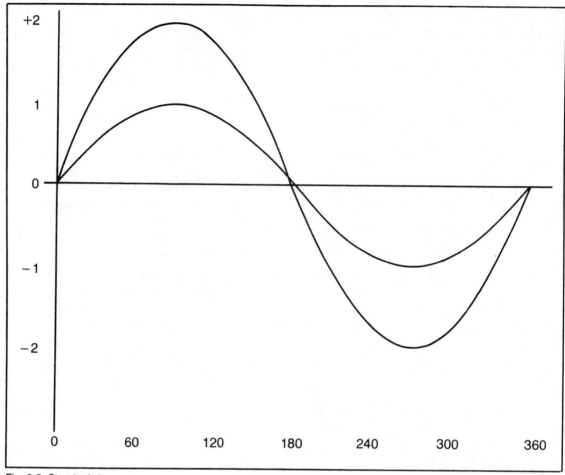

Fig. 6-5. Standard sinewaves.

1. $S2 = (A(X/I)) + ((1 - A)(S1 + B1))$
2. $B2 = (G(S2 - S1)) + (B1(1 - G))$
3. $I(T) = D(X/S2) + (I(T - L)(1 - D))$
4. $F = I(T - L \& M)(S2 + BM)$

where L is the length of seasonality (number of months, quarters, or days in a year), T is the

number of units since the beginning of the data, and $I(X)$ is the seasonal adjustment factor.

Listing 6-3 implements these sine wave and exponential smoothing techniques. Listing 6-4 handles a Ratio-to-Averages set.

Classic Decomposition Methods. Both the

Listing 6-3. Time-Series Smoothing

```
1  '************************************************
2  'TIME-SERIES SMOOTHING                          *
3  'LISTING 6-3                                    *
4  '************************************************
5  '
10 CLS
20 INPUT"HOW MANY DATA POINTS";K:DIMU(K),II(K)
```

108

```
30 FORI=1TOK:PRINT"ENTER VALUE FOR POINT #";I,:I
   NPUTV(I):NEXT
40 FORI=1TOK:PRINTI;V(I),:NEXT:PRINT
50 PRINT"ARE THESE ALL OK?  (Y/N)   ";
60 Q$=""+INKEY$:IFQ$=""THEN60    ELSEPRINTQ$
70 IFQ$="Y"THEN100
80 INPUT"ENTER NUMBER OF ITEM AND CORRECT VALUE"
   ;J,V(J):GOTO40
90 PRINT"PRINTING INPUT DATA":LPRINT"INPUT DATA"
   :FORI=1TOK:LPRINTI;V(I),:NEXT:LPRINT""
100 SM=V(1):PRINT:PRINT"(E)XPONENTIAL SMOOTHING
    (S)INEWAVE";
110 Q$=""+INKEY$:IFQ$=""THEN110   ELSEIFQ$="S"THE
    N270
120 PRINT:INPUT"ALPHA FACTOR";A:INPUT"BETA FACTO
    R";B:INPUT"GAMMA FACTOR";G
130 INPUT"LENGTH OF SEASON";L
140 INPUT"LENGTH OF LAG";M
150 S1=.5:B1=.5
160 FORI=0TOL:II(I)=1:NEXT
170 S1=V(L-1)
180 LPRINT"","",".            SMOOTHING"
190 LPRINT"PERIOD","ACTUAL","SINGLE","SEASONAL",
    "TREND","FORECAST"
200 FORI=LTOK-1
210   S2=(A*(V(I)/II(I-L)))+((1-A)*(S1+B1)):PRIN
    TS2,
220   B1=(G*(S2-S1))+((1-G)*B1):S1=S2:PRINTB1,
230   II(I+1)=(B*(V(I)/S2))+((1-B)*II(I-L)):PRIN
    TII(I+1),
240   F=(S2+(B1*I))*II(I-L+M)
250   PRINTF:LPRINTI,V(I),S2,II(I+1),B1,F
260 NEXT
270 FORI=1TOK
280   IFV(I)<=LGTHEN300
290   LG=V(I)
300   IFSM<=V(I)THEN320
310   SM=V(I)
320   T=T+V(I):X2=X2+(V(I)[2)
330 NEXT
340 M=T/K:SD=SQR((X2-((T[2)/K))/(K-1))
350 PRINT"SMALLEST = ";SM,"LARGEST = ";LG:PRINT"
    SUM = ",T,"MEAN = ";M,"STAND. DEV. = ";SD
360 GOTO380
370 LPRINT"SMALLEST = ";SM,"LARGEST = ";LG,"SUM
    = ";T,"MEAN = ";M,"STANDARD DEVIATON = ";SD

380 INPUT"DATA REPRESENT HOW MANY YEARS";NY
390 CLS:F=47/LG
400 FORI=1TOK
410   X=INT(127*(I/K)):Y=INT(47-(V(I)*F))
420   SET(X,Y)
430 NEXT
440 Z=NY*6.28318:TX=0:TY=0:X2=0:Y2=0:XY=0
450 FORI=1TOK
460   X=INT(127*(I/K)):XX=X+AD
470   Y=((SIN(.9865473321*((XX*Z)/(NY*127))))*(LG
```

Listing 6-3. Time-Series Smoothing (continued from page 109)

```
        -SM))+LG-SM)/2
480     SET(X,47-(Y*F)):X1=X1+X:X3=X3+(X[2):YY=YY+
        (X*Y)
490     X=V(I):TX=TX+X:TY=TY+Y:X2=X2+(X[2):Y2=Y2+(
        Y[2):XY=XY+(X*Y)
500 NEXT
510 R=((K*XY)-(TX*TY))/SQR(((K*X2)-(TX[2))*((K*Y
        2)-(TY[2)))
520 PRINT@0,"CORRELATION = ";R;
530 B=(YY-(K*((X1/K)*(TY/K))))/(X3-(K*((X1/K)[2)
        ))
540 A=(TY/K)-(B*(X1/K))
550 FORI=1TOK
560     X=INT(127*(I/K)):Y=A+(B*X):SET(X,47-(Y*F))

570 NEXT
580 PRINT@960,"(O)K  SHIFT (L)EFT  SHIFT (R)IGHT
        ";
590 S$=""+INKEY$:IFS$=""THEN590
600 PRINT@960,"AMOUNT OF SHIFT";:INPUTV
610 IFS$="R"THENAD=AD-V
620 IFS$="L"THENAD=AD+V
630 IFS$="O"THEN650
640 GOTO390
650 PRINT"THE EQUATION FOR THIS SEASONAL CYCLE I
        S: ((SIN(.9856473321 TIMES ((NUMBER OF DAYS
        SINCE JAN 1 TIMES";Z;") DIVIDED BY";NY*127
        ;")) TIMES";LG-SM;") PLUS";LG-SM;") DIVIDED
        BY 2"
660 GOTO580
```

Listing 6-4. Ratio-to-Moving Averages

```
1   '**********************************************
2   'RATIO-TO-MOVING AVERAGES                     *
3   'LISTING 6-4                                  *
4   '**********************************************
5   '
10 ONERRORGOTO940
20 @CLEAR
30 CLS
40 INPUT"NUMBER OF ITEMS";V:DIM M(V),Y(12),YY(V)
        ,D(V),F(V),MA(12),T(V),C(12),A(12),AM(V)
50 B$="YR.  JAN   FEB   MAR   APR   MAY   JUN
        JUL   AUG   SEP   OCT   NOV   DEC   TOTAL
        AVERAGE"
60 A$="### ##.#  ##.#  ##.#  ##.#  ##.#  ##.#  #
        #.#  ##.#  ##.#  ##.#  ##.#  ##.#  ######.#
        #  ###.##"
70 FA$="###.# ###.# ###.# ###.# ###.# ###.# ###.
        # ###.# ###.# ###.# ###.# ###.#    ####.##
        ###.##"
80 GA$="  #.### #.### #.### #.### #.### #.### #.
        ### #.### #.### #.### #.### #.###   ####.###
        ##.####"
```

```
90 PRINT@0,"INPUT DATA                    ";
100 @OPEN2
110 FORI=1TOV:@INPUTM(I):X=I+7:Y=65-M(I):SET(X,Y
    ):NEXT
120 @CLOSE
130 LPRINT"INPUT DATA":LPRINTB$:J=1
140 FORI=1TOVSTEP12
150    YT=0:FORJ=0TO11:YT=YT+M(I+J):Y(J+1)=Y(J+1)
    +M(I+J):TT=TT+M(I+J):NEXTJ
160     LPRINTUSINGA$;I/12;M(I);M(I+1);M(I+2);M(I+
    3);M(I+4);M(I+5);M(I+6);M(I+7);M(I+8);M(I+9
    );M(I+10);M(I+11);YT;YT/12
170 NEXT
180 LPRINT"SUM";USINGFA$;Y(1);Y(2);Y(3);Y(4);Y(5
    );Y(6);Y(7);Y(8);Y(9);Y(10);Y(11);Y(12);TT;
    TT/12
190 LPRINT"AVE";USINGFA$;Y(1)/10;Y(2)/10;Y(3)/10
    ;Y(4)/10;Y(5)/10;Y(6)/10;Y(7)/10;Y(8)/10;Y(
    9)/10;Y(10)/10;Y(11)/10;Y(12)/10;TT/10;TT/1
    20
200 LPRINT"":LPRINT"MOVING AVERAGES"
210 LPRINTB$:J=1:YT=0
220 PRINT@0,"MOVING AVERAGES                    ";
230 FORI=1TOV
240    T=T+M(I):IFI<12THEN260
250    Y(J)=T/12:YY(I)=M(I)/(T/12):T=T-M(I-11):C(
    J)=C(J)+Y(J):A(J)=A(J)+YY(I):GOTO270
260    Y(J)=T/I:YY(I)=M(I)/(T/I):A(J)=A(J)+YY(I)
270    TX=TX+I:X2=X2+(I[2):TY=TY+M(I):Y2=Y2+(M(I)
    [2):XY=XY+(I*M(I)):N=N+1
280    X=I+7:Y=Y(J):SET(X,65-M(I)):SET(X,65-Y):AM
    (I)=Y(J):J=J+1:IFJ<13THEN310
290     FORK=1TO12:YT=YT+Y(K):NEXT
300     LPRINTUSINGA$;INT(I/12.001);Y(1);Y(2);Y(3)
    ;Y(4);Y(5);Y(6);Y(7);Y(8);Y(9);Y(10);Y(11);
    Y(12);YT;YT/12:YT=0:J=1
310 NEXT
320 Z$="SUM"
330 FORI=1TO12:TA=TA+A(I):NEXT
340 IA=12/TA
350 FORI=1TO12:MA(I)=A(I)*IA:NEXT
360 FL=0
370 FORI=1TO12:CC=CC+C(1):NEXT
380 LPRINTZ$;USINGFA$;C(1);C(2);C(3);C(4);C(5);C
    (6);C(7);C(8);C(9);C(10);C(11);C(12);CC;CC/
    12:CC=0:IF FL=1THEN410
390 Z$="AVE"
400 FL=1:FORI=1TO12:C(I)=C(I)/10:NEXTI:GOTO370

410 LPRINT"":LPRINT"MOVING AVERAGES   (ACTUAL TO
    MOVING AVERAGE)"
420 LPRINTB$
430 FORI=0TOV-1STEP12
440    YR=0:FORJ=1TO12:YR=YR+YY(I+J):NEXT
450     LPRINTUSINGA$;I/12;YY(I+1);YY(I+2);YY(I+3)
    ;YY(I+4);YY(I+5);YY(I+6);YY(I+7);YY(I+8);YY
    (I+9);YY(I+10);YY(I+11);YY(I+12);YR;YR/12
```

Listing 6-3. Time-Series Smoothing (continued from page 111)

```
460 NEXT
470 LPRINT"SUM";USINGFA$;A(1);A(2);A(3);A(4);A(5
    );A(6);A(7);A(8);A(9);A(10);A(11);A(12);TA;
    TA/12
480 LPRINT"AVE";USINGGA$;MA(1);MA(2);MA(3);MA(4)
    ;MA(5);MA(6);MA(7);MA(8);MA(9);MA(10);MA(11
    );MA(12);TA/10;TA/120
490 LPRINTCHR$(140)
500 R=((N*XY)-(TX*TY))/SQR(((N*X2)-(TX[2])*((N*Y
    2)-(TY[2])))
510 B=(XY-((TX*TY)/N))/(X2-((TX[2])/N))
520 A=(TY/N)-(B*(TX/N))
530 MY=TY/N:SD=SQR((X2-((TX[2])/N))/(N-1))
540 SY=SD/SQR(N)
550 FORI=1TOV
560   Y=65-(A+(B*I)):X=I+7:SET(X,Y)
570 NEXT
580 PRINT@0,"LINEAR TREND                        "
590 PRINT"LINEAR TREND:   Y = ";A;" + ";B;" X"
600 PRINT"CORRELATION = ";R
610 PRINT"STANDARD ERROR = ";SY
620 PRINT"MEAN = ";MY,"STANDARD DEVIATION = ";SD

630 LPRINT"LINEAR TREND DATA"
640 LPRINT"MON DATA TREND DIFF  MON DATA TREND D
    IFF  MON DATA TREND DIFF  MON DATA TREND DI
    FF"
650 C$="### ### ###.# ###.#  ### ### ###.# ###.#
       ### ### ###.# ###.#  ### ### ###.# ###.#"
660 J=1
670 FORI=1TOVSTEP4
680   FORJ=ITOI+3
690     T(J)=A+(B*J):D(J)=M(J)-T(J)
700   NEXT
710   J=I+1:K=I+2:L=I+3
720   LPRINTUSINGC$;I;M(I);T(I);D(I);J;M(J);T(J)
      ;D(J);K;M(K);T(K);D(K);L;M(L);T(L);D(L)
730 NEXTI
740 LPRINT"LINEAR TREND:    Y = A + B X"
750 LPRINT"A = ";A,"B = ";B;"STANDARD ERROR = ";
    SY
760 LPRINT"CORRELATION = ";R,"MEAN = ";MY,"STAND
    ARD DEVIATION = ";SD:LPRINT"":LPRINTCHR$(14
    0)
770 D$="### ###   ###.### ###.### ##.### ###.###
       ###.##   ### ###   ###.### ###.### ##.### ###
    .### ###.##"
780 LPRINT"FORECAST STATISTICS"
790 LPRINT"MON DATA TREND 1  DIFF   CYCLE   TREND
     2 DIFF    MON DATA TREND 1  DIFF   CYCLE T
    REND 2  DIFF"
800 E$="         ###.###                ###.###
                    ###.###                ###.#
    ##"
810 GOTO830
820 CLS:PRINT@0,"RESIDUAL  (CYCLIC DATA + ERROR)";
```

```
830 FORI=0TOU-12STEP12
840   FORJ=1TO12STEP2
850     T1=A+(B*(I+J)):T2=A+(B*(I+J+1))
860     Y1=T1*MA(J)*(T1/AM(I+J)):Y2=T2*MA(J+1)*(
T2/AM(I+J+1))
870       F(I)=Y1:F(I+1)=Y2:D(1)=D(1)+M(I+J)-T1:D(
2)=D(2)+M(I+J)-Y1:D(3)=D(3)+M(I+J+1)-T2:D(4
)=D(4)+M(I+J+1)-Y2
880       LPRINTUSINGD$;I+J;M(I+J);T1;M(I+J)-T1;T1
/AM(I+J);Y1;M(I+J)-Y1;I+J+1;M(I+J+1);T2;M(I
+J+1)-T2;T2/AM(I+J+1);Y2;M(I+J+1)-Y2
890       SET(I+7,23-(M(I+J)-Y1)):SET(I+8,23-(M(I+
J+1)-Y2))
900   NEXTJ
910 NEXTI
920 LPRINT"NET DIFF.";USINGE$;D(1);D(2);D(3);D(4
)
930 END
940 RESUMENEXT
```

foregoing and the classic decomposition methods assume a given data point is the sum of the seasonal index value plus the computed trend plus the cycle component plus error

$$X = I + T + C + E$$

The following describes how an analysis using the classic decomposition method is performed. Given a set of data, the trend line ($Y = A + BX$) is computed as described in Chapter 4. Whether the trend line is in the linear form noted here or in one of the exponential or logarithmic forms is immaterial; the best version as dictated by the data must be used.

Secondly, a moving average value for each point is computed and that point is divided by the average. These ratio data are tabled according to season. That is, if the data are in monthly sums, a 12-column matrix is established; if they are quarterly, a 4-column matrix is established, and so forth. For an example, see Table 6-5.

Note that each column is totaled and averaged by the number of season cycles involved. This row of totals is totaled. The indexing (I) is accomplished by dividing the table total by 12 and multiplying the result times each of the column averages.

The computation of the preliminary forecast, then is:

Table 6-5. Seasonal Data Table for Indexing.

Quarterly Sales Data						
Year	Jan-Mar	Apr-Jun	Jul-Sep	Oct-Dec	Total	Mean
1971	240	267	440	538	1485	371.25
1972	276	244	460	525	1505	376.25
1973	262	240	440	567	1509	377.25
1974	278	239	446	576	1539	384.75
1975	264	265	463	561	1553	388.25
Total	1320	1255	2249	2767	7591	1897.75
Mean	264	251	449.8	553.4	1518.2	379.55

$$F = I (A + B X)$$

Subtracting this forecast from the actual data ordinarily leaves some residual data. It is recommended the analyst examine these residual values for randomness.

AUTOREGRESSION

In Chapter 5 we considered several multivariate regression techniques in which the normal form of the equation was

$$Y = A + B_1 X_1 + B_2 X_2 + \ldots . B_n X_n + e$$

Each value of X represents a different factor: price, temperature, etc., with its own beta weight. In a time-series regression analysis, each value of X is the magnitude of a given variable, but displaced over one or more periods of time. For example, we presume that the current value of the variable Y, using an offset of three periods, becomes

$$Y_t = A + B_1 Y_{t-3} + B_2 Y_{t-4} + \ldots . B_n Y_{t-n} + e$$

Since the different independent variables are nothing more than time-lagged values of the dependent variable, we can compute a correlation between these values. Such a process is known as an *autoregression* process. It should be evident that different lag factors are likely to produce different autoregressions. It is a fairly simple matter to use the microcomputer to evaluate the data and identify the optimum lag factor. The computation equations used in this process are:

$$r_k = \frac{\sum\limits_{T=1}^{n-k} (Y_T - \overline{Y}) (Y_{T+K} - \overline{Y})}{n_{(Y_T - \overline{Y})}}$$

$$T = \sqrt{\frac{\sum\limits^{T=1}(Y_T - \overline{Y})^2}{n - 1}}$$

From the study of statistics we can derive a principle that states that if a set of numbers is generated randomly, the autoregression of these values must lie within a range defined by the mean of the distribution plus 1.96 times the standard error. If all of the autoregressions are computed to fall within these limits, the data are accepted as randomly ordered. On the other hand, if one or more of the autoregressions fall outside this limit, the data are believed to contain some rational order. Success in forecasting is frequently based on the analyst's ability to distinguish random from rational or patterned data.

Listing 6-5 is a brief routine to determine the optimum lag factor to obtain the maximum correlation between the tabular data and to illustrate degree of randomness in the data.

Having built a predictive model and applied it against known data points, we are left with residual or error data. These are simply the dregs after we have made a prediction. For each data point for which we make a forecast, there is some degree of error. If we table these residuals and then compute an autoregression on these data, we are looking for a high degree of randomness in the error data. The smaller the amount of error and the greater the randomness of the data, the better our forecasting model.

Stationary

When the data are randomly ordered, the dis-

Listing 6-5. Autoregression

```
1  '**********************************************
2  'AUTOREGRESSION                               *
3  'LISTING 6-5                                  *
4  '**********************************************
5  '
10 CLS:PRINT"AUTOREGRESSION":PRINT:PRINT
20 INPUT"NUMBER OF ITEMS";N
30 DIM X(N),R(N-1)
40 FORI=1TON
50    PRINT"ENTER ITEM #";I,:INPUT X(I)
60    TX=TX+X(I)
```

```
70 NEXT
80 MX=TX/N
90 FORI=1TON
100    SY=SY+((X(I)-MX)[2)
110 NEXT
120 FORK=1TON-1
130    PRINTK;
140    FORI=1TON-K
150      SX=SX+((X(I)-MX)*(X(I+K)-MX))
160    NEXTI
170    R(K)=SX/SY:PRINTR(K):SX=0
180 NEXTK
190 CLS
200 PRINT"TIME LAG
                AUTOCORRELATON"
210 FORI=14TO1STEP-1
220    PRINT@960-(I*64),I;
230    PRINT@988-(I*64)+(25*R(I)),"*";
240    PRINT@1016-(I*64),USING"#.####";R(I);
250 NEXT
260 SE=1/SQR(N):ES=1.96*SE:LE=29-(25*ES):RE=29+(
    25*ES)
270 LX=LE*2:RX=RE*2
280 FORY=4TO47STEP2:SET(LX,Y):SET(RX,Y):NEXT
290 FORX=13TO111STEP4:SET(X,46):NEXT
300 PRINT@964,"-1";:PRINT@988,"-0-";:PRINT@1014,
    "+1";
310 FORI=15360TO16324STEP64
320    FORJ=ITOI+63
330      A=PEEK(J):IF A<32THEN370
340      IFA<58THEN360
350      IFA=32THENLPRINT" ";ELSELPRINT"I";:GOTO3
    80
360      LPRINTCHR$(A);:GOTO380
370      LPRINTCHR$(A+64);
380    NEXTJ
390    LPRINT""
400 NEXTI
410 LPRINT"":LPRINT"STANDARD ERROR = 0 +/-";ES
420 END
```

tribution of the various regressions will fall within the nominal limits defined above but in no apparent pattern about the mean. Such data are called *stationary*; that is, there is no growth or decline in the data. Charted, the data would be horizontal along the x-axis.

If the data patterns itself very neatly about the mean and useful forecasts can be computed from the linear or curvilinear trend, then, for practical purposes, we can leave this section of the data analysis. On the other hand, if there are autoregressions that are significant (greater than 1.96 times the standard error), we know the data contain some pattern. The basic procedure we use is

1. Compute the autoregressions. If they tend to cluster near zero, after one or two time lags, the table is said to be stationary. If it is stationary, go to rule 3; otherwise, go to rule 2.
2. Process the data using the principle of *differencing* described below. Return to rule 1.
3. If the first three time lags are significant, a nonseasonal pattern in the data is suggested. If these are not, but time lags

115

greater than three are, we assume a seasonal pattern with a length corresponding to the time lags of the largest autoregression. If none of the autoregressions are significant, then we believe no pattern exists in the data.

Differencing is a process by which the table is rebuilt by subtracting consecutive data points in successive periods. For example,

$$X'_T = X_{T+1} - X_T \qquad \text{First Difference}$$
$$X''_T = X'_{T+1} - X'_T = X_{T+2} - 2X_{T+1} + X_T$$
$$\text{Second Difference}$$

The new table is then run through the autoregression program to recompute the autoregressions. If this process should fail to achieve the desired stationarity, the table is differenced again.

In theory, this process can be continued until you run out of sufficient data or the table becomes stationary. In practice, however, it is rare to have to go beyond the second difference to achieve stationarity. Listing 6-6 includes lines that are meant to be appended to the program in Listing 6-5 and implement the differencing options.

As you may have concluded, time-series fore-

Listing 6-6. Autoregression

```
1    '***********************************************
2    'AUTOREGRESSION                               *
3    'LISTING 6-6                                  *
4    '***********************************************
5    '
10   CLS:PRINT"AUTOREGRESSION":PRINT:PRINT
20   INPUT"NUMBER OF ITEMS";N
30   DIM X(N),R(N-1)
40   FORI=1TON
50     X(I)=RND(100):GOTO70
60       PRINT"ENTER ITEM #";I,:INPUT X(I)
70       PRINTX(I),:TX=TX+X(I)
80   NEXT
90   MX=TX/N
100  FORI=1TON
110      SY=SY+((X(I)-MX)[2)
120  NEXT
130  FORK=1TON-1
140      PRINTK;
150      FORI=1TON-K
160        SX=SX+((X(I)-MX)*(X(I+K)-MX))
170      NEXTI
180      R(K)=SX/SY:PRINTR(K):SX=0
190  NEXTK
200  CLS
210  PRINT"TIME LAG
                  AUTOCORRELATON"
220  FORI=14TO1STEP-1
230      PRINT@960-(I*64),I;
240      PRINT@988-(I*64)+(25*R(I)),"*";
250      PRINT@1016-(I*64),USING"#.####";R(I);
260  NEXT
270  SE=1/SQR(N):ES=1.96*SE:LE=29-(25*ES):RE=29+(
         25*ES)
280  LX=LE*2:RX=RE*2
290  FORY=4TO47STEP2:SET(LX,Y):SET(RX,Y):NEXT
300  FORX=13TO111STEP4:SET(X,46):NEXT
310  PRINT@964,"-1";:PRINT@988,"-0-";:PRINT@1014,
         "+1";
```

116

```
320 FORI=15360TO16324STEP64
330   FORJ=ITOI+63
340     A=PEEK(J):IF A<32THEN380
350     IFA<58THEN370
360     IFA=32THENLPRINT" ";ELSELPRINT"I";:GOTO3
      90
370     LPRINTCHR$(A);:GOTO390
380     LPRINTCHR$(A+64);
390   NEXTJ
400   LPRINT""
410 NEXTI
420 LPRINT"":LPRINT"STANDARD ERROR = 0 +/-";ES
430 IF FL<>0THEN700
440 PRINT@0,"DIFFERENCING REQUIRED?   (Y/N)";
450 Q$=""+INKEY$:IFQ$=""THEN450
460 PRINTQ$:IFQ$="N"THEN780
470 FL=11:DIM XX(N),RR(N):K=1:TX=0
480 FORI=1TON-1
490   XX(I)=X(I+1)-X(I):TX=TX+XX(I)
500 NEXT
510 SY=0:MX=TX/(N-K):SX=0
520 FORI=1TON-K
530   SY=SY+((XX(I)-MX)[2)
540 NEXT
550 FORI=1TON-K
560   PRINTI,
570   FORJ=1TON-I
580     SX=SX+((XX(J)-MX)*(XX(J+I)-MX))
590   NEXTJ
600   RR(I)=SX/SY:PRINTRR(I):SX=0
610 NEXTI
620 CLS
630 PRINT"TIME LAG
               AUTOCORRELATION"
640 FORI=14TO1STEP-1
650   PRINT@960-(I*64),I;
660   PRINT@988-(I*64)+(25*RR(I)),"*";
670   PRINT@1016-(I*64),USING"#.####";RR(I);
680 NEXTI
690 GOSUB290
700 PRINT@0,"ADDITIONAL DIFFERENCING?   (Y/N)";
710 Q$=""+INKEY$:IFQ$=""THEN710
720 PRINTQ$:IFA$="N"THEN780
730 K=K+1:TX=0
740 FORI=1TON-K-1
750   XX(I)=XX(I+2)-(2*XX(I+1)+XX(I))
760 NEXT
770 GOTO510
780 END
```

casting is, in many respects, a special case of the use of forecasting techniques in general. In place of an independent variable, we use time periods. This is not without some problems, but none that normally outweigh the advantages of the techniques.

S-CURVE OF ADOPTION

Virtually every new innovation goes through a process of adoption consisting of three stages: initial exposure, experimentation, and limited acceptance; wide-spread acceptance and acquisition; and stabilization to a normal level of use. If we introduce a new product to an identified population of consumers and then plot the number of consumers using the product as a percent of the total population, over a period of time, the graph will almost always resemble the form in Fig. 6-6.

This relationship is observed in studies of the adoption of new hybrid grains and farming techniques among Iowa farmers, the adoption of skateboards among youngsters throughout the country, the adoption of microcomputers as working aids in small businesses, and in the adoption of any number of similar innovations. The only factor that really varies from innovation to innovation is the scale of the independent variable, time. It may take a decade or two for a new grain or technique to become dominant among a community of farmers, yet only a matter of weeks for skateboards or pet rocks to sweep through the nation. Affecting the rate of acceptance are such factors as the actual cost of the new item, the risk (cost) of adoption as opposed to the known profit of not changing, the perceived profit potential of the innovation, and other social or cultural factors resisting or supporting change. A skateboard is relatively inexpensive. To make the purchase is fairly easy. Not to buy the board is to isolate oneself from a peer activity. It might be fun to use, and there is no great loss if it doesn't work out. At the other end of the spectrum, let's hypothesize an improved farming technique that we want to introduce in India. Unfortunately, a part of the process requires the slaughter and pro-

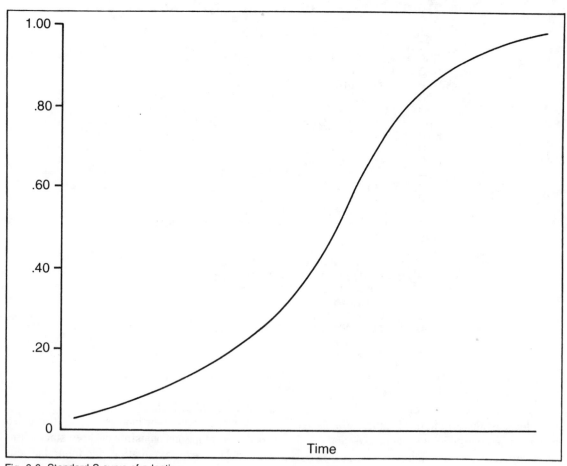

Fig. 6-6. Standard S-curve of adoption.

cessing of cattle for certain necessary chemicals to be used in the improved technique. Not only will there be a predictable resistance to new ideas, but there will also be the religious or cultural opposition to the use of the sacred cattle in the process. It might require generations before any significant progress is made in adoption of the technique. Interestingly enough, after an initial breakthrough in attitude and acceptance, a bandwagon effect can sometimes be seen, and that which has been resisted for decades will be warmly embraced by almost everyone within the year. During that last period, the adoption rate will resemble the standard "S" or ogive curve of acceptance.

The function of this section, however, is not to devise strategies for acceptance of innovations, but to provide a way to use the microcomputer to fit an ogive shape to data available early in the history of an innovation, so that a projected acceptance pattern can be constructed.

The ogive curve closely resembles the arctangent family of curves. A program that exploits this information by overlaying a plotting of the available acceptance data with an arctangent curve and then adjusting the curve for a best-fit of the data can be devised. The resulting coefficients let us extrapolate the balance of the acceptance pattern.

In addition to the arctangent family of curves, we also have some other equations that can be used in projecting an acceptance pattern. They are

1. $Y = ae^{bx}$ Exponential

2. $Y = \dfrac{L}{1 + ae^{-bt}}$ Pearl's equation

3. $Y = Le^{-ae^{-bt}}$ Gompertz's equation

4. $Y = (1 - ae^{-bt})^3$ Von Bertalanffy's Curve

where a is the intercept of the S-curve; b is the slope; L is the upper limit; and t is the time period.

A little trial and error will produce the coefficients for the first equation. If L = 1, the second and third equations can be transformed into a more standard form $(Y = A + B X)$ and the coefficients solved as in the least squares linear trend.

Both of the foregoing approaches are burdened by the same defect: to be of value, the projection must be made so early in the process of acceptance that computations of curves based on available data may be terribly misleading. By the time sufficient data have been collected from which to compute a reliable curve, the utility of the forecast may only be nominal. About the only thing that can be done about this is to run one or the other of the programs you have devised once or twice a week from the beginning of the innovation and revise the long-term forecast accordingly. After a time, the projected data for acceptance by a specified percentage will begin to stabilize. Hopefully, the stabilization will occur prior to the need for the forecast.

LINEAR REGRESSION AND TIME-SERIES FORECASTING

In normal regression analysis, two variables (such as GNP, market prices, weather conditions, etc.), are correlated one to another, one of them being the independent variable and the other being the dependent variable, that is, it is dependent on a value of the independent variable for its magnitude. Such a relationship is known as a *causal model*. Correlations developed using time as the independent variable are known as *time-series models*.

The time-series model has proven to be a powerful predictor in long range forecasts. Its main shortfall results from the error induced by the rise and fall of seasonal data; such as daily and monthly variations. For this reason, the longer the forecast, in numbers of years, the less likely there will be significant long-term error. Chapter 5 included some useful techniques for this kind of trend analysis. Especially useful are the routines supporting nonlinear curve-fitting.

EXERCISES

1. Contact your local weather station and obtain daily temperature records for the last five years. Compute the seasonal indices, mean daily temperatures and short-term

Table 6-6. 5-Year Shoe Sales Record.

JAN	FEB	MAR	APR	MAY	JUN	JUL	AUG	SEP	OCT	NOV	DEC	TOT
362	415	500	422	430	286	223	166	141	89	169	276	3479
423	510	471	427	356	318	173	154	105	149	179	312	3577
361	476	467	423	438	255	165	75	141	126	227	311	3465
426	513	468	497	423	292	168	151	132	120	171	251	3612
401	457	447	431	382	262	220	134	148	142	192	348	3564
1973	2371	2353	2200	2029	1413	949	680	667	626	938	1498	17697

trend, and forecast next month's temperatures. Correlate your forecast with the actual outcome.

2. From the data above, simply smooth the data using a seasonal smoothing technique and forecast next month's temperature from a graph of the smoothed data. Compare this value with the best estimate from item 1.

3. Table 6-6 contains the five-year sales record of a shoe store. Prepare an analysis of the sales to include the seasonal indexing, long term trend, and nonseasonal cyclic influence, if any.

4. Census II is a technique developed and used by the federal government to compute populations and population trends using a decomposition method similar to but more complicated than the ones shown in this chapter. Locate a funtional description of the technique, and write a routine to implement it.

SUGGESTED READING

Brown, R. G., 1963. *Smoothing, Forecasting, and Prediction.* Englewood Cliffs, NJ: Prentice-Hall.

Byrkit, D. R., 1972. *Elements of Statistics.* New York: Van Nostrand Reinhold Company.

McFadden, J. A., 1971. *Physical Concepts of Probability.* New York: Van Nostrand Reinhold Company.

Mendenhall, W. and J. E. Reinmuth, 1971. *Statistics for Management and Economics.* Belmont, CA: Wadsworth Publishing Co.

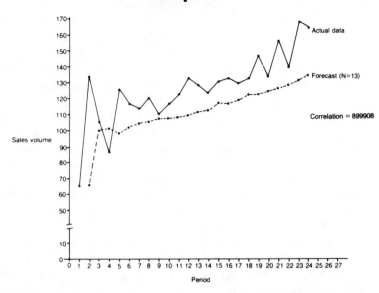

Chapter 7

Modeling and Simulations

In the preparation of this book, especially the supporting programs, I have come upon problems the solutions to which were not self-evident or easily found in a simple equation. The first exercise item in Chapter 10 grew out of just such a problem. I knew that I could reduce the expression for computing the relative appreciated values to m Log 2(1 + R_1) and m Log (1 + R_2). I was looking for the date at which the two lines would intersect, which would be when

$$m \text{ Log } 2(1 + R_1) = m \text{ Log } (1 + R_2)$$

I wanted a short algebraic solution to this relationship, but nothing presented itself. The only solution that I was aware of was an iterative approach wherein I used trial values of m to approach the relationship described. The experience taught me several lessons.

First, it illustrated the utility of a model. By constructing a numerical equivalent of the real life situation we can step through the process rapidly to determine conditions that satisfy our objectives. Second, we can probably save ourselves a lot of time. Elegant solutions to a variety of problems probably exist throughout a lot of our daily work. Yet, the time required to come to a workable understanding of these solutions may be more than we have available. As a practical matter, the brute-force solution may be the most expedient solution, and we shouldn't be too proud to use it. To the extent that the difference in processing time within the microcomputer is measured only in a few milliseconds, technique selection is determined by the availability and understandability of the solutions. This is not an argument for sloppy science or a cop-out but it is encouragement to the reader who may have a workable solution to a problem but is spending considerable time seeking a more elegant solution. If the enjoyment you receive from microcomputer programming comes from solving such problems in the most elegant fashion, I applaud the effort. On the other hand, if the objective is to get a job done and the program works, leave it alone and get on with the main tasks.

Modeling and simulations frequently offer solutions to problems that would otherwise be too tedious to unravel in the time alloted to the task. The exercise item just mentioned and several of the approaches in a number of the chapters rely upon mathematical models to provide the desired answers. We may not know all of the components of buyer behavior, relevant weather patterns, and other economic elements and interactions, but if we can predict trends in these variables, we can build effective marketing models.

Models allow us to experiment with objects and systems that are otherwise too large or unwieldy to deal with. Models allow system or organizational managers to play the "what if" game. What if we raise salaries 12 percent? What if we raise salaries and increase and achieve production quotas? What if we switch to a new plastic in lieu of the sheet metal we've been using for fifty years? Unfortunately, its Board of Directors would never allow us to tinker with the operational components of General Motors, no matter how honorable our intentions. On the other hand, if we build a model of General Motors in our computer systems, we can tinker to our hearts' delight. Through this process, assuming our computer can handle all of the relevant data, we have the ability to devise winning management strategies.

The problem with models is that they are simply rough representations of the real thing. Seldom do they contain the level of detail and the comprehensive coverage of the "real thing" necessary to assure us that all contingencies can be anticipated. In large corporate settings, the complexity of the total system is such that to develop a program accounting for all aspects would often exceed the capacity of the supporting computer and far exceed the time available for analysis. Rather, in using models, we make every effort to give adequate consideration to significant factors and trust that what is left unaccounted for will not result in unacceptable consequences.

Beyond this, there are few specific rules for model makers to follow. To be useful for microcomputer applications, the model should be quantifiable; that is, the components should be able to be expressed in numerical relationships. Also, given known "settings" or relationships, the model should yield known and corresponding outputs. For example, if we know that in real life the number of eggs produced by a given number of chickens is partly a function of the quantity of grain consumed in a day, any model we construct of the chicken yard should yield accurate results given known conditions. If, in real life, the normal level of grain consumption will yield 100 eggs, then the computer model, using the normal level of grain as a beginning parameter, should produce the same results. This is especially important within the model. If the state or condition of one component is the function of another, we must fine tune the corresponding mathematical relationships to yield the same results.

While most of the chapters contain major programs to support the objective of the given chapter, this chapter will not lead to an all-purpose model-making program. Instead, we will use several case studies to illustrate various microcomputer applications of modeling and simulations.

THE "LIFE" SIMULATION

A popular computer programming exercise first inspired by an article in *Scientific American* a number of years ago, Life is an abstraction of the present world in which the prime determinants of existence are overcrowding and isolation. The rules are quite simple:

1. The "world" is represented by a matrix. At any given instant, one or more of the matrix cells will be populated.
2. If that cell has more than three contiguous (touching) neighbors, it will die from overcrowding before the next generation is produced.
3. If that cell has less than two contiguous neighbors, it will die from isolation.
4. If a cell is not populated (not filled) and has exactly three neighbors, a new cell will be created.

The normal process is to establish the matrix, randomly populating the field, and then to check each cell in turn against the rules stated above. Before the text generation is displayed, each overcrowded or isolated cell is removed from the matrix (killed). Each cell with three neighbors generates a new cell occupant.

Listing 7-1 contains a simple program for playing Life. Figure 7-1 shows a flowchart of the program. It will create interesting shapes and forms such that only the most esoterically trained mathematician, using little-known techniques, could begin to predict the actual shape of the population distribution at any given moment. Assembly

Listing 7-1. Life Simulation

```
1  '***********************************************
2  'LIFE SIMULATION                               *
3  'LISTING 7-1                                   *
4  '***********************************************
5  '
10 CLS:RANDOM
20 PRINT"LIFE SIMULATION":PRINT:PRINT
30 INPUT"WHAT IS THE HORIZONTAL DIMENSION SIZE (
        0 < X < 120 )";H
40 IF 0<H AND H<121 THEN 60
50 PRINT"SORRY, MUST BE 0 < D < 121":PRINT:GOTO3
        0
60 INPUT"WHAT IS THE VERTICAL DIMENSION SIZE ( 0
        < Y < 40 )";V
70 IF 0<V AND V<41 THEN 90
80 PRINT"SORRY, MUST BE 0 < D < 41":PRINT:GOTO60

90 PRINT:PRINT"WE WILL CREATE A MATRIX";H;"CELLS
        WIDE
BY";V;"CELLS HIGH.    THIS CREATES A UNIVERSE
OF";V*H;"CELLS.":PRINT:PRINT"WHAT PERCENTAGE OF
        THESE SHOULD
BE  'ALIVE' AT THE BEGINNING OF THE RUN   (5%=5)"
        ;:INPUTP:P=P/100
100 HC=INT((127-H)/2):VC=INT((47-V)/2)
110 BP=INT(H*V*P):AP=BP:CLS
120 FORI=1TOBP
130   X=RND(H)+HC:Y=47-RND(V)-VC
140    IFPOINT(X,Y)THEN130
150    SET(X,Y)
160 NEXT
170 X=RND(H)+HC:Y=47-RND(V)-VC
180 A=X-1:B=Y-1
190 T=0
200 FORX=A-1TOA+1
210   FORY=B-1TOB+1
220     IFX=A AND Y=B THEN 240
230       IF POINT(X,Y) THEN T=T+1
240     NEXTY
250 NEXTX
260 PRINT@0,"ACTUAL POPULATION =";AP;
270 IFPOINT(X,Y)THEN300
280 IFT<>3THEN170
290 SET(X,Y):AP=AP+1:GOTO170
300 IFT>3THEN320
310 IFT=>2THEN170
320 RESET(X,Y):AP=AP-1
330 GOTO170
```

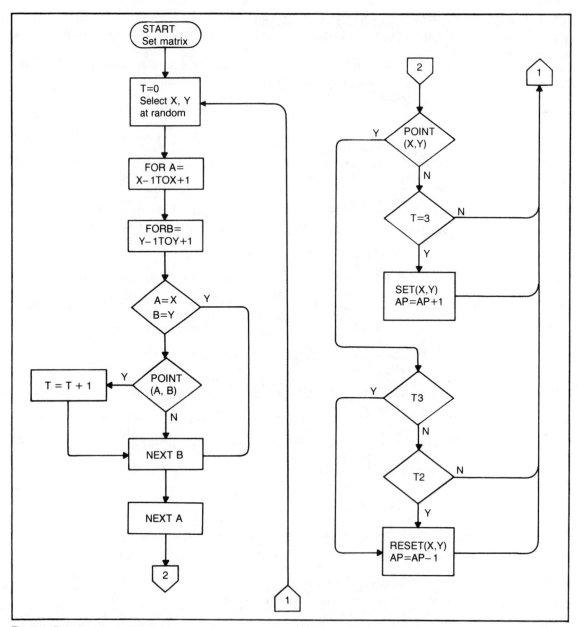

Fig. 7-1. Flowchart for Listing 7-1.

language routines that enable the user to see the evolution of generations by accelerating the process have been constructed.

SWAMP MANAGER

This is a simple simulation of an environmental control problem. The premise is this: you own land upon which there is a swamp in which malaria-bearing mosquitoes breed profusely; additionally, the community leaders hold you responsible for the control of the mosquitoes or the compensation for the medical expenses of your neighbors. Your only source of income is through development and leasing of the property. You specify all input values. The objective is to achieve a maximum positive cash flow in minimum time. Of course, you can contrive to reach the objective by manipulation of the input values. So long as the simulation is only a game, that is up to you, but, to the extent that you have a serious interest in the outcome, you must be as realistic as possible about the input values.

ISLAND

There is a remote island that you own. You would like to purchase a certain number of cattle, sheep, or a combination of both, which you would transport to the island for grazing until market time. The objective of the island is to determine the optimum starting population of the herd of livestock such that a maximum herd size is obtained in minimum time without creating a herd so large that

Listing 7-2. Swamp Simulation

```
1  '**********************************************
2  'SWAMP SIMULATION                            *
3  'LISTING 7-2                                 *
4  '**********************************************
5  '
10 CLS:PRINT"SWAMP SIMULATION":PRINT:PRINT
20 INPUT"AVERAGE MOSQUITO POPULATION PER ACRE";M
     A
30 INPUT"NUMBER OF ACRES";NA:MP=NA*MA
40 INPUT"MOSQUITO REPRODUCTION RATE (NEW MOSQUIT
     OES PER 1000)";RR:R=1+(RR/1000)
50 INPUT"COST TO DESTROY 1000 MOSQUITOES";CD
60 INPUT"COST OF MEDICAL CARE FOR ONE MALARIA VI
     CTIM";CM
70 INPUT"NUMBER OF MALARIA VICTIMS PER 1000 MOSQ
     UITOES";MV:VM=MV/1000:INPUT"BEGINNING BANK
     BALANCE";BB:B=BB
80 INPUT"COST TO PREPARE AN ACRE FOR LEASING";CP
90 INPUT"NET PROFIT FROM SUBLEASE OF ONE MOSQUIT
     O-FREE ACRE";NP:CLS
100 PRINT:PRINT"GENERATION # ";G:B=B+(AD*NP)
110 PRINT"MOSQUITO POPULATION =";MP,:AI=INT(MP/M
     A)+1:IFAI>NATHENAI=NA
120 PRINT"TOTAL ACRES INFESTED =";AI
130 CV=INT(VM*(MP/1000))+1:B=B-(CM*CV)
140 PRINT"CURRENT NUMBER OF MALARIA VICTIMS =";I
     NT(VM*(MP/1000))+1:G=G+1
150 PRINT"BANK BALANCE (AFTER MEDICAL EXPENSES)
     = $";B
160 PRINT:INPUT"NUMBER OF MOSQUITOES TO BE DESTR
     OYED";N
170 C=CD*(N/1000):IFC<=BTHEN210
180 IFB<0THEN200
190 PRINT"SORRY, YOU ONLY HAVE THE CASH TO DESTR
     OY";1000*(B/CD);"MOSQUITOES":GOTO160
200 PRINT"SORRY, NO CASH AVAILABLE THIS PERIOD":
     GOTO260
210 B=B-C:MP=INT(MP*R)-N
220 AF=NA-(MP/MA)
230 PRINTAF;"ACRES ARE FREE FOR DEVELOPMENT.   ";
240 IFAF<0THEN100
250 IFB=>0THEN270
```

Listing 7-2. Swamp Simulation (continued from page 125)

```
260 PRINT"NO CASH IS AVAILABLE FOR DEVELOPMENT":
    GOTO100
270 INPUT"NUMBER DESIRED";N:C=CP*N:IFC<=BTHEN290
280 PRINT"SORRY, YOU ONLY HAVE THE CASH TO DEVEL
    OP";B/CP;"ACRES":GOTO270
290 B=B-C+(N*NP):AD=AD+N
300 GOTO100
```

it exceeds the island's capability to generate sufficient vegetation to sustain the herd.

QUEUING THEORY

We fully suspect that the first theory related to *queues* (lines of people or items awaiting some sort of processing or service) was developed by a mathematician waiting in line at a bank or supermarket. What began as a trivial exercise to pass the time of day has evolved into a serious science with useful and practical applications. Use of the modern queuing theories has enabled engineers and managers make optimum use of people and resources so that customers receive prompt service, without

Listing 7-3. Island

```
1  '*********************************************
2  'ISLAND                                      *
3  'LISTING 7-3                                 *
4  '*********************************************
5  '
10 CLS:PRINT"ISLAND":PRINT:PRINT
20 PRINTAA,:INPUT"WHAT IS THE AREA, IN ACRES, OF
    THE ISLAND";AA
30 IA=AA*43560
40 PRINTNA,:INPUT"NUMBER OF ANIMALS TO BE INTROD
    UCED";NA
50 PRINTSF,:INPUT"SQUARE FOOTAGE COVERED BY EACH
    ANIMAL";SF
60 PRINTBR,:INPUT"NUMBER OF BIRTHS PER 1000 ANIM
    ALS PER MONTH";BR:R1=1+(BR/1000)
70 PRINTDR,:INPUT"NUMBER NATURAL DEATHS PER 1000
    PER MONTH";DR:R2=1+(DR/1000)
80 PRINTRS,:INPUT"NUMBER OF ANIMALS TO BE REMOVE
    D MONTHLY FOR SALE";RS
90 PRINTVC,:INPUT"SQUARE FEET OF VEGETATION CONS
    UMED PER ANIMAL PER MONTH";VC
100 PRINT"TOTAL VEGETATION REQUIRED AT START";VC
    *NA
110 PRINTVG,:INPUT"GROWTH RATE OF VEGETATION IN
    SQUARE FEET PER MONTH";VG
120 LS=NA*SF:VS=IA-LS:VV=VS:P=NA:G=0
130 PRINT"AT THE BEGINNING, THE ANIMALS WILL REQ
    UIRE";LS;"SQUARE FEET
OF LIVING SPACE.   THIS LEAVES";VS;"SQUARE
FEET FOR VEGETATION."
140 PRINT:PRINT"ANY KEY TO CONTINUE ";
150 Q$=""+INKEY$:IFQ$=""THEN150
160 CLS:PRINT@0,"","NUMBER","SQR FEET":PRINT"GEN
    ERATION","ANIMALS","VEGETATION"
170 VV=VV-(P*VC)+VG:NB=P*R1:ND=P*.   :P=P+NB-ND-RS
180 IFVV>0THEN200
```

```
190 ND=ABS(UU/UC):P=P-ND
200 IFP<=0THEN240
210 LS=P*SF:US=IA-LS:G=G+1:IFUU>USTHENUU=US
220 PRINT@128,G,P,UU,
230 GOTO170
240 PRINT@128,G,P,UU:PRINT@512,"SORRY, HERD HAS
    DIED.  TRY NEW STARTING VALUES":PRINT:GOTO2
    0
```

using an excessive number of salespeople. Likewise, appliances awaiting repair or goods awaiting a manufacturing process are handled without unnecessary delay or excessive use of capital equipment.

The processing of queuing problems normally begins with the user specifying two values: L, the average number of customers arriving per unit of time (normally per hour) and M, the maximum number of customers the queue can process in one hour, or S, the average time to serve one customer, from which M can be computed. From these values, a number of other values can be computed. These include:

$U = L/M$ — Queue utilization factor.

$S = 60/M$ — Average processing time.

$M = 60/S$ — Maximum number of customers a queue can process in one unit of time.

$PW = 1 - U$ — The probability that a customer will not have to wait.

$PN = U^N (1 - U)$ — The probability of N customers in the system at one moment.

$EN = \dfrac{L}{M - L}$ — Mean number of customers in the total system.

$EL = \dfrac{L^2}{M(M - L)}$ — Mean length of waiting time, not including those being served.

$EW = \dfrac{L}{M(M - L)}$ — Mean waiting time in queue.

$ET = \dfrac{1}{M - L}$ — Mean total time in system.

In addition, queuing theory includes the value of Q, the *balk point*, which is the number of persons in a queue that will normally cause the next cus-

tomer who enters the facility and views the queue to balk and leave without waiting for service. As with L and M, this value is normally determined by observation. Alternatively, the analyst may wish to experiment with different values of Q. At any rate, the equations given above can be modified to accommodate Q and are shown below. In the first column is the standard notation. In the second column is the notation used in this book for equations with a balk point.

$$EN \quad NE \quad = \frac{U}{1 - U} - \frac{U^{Q+1} (1 + Q)}{1 - U^{Q+1}}$$

$$EL \quad LE \quad = NE - 1 + \frac{1}{1 - U^{Q+1}}$$

$$ET \quad TE \quad = \frac{1}{M(1 - U)} - \frac{Q U^Q}{M(1 - U^Q)}$$

$$EW \quad WE \quad = TE - \frac{1}{M}$$

The other equations remain the same as before.

To this point, the assumption has been that there was only one server and that customers arrived at normal or even intervals. In many instances, however, there are two or more servers and customers tend to arrive in a Poisson distribution instead of a normal distribution. If we designate the number of servers as K, where K is greater than one and KM is greater than L, we can compute the value P_0, which is the probability of zero customers in the system at a given instant, from

$$P_0 = \frac{1}{\displaystyle\sum_{N=0}^{K-1} \frac{U^N}{N!} + \frac{U^K}{K!}\left(\frac{K M}{K M - L}\right)}$$

Using this value, we can now compute the other basic queue factors from

$$\text{EN} \quad E_1 = \frac{L\,M\,U^K}{(K-1)!\,(K\,M-L)^2}\,P_0 + U$$

$$\text{EL} \quad E_2 = E_1 - U$$

$$\text{ET} \quad E_3 = \frac{M\,U^K}{(K-1)!\,(K\,M-L)^2} + P_0 + \frac{1}{M}$$

$$E_4 = E_3 - \frac{1}{M}$$

Listing 7-4 implements the foregoing queuing equations. From the program, the analyst can estimate the various factors in a given system. When the processing time, S, grows relatively large, to the extent there are normally three or more persons in the queue, the likelihood is high that a balk point exists. When the observed data deviate from the predicted data, there is a good possibility that a balk point exists in reality and that it is reached often enough to have an operational impact. In this instance, the analyst should use actual data, such as the actual mean number of customers in the total system at a given time, NE, and solve the equation for Q. The problem with the quations involving Q is that they use exponential forms of Q that are difficult to factor out. The easier solution is to use an iterative solution for the equation:

$$\text{NX} = \frac{\dfrac{U}{1-U} - U^{Q+1}\,(Q+1)}{1 - U^{Q+1}}$$

Using trial values of Q until NX = NE.

With these basic data, the analyst can design a model of the operation and vary the magnitude of the controllable elements and thereby discover optimum components. For example, knowing the basic variables for a retail operation with two cashiers, the analyst can compute the effect of varying the number of cashiers (K) to determine the optimum number to have on duty at a given time so that the actual number of balks (walk-away business) is minimized. Each walk-away (WA) represents an average sales dollar volume (SD). Each cashier represents a known wage per customer (WC). The objective of the analyst, then, is to compute K where K × WC is equal to or less than SD × WA. The implication of the relationship is fairly clear: an infinite number of cashiers will eliminate the possibility of walk-aways but at an unacceptable wage cost. Too few cashiers could result in an unnecessary profit loss. There may never be a point where K × WC is less than SD × WA, but we should always be able to locate the point where the difference is minimized. Such is the value of using the microcomputer for simulations.

Listing 7-4. Queuing

```
1  ´***********************************************
2  ´QUEUING                                      *
3  ´LISTING 7-4                                  *
4  ´***********************************************
5  ´
10 CLS:PRINT"QUEING":PRINT:PRINT
20 INPUT"AVERAGE NUMBER OF CUSTOMERS ARRIVING PE
     R HOUR";L
30 PRINT"EXPECTED INTERVAL BETWEEN CUSTOMERS =";
     60/L;"MINUTES"
40 INPUT"AVERAGE NUMBER OF MINUTES TO SERVE ONE
     CUSTOMER";S:INPUT"NUMBER OF SERVERS";K
50 M=K*(60/S):PRINT"MAXIMUM NUMBER OF CUSTOMERS
     PER HOUR PER SERVER =";M
60 U=L/M:ST=(K*60)-(L*S)
70 PRINT"UTILIZATION FACTOR (U) =";U
80 PRINT"MAXIMUM SLACK TIME (ST) =";ST;"MINUTES
     (";ST/60;"SERVER(S) )"
90 PW=1-U:INPUT"TRIAL NUMBER OF CUSTOMERS (N)";N
     :PN=PW*(U[N)
```

```
100 IFK>1ANDM>LTHEN360
110 EN=L/(M-L):EL=(L[2)/(M*(M-L)):EW=L/(M*(M-L))
    :ET=1/(M-L)
120 PRINT"PROBABILITY OF";N;"CUSTOMERS IS ";PN
130 PRINT"MEAN NUMBER OF CUSTOMERS IN TOTAL SYST
    EM =";EN
140 PRINT"MEAN LENGTH OF WAITING TIME =";EL*60;"
    MINUTES"
150 PRINT"MEAN WAITING TIME IN QUEUE =";EW*60;"M
    INUTES"
160 PRINT"MEAN TOTAL TIME IN SYSTEM =";ET*60;"MI
    NUTES"
170 INPUT"VALUE OF BALK POINT (0 IF UNKNOWN)";Q
180 IFQ=0THEN300
190 PRINT"COMPUTATIONS USING A BALK POINT OF ";Q
200 NE=(U/(1-U))-((Q+1)*(U[(Q+1))/(1-(U[(Q+1))))
210 LE=NE-1+((1-U)/(1-(U[(Q+1))))
220 TE=(1/(M*(1-U)))-((Q*(U[Q))/(M*(1-(U[Q))))
230 WE=TE-(1/M)
240 PRINT"USING A BALK POINT OF";Q;":"
250 PRINT"MEAN NUMBER OF CUSTOMERS IN SYSTEM =";
    NE
260 PRINT"MEAN LENGTH OF WAITING TIME =";LE*60;"
    MINUTES"
270 PRINT"MEAN TOTAL TIME IN SYSTEM =";TE*60;"MI
    NUTES"
280 PRINT"MEAN WAITING TIME IN QUEUE =";WE*60;"M
    INUTES"
290 END
300 INPUT"OBSERVED MEAN NUMBER OF CUSTOMERS IN S
    YSTEM";NE:Q=10:DQ=2
310 NX=(U/(1-U))-((Q+1)*(U[(Q+1))/(1-(U[(Q+1))))
320 IFNX>NETHEN350
330 IFQ>(NE[3)THEN200
340 Q=Q+DQ:GOTO310
350 Q=Q-DQ:DQ=DQ/2:IFDQ>.0001THEN340  ELSE200
360 M=M/K
370 FORN=0TOK-1
380   A=U[N
390   B=1
400   FORF=1TON:B=B*F:NEXT
410   B=1/B:C=C+(A*B)
420 NEXTN
430 KF=1
440 FORF=1TOK:KF=KF*F:NEXT
450 A=1/KF:B=(K*M)/((K*M)-L):D=A*B
460 P0=1/(C+D)
470 PRINT"PROBABILITY OF ZERO CUSTOMERS =";P0
480 A=L*M*(U[K)
490 B=1
500 FORF=1TOK-1:B=B*F:C=B*(((K*M)-L)[2)
510 E1=((A/C)*P0)+U:E2=E1-U
520 E3=(((M*(U[K))/(B*(((K*M)-L)[2)))*P0)+(1/M):
    E4=E3-(1/M)
530 NE=E1:LE=E2:TE=E3:WE=E4:GOTO250
```

FORECASTING USING AN ECONOMIC MODEL

Figure 7-2 illustrates the cash flow of a simple retail operation. At the center of the figure is the retail operation itself. It consists of a proprietor and one or more employees. The proprietor will draw his earnings from the net profit, if any, and will pay personal income tax on that amount. The only source of cash income is from the customers. From this amount must be paid all of the various expenses. Off the top will normally come one or more operating taxes or fees paid to city, county, state, and federal taxing and licensing authorities. These will take two forms. The first will be fixed fees independent of sales volume. The second will be taxes based on the size of the plant facility and the sales volume. The wholesaler, of course, is an essential factor in the successful retail operation. Whether the wholesaler will extend terms (credit) to the retailer or give discounts for quantity purchases or prompt payment are central to the success or failure of both new and existing businesses.

The retail process begins with a decision to purchase a certain quantity of goods from the wholesaler. This quantity is a function of the retailer's anticipation of probable sales volume, capital resources, available lines of credit, and the wholesaler's terms. Subsequent purchases from the wholesaler are a function of actual sales volume experience. Initially, the new retailer's objective is to buy sufficient merchandise from the wholesaler to fill the store well enough to encourage customers to think they are dealing with an established business and to satisfy buyer demand. Yet the retailer must not buy so much that the tie-up lines of credit unnecessarily. This is often one of the really tricky problems in retailing.

Utilities include gas and electricity for heat and air conditioning, telephone service, and water. Generally speaking, the amount paid for utilities will be a function of the size of the retail operation, which is a function of the size of the retail operation, which is a function of sales volume. (This is not

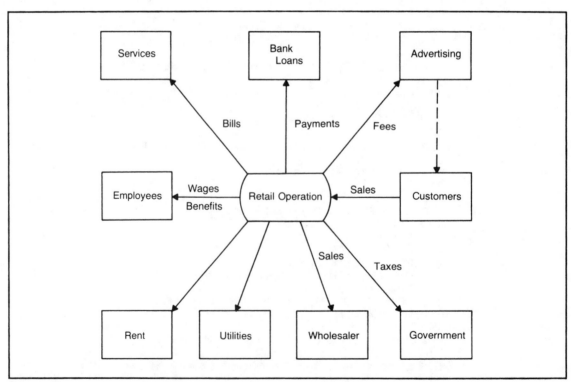

Fig. 7-2. Cash flow model, retail sales.

quite true. A number of large corporate retail operations mandate a certain square footage regardless of actual market, and then set as a management goal a sales volume to justify the space. In this model we are not concerned with how a national chain establishes a new outlet, but how the sole proprietor of a specialty shop might start up and operate a business.) A large store with tens of thousands of square feet will have to pay proportionately more for utilities than a small shop. Likewise, rent is normally a function of square footage.

The number of employees is a function of the anticipated number of sales and the time required to complete a sale, rather than the total dollar amount of sales. A jewelry store, with a number of big ticket items, needs fewer employees to support a dollar income equal to that of a cookie shop with more employees. If T is the time in minutes required to complete a sale; H is the number of hours the shop is open daily; and A is the average anticipated daily sales volume, the maximum number of sales staff, S, can be computed from

$$S = 1 + INT \frac{A \times T}{60 \times H}$$

The smaller the anticipated sales volume, the more demanding personnel management will become. If S is computed to be 1, problems will occur during that person's absence due to vacation or illness. The proprietor will have to either undertake sales duties or hire temporary help. On the other hand, as the value of S increases, the easier it should be to manage absences due to vacation or illness.

In addition to wages, the model must account for employer Social Security contributions, retirement fund payments, medical benefits, and other employee-related expenses.

Although smaller businesses often maintain a working ledger system, it is often prudent or neces-

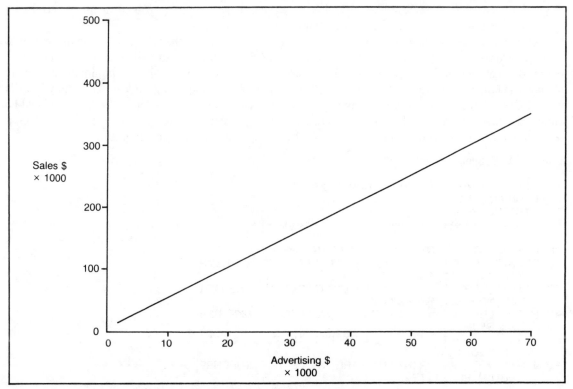

Fig. 7-3. Sales volume as a function of advertising expenditures, nominal form.

sary to retain the services of a professional accountant, at least at year's end to handle tax matters. Other services the business may require are legal, catering, and printing services.

It does pay to advertise. Time and time again a clear relationship can be shown between the number of dollars spent for advertising and sales volume. Industry-wide, the relationship is fairly linear; that is, when you plot the amount of sales receipts against the related amount spent for advertising, the general relationship that results is shown in Fig. 7-3.

It would be misleading, however, to suggest that a given store solve its cash flow problems simply by pumping cash into advertising. A number of nonadvertising aspects may be adversely affecting sales volume. These include: market size, competition, location, local employment levels, and so forth. For this reason, we suggest this model use a variation of the linear trend equation $(Y = A + B X)$ to limit the utility of advertising to a practical level. the form recommended is: $Y = A + B \log X$, in which X is the dollar amount of the advertising budget and Y is the anticipated sales volume.

Bank loans are frequently used by the retail operation to bridge the time between the purchase of goods and the time these goods are sold at retail prices. This approach is most often encountered in situations where the wholesaler will not grant extension of terms to the retailer but insists on cash

payment on or before shipment. Normally, the bank will extend a line of credit to the merchant which requires that the payments, which are computed using the actual amount of the credit used, be paid over 12 to 60 months. The interest rate will vary considerably, depending on the bank's objectives (whether it wants to encourage or discourage small business accounts). While rates below commercial levels are possible to negotiate with a friendly banker, a retailer should normally anticipate paying a premium interest rate. Remember, usury laws don't apply to commercial transactions.

We've gone around the model and have returned to the customer. The level of sales is assumed to be a function of the amount spent on advertising. For purposes of simplicity, we include in advertising the money spent to decorate the shop, purchase attractive shopping bags, and to provide other features to attract customers and to make them feel comfortable in the store. In more elaborate models of this retail operation, some of these costs might be placed in other accounting areas.

As with the other models, it is up to the user to specify all of the input variables with the objective to maximizing profits in the minimum amount of time. As a game it is fairly easy to specify a set of no-lose input factors. As a device to aid a would-be entrepreneur, the key element is an honest estimate of the actual components.

Listing 7-5. Economic Model

```
1  '**********************************************
2  'ECONOMIC MODEL                              *
3  'LISTING 7-5                                 *
4  '**********************************************
5  '
10 CLS:PRINT"ECONOMIC MODEL":PRINT:PRINT
20 PRINT"DEFAULT =";IC,:INPUT"INITIAL CAPITALIZA
      TION";IC:I1=IC
30 PRINT"DEFAULT =";MS,:INPUT"ANTICIPATED NUMBER
      OF MONTHLY SALES";MS
40 PRINT"DEFAULT =";AI,:INPUT"AVERAGE INCOME PER
      SALE";AI
50 PRINT"DEFAULT =";RW,:INPUT"RETAIL TO WHOLESAL
      E RATIO";RW
60 IP=(MS*AI)/RW:PRINT"INITIAL WHOLESALE PURCHAS
      E WILL BE $";IP
```

```
70 PRINT"WILL THE WHOLESALER EXTEND TERMS (SHIP
   ON CONSIGNMENT)?   (Y/N)";
80 Q1$=""+INKEY$:IFQ1$=""THEN80
90 PRINT" ";Q1$
100 IFQ1$="N"THEN120
110 PRINT"DEFAULT =";WL,:INPUT"CREDIT LIMIT EXTE
    NDED BY WHOLESALER";WL
120 PRINT"IS THERE A BANK LINE OF CREDIT AVAILAB
    LE  (Y/N)";
130 Q2$=""+INKEY$:IFQ2$=""THEN130
140 PRINT" ";Q2$
150 IFQ2$="N"THEN180
160 PRINT"DEFAULT =";CL,:INPUT"AMOUNT OF CREDIT
    LINE";CL
170 PRINT"DEFAULT =";TC,:INPUT"TERM OF CREDIT IN
    MONTHS";TC:PRINT"DEFAULT =";MR*1200,:INPUT
    "ANNUAL INTEREST RATE (5%=5)";AR:MR=AR/1200

180 PRINT"SQUARE FOOTAGE NECESSARY TO SUPPORT";M
    S;"SALES MONTHLY",:PRINT"DEFAULT =";SF,:INP
    UTSF
190 PRINT"DEFAULT =";MU,:INPUT"MONTHLY UTILITIES
    PAYABLE PER SQUARE FOOT";MU
200 PRINT"DEFAULT =";NR*12,:INPUT"NORMAL ANNUAL
    RENTAL PER SQUARE FOOT";NR:NR=NR/12
210 R=SF*NR:U=MU*SF:MP=(MR*((1+MR)[TC))/(((1+MR)
    [TC)-1)
220 PRINT"YOUR RENT WILL BE APPROXIMATELY $";R;"
    MONTHLY"
230 PRINT"UTILITIES WILL AVERAGE APPROXIMATELY $
    ";U;"MONTHLY"
240 PRINT"DEFAULT =";T,:INPUT"AVERAGE TIME TO CO
    MPLETE ONE SALE";T
250 PRINT"DEFAULT =";D,:INPUT"NUMBER OF DAYS PER
    WEEK STORE IS OPEN";D
260 D=D*4.333:PRINT"DEFAULT =";H,:INPUT"NUMBER O
    F HOURS PER DAY STORE IS OPEN";H          .
270 S=1+INT(((MS/D)*T)/(60*H)):PRINT"ESTIMATED M
    AXIMUM STAFF =";S:PRINT"IS THIS ACCEPTABLE
    (Y/N)";
280 Q3$=""+INKEY$:IFQ3$=""THEN280
290 PRINT" ";Q3$:IFQ3$="Y"THEN310
300 PRINT"DEFAULT =";S,:INPUT"ENTER ACTUAL STAFF
    ";S
310 PRINT"DEFAULT =";AW,:INPUT"AVERAGE WAGE PER
    STAFF MEMBER";AW
320 PRINT"DEFAULT =";EB,:INPUT"AVERAGE DOLLAR CO
    ST PER MONTH OF EMPLOYEE
BENEFITS";EB:EC=((AW*S)*1.17)+EB:PRINT"MONTHLY E
    MPLOYEE COST = $";EC
330 PRINT"DEFAULT =";CS,:INPUT"MONTHLY COST OF S
    ERVICES";CS
340 PRINT"DEFAULT =";Y1,:INPUT"# CUSTOMERS RESUL
    TING FROM $20,000 IN
ADVERTISING";Y1
350 PRINT"DEFAULT =";Y2,:INPUT"# CUSTOMERS RESUL
```

Listing 7-5. Economic Model (continued from page 133)

```
      TING FROM $40,000 IN
ADVERTISING";Y2
360 B=(((Y1*LOG(20000))+(Y2*LOG(40000)))-(.5*((L
    OG(20000)+LOG(40000))*(Y1+Y2))))/(((LOG(200
    00)[2)+(LOG(40000)[2))-(.5*(LOG(20000)+LOG(
    40000))[2))
370 A=.5*((Y1+Y2)-(B*(LOG(20000)+LOG(40000))))
380 IA=EXP((MS-A)/B)
390 PRINT"INITIAL ADVERTISING SHOULD BE = $";IA:
    PRINT"ACCEPTABLE   (Y/N) ";
400 Q4$=""+INKEY$:IFQ4$=""THEN400
410 PRINTQ4$:IFQ4$="Y"THEN430
420 PRINT"DEFAULT =";X,:INPUT"ADVERTISING DESIRE
    D";X:Y=A+(B*LOG(X)):PRINT"ANTICIPATED SALES
     = $";Y*AI,"=";Y;"CUSTOMERS"
430 PRINT"DEFAULT =";(IR-1)*1200,:INPUT"ANNUAL I
    NFLATION RATE
TO BE APPLIED TO COSTS (5%=5)";IR:IR=1+(IR/1200)
    :LW=WL:LC=CL:CLS
440 IC=IC-R-U-IA-(S*EC)-CS-MP
450 IFIP>LWTHEN470
460 LW=LW-IP:GOTO510
470 IF(IP-LW)>CLTHEN490
480 LC=LC+(IP-LW):CL=CL-(IP-LW):GOTO500
490 LC=LC+CL:CL=0
500 MP=LC*MR:LW=0
510 IC=IC+(MS*AI):I2=IC:PRINT@0,"CAPITAL AVAIL.
    = $";IC,"NET CHANGE = $ ";I2-I1:IN=I2-I1:IF
    IN<0THEN540
520 TX=IN/10000:IFTX>.5THENTX=.5
530 IC=IC*(1-TX)
540 IC=IC-WL:LW=LW+WL:CL=(CL*(1-MR))+MP
550 I1=I2:R=R*IR:U=U*IR:EC=EC*IR:CS=CS*IR:IP=IP*
    IR
560 IFIC>0THEN440
570 PRINT@512,"OPPS.   YOU'VE JUST LOST YOUR SHIR
    T.   REPROGRAM STARTING VALUES"
580 PRINT:PRINT"TOUCH ANY KEY TO CONTINUE";
590 Q$=""+INKEY$:IFQ$=""THEN590  ELSE10
```

EXERCISES

1. Identify a small business in your neighborhood. Interview the owner to determine the general operations routine of his business in sufficient detail to develop a computer model of his business. In this project, remember that many business people, while willing to discuss their business (during slow or quiet periods), are reluctant to discuss specific costs and wholesale prices. In such instances, be willing to settle for approximate cost data or ranges of prices. In exchange for greater candor from the merchant, you may want to offer to share the model and the results of your work with him.

2. Develop a cash flow model of your own finances. Show the source(s) of income and the disposition of it. If you have a savings account or investments, be sure to show the interest paid as a source of income.

3. Write a program to simulate the operation of a roulette wheel. Include in the program a system to keep track of the numbers that

appear and the betting options and odds available. Your research should quickly lead you to the fact there are at least two types of wheel layouts, European and American. Determine which one tends to favor the player more.

4. Develop a program to "deal" a complete bridge hand; i. e., 13 cards dealt from a shuffled deck to each of four players (see Chapter 15 for shuffling routines). Display each card by suit and in descending order from right to left in each hand. Show the hands at the top, bottom, and either side of the screen, labeled N, E, W, and S for the compass direction of the hands.

5. If you understand the game well enough, develop a subroutine in the program in item 4 so the computer can participate in the bidding of the hands.

SUGGESTED READING

Adler, I., 1957. *Magic House of Numbers*. New York: The John Day Company, Inc.

Dusenberry, J. S., et al., 1965. *The Brookings Quarterly Economic Model of the United States*. Chicago: Rand-McNally.

Epstein, R. A., 1967. *The Theory of Gambling and Statistical Logic*. New York: Academic Press.

Pindyck, R. S. and D. L. Rubenfeld, 1976. *Econometric Models and Economic Forecasts*. New York: McGraw-Hill.

Chapter 8

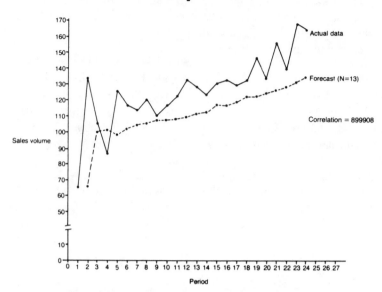

Numerical Analysis

In the real world of higher mathematics, the term *numerical analysis* refers to quite a family of sophisticated equations and complex relationships. Those who have mastered calculus get bogged down in cluster analysis and linear transfer functions. You will find very few such references in this chapter. Instead, what we will present are some practical ways to use fundamental numerical relationships and distributions to assist in a forecasting effort where other techniques fall short of being satisfactory or appear so tedious to implement that it doesn't appear cost/time effective to do it the long way. We offer these techniques from the pragmatic perspective: if it works, use it. The responsible researcher must make every effort to go beyond establishing the means to make a forecast and identify, if at all possible, the casual relationships between the predictor and the dependent variable.

Nonetheless, the techniques that follow often yield useful forecasting tools. We will start with a technique that can deal with rationally related variables and nth order polynomials, and then work to more abstract approaches, including geometric sec-

tions. Along the way we will consider a variety of distributions, trigonometric functions, and Fast Fourier Transforms.

NTH ORDER POLYNOMIALS

The underlying assumption with this technique is that the dependent variable, Y, is primarily a function of one independent variable, X. The computation, however, is not simply in the form of the linear trend, $Y = A + BX$, but in the expanded form:

$$Y = A_0 + A_1 X + A_2 X^2 + A_3 X^3 + \ldots + AN X^n$$

Assuming one chooses to use this approach, the tricky part is to properly identify the appropriate order of the equation. Many values of n will result in a curve form that will fit the sample data points, yet go wandering off in some very esoteric wavy form in between (see Fig. 8-1). Listing 8-1 offers a routine to evaluate sample data points in the sense and form of the nth order polynomial. It will begin by asking for the order of the equation, N, and then insist that the user enter at least N + 2 sample data points. The first action, then, is the evaluation

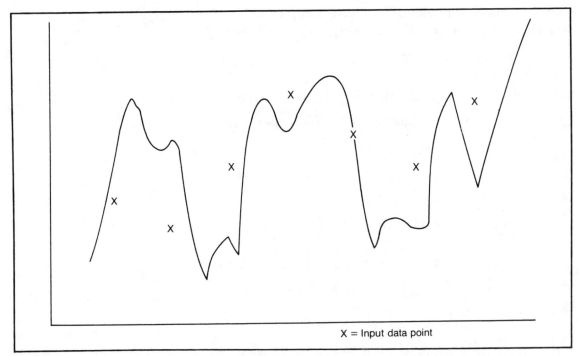

X = Input data point

Fig. 8-1. Graph of polynomial.

of the polynomial as described above. The program outputs the constant or *residual,* and then specifies the various coefficients. These are followed by the computed coefficient of determination and the coefficient of correlation. Having completed the assigned task, the program goes on to compute all of the possible orders of the equation from n = 1 to n = N − 1. In each instance, the program computes the coefficients of determination and correlation. It is up to the user to choose which form is optimum for the present task.

The user may want to add the subroutine

Listing 8-1. Nth Order Polynomial

```
1  '*********************************************
2  'NTH ORDER POLYNOMIAL                        *
3  'LISTING 8-1                                 *
4  '*********************************************
5  '
10 CLS:INPUT"DEGREE OF EQUATION";D
20 INPUT"NUMBER OF KNOWN POINTS";N
30 IFN>(D+1)THEN50
40 PRINT"SORRY--WE NEED AT LEAST";D+2;"POINTS":G
   OTO20
50 DIM XX(N),YY(N),A((2*(N))+1),R(N,N),T(N):A(1)
   =N
60 FORI=1TON:PRINT"X, Y OF POINT #";I;:INPUTXX(I
   ),YY(I):NEXT
70 FORI=1TON:PRINTI;XX(I);YY(I),:NEXTI
80 PRINT:PRINT"ARE THESE CORRECT?  (Y/N)"
90 Q$=""+INKEY$:IFQ$=""THEN90    ELSEIFQ$="Y"THEN
   110
```

137

Listing 8-1. Nth Order Polynomial (continued from page 137)

```
100 PRINT:INPUT"ITEM #, X, Y";I,XX(I),YY(I):GOTO
    70
110 CLS:PRINT"COMPUTING...":PRINT
120 FORI=1TON
130    X=XX(I):Y=YY(I)
140    FORJ=2TO((2*D)+1):A(J)=A(J)+(X[(J-1)):NEXT

150    FORK=1TOD+1:R(K,D+2)=T(K)+(Y*(X[(K-1)))):T(
    K)=T(K)+(Y*(X[(K-1))):NEXTK
160    T(D+2)=T(D+2)+(Y[2)
170 NEXTI
180 FORJ=1TOD+1:FORK=1TOD+1:R(J,K)=A(J+K-1):NEXT
    K:NEXTJ
190 FORJ=1TOD+1
200    FORK=JTOD+1
210       IFR(K,J)<>0THEN240
220    NEXTK
230    PRINT"NO UNIQUE SOLUTION":GOTO510
240    FORI=1TOD+2:S=R(J,I):R(J,I)=R(K,I):R(K,I)=
    S:NEXTI
250    Z=1/R(J,J):FORI=1TOD+2:R(J,I)=Z*R(J,I):NEX
    TI
260    FORK=1TOD+1
270       IFK=JTHEN300
280       Z=-R(K,J)
290       FORI=1TOD+2:R(K,I)=R(K,I)+(Z*R(J,I)):NEX
    TI
300    NEXTK
310 NEXTJ
320 IFQ$="C"THEN350
330 PRINT"              CONSTANT = ";R(1,D+2)
340 FORJ=1TOD:PRINTJ;"DEGREE COEFFICIENT = ";R(J
    +1,D+2):NEXTJ:PRINT
350 P=0
360 FORJ=2TOD+1:P=P+(R(J,D+2)*(T(J)-(A(J)*(T(1)/
    N)))):NEXTJ
370 Q=T(D+2)-((T(1)[2)/N):Z=Q-P:I=N-D-1:J=P/Q:PR
    INT
380 IFQ$="C"THEN400
390 PRINT"COEFFICIENT OF DETERMINATION (R[2) = "
    ;J
400 IFJ=>0THEN420
410 PRINT"COEFFICIENT OF CORRELATION          = "
    ;-1*SQR(ABS(J)):GOTO430
420 PRINT"COEFFICIENT OF CORRELATION          = "
    ;SQR(J)
430 IFQ$="C"THEN580  ELSEIFZ=>0THEN450
440 PRINT"STANDARD ERROR OF ESTIMATE          =";
    -1*SQR(ABS(Z/I)):GOTO460
450 PRINT"STANDARD ERROR OF ESTIMATE          = "
    ;SQR(Z/I)
460 PRINT:PRINT"(I)NTERPOLATION     (C)ORRELATION
    ANALYSIS    (N)EW
470 Q$=""+INKEY$:IFQ$=""THEN470  ELSEIFQ$="N"THE
    N510  ELSEIFQ$="C"THEN530  ELSEIFQ$<>"I"THE
    N470
```

```
480 PRINT:P=R(1,D+2):INPUT"ENTER X VALUE";X
490 FORJ=1TOD:P=P+(R(J+1,D+2)*(X[J)):NEXTJ
500 PRINT"Y = ";P:GOTO460
510 RUN10
520 END
530 PRINT:PRINT"COMPUTING";N-2;"REGRESSION CORRE
    LATION COMPARISONS"
540 FORD=1TON-2
550   FORI=2TO((2*N)+1):A(I)=0:NEXTI
560   FORI=1TON:FORJ=1TON:R(I,J)=0:NEXTJ:T(I)=0:
    NEXTI
570   PRINT"D =";D,:GOTO120
580 NEXTD
590 PRINT:INPUT"COMPLETE STATISTICS FOR WHAT DEG
    REE";D:Q$="":GOTO120
600 GOTO460
```

shown in Listing 8-2 to graphically illustrate the sample data points and the interpolated points resulting from the chosen polynomial form.

DISTRIBUTIONS

Data, especially large amount of data, frequently fall into one of several easily described distribution forms. If we know the basic form, we can forecast or interpolate the unknown points. Types of distributions include, but are not limited to the normal, binomial, Poisson, and random.

The Normal Distribution

Otherwise known as the *bell curve,* the normal

Listing 8-2. Modification to Nth Order Polynomial

```
1 '**********************************************
2 'MODIFICATION TO NTH ORDER POLYNOMIAL       *
3 'LISTING 8-2                                 *
4 '**********************************************
5 '
10 CLS:INPUT"DEGREE OF EQUATION";D
20 INPUT"NUMBER OF KNOWN POINTS";N
30 IFN>(D+1)THEN50
40 PRINT"SORRY--WE NEED AT LEAST";D+2;"POINTS":G
    OTO20
50 DIM XX(N),YY(N),A((2*(N))+1),R(N,N),T(N):A(1)
    =N
60 FORI=1TON:PRINT"X, Y OF POINT #";I;:INPUTXX(I
    ),YY(I):NEXT
70 FORI=1TON:PRINTI;XX(I);YY(I),:NEXTI
80 PRINT:PRINT"ARE THESE CORRECT?  (Y/N)"
90 Q$=""+INKEY$:IFQ$=""THEN90      ELSEIFQ$="Y"THEN
    110      '
100 PRINT:INPUT"ITEM #, X, Y";I,XX(I),YY(I):GOTO
    70
110 CLS:PRINT"COMPUTING...":PRINT
120 FORI=1TON
130   X=XX(I):Y=YY(I)
140   FORJ=2TO('2*D)+1):A(J)=A(J)+(X[(J-1)):NEXT

150   FORK=1TOD+1:R(K,D+2)=T(K)+(Y*(X[(K-1))):T(
    K)=T(K)+(Y*(X[(K-1))):NEXTK
160   T(D+2)=T(D+2)+(Y[2)
170 NEXTI
```

139

```
180 FORJ=1TOD+1:FORK=1TOD+1:R(J,K)=A(J+K-1):NEXT
    K:NEXTJ
190 FORJ=1TOD+1
200   FORK=JTOD+1
210     IFR(K,J)<>0THEN240
220   NEXTK
230    PRINT"NO UNIQUE SOLUTION":GOTO520
240    FORI=1TOD+2:S=R(J,I):R(J,I)=R(K,I):R(K,I)=
    S:NEXTI
250   Z=1/R(J,J):FORI=1TOD+2:R(J,I)=Z*R(J,I):NEX
    TI
260   FORK=1TOD+1
270     IFK=JTHEN300
280     Z=-R(K,J)
290     FORI=1TOD+2:R(K,I)=R(K,I)+(Z*R(J,I)):NEX
    TI
300   NEXTK
310 NEXTJ
320 IFQ$="C"THEN350
330 PRINT"              CONSTANT = ";R(1,D+2)
340 FORJ=1TOD:PRINTJ;"DEGREE COEFFICIENT = ";R(J
    +1,D+2):NEXTJ:PRINT
350 P=0
360 FORJ=2TOD+1:P=P+(R(J,D+2)*(T(J)-(A(J)*(T(1)/
    N)))):NEXTJ
370 Q=T(D+2)-((T(1)[2)/N):Z=Q-P:I=N-D-1:J=P/Q:PR
    INT
380 IFQ$="C"THEN400
390 PRINT"COEFFICIENT OF DETERMINATION (R[2) = "
    ;J
400 IFJ=>0THEN420
410 PRINT"COEFFICIENT OF CORRELATION        = "
    ;-1*SQR(ABS(J)):GOTO430
420 PRINT"COEFFICIENT OF CORRELATION        = "
    ;SQR(J)
430 IFQ$="C"THEN590  ELSEIFZ=>0THEN450
440 PRINT"STANDARD ERROR OF ESTIMATE          =";
    -1*SQR(ABS(Z/I)):GOTO460
450 PRINT"STANDARD ERROR OF ESTIMATE          = "
    ;SQR(Z/I)
460 PRINT@960,"(I)NTERPOLATION    (C)ORRELATION A
    NALYSIS   (N)EW    (G)RAPHICS"
470 Q$=""+INKEY$:IFQ$=""THEN470   ELSEIFQ$="N"THE
    N520   ELSEIFQ$="C"THEN540   ELSEIFQ$="I"THEN
    490   ELSEIFQ$<>"G"THEN470
480 GOTO620
490 PRINT:P=R(1,D+2):INPUT"ENTER X VALUE";X
500 FORJ=1TOD:P=P+(R(J+1,D+2)*(X[J)):NEXTJ
510 PRINT"Y = ";P:GOTO460
520 RUN10
530 END
540 PRINT:PRINT"COMPUTING";N-2;"REGRESSION CORRE
    LATION COMPARISONS"
550 FORD=1TON-2
560   FORI=2TO((2*N)+1):A(I)=0:NEXTI
```

```
570     FORI=1TON:FORJ=1TON:R(I,J)=0:NEXTJ:T(I)=0:
        NEXTI
580     PRINT"D =";D,:GOTO120
590 NEXTD
600 PRINT:INPUT"COMPLETE STATISTICS FOR WHAT DEG
    REE";D:Q$="":GOTO120
610 GOTO460
620 PRINT:INPUT"DEGREE DESIRED";D:CLS:PRINT@0,"C
    OMPUTING VALUES OF X FROM 0 TO 120"
630 DIM Y(120)
640 FORI=1TO120
650     P=R(1,D+2)
660     FORJ=1TOD
670         P=P+(R(J+1,D+2)*(I[J))
680     NEXTJ
690     Y(I)=P:PRINT@128,Y(I);:IFY(I)<LGTHEN710
700     LG=Y(I)
710     IFY(I)=>SMTHEN730
720     SM=Y(I)
730 NEXTI
740 LY=0:SY=0:SX=0:LX=0
750 FORI=1TON
760     IFXX(I)<LXTHEN780
770     LX=XX(I)
780     IFSX<XX(I)THEN800
790     SX=XX(I)
800     IFYY(I)<LYTHEN820
810     LY=YY(I)
820     IFSY<YY(I)THEN840
830     SY=YY(I)
840 NEXTI
850 CLS
860 PRINT@0,"DATA";
870 FORI=1TON
880     X=120*(XX(I)/(LX-SX))
890     Y=47-(47*(YY(I)/(LY-SY)))
900     SET(X,Y)
910 NEXTI
920 PRINT@0,"POLYNOMIAL";
930 FORX=1TO120
940     Y=47-(47*(Y(X)/(LG-SM)));:SET(X,Y)
950 NEXT
960 PRINT@0,"";:GOTO460
```

distribution is the most commonly used form of data distribution. (See Fig. 2-3). For many statistical functions we assume the data to be normally distributed, even though we know the distribution is not precisely so distributed. The equation of the normal distribution is:

$$Y = f(x) = \frac{1}{2\,\pi}e^{-x/2}$$

The value of x is expressed in standard deviations from the mean and the magnitude of Y is expressed as a fraction of the total data set. That is, when x = 1.18, Y = .2. If we have reason to believe our data are normally distributed, we can interpolate a point from the equation above.

Binomial Distribution

In this form, the data conform to the shape defined by the probability of a given variable, P. The basic form of the equation is

$$Y = p(x) = \binom{n}{x} p^x (1 - p)^{n - x} \quad x = 0, 1, 2 \ldots n$$

For example, a card is drawn from a standard deck of 52 playing cards. If it is a heart, a success, S, is recorded; if not, a failure is recorded. After n trials, we have a sum, S, representing the number of success. This is a binomial variable because the probability of success is constant ($p = \frac{1}{4}$). The mean and the variance of such a distribution is

$$m = n p$$
$$s^2 = n p (1 - p)$$

The key element in this distribution is the probability (p) of a given happening. If the other features of the distribution are given, the value of p is all that is necessary to compute the probability of any value of n events. The computation gives the probability of exactly n events happening. If n is the maximum number of possibilities and k is some intermediate value, then by computing all of the values of p(x) for x = 0 to k and summing the result,

the computation yields the probability of at least k events happening. By computing the value of p(x) for x = k to n, the probability of having at most k events is calculated.

Poisson Distribution

This distribution is far less known and understood than the binomial distribution, but it is at least as useful. When graphed, the distribution resembles the normal distribution with a skew, normally to the right. The key element in this distribution is the mean, normally designated by the Greek letter lambda, λ. An interesting feature is that the variance is the same as the mean. Its utility comes from the fact that a lot of behavioral data tends to be distributed more according to the Poisson than the normal distribution. People tend to arrive for work or other formal gatherings according to the Poisson distribution. That is, if the designated starting time for work is 8:00 AM, a tally of actual numbers of arrivals at or near that time would look like that in

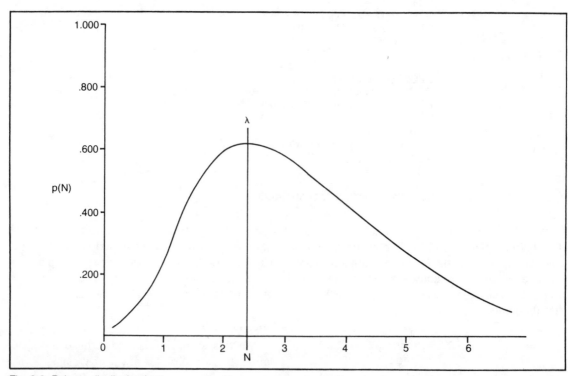

Fig. 8-2. Poisson distribution form.

Fig. 8-2. Most of the people arrive shortly before the cutoff time, with the balance arriving at extended times beyond the mean.

The basic equation for the Poisson distribution is:

$$Y = f(x) = \frac{L^x e^{-L}}{X!} \text{ where } X = 0, 1, 2, \dots$$

Listing 8-3 is a useful routine to compute and display various elements of the Poisson distribution. The screen display is shown in Fig. 8-3.

Chi-Square Distribution

Figure 8-4 illustrates the general form of the chi-square distributions. In these, the key variable is the degrees of freedom, v, in each distribution. For example, if there are ten items in a table for

Listing 8-3. Poisson Distributions

```
1  '*********************************************
2  'POISSON DISTRIBUTIONS                       *
3  'LISTING 8-3                                 *
4  '*********************************************
5  '
10 CLS:CLEAR 1000
20 INPUT"ENTER NUMBER OF TERMS";T
30 DIM M(T),N(T),TX(50),FX(50)
40 FOR I=1 TO T
50     PRINT@128,"ENTER TERM NUMBER";I;"    ":INP
   UTN(I)
60     S=S+N(I):Q=Q+(N(I)[2)
70 NEXT I
80 L=S/T
90 IF L>20THEN100   ELSE120
100 L=L/10:F=F+1
110 GOTO90
120 E=2.71828
130 PRINT:PRINT"THE FOLLOWING COMUPATION WILL TA
    KE 2 MINUTES OR LESS:":PRINT:PRINT"X","J","
    X!","P(X-1)";:PRINT
140 ONERRORGOTO240
150 FOR X=1 TO 50
160     XX=1
170     FOR J=1 TO X
180         XX=XX*J
190         PRINT@512,X,J,XX,TX(X-1);
200     NEXT J
210     TX(X)=((L[X]*(1/(E[L)))/XX:FX(X)=INT(TX(
    X)*100)
220     IF TX(X)<.000001 AND X>10THEN240   ELSE23
    0
230 NEXT X
240 CLS
250 FOR X=20 TO 21
260     FOR Y=5 TO 35 STEP 5
270         SET(X,Y)
280     NEXT Y
290 NEXT X
300 X=22
310 FOR Y=3 TO 40
320     SET(X,Y)
330 NEXT Y
340 Y=40
```

Listing 8-3. Poisson Distributions (continued from page 143)

```
350 FOR X=23 TO 117
360     SET(X,Y)
370 NEXT X
380 Y=41
390 FOR X=23 TO 113 STEP 4
400     SET(X,Y)
410 NEXT X
420 PRINT@198,".30";:PRINT@518,".15";:PRINT@838,
    ".00";:PRINT@448,"P(X)";
430 Z=5
440 FOR I=18 TO 56 STEP 10
450     PRINT@896+I,Z;:Z=Z+5
460 NEXT I
470 PRINT@990,"X *";10[F;
480 FOR I=1 TO 20
490     SET((I*4)+19,40-INT((TX(I)/.45)*38))
500 NEXT I
510 PRINT@11,"MEAN =";L;"X";10[F;
520 PRINT@40,"'C' TO CONTINUE";
530 Q$=INKEY$:IFQ$=""THEN530
540 IFQ$="C"THEN550  ELSE530
550 CLS
560 PRINT@220,"OPTIONS"
570 PRINT:PRINT"                        1 -- LINE PR
    INTER
                    2 -- VIDEO PLOT
                    3 -- PROBABILITY COMPUTATION

                    4 -- END"
580 PRINT:PRINT"ENTER NUMERICAL CHOICE"
590 N$=INKEY$:IFN$=""THEN590
600 NC=VAL(N$)
610 ONNCGOTO840  ,240  ,620  ,1120
620 CLS
630 PRINT@512,"ENTER INTERGER VALUE FOR WHICH PR
    OBABILITY IS DESIRED:"
640 INPUT IV:IV=INT(IV)
650 IV=IV/(10[F)
660 IF IV>30THEN740
670 FOR I=1 TO 30
680     IF IV=ITHEN690  ELSE730
690     PRINT:PRINT"THE PROBABILTY OF";IV*(10[F)
    ;" EVENTS IS =";TX(I)
700     PRINT:PRINT"ANOTHER VALUE?   (Y/N)"
710 Q$=INKEY$:IFQ$=""THEN710
720 IFQ$="Y"THEN620  ELSE550
730 NEXT I
740 XX=1
750 ONERRORGOTO820
760 FOR J=1 TO IV
770     XX=XX*J
780 NEXT J
790 TT=((L[IV)*(1/(E[L)))/XX
800 PRINT:PRINT"THE PROBABILITY OF";IV*(10[F);"
    EVENTS IS =";TT
```

```
810 GOTO700
820 PRINT:PRINT"THE COMPUTATIONS INVOLVED WITH T
        HE SOLUTION OF P(";IV;") CAUSE THE COMPUTER
        TO 'OVERFLOW.'  SORRY.?"
830 GOTO700
840 LPRINTSTRING$(2,10)
850 LPRINT"POISSON DISTRIBUTION ANALYSIS"
860 LPRINT" "
870 LPRINT"MEAN OF DISTRIBUTION OF";T;" ITEMS IS
        =";L*(10[F)
880 LPRINT" "
890 LPRINTTAB(60)"P(X)"
900 LPRINTSTRING$(19,32);:LPRINT"0.0
                .1                              .2
                .3                              .4"
910 LPRINTSTRING$(19,32);:LPRINT" I
                I                               I
                I                               I"
920 LPRINTSTRING$(18,32);:LPRINT"---------------
        -----------------------------------------
        ---------------------------""
930 FOR X=1 TO 25
940     LPRINTSTRING$(20,32);"I";:LPRINTSTRING$(I
        NT(100*(TX(X)*2)),32);X
950     LPRINTSTRING$(20,32);"I"
960     IF TX(X)<.0045 AND X>10THEN980  ELSE970

970 NEXT X
980 LPRINT" ":LPRINTSTRING$(25,32);"PROBABILITY
        OF LAST VALUE IS =";TX(X)
990 LPRINTSTRING$(3,10)
1000 LPRINT"TABLE OF INPUT VALUES AND PROBABILIT
        IES"
1010 LPRINT" "
1020 LPRINT"INPUT VALUE, X","P(X)=","INPUT VALUE
        , X","P(X)=","INPUT VALUE, X","P(X)=","INPU
        T VALUE, X","P(X)="
1030 FOR I=1 TO T
1040     LPRINTN(I),TX(I),
1050 NEXT I
1060 LPRINT" "
1070 LPRINT"MEAN OF DISTRIBUTION =";L*(10[F)
1080 LPRINT"POISSON STANDARD DEVIATION =";SQR(L*
        (10[F))
1090 LPRINT"'NORMAL' STANDARD DEVIATION =";SQR((
        Q-((S/T)[2))/(T-1))
1100 LPRINTSTRING$(10,10)
1110 GOTO240
1120 END
```

which we compute a mean value of 1345.6678, any nine of those values can be any value we want, but those nine values define the tenth value such that the mean remains 1345.6678. Accordingly, we have nine degrees of freedom; $v = 9$. The equation for the general form of these equations is

$$\chi^2 = \Sigma \frac{(O_i - E_i)^2}{E_i}$$

$$f(x) = \frac{x^{\frac{v}{2} - 1}}{2^{\frac{v}{2}} \ \Gamma\left(\frac{v}{2}\right) e^{\frac{x}{2}}}$$

145

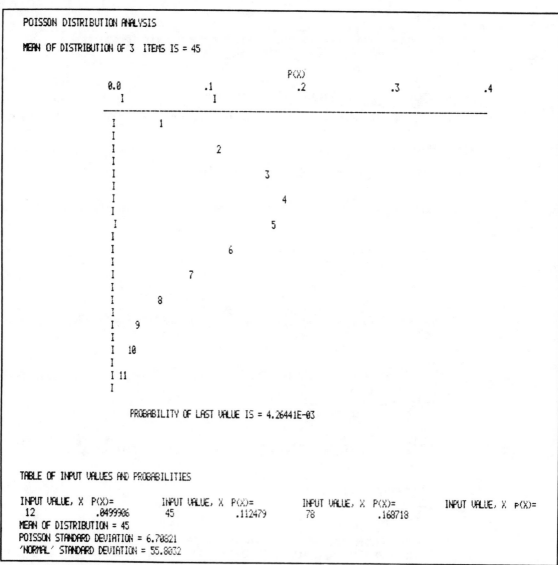

POISSON DISTRIBUTION ANALYSIS

MEAN OF DISTRIBUTION OF 3 ITEMS IS = 45

```
                                              P(X)
           0.0                 .1              .2              .3              .4
            I                  I
           _____
            I        1
            I
            I                  2
            I
            I                        3
            I
            I                           4
            I
            I                        5
            I
            I                  6
            I
            I           7
            I
            I        8
            I
            I     9
            I
            I  10
            I
            I 11
            I
```

PROBABILITY OF LAST VALUE IS = 4.26441E-03

TABLE OF INPUT VALUES AND PROBABILITIES

INPUT VALUE, X P(X)=	INPUT VALUE, X P(X)=	INPUT VALUE, X P(X)=	INPUT VALUE, X P(X)=
12 .0499986	45 .112479	78 .168718	

MEAN OF DISTRIBUTION = 45
POISSON STANDARD DEVIATION = 6.70821
'NORMAL' STANDARD DEVIATION = 55.8032

Fig. 8-3. Results of the Poisson distribution program.

The Gamma value is fairly easy to compute from the relationship

$$\Gamma\left(\frac{v}{2}\right) = \left(\frac{v}{2} - 1\right)! \quad \text{when v is even}$$

or

$$\Gamma\left(\frac{v}{2}\right) = \left(\frac{v}{2} - 1\right)\left(\frac{v}{2} - 2\right)\ldots .8862269$$

when v is odd.

The area under the chi-square up to the value of chi-square is given by the equation

$$P(x) = \frac{2x}{v}f(x)\left[1 + \sum_{k=1}^{\infty}\frac{x^k}{(v+2)(v+4)\ldots(v+2k)}\right]$$

Listing 8-4 is an extensive program enabling the user to evaluate data according to the foregoing

146

Listing 8-4. Distributions

```
1  '***************************************************
2  'DISTRIBUTIONS                                    *
3  'LISTING 8-4                                      *
4  '***************************************************
5  '
10 CLS:PRINT"      ****  DISTRIBUTIONS   ****
20 DIM U(100),X(100),AA(20),RR(30),M(3)
30 PRINT:PRINT"THESE ROUTINES ALLOW THE USER TO
      INPUT VARIABLES TO SEVERAL      COMMON DISTR
      IBUTIONS AND FIND THE RESULTING Y-COMPONENT
      ."
40 PRINT
50 PRINT"           1 -- BINOMIAL"
60 PRINT"           2 -- POISSON"
70 PRINT"           3 -- NORMAL"
80 PRINT"           4 -- CHI-SQUARE"
90 PRINT"           5 -- RAW DATA INPUT"
100 PRINT:PRINT"ENTER NUMBER OF THE DESIRED DIST
      RIBUTION:"
110 X$=INKEY$:IFX$=""THEN110
120 X=VAL(X$):IFX>5GOTO10
130 ONXGOTO140 ,470 ,700 ,1050 ,2830
140 CLS:PRINT"   ***  BINOMIAL  ***"
150 PRINT:PRINT"ROUTINE COMPUTES THE PROBABILITY
      OF OBTAINING A GIVEN NUMBER OF SUCCESSES I
      N A GIVEN NUMBER OF BERNOULLI TRIALS."
160 PRINT
170 ZA=1
180 GOSUB1380
190 PRINT"(TO END PROGRAM TYPE 0)"
200 PRINT"NUMBER OF TRIALS?"
210 INPUTN$:IFN$="0"THEN460
220 IFN$="G"THEN1410
230 N=VAL(N$)
240 PRINT"EXACT NUMBER OF SUCCESSES";
250 INPUT X
260 PRINT"PROBABILITY OF SUCCESS";
270 INPUT P
280 M(1)=N
290 M(2)=X
300 M(3)=N-X
310 FOR I=1 TO 3
320    IF M(I)>33THEN330   ELSE350
330    PRINT"INPUT VALUE,";M(I);", IS TOO BIG.
      TRY ANOTHER."
340    GOTO200
350    IF M(I)=0 THEN410
360    A=1
370    FOR J=1 TO M(I)
380       A=A*J
390    NEXT J
400    M(I)=LOG(A)
410 NEXT I
420 R=EXP(M(1)-M(2)-M(3)+X*LOG(P)+(N-X)*LOG(1-P)
      )
```

Listing 8-4. Distributions (continued from page 147)

```
430 PRINT"PROBABILITY OF ";X;" SUCCESSES IN ";N;
     " TRIALS = ";R
440 PRINT@576,""
450 GOTO200
460 END
470 CLS
480 PRINT"          **** POISSON ****"
490 PRINT:PRINT"THIS ROUTINE COMPUTES THE PROBAB
    ILITY
OF AN EVENT OCCURRING A GIVEN NUMBER OF TIMES."
500 ZA=2
510 PRINT:PRINT"(TO END TYPE A 0)"
520 PRINT"CALCULATED MEAN"
530 INPUT L
540 IF L=0 THEN690
550 GOSUB1380
560 PRINT"TEST FREQUENCY?"
570 INPUT X$:IF X$="G"THEN1410
580 X=VAL(X$):IFX=>34THEN590   ELSE600
590 PRINT"INPUT VALUE,";X;" IS TOO LARGE.   MUST
     BE LESS THAN 34.":GOTO560
600 A=1
610 FOR I=1 TO X
620 A=A*I
630 NEXT I
640 A=LOG(A)
650 A=EXP(-L+X*LOG(L)-A)
660 PRINT"PROBABILITY OF ";X;"OCCURRENCES = ";A
670 PRINT
680 GOTO520
690 END
700 CLS:PRINT"          **** NORMAL ****"
710 ZA=3
720 PRINT:PRINT"ROUTINE COMPUTES THE PROBABILTY
    AND FREQUENCY OF GIVEN VALUES ON A STANDARD
      NORMAL DISTRIBUTION CURVE."
730 PRINT
740 PRINT"(S=STANDARD, N=NON-STTANDARD (IF YOU K
    NOW THE MEAN AND SD)"
750 PRINT"WHICH TYPE OF VARIABLE?"
760 S$=INKEY$:IFS$=""THEN760
770 IF S$="S"THEN830
780 PRINT"MEAN?"
790 INPUT M
800 PRINT"STANDARD DEVIATION?"
810 INPUT S
820 GOTO880
830 S=1
840 GOSUB1380
850 INPUT"ENTER 'Z' SCORE VALUE";Y$
860 IFY$="G"THEN1410
870 Y=VAL(Y$):GOTO950
880 PRINT
890 PRINT"TO END PROGRAM ENTER 'E'"
900 PRINT"ENTER TRIAL VALUE";
```

```
910  INPUTY$:IFY$="E"THEN1040
920  IFY$="L"THEN1410
930  Y=VAL(Y$)
940  Y=(Y-M)/S:PRINT"THE 'Z' SCORE IS =";Y
950  R=EXP(-Y[2/2)/2.5066232746
960  PRINT"FREQUENCY  F(X) = ";R
970  R1=.2316419:B1=.31938153:B2=-.356563782:B3=1
     .781477937:B4=-1.821255978:B5=1.330274429
980  T=1/(1+(R*Y))
990  QX=R*((B1*T)+(B2*(T[2))+(B3*(T[3))+(B4*(T[4)
     )+(B5*(T[5)))
1000 PRINT"PROBABILITY  Q(X) = ";QX;"      ( 1 - Q
     =";1-QX;")"
1010 PRINT
1020 IFS$="S"THEN850
1030 GOTO900
1040 END
1050 CLS:PRINT"              **** CHI-SQUARE  ****"

1060 ZA=4
1070 GOSUB1380
1080 PRINT:PRINT"THIS ROUTINE COMPUTES THE TAIL-
     END VALUE FOR POINTS ON A CHI-SQUARE DISTRI
     BUTION."
1090 PRINT
1100 PRINT"(TO END TYPE A 0)"
1110 PRINT"DEGREES OF FREEDOM?"
1120 INPUT V:UU=V
1130 IF V=0 THEN1370
1140 PRINT"CHI-SQUARE VALUE?"
1150 INPUTW$:IFW$="G"THEN1410
1160 W=VAL(W$):WW=W:WV=W
1170 R=1
1180 FOR I=V TO 2 STEP -2
1190 R=R*I
1200 NEXT I
1210 K=W[(INT((V+1)/2))*EXP(-W/2)/R
1220 IF INT(V/2)=V/2 THEN 1250
1230 J=SQR(2/W/3.141592653599)
1240 GOTO1260
1250 J=1
1260 L=1
1270 M=1
1280 V=V+2
1290 M=M*W/V
1300 IF M<.0000001 THEN1330
1310 L=L+M
1320 GOTO1280
1330 PRINT"TAIL-END VALUE = ";1-J*K*L
1340 PRINT"PERCENTILE VALUE = ";J*K*L:WP=J*K*L
1350 PRINT
1360 GOTO1110
1370 END
1380 PRINT@960,"(G)RAPHICS";
1390 PRINT@192,""
1400 RETURN
1410 CLS
```

Listing 8-4. Distributions (continued from page 149)

```
1420 D$(1)="BINOMIAL":D$(2)="POISSON":D$(3)="NOR
     MAL":D$(4)="CHI-SQUARE"
1430 PRINT"GRAPHIC DISPLAY OF A ";D$(ZA);" DISTR
     IBUTION"
1440 ONZAGOTO1450 ,1700 ,2050 ,2390
1450 '
1460 GOSUB4220
1470 PRINT@512,"P(X)";
1480 FORJ=0TO6:PRINT@65+(J*128),.05*(6-J);:NEXTJ

1490 Z=5:FORJ=18TO56STEP10:PRINT@896+J,Z;:Z=Z+5:
     NEXTJ
1500 FOR I=1 TO N
1510     M(1)=N:M(2)=I:M(3)=N-I
1520     FOR J=1 TO 3
1530         IF M(J)=0THEN1590
1540         A=1
1550         FOR K=1TOM(J)
1560             A=A*K
1570         NEXT K
1580         M(J)=LOG(A)
1590     NEXT J
1600     PRINT@478,I/N;"% STILL TO GO...";
1610     RR(I)=EXP(M(1)-M(2)-M(3)+I*LOG(P)+(N-I)*
     LOG(1-P))
1620 NEXT$I
1630 PRINT@478,"                         ";
1640 FOR I=1 TO 24
1650     SET((I*4)+19,40-INT((RR(I)/.30)*38))
1660 NEXT I
1670 PRINT@960,"'A' FOR ANOTHER SET";
1680 A$=INKEY$:IFA$=""THEN1680
1690 GOTO140
1700 'POISSON GRAPHICS
1710 GOSUB4220
1720 PRINT@512,"P(X)";
1730 FORJ=0TO6:PRINT@65+(J*128),.075*(6-J);:NEXT
     J
1740 Z=5:FORJ=18TO56STEP10:PRINT@896+J,Z;:Z=Z+5:
     NEXTJ
1750 F=0:G=1
1760 FOR I=1 TO 20
1770     A=1
1780     FOR J=1 TO 1
1790         A=A*J
1800     NEXT J
1810     A=LOG(A)
1820     AA(I)=EXP(-L+I*LOG(L)-A)
1830     PRINT@478,I/20;"% STILL TO GO...";
1840 NEXT I
1850 CC=0
1860 FORI=1TO20
1870     IFAA(I)<.01125THEN1880 ELSE1890
1880     CC=CC+1
1890 NEXTI
```

```
1900 IFCC<15THEN1930
1910 PRINT@468,"NO DATA POINTS AVAILABLE AT THIS
     SCALE";
1920 F=F+1:G=10[F:GOTO2000
1930 PRINT@468,"
               ";
1940 ONERRORGOTO2010
1950 FOR I=1 TO 20
1960    SET((I*4)+19,40-1NT((AA(I)/.45)*38))
1970 NEXT I
1980 IFF>0THENPRINT@995,"DIVIDE P(X) BY";G;
1990 GOTO2020
2000 FORI=1TO20:AA(I)=AA(I)*G:NEXTI:GOTO1850
2010 RESUMENEXT
2020 PRINT@960,"'A' FOR ANOTHER SET";
2030 A$=INKEY$:IFA$=""THEN2030
2040 GOTO470
2050 'NORMAL DISTRIBUTION GRAPHICS
2060 GOSUB4220
2070 PRINT@512,"F(X)";
2080 FORJ=0TO6:PRINT@65+(J*128),.075*(6-J);:NEXT
     J
2090 IFS$="S"THEN2250
2100 MM=M-(3*S)
2110 Z=MM:FORJ=14TO52STEP6:PRINT@896+J,Z;:Z=Z+S:
     NEXTJ
2120 Y=41:FORX=23TO113STEP12:RESET(X,Y):NEXTX
2130 FORX=27TO113STEP12:RESET(X,Y):NEXTX
2140 PRINT@990,"      X";
2150 I=0
2160 FORY=MMTOM+(3*S)STEP(((M+(3*S))-MM)/20)
2170    Q=(Y-M)/S
2180    RR(I)=EXP(-Q[2/2)/2.5066232746
2190    PRINT@476,"COMPUTING F(X)=";RR(I);"     "
     ;
2200    I=I+1
2210 NEXTY
2220 PRINT@476,"
               ";
2230 GOTO2330
2240 GOTO2240
2250 FORY=-4TO4STEP.3333333
2260    RR(I)=EXP(-Y[2/2)/2.5066232746
2270    PRINT@476,"COMPUTING F(X)=";RR(I);"    ";
2280    I=I+1
2290 NEXT Y
2300 PRINT@476,"
                ";
2310 PRINT@984,"SD OF";
2320 Z=-3:FORJ=14TO56STEP6:PRINT@896+J,Z;:Z=Z+1:
     NEXTJ
2330 FOR J=0TOI
2340    SET((J*4)+23,40-1NT((RR(J)/.45)*38))
2350 NEXT J
2360 PRINT@960,"'a' FOR ANOTHER SET.";
2370 A$=INKEY$:IFA$=""THEN2370
```

Listing 8-4. Distributions (continued from page 151)

```
2380 RUN700
2390 'CHI-SQUARE DISTRIBUTION GRAPHICS
2400 B$="#.####"
2410 GOSUB4220
2420 FORJ=0TO6:PRINT@65+(J*128),"";:PRINTUSINGB$
     ;.166666*(6-J);:NEXTJ
2430 PRINT@512,"P(X)";
2440 Z=5:FORJ=18TO56STEP10:PRINT@896+J,Z;:Z=Z+5:
     NEXTJ
2450 PRINT@988,"CHI-SQUARE";
2460 X=0
2470 IFU>33THEN2770
2480 FORW=1TO24
2490     R=1:U=UU
2500     FORI=UTO2STEP-2
2510        R=R*I
2520     NEXTI
2530     K=W[(INT((U+1)/2))*EXP(-W/2)/R
2540     IF INT(U/2)=U/2THEN2570
2550     J=SQR(2/W/3.141592653599)
2560     GOTO2580
2570     J=1
2580     L=1
2590     M=1
2600     U=U+2
2610     M=M*W/U
2620     IFM<.0000001THEN2650
2630     L=L+M
2640     GOTO2600
2650     RR(X)=J*K*L
2660     X=X+1
2670     PRINT@466,"COMPUTATION IS";(W/24)*100;"%
     COMPLETE";"       ";
2680 NEXTW
2690 PRINT@464,"
     ";
2700 FOR J=0TOX
2710     SET((J*4)+23,40-INT(RR(J)*38))
2720 NEXTJ
2730 PRINT@960,"'A' FOR ANOTHER SET.";
2740 PRINT@0,"TABLE SHOWS % CONFINDENCE IN DATA
     FOR";UU;" DEGREES OF FREEDOM";
2750 A$=INKEY$:IFA$=""THEN2790 ELSE2760
2760 GOTO1050
2770 PRINT@476,"SORRY.  DEGREES OF FREEDOM
                        MUST BE 33 OR LESS"
2780 FORI=1TO2000:NEXTI:GOTO1050
2790 IFWP>0ANDWU<24THEN2800 ELSE2750
2800 SET(INT(WU*4)+19,40-INT(WP*38)):FORX=1TO10:
     NEXTX
2810 RESET(INT(WU*4)+19,40-INT(WP*38))
2820 GOTO2750
2830 'RAW DATA INPUT
2840 CLS
2850 PRINT"IN THIS SECTION THE USER CAN INPUT RA
```

```
      W DATA TO OBTAIN THE
BASIC DATA REQUIRED TO RUN THE OTHER OPTIONS IN
      THIS LIBRARY."
2860 PRINT:PRINT
2870 PRINT"           1 -- BINOMIAL"
2880 PRINT"           2 -- CHI-SQUARE"
2890 PRINT"          3 -- ALL OTHER"
2900 PRINT:PRINT"ENTER SUBROUTINE DESIRED:"
2910 A$=INKEY$:IFA$=""THEN2910
2920 A=VAL(A$)
2930 ONAGOTO2940 ,3050 ,3090
2940 CLS:PRINT"BINOMIAL DISTRIBUTION INPUT"
2950 PRINT:PRINT"THIS DISTRIBUTION ASKS THE USER
      TO PROVIDE THREE PIECES OF
INFORMATION.  THE OUTPUT IS THE PROBABILITY THAT
      , GIVEN THE
CHANCE THAT AN EVENT WILL HAPPEN, X NUMBER OF LI
      KE EVENTS, OUT
OF A SPECIFIED NUMBER OF TRIALS, WILL HAPPEN."
2960 PRINT:PRINT"TO ANSWER THE INPUT QUESTIONS,
      YOU NEED TO KNOW THE
PROBABILITY THAT AN EVENT (E.G., 'HEADS' ON A CO
      IN, WHICH OF 8
HORSES WINNING IN A RACE...) WILL OCCUR.  TAKE T
      HE HORSE RACE
EXAMPLE.  THE QUESTION THE BINOMIAL ROUTINE ATTE
      MPTS TO"
2970 PRINT"TO ANSWER IS: WHAT IS THE PROBABILITY
      THAT A HORSE
WILL WIN 3 (OR 1 OR 5 OR 6...) OUT OF (AT LEAST)
      3 (OR 1 OR 5
OR 6) RACES.  IF YOU HAVE 'HANDICAPPED' THE HORS
      E, USE THOSE
ODDS OR PROBABILITIES.  IF YOU HAVEN'T, ASSUME A
      N EVEN"
2980 PRINT"DISTRIBUTION OF ODDS.  (HIT 'ENTER' T
      O CONTINUE)";
2990 INPUTZZ
3000 PRINT"IF THERE ARE 8 HORSES, THE CHANCE OF
      ANY ONE HORSE WINNING,
ALL OTHER THINGS BEING EQUAL, IS P=.125.   IF YO
      U WANT TO KNOW
WHAT THE PROBABILITY OF A HORSE WINNING 3 OUT OF
      7 RACES, USE:
      NUMBER OF TRIALS = 7
      NUMBER OF SUCCESSES";
3010 PRINT" = 3
      PROBABILITY OF SUCCESS = .125"
3020 PRINT:PRINT"USING THE PROGRAM, YOU'LL SEE T
      HE CHANCE OF YOUR HORSE,CHOSEN
AT RANDOM, OF WINNING ANY 3 RACES IS P=.040071."
HOPE THIS HELPS."
3030 PRINT:PRINT:INPUT"'ENTER' WHEN READY.";ZZ
3040 RUN
3050 'CHI-SQUARE DATA INPUT
3060 CLS
3070 PRINT:INPUT"'ENTER' WHEN READY.";ZZ
```

Listing 8-4. Distributions (continued from page 153)

```
3080 RUN
3090 'RAW DATA INPUT
3100 CLS
3110 INPUT"HOW MANY DATA ELEMENTS ARE TO BE ENTE
     RED";N
3120 IF N>100THEN3130 ELSE3140
3130 PRINT"PLEASE LIMIT INPUT TO 100 ITEMS OR LE
     SS.":GOTO3090
3140 FOR I=1TON
3150    PRINT"ENTER DATA ELEMENT #";I;:INPUT X(I
     )
3160 NEXT I
3170 FORI=1TON
3180    IF X(I)=0THEN3190 ELSE3200
3190    LL=LL+1
3200 NEXTI
3210 IF LL<>0THEN3220 ELSE3230
3220 SM=0:GOTO3240
3230 SM=X(1)
3240 FOR I=1 TO N
3250    SX=SX+X(I)
3260    QX=QX+X(I)[2
3270    IF X(I)<=SMTHEN3280 ELSE3290
3280    SM=X(I)
3290    IF X(I)>=LGTHEN3300 ELSE3310
3300    LG=X(I)
3310 NEXT I
3320 AV=SX/N:SD=SQR((QX-(SX[2)/N)/N-1)
3330 PA=SQR(AV)
3340 CLS
3350 GOSUB3620
3360 PRINT
3370 PRINT"THERE WERE";N;" ELEMENTS ENTERED.
             THE SMALLEST WAS: ";SM;"
             THE LARGET WAS: "LG;"
             THE SUM WAS =";SX;" AND THE AVERAGE W
     AS =";AV"
3380 PRINT"            THE MEDIAN WAS =";ME;"
             THE MODE WAS =";MD;"
             THE SKEW WAS =";SK;
3390 PRINT:PRINT"IN A NORMAL DISTRIBUTION, THE S
     TANDARD DEVIATION IS =";SD;".
THE DISTRIBUTION IS SKEWED TO THE ";SK$;".

IN A POISSON DISTRIBUTION, THE STANDARD DEVIATIO
     N IS =";
PA;"."
3400 PRINT
3410 A$="":B$=""
3420 PRINT"DO YOU WANT TO USE THESE VALUES IN TH
     E BASIC ROUTINE? (Y/N)"
3430 A$=INKEY$:IFA$=""THEN3430
3440 IFA$="Y"THEN3450 ELSE3550
3450 PRINT"CHOOSE:   (N)ORMAL OR (P)OISSON DISTRI
     BUTIONS"
```

```
3460 B$=INKEY$:IFB$=""THEN3460
3470 IFB$="N"THEN3510
3480 L=AV
3490 ZA=2
3500 GOTO560
3510 M=AV:S=SD
3520 ZA=3
3530 GOTO880
3540 END
3550 PRINT"DO YOU WANT TO SEE THE INPUT DATA (Y/
     N)"
3560 Q$=INKEY$:IFQ$=""THEN3560
3570 IF Q$="Y"THEN3580 ELSERUN
3580 PRINT"OUTPUT TO PRINT ALSO"
3590 QQ$=INKEY$:IFQQ$=""THEN3590
3600 IFQQ$="Y"THENLP=1ELSELP=0
3610 GOTO3920
3620 'SORTING ROUTINE
3630 CLS:PRINT@512,"SORTING INPUT VALUES:";
3640 FOR I=1TON
3650     U(I)=X(I)
3660 NEXTI
3670 D=1
3680 D=2*D:IFD<NTHEN3680
3690 D=INT((D-1)/2)
3700 IF D=0THEN3790
3710 IT=N-D
3720 FORI=1TOIT
3730     J=I
3740     L=J+D
3750     IF U(L)<U(J)THENTEMP=U(J):U(J)=U(L):U(L)
     =TEMP:J=J-D:IFJ>0THEN3740
3760 NEXTI
3770 GOTO3690
3780 END
3790 'PRINT SORTED ARRAY
3800 PRINT
3810 FORI=1TON
3820     PRINTU(I),
3830 NEXTI
3840 IF INT(N/2)=N/2THEN3900
3850 ME=U(((N-1)/2)+1)
3860 SK=(3*(AV-ME))/SD:MD=AV-(SK*SD)
3870 IFSK<0THENSK$="LEFT (PEAK TO THE RIGHT)"ELS
     ESK$="RIGHT (PEAK TO THE LEFT)"
3880 FORI=1TO1500:NEXTI
3890 RETURN
3900 ME=(U(N/2)+U((N/2)+1))/2
3910 GOTO3860
3920 CLS
3930 PRINT"UNSORTED INPUT"
3940 FORI=1TON
3950     PRINTX(I),
3960 NEXTI
3970 PRINT
3980 PRINT"SORTED DATA"
3990 FOR I=1 TO N
```

Listing 8-4. Distributions (continued from page 155)

```
4000      PRINTU(I),
4010 NEXTI
4020 PRINT
4030 FORI=1TO1000
4040 NEXTI
4050 IFLP=1THEN4070 ELSE3360
4060 LPRINTSTRING$(3,10)
4070 LPRINT"UNSORTED"
4080 FORI=1TON
4090      LPRINTX(I),
4100 NEXTI
4110 LPRINT" ":LPRINT" "
4120 LPRINT"SORTED"
4130 FORI=1 TON
4140      LPRINTU(I),
4150 NEXTI
4160 LPRINT" ":LPRINT" "
4170 LPRINTN;" ITEMS ENTERED, THE SMALLEST BEING
     ;";SM;", THE LARGEST BEING";LG;".  THE FOLL
     OWING ITEMS WERE COMPUTED:
     SUM =";SX;"    AVERAGE";AV;"   MEDIAN";ME;"
        MODE =";MD;"   SKEW =";SK;"    STANDARD D
     EVIATION =";SD
4180 LPRINT" ":LPRINT"IN A POISSON DISTRIBUTION
     THE STANDARD DEVIATION WOULD BE =";PA
4190 LPRINTSTRING$(3,10)
4200 GOTO3360
4210 END
4220 FORX=20TO21:FORY=4TO37STEP3:SET(X,Y):NEXTY:
     NEXTX
4230 X=22:FORY=3TO40:SET(X,Y):NEXTY
4240 Y=40:FORX=23TO117:SET(X,Y):NEXTX
4250 Y=41:FORX=23TO113STEP4:SET(X,Y):NEXTX
4260 PRINT@990,"X";
4270 RETURN
```

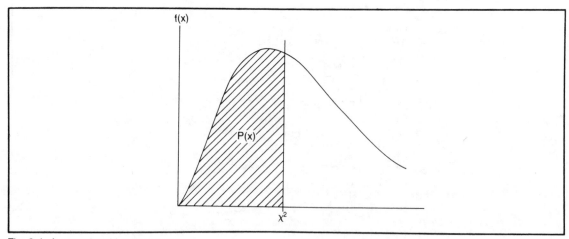

Fig. 8-4. Area under chi-square curve.

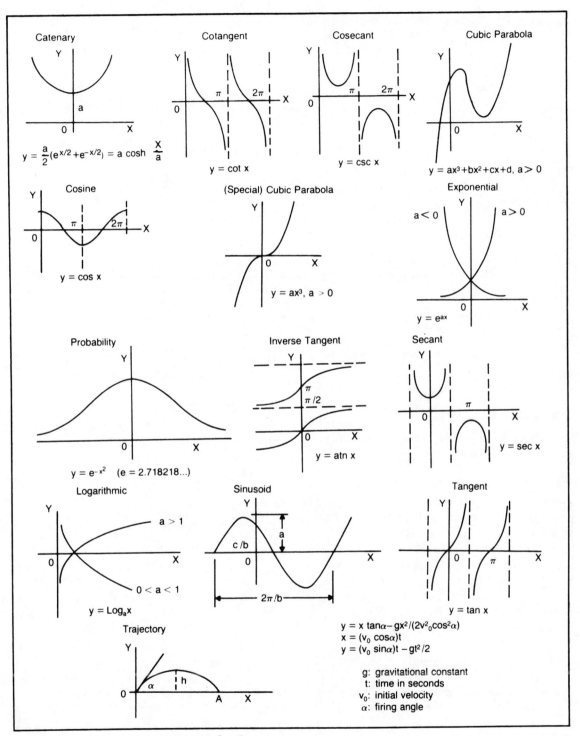

Catenary

$$y = \frac{a}{2}(e^{x/2} + e^{-x/2}) = a \cosh \frac{x}{a}$$

Cotangent

$$y = \cot x$$

Cosecant

$$y = \csc x$$

Cubic Parabola

$$y = ax^3 + bx^2 + cx + d, \ a > 0$$

Cosine

$$y = \cos x$$

(Special) Cubic Parabola

$$y = ax^3, \ a > 0$$

Exponential

$a < 0$ $a > 0$

$$y = e^{ax}$$

Probability

$$y = e^{-x^2} \quad (e = 2.718218...)$$

Inverse Tangent

$$y = \text{atn} \ x$$

Secant

$$y = \sec x$$

Logarithmic

$a > 1$

$0 < a < 1$

$$y = \text{Log}_a x$$

Sinusoid

$2\pi/b$

Tangent

$$y = \tan x$$

Trajectory

$$y = x \tan\alpha - gx^2/(2v^2_0 \cos^2\alpha)$$
$$x = (v_0 \cos\alpha)t$$
$$y = (v_0 \sin\alpha)t - gt^2/2$$

g: gravitational constant
t: time in seconds
v_0: initial velocity
α: firing angle

Fig. 8-5. Standard curves and trigonometric functions.

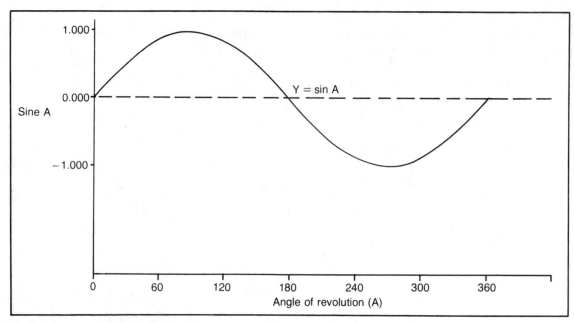

Fig. 8-6. Sine wave relationships.

TRIGONOMETRIC FUNCTIONS

Figure 8-5 illustrates a number of curves that are generated by functions of various algebraic and trigonometric relationships. Numerous reference works in mathematics continue this series with countless fascinating shapes and curves. Our purpose here is not to present an encyclopedic catalog of the various possibilities, but simply to alert the reader to the option of using such forms.

Many of the equations can be modified to better fit your data by the simple addition of various coefficients. For example, the normal equation for the coordinates of a sine curve are: $X = \cos A$ and $Y = \sin A$, where A is the angle of revolution. (See Fig. 8-6).

We can modify the position of the curve on the chart by adding a constant, K, as in: $X = \cos A$ and $Y = K + \sin A$. This has the effect of raising the whole curve upward K units. We can also multiply the function by a constant: $X = \cos A$ and $Y = K \sin A$. The center line of the curve remains at zero, but the

absolute magnitude of the vertical component is increased as a function of K. (See Fig. 8-7).

FAST FOURIER TRANSFORMS

Scientists have known for a long time that many complex wave forms in acoustics and electronics are really the result of combining two or more simple sine or cosine wave forms. They say that in general, the complex wave should be able to be represented by the equation.

$$Y = K_1 \cos A_1 + L_1 \sin A_1 + K_2 \cos A_2 + L_2 \sin A_2 \ldots$$

Figure 8-8 illustrates this combination.

The problem with this concept is that a trial and error approach to defining the coefficients is very frustrating and time-consuming. The classic approaches to the solution of the problem using calculus are beyond the skills of many of us and remain quite tedious even for those who can handle the mathematics. The Fast Fourier transform (FFT) is a working alternative to both the trial and error method and the use of calculus.

Named after the famous French mathematician, the process is faster than the other techniques. Economists have used the technique in various efforts to analyze the stock market as a complex wave constituted of a number of identifiable and simple cyclic waves. As with all other efforts to determine a predictive key to the market, though, we seldom hear of the successes. Those finding such a key are unlikely to share it openly.

EXERCISES

1. The catenary curve, which describes the natural shape of a rope or chain hanging suspended between two posts or supports, is useful in determining the shape and dimensions of the suspension cables on a bridge. Describe two other applications of the catenary form and equations.

2. Write a program, based on one of the various forms of the spiral to help make search operations for lost persons more efficient.
3. Maintain a record of the stock market average or the price of one stock for a month or so. Use the polynomial program to evaluate these data in order to determine the utility of the approach. Explain the results.
4. Count the number of people arriving at the front door of a place of business from thirty minutes before to thirty minutes after the nominal opening or start of the work day. Determine the mean number of arrivals during each time interval. Assume the arrival times resemble those predicted by a

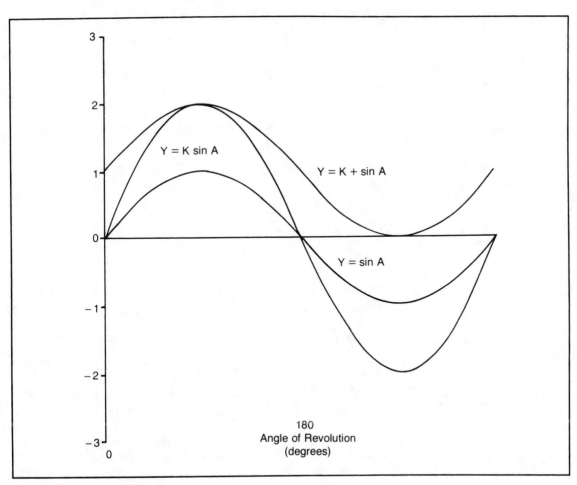

Fig. 8-7. Sine wave variations.

159

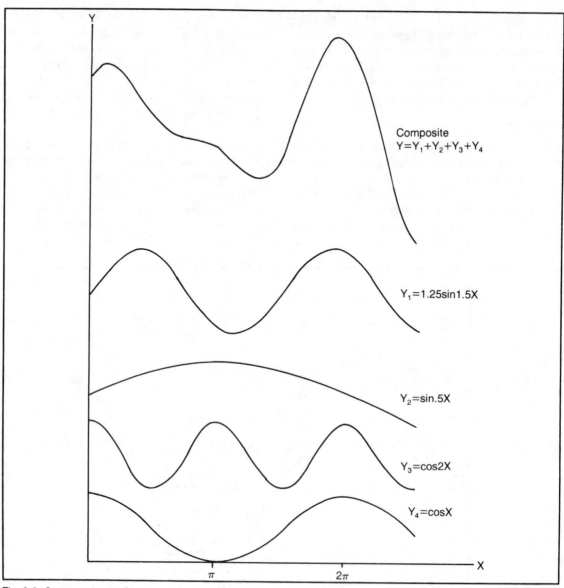

Fig. 8-8. Compound wave form.

Poisson distribution. From these data, compute the expected number of arrivals sixty minutes on either side of the nominal start time. Validate your forecast, if possible.

5. Repeat the exercise in item 4, but use the normal distribution as the predictor format. Which approach gives better results? Why?

SUGGESTED READING

Adler, I., 1957. *Magic House of Numbers.* New York: The John Day Company, Inc.

Bruning, J. L. and B. L. Kintz, 1968. *Computational Handbook of Statistics.* Glenview, IL: Scott, Foresman Company.

Selby, S., 1973. *Standard Mathematical Tables.* Cleveland: The Chemical Rubber Co.

Chapter 9

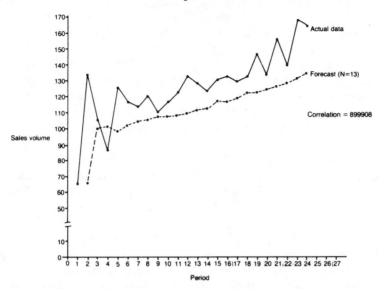

Opinion and Survey Research

One of the more significant applications of the forecasting techniques presented in this book is in opinion, survey, or market research. The basic approach is fairly straightforward: question a convenient number of people from a larger population on how they feel about a thing, subject, or person and generalize the answers to the whole population. Want to know who will be the next president? Stop the next five people you see and ask them. To a certain degree, the composite of their answer will reflect how the nation will vote in the next election. Admittedly, this approach leaves something to be desired as a technique for predicting national elections, but only in a relative sense. The objective of this chapter is to provide the reader with fundamental, but sufficient, statistical and research tools with which to conduct usable and responsible survey research. These tools include: planning, sample size, survey questionnaire, interviewing considerations and data collection, and data analysis.

SURVEY PLANNING

It is possible for you to conduct a complete political survey in the next ten minutes. Just pick up the telephone or walk down the street and spend six minutes talking to whoever will answer. Spend the last four minutes summarizing the responses. We suggest, however, that a more insightful and cost-effective survey can be conducted with a reasonable amount of preplanning. Before rushing out, the prudent researcher gives consideration to the following items.

Objective

What is the purpose of the survey? This is perhaps the most difficult and vital aspect of the research effort. Until you can give a good, solid answer to this question, everything else you do will be of little value. Identifying the objective will give a focus to the rest of your planning and make many decisions very simple. Is your objective to identify the true voter intent with regard to your client? Or, is your objective to give your client a sense of support and confidence, regardless of the real voter intent? If it is the former, select a good sample from the relevant population, and measure the proportion favoring your client. On the other hand, if the objective is the latter, select a sample from those voters known to be solidly on your side (such as known straight ticket voters, voters who have publicly supported your client, etc.), measure the proportion favoring your client, and apply this to the voting population as a whole. If you are doing a market survey, is your objective to identify consumer behavior, consumer preference for your client's product, consumer preference for the competition's product, consumer desires as opposed to consumer actions . . . . ? How you answer these kinds of questions will give shape and meaning to the balance of your efforts. As concisely and concretely as possible, define your objective.

Techniques and Limitations

There are a number of techniques available to the researcher. Each one serves a useful purpose if properly applied and has significant limitations. Just as a mechanic has a box filled with tools, each having a specific function, the researcher has quite an arsenal of techniques. To use one simply because you understand how to do it is shortsighted. Instead, you should use the technique best suited to the objective. Some of the techniques, with their applications and limitations, are described on the following pages.

Telephone Interviews. The telephone survey is useful for short questionnaires with fairly easy to understand questions and in surveys looking for gross statistical generalities. Interviewers must have a pleasant telephone personality and be able to read well and to record responses accurately and quickly, but otherwise they are not required to have exceptional research skills. This technique is handy for quick surveys, but can easily be criticized for excluding from your sample a portion of population either too poor or too transient to have a telephone, yet who might otherwise be suitable subjects. To overcome this limitation, the next option can be used.

Interviews In-depth. This method involves meeting the people to be surveyed face-to-face and asking them the relevant questions. The advantage of this method is that the questionnaire can go into

greater subtlety and depth, and take more time, covering a broader range of subject matter. It overcomes the criticism of exclusion in the telephone technique. On the other hand, it is a very time-consuming technique, which requires a much larger number of interviewers in order to contact the same number of subjects in the same time as a telephone survey. The interviewers in this approach must present a clean and professional appearance as well as a pleasing personality. They must understand survey techniques well-enough to deal with the unexpected quickly and without extraordinary resort to notes or other guidance. Volunteers can generally be trained quickly to do telephone work, but effective and reliable field survey work generally requires a paid staff.

Mail Surveys. This technique shifts the emphasis from interviewer skill to skill in questionnaire design. Compared to field survey work, it is a very inexpensive technique. Large portions of the population can be contacted in fairly short order and asked a broad range of questions of exceptional depth and sophistication. The primary objection to this technique is that the response to the questionnaire is likely to be only a slight fraction of the total number contacted. Professionals in mail survey work consider a five percent response to be quite good. This means that, if you have determined the proper sample size to be 1000, you need to contact at least 20,000 addresses. Using a printing and postage cost of $0.50 for each questionnaire mailed out, this implies a research cost starting at $10,000. If an interviewer can complete an average of twelve interviews a day, at $5 an hour, $10,000 would obtain 2000 in-depth interviews in a little over 166 interview days. The second criticism to this technique is one of validation. There is no satisfactory way to know that the person identified on the questionnaire actually answered the items or that the answers are truthful. The surveyor must accept on faith the accuracy and honesty of the responses. Selection of this technique should be in part a function of the degree to which accuracy and honesty in response are rewarded. A survey asking the subject's age and sex, as well as suggestions for five kinds of television programs desired, sponsored by a television station or network is more likely to receive valid responses than one offering a prize for a paragraph on why a certain product is better than another. Using this technique, the surveyor must assume that if it is in the interests of the subjects to lie, they will.

Observation Analysis. There are a number of variations on this basic technique, but what they have in common is a period during which the social system under investigation is observed by a data collector. Political influence analysis, for example, is conducted by observing participants in a political matrix and recording very carefully who initiates different sorts of interactions with what sort of consequences. This technique normally requires a considerable amount of time and training effort to prepare the observers for their duties. Even under fairly ideal conditions, the observations can become very subjective in nature unless strict controls are applied.

Archive Analysis. The determination of voter trends is often better computed from historical records than from interview research. This approach is often implemented as part of a larger effort in voter analysis in which current trends or preferences (obtained from interviews) are contrasted with historical trends identified from data in voting record archives.

Cost Considerations

As noted several times above, each technique carries with it certain predictable costs. Before making a selection, the surveyor should first determine the degree of precision necessary and the level of confidence desired in the outcome of the research. Then, given two or more techniques which are adequate to the task (that is, they yield results within the required range), the researcher should select the technique costing the least—even though its results may not be quite as good as another. Since people come in integer units, an expensive technique that promises precision to five decimal places is no more valuable than an inexpensive technique promising precision to only one or two decimal places. In counting potential voters, for example, 233.4232934366 voters are essentially equivalent to 233.42 voters. Table 9-1 offers a nominal matrix for estimating personnel requirements and costs for a survey effort.

To this figure is added the administrative costs that are associated with the selected technique. For example, if the technique of choice is a mail survey, printing and postage costs are likely to be quite high. Listing 9-1 provides computer assistance in evaluating two or more alternative techniques based on the format in Table 9-1.

Table 9-1. Survey Time Scheduling.

Operation	-Working Days				Total Pers.	$ Admin. Costs
	Study Director	Research Associate	Interviewer	Clerks		
Formulation and Design:	60	60	5	30	155	100
Development of Materials:	15	15	15	30	75	200
Development of Interview:	15	15	5	45	80	450
Data Collection:	30	30	120	15	195	600
Data Coding/Compiling:	5	10	5	60	80	450
Statistical Analysis:	10	20	0	20	50	300
Report Writing:	30	45	0	60	135	200
Final Admin Work:	5	5	0	5	15	50
Total Working Days:	170	200	150	265	785	2350
Wage Factor:	5	4.5	1.5	1	n/a	n/a
Product:	850	900	225	265	n/a	n/a

Sum of Column Products = 2240 × Basic Wage (3.50) = Labor Cost = $7840.99
Total Labor Cost + Total Admin. Cost = Total Research Cost = 7840 + 2350 = 10,190

Listing 9-1. Survey Estimator

```
1 '**********************************************
2 'SURVEY ESTIMATOR                              *
3 'LISTING 9-1                                   *
4 '**********************************************
5 '
10 CLS:PRINTCHR$(210);"SURVEY TIME/COST ESTIMATE
    S":PRINT:PRINT
20 P$(1)="DIRECTOR":P$(2)="ASSISTANT":P$(3)="INT
    ERVIEWER":P$(4)="CLERKS"
30 FORI=1TO4
40   PRINT"WHAT IS THE WAGE FACTOR FOR THE ";P$(
    I);:INPUTW(I)
50 NEXT
60 PRINT:INPUT"WHAT IS THE BASE WAGE";BP:PRINT
70 F$(1)="FORMULATION AND DESIGN":F$(2)="DEVELOP
    MENT OF MATERIALS":F$(3)="DEVELOPMENT OF IN
    TERVIEW":F$(4)="DATA COLLECTION":F$(5)="DAT
    A CODING":F$(6)="STATISTICAL ANALYSIS":F$(7
    )="REPORT WRITNG":F$(8)="FINAL ADMIN WORK"
80 PRINT"PHASE"
90 FORJ=1TO8
100   PRINTF$(J)
110   FORI=1TO4
120    PRINT"        ";P$(I);": HOW MANY WORK DA
    YS TOTAL  ";
130    INPUTV
140    R(J)=R(J)+V:TD=TD+V:P(J,I)=V:P(0,I)=P(0,I)
    +V
150   NEXT
160   PRINT"     TOTAL MANPOWER THIS PERIOD = ";
    R(J);"MAN-DAYS"
170   PRINT"      ADMIN COSTS";
180   INPUTAC(J)
190   TA=TA+AC(J)
200   PRINT
210 NEXTJ
220 Z$="%              %  ###        ##.##       ##
    ###.##     ######.##"
230 A$="                  MAN        WAGE
             ACTUAL"
240 B$="                 DAYS       FACTOR      P
    RODUCT      WAGES"
250 CLS:PRINTA$:PRINTB$:PRINT
260 FORI=1TO4
270   PRINTUSINGZ$;P$(I);P(0,I);W(I);W(I)*P(0,I)
    ;W(I)*P(0,I)*BP:TW=TW+(W(I)*P(0,I)*BP)
280 NEXT
290 PRINTUSINGZ$;"TOTAL";TD;TW/(TD*BP);TW/BP;TW
300  PRINT:PRINT"TOTAL ADMIN = ";TA
310 PRINT"TOTAL WAGES = ";TW
320 PRINT"               ----------------"
330 PRINT"TOTAL COSTS = ";TW+TA
340 PRINT@960,"(C)ONTINUE  (P)RINT    (N)EW";
350 Q$=""+INKEY$:IFQ$=""THEN350
```

```
360 IFQ$="P"THEN480    ELSEIFQ$="C"THEN380    ELSEIF
       Q$<>"N"THEN350
370 RUN
380 CLS
390 PRINTA$:PRINTB$:PRINT
400 FORI=1TO8
410    FORJ=1TO4:W=W(J)*P(I,J)*BP:TT=TT+W:NEXT
420    WF=TT/(BP*R(I)):PF=WF*R(I):TC=TC+TT+AC(I)
430    PRINTUSINGZ$;RIGHT$(F$(I),15);R(I);WF;PF;T
       T+AC(I):TT=0
440 NEXT
450 PRINT:PRINTUSINGZ$;"TOTAL";TD;TW/(TD*BP);TW/
       BP;TC
460 TC=0
470 GOTO340
480 FORR=0TO14
490    FORC=0TO63
500       A=PEEK(15360+(R*64)+C):IFA<32THENA=A+64
510       LPRINTCHR$(A);
520    NEXTC
530    LPRINT""
540 NEXT
550 LPRINT"":GOTO340
```

Sponsorship

While not strictly a part of the statistical aspect of forecasting, it is appropriate to enter a word here on the ethical responsibility to identify yourself to the subject of the interview. While it is not necessary to give your personal identity to those you interview, it is responsible to identify the organization for which you are working or the agency sponsoring the research. If your research is self-initiated, you may want to create a business or small corporation as a sponsor. Failure to do so is not grave, but might limit the number of people willing to respond. Many people are properly concerned about revealing personal information to strangers. If you are able to provide some credential the subject could contact or refer to later, you are likely to realize greater success. If you create your own business framework, whether a proprietorship or a corporation, it should be legitimate to the extent that should your subject contact the local state or county registry, they would have the proper documentation, and that your telephone or mailing addresses be authentic. A person who has responded to your survey and then investigates your credentials and finds them wanting may well initiate complaints against you with the police or other authorities. The business you establish need not be an expensive proposition involving rented offices and furniture. You can do a very respectable business from a room of your home. Simply represent yourself with the truth so that your subject perceives that you have a legitimate purpose in your inquiries, and you should realize reasonable success.

Listing 9-2 is a short routine using the computer to help you chart out the project development through the different phases. It is offered more as an example of how to implement such a program than as a finished program, although it is complete within a limited scope.

Listing 9-2. Survey Scheduling

```
1 '***********************************************
2 'SURVEY SCHEDULING                            *
3 'LISTING 9-2                                  *
4 '***********************************************
```

Listing 9-2. Survey Scheduling (continued from page 165)

```
5  '
10 CLS:PRINTCHR$(210);"SURVEY SCHEDULING":PRINT:
      PRINT
20 F$(1)="DESIGN":F$(2)="MATERIALS":F$(3)="INTER
      VIEW":F$(4)="COLLECTION":F$(5)="CODING":F$(
      6)="ANALYSIS":F$(7)="REPORT ":F$(8)="FINAL
      WORK"
30 INPUT"HOW MANY DAYS ARE ALLOWED FOR THE PROJE
      CT";D:TD=0
40 PRINT:PRINT"WHAT IS YOUR ESTIMATE OF THE TIME
       REQUIRED FOR:?
50 FORI=1TO8
60    PRINT"        ";F$(I),:INPUT V:T(I)=V:TD=TD+V
70 NEXT
80 CLS:S=TD-D:IFTD=DTHEN120
90 IFTD<DTHEN110
100 PRINT:PRINT"SORRY, THESE ESTIMATES REQUIRE";
      TD-D;" MORE DAYS THAN ALLOWED":PRINT:GOTO30

110 PRINT"CONGRATULATIONS, YOU HAVE";D-TD;"DAYS
      SLACK AVAILABLE":GOTO130
120 PRINT"THE PROGRAM CAN BE COMPLETED ON SCHEDU
      LE"
130 FORX=0TO127:SET(X,14):NEXT
140 FORX=32TO127STEP10:SET(X,13):NEXT
150 PRINT@384,"";
160 FORI=1TO8:PRINTF$(I):NEXT
170 FORY=12TO45:SET(32,Y):NEXT
180 PRINT@158,"DAYS FROM START";
190 PRINT@192,"PHASE";
200 J=0:FORI=0TODSTEP(D/10):PRINT@208+INT((95*(I
      /D))/2),INT(I);:J=J+1:IFJ=10THEN210   ELSENE
      XT
210 A=0
220 FORI=1TO8
230    S(I)=A:C(I)=S(I)+T(I)-1
240    PRINT@336+(I*64)+INT((95*(A/D)/2)),"[";
250    FORJ=ATOD
260      IFJ<(A+T(I))THEN280
270      PRINT@336+(I*64)+INT((95*(J/D))/2),"[ ";
      :A=J:GOTO300
280      PRINT@336+(I*64)+INT((95*(J/D))/2)+1,"."
      ;
290    NEXTJ
300 NEXTI
310 IFS=0THEN360
320 PRINT@896,"SLACK";
330 PRINT@912+INT((95*(J/D))/2),"[ ";
340 FORI=J+2TOD:PRINT@912+INT((95*(I/D))/2)+1,".
      ";:NEXT
350 PRINT@959,"[    ";
360 PRINT@0,"(P)RINT    (N)EW
                         ";
370 Q$=""+INKEY$:IFQ$=""THEN370
380 IFQ$="P"THEN400
```

```
390 RUN
400 PRINT@85,"PROJECT SCHEDULE";
410 FORR=1TO15
420    FORC=0TO63
430       A=PEEK(15360+(R*64)+C):IFA<32ANDA<90THEN
    A=A+64
440       LPRINTCHR$(A);
450    NEXTC
460    LPRINT""
470 NEXT
480 LPRINT""
490 LPRINT"PHASE","START DAY","COMPLETION","TIME
       REQUIRED"
500 FORI=1TO8:LPRINTF$(I),S(I),C(I),T(I):NEXT:LP
    RINT""
510 RUN
```

THE SAMPLE

It is almost inevitable that to survey an entire population would require more time and resources than we could ever muster. If the target area for a telephone survey, for example, has a million people, and each interview takes five minutes, the survey would take one interviewer, working eight hours a day, seven days a week, better than twenty-eight and a half years to complete. To complete the survey in one week would require at least 1488 interviewers working in eight-hour shifts, 496 at a time. These computations leave no room for slippage or error. Nor do they contemplate the problems of interviewing people at 3:00 AM.

A practical alternative is to select a portion of the population and survey the sample. In doing so, we assume that if 35 percent of the sample indicate preference for a given political candidate, then 35 percent of the entire electorate will be for the same candidate. How reasonable this assumption is will be a function of several factors: homogeneity of the population, size of the sample, size of the population, the allowable degree of error, the level of confidence required, and the sampling procedure.

Homogeneity

The homogeneity of a population is the degree to which the members of the population are alike with respect to the subject of the survey. The more alike a population is on a given subject, the smaller the sample needed to achieve desirable results. For example, we could assume that attitudes toward farming would be as easily defined from a small sample in Des Moines as from a large sample in New York City.

Sample Size

In general, the larger the sample, the more reliable the findings. At the same time, the cost of the survey is most often a direct function of sample size; that is, the larger the sample, the more expensive the research. In this chapter we will present techniques to optimize sample size relative to the other parameters of the research.

Population Size

Up to a point, the size of the sample as a percentage of the population is critical. When the population begins to be considerable (that is, greater than one hundred thousand or a million), sample size as a percentage of the population is negligible. For example, if the population is 100, then a reliable sample size might have to be 30 to 60 percent of the total. On the other hand, the Gallup and Roper polls both do very reliable research work using a sample of less than 1900, or less than 0.00088 percent of the national population.

Allowable Error

No experiment or research effort is totally free from error. No research sponsor should expect error-free research data. It is far more responsible to specify the degree of allowable error. How much this should be is a function of the type of research undertaken. If we are examining certain phenomena in the physical sciences, we normally demand a very small degree of allowable error, perhaps less than one-tenth of one percent. On the other hand, research work in the social sciences must tolerate considerable error, perhaps as much as 5 to 10 percent, or 20 percent in some difficult situations. One equation computes the standard error of a percentage as:

$$S = \sqrt{\frac{PQ}{N}}$$

where P = percentage (45% = .45) Q = 1 − P, and
N is the population.

Level of Confidence

As a particular subject of research moves away from the mean of the population or the sample, the amount of error increases. That is, if we are studying the relationship between level of education and income, we will compute a mean educational and income level from the sample data. An individual whose education is near the educational mean will normally have an income level not too far from the income mean. We say the error, the difference between the actual data and the forecast or mean is small. On the other hand, the difference between the income of a person at one extreme of the educational spectrum or the other and the mean income for all those at that educational level will be greater. So, we usually combine allowable error and level of confidence into one expression and say that we will accept the data as being valid if it applies to 95 percent of the population (or 99 percent, or whatever) within 1 (or 5) percent error. For example, a political survey of 100 people indicates that 57.63 percent of the sample prefer candidate Able over candidate Baker. When we report this finding to the media and our client, what we really are saying is that 95 percent of the population prefer candidate Able by 57.63 percent, plus or minus 5 percent. What the remaining 5 percent of the population choose to do is not forecast. Given these data and a population of one million voters, the outcome could range from 499,999 ((.5763 − .05) × 950000) to 644,998 ((((.5763 + .05) × 950000) + (.05 × 1000000)) votes for Able. In this fashion, an electorial defeat could occur despite a positive forecast, although, given these data, this is not likely. By increasing the sample size to 200, the sample error drops to 3.5 percent, thus (if the basic percentage for Able remains at 57.634) the expectation ranges from 514,249 to 630,748—a sure win!

Sampling Procedure

There are several techniques for drawing a sample from a population: simple random selection, stratified samples, and cluster samples, to mention three. Each approach has an effect on the desirable sample size.

Simple Random Selection. In this process the sample is drawn or selected from the general population at random. If you throw a dart at a page selected at random from the telephone directory and dial the number closest to the embedded point of the dart, you are selecting the sample randomly. Each member of the population has an equal probability of selection. To implement this approach on a more rational basis than dart throwing, however, is rather tedious and generally requires identifying each memory of the population with some sort of an identification number and then generating as many random numbers as required for an adequate sample size. We then interview each member of the population whose identification number matches one on the list of random numbers. Listing 9-3 is a simple program that generates random telephone numbers that can be used as identification numbers.

Listing 9-3. Telephone Selector

```
1  ′***********************************************
2  ′TELEPHONE SELECTOR                            *
3  ′LISTING 9-3                                   *
4  ′***********************************************
```

```
5 '
10 CLS:RANDOM
20 PRINT"THIS ROUTINE GENERATES A RANDOM SET OF
       TELEPHONE NUMBERS
AT RANDOM, WITH REPLACEMENT.  IF A SET WITHOUT R
       EPLACEMENT IS
DESIRED, INSERT CHECKING LOOP BETWEEN LINES 130
       AND 140":PRINT
30 INPUT"ENTER NUMBER OF TELEPHONE EXCHANGES TO
       BE SURVEYED";TE
40 DIM E$(TE)
50 FORI=1 TO TE
60    PRINT"ENTER THE THREE DIGIT EXCHANGE # ";I,
       :INPUTE$(I)
70 NEXTI
80 INPUT"HOW MANY NUMBERS ARE TO BE GENERATED";N

90 FORI=1 TO N
100    A=RND(TE):A$=E$(A)+" -"
110    FORJ=1 TO 4
120       B=RND(9):A$=A$+STR$(B)
130    NEXTJ
135    'ENTER LOOP TO CHECK FOR DUPLICATE NUMBERS
       HERE.
140    PRINT A$,:LPRINTA$,
150 NEXT
160 END
```

Cluster Samples. This procedure simplifies the task a bit. By some definable process, we group people into manageable-size clusters and then select clusters randomly and interview everyone in that cluster.

Stratified Samples. This method is often used in an effort to ensure that the sample resembles the population in terms of various demographic characteristics: sex, race, age, occupation, and so forth. Each characteristic adds another dimension to the sample matrix. For example, with the four categories above, we might have a matrix to fill that has two sexes times three basic racial groups times eighty age categories times x number of possible occupation groups. Each cell need not be filled (we suspect there will be few 2-year old bank directors) except to the same proportion as in the general population.

The stratified sample, properly constructed, requires the smallest sample size for a given allowable error and level of confidence. Cluster samples, on the other hand, usually require a larger sample than either the stratified or simple random sample.

As a practical matter, however, the cluster sample approach is often selected as the most feasible and cost-effective approach.

Computation of Sample Size

Listing 9-4 offers an extensive routine for computing a variety of statistics related to sample size. Underlying this program is the assumption that, in terms of the research characteristics, the population is normally distributed. If this is true, 95 percent of the population will lie within 1.9208 standard deviations from the mean, 98 percent within 2.71445 standard deviations, and 99 percent within 3.3282 standard deviations. These values are referred to in the program by the variable Z. The portion of the population to which the data are to apply (level of confidence) is P (95% = .95). The allowable error is E (1% = .01). We compute: Q = 1 − P. The minimum sample size is estimated from

$$S = (Z \, P \, Q) / E^2$$

To compute the minimum sample size to be applicable to 95 percent (Z = 3.8416 and P = .95, Q = .05) of the population with an error of plus or minus 2 percent (E = .02), we compute

$$S = (3.8416 \times .95 \times .05)/ (.02^2)$$
$$= .182476 / .0004$$

$$= 456.19$$

Therefore, we should sample at least 457 subjects in order to reach the level of confidence stated. The balance of the equations in the program are built around this basic relationship.

Listing 9-4. Sample Size

```
1    '*********************************************
2    'SAMPLE SIZE                                 *
3    'LISTING 9-4                                 *
4    '*********************************************
5    '
10   CLS:PRINTCHR$(210);"SAMPLE SIZE":PRINT:PRINT
20   Z(1)=3.8416:Z(2)=5.4289:Z(3)=6.6564
30   INPUT"ENTER POPULATION SIZE";PS
40   PRINT"OUTPUT TO PRINTER?   (Y/N)":PRINT
50   Q$=""+INKEY$:IFQ$=""THEN50    ELSEIFQ$="Y"THEN
        LP=1ELSELP=0
60   P=.5:Q=.5
70   PRINT:INPUT"WHAT IS THE ALLOWABLE PER CENT OF
        ERROR (5%=5)";E:E=E/100
80   PRINT:PRINT"",""        DEGREE OF CONFIDENCE":PR
        INT"","95 %","98 %","99 %":PRINT:PRINT"NUMB
        ER",
90   FORI=1TO3
100     SS(I)=INT((Z(I)*.25)/(E[2))+1:IFSS(I)>PSTH
        ENSS(I)=PS
110     PRINTSS(I),
120  NEXT
130  PRINT:PRINT"PER CENT",
140  FORI=1TO3:PRINT100*(SS(I)/PS),:NEXTI:PRINT
150  GOTO240
160  FORR=0TO14
170     FORC=0TO63
180        L=PEEK(15360+(R*64)+C):IFL<32THENL=L+64
190        LPRINTCHR$(L);
200     NEXTC
210     LPRINT""
220  NEXT
230  LPRINT"":RETURN
240  PRINT:INPUT"DESIRED SAMPLE SIZE";DS
250  PRINT:PRINT"","    DEGREE OF CONFIDENCE"
260  PRINT"","95 %","98 %","99 %":PRINT:PRINT"% E
        RROR",
270  FORI=1TO3
280     B=SQR((Z(I)*.25)/DS):PRINT100*B,
290  NEXTI
300  PRINT:IFLP=1THENGOSUB160
310  IFB>ETHEN330
320  PRINT:PRINT"SAMPLE SIZE IS ADEQUATE":PRINT:G
        OTO370
330  PRINT:PRINT"THE SAMPLE SIZE OF";DS;"IS INADE
        QUATE IN TERMS
```

```
      YOU'VE SPECIFIED.    TO STAY WITHIN THE LIMITS YO
          U'VE CITED,
      THE SAMPLE SIZE MUST BE AT LEAST ";(Z(1)*.25)/(E
          [2];", OTHERWISE
      THE DEGREE OF CONFIDENCE WILL ONLY BE ";
  340 Z=SQR((DS*(E[2])/(P*Q))
  350 FX=.398942*(2.71828[-((Z[2])/2)):T=1/(1+(.231
          64*Z)):QX=FX*((.319382*T)+(-.356564*(T[2]))+
          (1.781478*(T[3]))+(-1.821256*(T[4]))+(1.33027
          4*(T[5])))+7.5E-8:PRINT100*(1-(2*QX));" %"
  360 PRINT:RUN30
  370 PRINT:PRINT"THIS SECTION WILL ASSIST YOU IN
          THE SELECTION OF";DS;"SURVEY SUBJECTS.    YOU
          HAVE THE CHOICE OF:

                    1    ---    SAMPLE WITH REPLACEMENT
                    2    ---    SAMPLE WITHOUT REPLACEME
          NT

      PLEASE SELECT    ";
  380 Q$=""+INKEY$:IFQ$=""THEN380
  390 PRINT:PRINT"SURVEY THE FOLLOWING MEMBERS OF
          THE POPULATION:":PRINT
  400 LPRINT"SURVEY THE FOLLOWING MEMBERS OF THE P
          OPULATION:":LPRINT""
  410 ONVAL(Q$)GOTO420  ,520
  420 PRINT"SAMPLING WITH REPLACEMENT":LPRINT"SAMP
          LING WITH REPLACEMENT":LPRINT""
  430 IFPS>32767THEN480
  440 FORI=1TODS
  450    S=RND(PS):PRINTI;S,:LPRINTI;S,
  460 NEXT
  470 RUN30
  480 FORI=1TODS
  490    S=INT(RND(0)*PS):PRINTI;S,:LPRINTI;S,
  500 NEXT
  510 RUN30
  520 PRINT"SAMPLING WITHOUT REPLACEMENT":LPRINT"S
          AMPLING WITHOUT REPLACEMENT":LPRINT""
  530 DIM S(DS)
  540 FORI=1TODS
  550    S=RND(PS)
  560    FORJ=0TOK
  570      IFS(J)=STHEN550
  580    NEXT
  590    S(J)=S:K=J:PRINTI;S,:LPRINTI;S,
  600 NEXTI
  610 RUN30
  620 FORI=1TODS
  630    S=INT(RND(0)*PS)
  640    FORJ=0TOK
  650      IFS(J)=STHEN630
  660    NEXT
  670    S(J)=S:K=J:PRINTI;S,:LPRINTI;S,
  680 NEXTI
  690 RUN30
```

Before we leave the enchanted land of samples, we offer the following footnote concerning the probability of having no repetitions in a sample. If a sample of n items is taken from a population of m objects, the probability (P) of finding an object in the sample that meets a particular criterion is P = 1 / m. The probability (Q) of finding two or more items in the sample which meet the criterion is given in:

$$Q = 1 - ((1 - \frac{1}{m})(1 - \frac{2}{m}) \ldots (1 - \frac{n-1}{m}))$$

The common illustration of this routine is that of computing the probability of two or more people at a party sharing the same birthday. In this example, m is the number of days in the year and the sample size, n, is the number of people at the party. Without further illustration, we note that if n = 48, P = .96. A lot of wagers have been won on this equation and its implications.

(The normal form of the equation is for the value P, which is the complement of Q: P = 1 − Q. We offer the present form because Q is more often the value of common interest.)

Listing 9-5. Probability No Repetitions in a Sample

```
1   '*** '******************************************
2   'PROBABILITY NO REPETITIONS IN A SAMPLE    *
3   'LISTING 9-5                               *
4   '*********************************************
5   '
10  CLS:PRINT@512,"     * * * PROBABILITY OF NO R
    EPETITIONS IN A SAMPLE * * *":FOR I=1TO500:
    NEXTI
20  CLS
30  PRINT@128," ":INPUT"ENTER THE SIZE OF THE ENT
    IRE POPULATION TO BE EVALUATED:";M
40  PRINT:INPUT"ENTER THE SAMPLE SIZE:";N
50  CLS:PRINT@128,"IF THERE IS ONE ELEMENT OF THI
    S POPULATION OF";M;"ITEMS
THAT SATISFIES YOUR CRITERION, YOU HAVE A PROBAB
    ILITY
OF";1/M;"OF FINDING IT ON ANY ONE TRY."
60  P=1
70  FOR A=1 TO N-1
80      P=P*(1-(A/M))
90      IFN<50THEN110
100     PRINT@640,"STILL WORKING. PLEASE BE PATIE
    NT.";
110 NEXT A
120 PRINT@512,"OUT OF A POPULATION OF";M;"ITEMS,
        THE PROBABILITY
THAT THERE WILL BE TWO OR MORE ELEMENTS THAT WIL
    L
FIT YOUR CRITERION IS =";1-P
130 PRINT:PRINT"(PROBABILITY OF NO REPITIONS IN
    SAMPLE =";P;")"
140 PRINT:PRINT:INPUT"DO YOU WANT TO TRY ANOTHER
    (Y OR N)";Q$
150 IF Q$="Y"THEN10    ELSE160
160 CLS:PRINT@512,"THANK YOU !!!"
170 FOR I=0TO500:NEXTI
180 END
```

THE SURVEY QUESTIONNAIRE

A congressional personality appeared on national television recently and was asked his opinion concerning an opinion survey showing a lack of support for a program with which he was associated. The Congressman's response was to the effect that, given control of the writing of the questionnaire, he could guarantee any desired outcome of a survey. An artful evasion indeed, but not without some validity.

We assume your interest in this subject is honest and straightforward. Your objective is to obtain unbiased and comprehensive information with regard to a given subject. We also assume you are primarily interested in quantitative research instead of anecdotal inquiry. Considerable valid research has been conducted using the case study method or an anecdotal approach in which essential elements of a subject are elicited in a conversational manner, but the results are generally unsuitable for statistical analysis. Microcomputers can assist in anecdotal research by keeping track of the archival data related to the study (names, dates, addresses, and phone numbers of interviewees, location of reference documents, etc.), and by performing text evaluation studies. That is, a verbatim transcript of a interview can be statistically evaluated by a microcomputer to identify particular word selections, speech patterns, and similar data. Nonetheless, this book will limit the applications to quantifiable research. This limitation will make the questionnaire preparation process a lot easier.

The first "rule" of questionnaire design, then, is to include only those questions the answers to which can be quantified, that is, turned into some sort of a number. We can have three kinds of numbers: scalar values, dichotomous values, and demographic values.

Scalar Values. We use scalar values to measure things: attitudes, social values or rankings, income, educational levels, and so forth. Chapter 2 contains a comprehensive review of the different sorts of scales we use to measure attitudes, tell time, weigh fish, or count automobiles. It is in this process of survey design that such distinctions are critical. The questionnaire writer must pay scrupulous attention to the advantages and shortfalls of each of the types of scalar data. Of particular concern are attitudinal type questions: "On a scale from 1 to 10...." In such cases there is a strong temptation to subject the responses to rigorous statistical analysis in an effort to summarize the study by saying: "The mean response was 4.988856 or slightly below "no opinion" with a standard deviation of 1.02345." Unfortunately, ordinal scale data cannot rationally be subjected to this level of analysis. It is acceptable to determine the median response to a given item using an ordinal scale. It is also acceptable to compare median responses to the same item over a period of time. This is frequently done in national newspaper political polls attempting to determine how the citizens feel about the candidates for president or how well the incumbent president is performing. Although much is made of a percentage point shift up or down, it is really more fair simply to note a shift has taken place.

Dichotomous Values. Questions that seek yes/no, true/false, male/female, accept/reject type answers are seeking dichotomous responses. We can use the results to divide the population into proportionate quantities: X% are for candidate Y (therefore, $(100 - X)$% are either neutral or against), A% are females and $100 - A$% are either males or transsexuals. The standard error of the results of a survey can be computed from this kind of a proportion. The basic equation is

$$S = \sqrt{\frac{P\,Q}{n}}\,\%$$

Notice that as the value of P moves toward either extreme, the value of the standard error gets much smaller. For example, if a political poll of 1000 people reveals a 49-51% split on an issue. The standard error in this instance is $= +/- 1.58082$%. This means the actual division of public opinion could reasonably fall anywhere between 47.41918 to 50.58082% against, and 49.41618 to 52.58082%. On the other hand, if the same 1000 people are surveyed later and found to be split 36-64 on an issue, the standard error is computed to be 1.51789%. The actual split is estimated to be from

34.48211 to 37.51789% against, and 61.48211 to 65.51789% for.

As with ordinal data, there are strict limits on the kinds of mathematical manipulations to which you can subject dichotomous data. It is not acceptable to compute the mean, median, or standard deviation of such data. What is relevant is the proportion computed.

Demographic Values. These include a number of quantities related to the natural characteristics of the people in the survey. Age, height, weight, sex, educational level, number (population), and so forth. While sex, male or female is a dichotomous variable, the remaining values are generally adequate for detailed statistical computations of mean, standard deviation, median, mode, distribution analysis, percentages, percentiles, etc. It is entirely acceptable to compute correlations between these types of demographic data and the dichotomous data obtained in true/false, accept/reject type of questions by using the Point-Biserial correlation tests discussed in Chapter 5.

Length of Questionnaire

The questionnaire must be long enough to obtain the essential answers concerning the main objective of the survey. It shouldn't be longer than necessary to collect relevant data. If it's too short, the survey is pointless. If it's too long the subject will become annoyed and the quality of answers will suffer. Just how long is too long depends a lot on the setting for the interview. The longest interviews are usually most successfully completed in the subject's home with an in-person interview. They are even more successful if the interview is of interest to the subject or one in which the subject perceives some personal gain or reward for participation.

At the other extreme are surveys conducted in shopping malls or other public areas. In these settings there are frequently a large number of potential respondents, especially if the survey is a marketing survey. The trouble is that most of these people are going somewhere and have little time to answer a questionnaire. Often, it's easier to plot a course around the interviewer or simply ignore their request for time. What is the significance on the outcome of such research when a portion of the crowd can avoid the interview?

Telephone surveys are somewhere in between the interview on the street and the interview in the home. Because the subject is at home, a longer questionnaire can be used, but the impersonality of the telephone limits that benefit and permits the subject to hang up at any time. Telephone surveys also tend to eliminate from the sample the poor and the transient. To the extent the survey can afford to let this portion of the population pass unsampled, there is little problem.

Questionnaire Completion

Unless mandated by circumstances, the interviewer should complete the survey form. This is done for several reasons. First, many of the answers may require special coding. Second, the data should be in a consistent form. Third, the interviewer will provide some measure of subjective validation. Only in the most extreme cases should the survey be mailed to the respondents. In a blind survey, wherein the respondents are chosen at random, the response is likely to be quite poor, 5-7 percent at best. On the other hand, in the worst case, 20 percent of those called in telephone surveys respond, and 80 percent in the house-to-house survey respond.

DATA ANALYSIS

Given the task of data analysis, you should select those techniques which are:

— Logically related to the desired output.
— Precise enough to satisfy program objectives.
— Simple enough to be completed with available resources.
— Short enough to be completed within the specified schedule.
— Inexpensive enough to fit within the project budget.

Analysis techniques will vary with the data to be analyzed. That is, demographic data are suitable for one set of techniques, while subjective attitude study data are suitable for another.

Demographic Analysis

A frequent component of a research report is a description of the sample in fairly straightforward, quantifiable terms such as age, sex, race, height, weight, economic status, and educational level. It is frequently useful to compare these data with the corresponding data for the general population. Normally, the more the sample demographic data resemble those of the general population the more ready we are to accept the attitudes of the sample as representative of those of the general population.

Researchers often don't know what parameters of the general population are. That is, we can note in our research report that the mean age of the respondent was 42.45 years. How this compares to the population at large depends on the nature of that population. If we are referring to the national population, we are really just comparing the mean from one sample of the population to another. We really don't know exactly how many people there are in the country, nor, therefore, do we know exactly how old we all are, so we can't compute a true mean national age. Instead, we estimate it from various census activities. On the other hand, if the sample is from a small college enrollment, it may be possible to make a more precise comparison. Listing 9-6 is a general purpose routine meant to illustrate an approach to evaluating demographic data. It does require that the user has available not only the sample demographic data but also the corresponding population data, whether actual or estimated.

Listing 9-6. Demographic Analysis

```
1  '***********************************************
2  'DEMOGRAPHIC ANALYSIS                          *
3  'LISTING 9-6                                   *
4  '***********************************************
5  '
10 CLEAR2500:@CLEAR
20 CLS:PRINT"DEMOGRAPHIC ANALYSIS":
30 PRINT:PRINT"ENTER VALUES IN NEAREST INTEGER V
      ALUE.  FOR DICHOTOMOUS VALUES
ASSIGN ONE ASPECT '1' AND THE OTHER, '0'.  FOR M
      EAN VALUE,
ENTER 'D'":PRINT:PRINT
40 INPUT"ENTER NUMBER OF SUBJECTS IN SAMPLE";NS
50 INPUT"NUMBER OF PEOPLE IN GENERAL POPULATION"
      ;NP
60 INPUT"ENTER NUMBER OF DEMOGRAPHIC CHARACTERIS
      TICS";C
70 DIM QC(C),C$(C),D$(NS,C),PM$(C):CLS
80 FORI=1 TO C:PRINT"NAME OF CHARACTERISTIC #";I
      ,:INPUTC$(I):INPUT"POPULATION MEAN FOR THIS
      VALUE";PM$(I):NEXT:CLS
90 FORI=1 TO NS
100   PRINT"SUBJECT #";I
110   FORJ=1 TO C
120     PRINT"",C$(J)
130     INPUT"ENTER SPECIFIC VALUE";D$(I,J):
140   NEXTJ
150 NEXTI
160 PRINT:PRINT:PRINT"(R)EVIEW ALL INPUT DATA  (
      C)ORRECT SELECTED DATA  (E)ND INPUT";
170 Q$=""+INKEY$:IFQ$=""THEN170
180 IFQ$="E"THEN300  ELSEIFQ$="C"THEN290
190 FORI=1 TO NS
```

175

Listing 9-6. Demographic Analysis (continued from page 175)

```
200    CLS:PRINTI;
210    FORJ=1 TO C
220      PRINTC$(J);"   ";D$(I,J),
230    NEXTJ
240    PRINT:PRINT"ALL OK?  (Y/N)";
250    Z$=""+INKEY$:IFZ$=""THEN250
260    IFZ$="Y"THEN280
270      INPUT"ENTER NUMBER OF ITEM TO BE CHANGED,
         AND CORRECT VALUE";X,D$(1,X):GOTO200
280  NEXTI
290  PRINT:INPUT"ENTER SUBJECT NUMBER, ITEM NUMBE
       R, AND CORRECT VALUE";X;Y;D$(X,Y):GOTO160

300  @OPEN2
310  @PRINT NS,C
320  FORI=1 TO NS
330    FORJ=1 TO C
340      @PRINTD$(1,J)
350    NEXTJ
360  NEXTI
370  @CLOSE
380  CLS:PRINT"PRELIMINARY ASSESSMENT.  NOW COMPU
       TING.":PRINT:PRINT
390  FORI=1 TO C
400    PRINTC$(I),:LG=0
410    FORJ=1 TO NS
420      D=VAL(D$(J,I)):IFD<LGTHEN440
430      LG=D
440    NEXTJ
450    FORJ=1 TO LG
460      FORK=1 TO NS
470        D=VAL(D$(K,I))
480        IFD<>JTHEN500
490        JJ=JJ+1:PRINT@144+(64*R),JJ,JJ/NS;
500      NEXTK
510    NEXTJ
520    JJ=0:R=R+1
530    PRINT@960,"(C)ONTINUE   (P)RINT";
540    Q$=""+INKEY$:IFQ$=""THEN540
550    IFQ$="C"THEN620
560    FORW=0 TO R+2
570      FORL=0TO63
580        A=PEEK(15360+(W*64)+L)
590        LPRINTCHR$(A);
600      NEXTL
610    NEXTW
620  NEXTI
```

Evaluating Subjective Data

Due to the slippery nature of attitude scales and the variations within these kinds of scales, it is difficult at best and often ill-advised to attempt the mathematical evaluations of such scalar data to compute means and standard deviations. What does have greater meaning and utility is to make comparisons between people with identifiable demographic differences or to make comparisons of the differences in attitudes among the same group of people over a period of time. Listing 9-7 facilitates this sort of processing. As with the program in

Listing 9-6, it is more illustrative than utilitarian. It works well with the data we contrived for the purpose of demonstrating the program, but probably should be modified to suit your own program requirements better.

CASE STUDY: WHAT MIGHT HAVE BEEN

During the campaign for the 1980 primary elections in a southwestern state, one of the candidates, a popular favorite, suffered a back injury in an

Listing 9-7. Attitude Analysis

```
********************************************
2 'ATTITUDE ANALYSIS                        *
3 'LISTING 9-7                              *
4 '******************************************
5 '
10 CLEAR2500:@CLEAR
20 CLS:PRINT"ATTITUDE ANALYSIS":PRINT
30 INPUT"ENTER NUMBER OF SUBJECTS IN SAMPLE";NS
40 INPUT"ENTER NUMBER OF ITEMS IN SURVEY";S
50 DIM V$(NS,S):CLS
60 FORI=1 TO NS
70    PRINT"SUBJECT #";I
80    FORJ=1 TO S
90      PRINT"ENTER RESPONSE TO ITEM #";J,:INPUT
      V$(I,J)
100   NEXTJ
110 NEXTI
120 PRINT:PRINT:PRINT"(R)EVIEW ALL INPUT DATA   (
      C)ORRECT SELECTED DATA  (E)ND INPUT";
130 Q$=""+INKEY$:IFQ$=""THEN130
140 IFQ$="E"THEN260   ELSEIFQ$="C"THEN250
150 FORI=1 TO NS
160   CLS:PRINTI;
170   FORJ=1 TO S
180     PRINTJ;V$(I,J),
190   NEXTJ
200   PRINT:PRINT"ALL OK?   (Y/N)";
210   Z$=""+INKEY$:IFZ$=""THEN210
220   IFZ$="Y"THEN240
230   INPUT"ENTER NUMBER OF ITEM TO BE CHANGED,
      AND CORRECT VALUE";X,V$(I,X):GOTO160
240 NEXTI
250 PRINT:INPUT"ENTER SUBJECT NUMBER, ITEM NUMBE
      R, AND CORRECT VALUE";X;Y;V$(X,Y):GOTO120
260 @OPEN2
270 @PRINT NS,S
280 FORI=1 TO NS
290   FORJ=1 TO S
300     @PRINTV$(I,J)
310   NEXTJ
320 NEXTI
330 @CLOSE
340 INPUT"LARGEST NUMBER OF OPTIONS";N:DIM A$(S,
      N),A(S,N)
350 FORI=1 TO S:FORJ=1 TO N:A$(I,J)=STR$(J):NEXT
      J:NEXTI
360 CLS:PRINT"PRELIMINARY ASSESSMENT.  NOW COMPU
      TING.":PRINT:PRINT
```

Listing 9-7. Attitude Analysis (continued from page 177)

```
370 FORI=1 TO NS
380    FORJ=1 TO S
390       V=VAL(U$(I,J)):A(J,U)=A(J,U)+1
400    NEXTJ
410 NEXTI
420 CLS
430 PRINT"ITEM","OPTION","NUMBER","PER CENT"
440 FORI=1 TO S
450    PRINTI,
460    FORJ=1TO N
470    . PRINTJ,A(I,J),100*(A(I,J)/N)
480    NEXT
490    PRINT:PRINT"(C)ONTINUE   (P)RINT";
500    Q$=""+INKEY$:IFQ$=""THEN500
510    IFQ$="C"THEN550
520    LPRINT"ITEM # ";I
530    FORJ=1TON:LPRINTJ,A(I,J),100*(A(I,J)/N):NE
    XTJ
540    LPRINT""
550 NEXTI
```

automobile accident. One of the consequences of the injury was that it made it impossible for the candidate to walk through each of the precincts to personally meet with residents at their homes. In past elections this technique had been perceived as vital to establishing an effective rapport with the voters. The candidate, a woman, felt it essential to meet the voters on a personal level to overcome chauvinist attitudes in several ethnic neighborhoods in which being male, in the absence of any other influence, was considered an asset. Her personality was such that personal contact with the voters was normally sufficient to offset this attitude. Although she won the election on the basis of votes registered in the polls, she lost the total vote with the addition of the absentee vote. After reviewing the election returns, she was convinced that her inability to walk through a good portion of the precincts made the difference between winning and losing the election. That is, she and her staff believed that if she had been able to walk through the precincts, enough additional votes could have been collected to offset the impact of the absentee vote. A lawsuit was initiated against the driver of the other car involved in the accident for damages and lost potential income on this basis. To support the lawsuit, we were retained by her legal counsel to perform a statistical analysis of the election results to determine if there was any quantitative basis to the action. What follows is an abridged version of the report to the attorney. Although names have been changed at the request of those involved, the numerical data is exactly as it was provided and analyzed. While we would have preferred to see the candidate win the lawsuit, we had to approach the study from strictly objective perspective. We anticipated that the defense counsel would retain a statistician to evaluate any work we submitted and that any effort to slant the data in favor of our client would have been detected and the whole work, rightly or wrongly, discredited. Accordingly, in each test that suggested support for our client, we devised a counter-test to at least challenge the first finding.

Abstract

Election results from the 39 precincts which constitute Area H in the State Legislature are statistically reviewed and evaluated. One candidate, Mary Smith, was forced to withdraw from active compaigning after making personal appearances in 12 precincts due to injuries received in an automobile accident. Analysis reveals the vote for Smith to be significantly higher in those precincts where she made personal appearances than in those where she did not. The data suggest and support the notion that had Smith been able to appear in all of the precincts the vote in her favor would have been as much as 5000 to 7000 votes greater.

Summary

This study reviews the election results in the legislative district from the 1980 General Election. In particular, we review those results related to the race between the candidates for the House seat, Smith (D) and Jones (R). The results are especially interesting in that those voting at the polls clearly preferred Smith over Jones (21313 to 19236) by a margin of 2077 votes. When the absentee ballots are counted, however, the outcome swings to favor Jones (25807 to 24674) by 1133 votes. A change in 567 votes would have altered the outcome of this race. These data are shown in Table 9-2.

It is interesting to note that early in the campaign, Smith was seriously injured in an automobile accident and, as a consequence, was unable to make personal appearances in nearly two-thirds of the precincts. It is even more interesting to note that in those precincts where Smith had made an appearance, walking door-to-door, the average vote in her favor (56.0714%) was 5.940% higher than in the precincts where she didn't walk (50.1315%). We believe the data support two hypotheses:

A — The absentee vote results reflect the overall political mood of the country in general at the time of the election, and the partisan attitudes of the electorate in the county without particular regard for Jones specifically.

B — A personal appearance in a given precinct by Smith was likely to result in a more favorable walk-in vote for her at the polls.

The implications of these findings are significant: it is not unreasonable to conclude that had Smith been able to appear in all of the precincts, then, providing the remaining precincts voted as the first twelve did, the result would have been a win for Smith, not Jones. Applying the percentages, 56.0714 percent of the 40549 walk-in votes cast is 22736 votes, while Jones' share would have been 17813. Adding the absentee votes (without modifi-

cation) the final tally would have been: Smith 26097, Jones 24384—Smith by a margin of 1713 votes. An even finer estimate of voter behavior will be illustrated later in this paper in which a linear regression estimate is computed based on the number of registered voters in a given precinct. In this particular estimate the outcome would have been: Smith 28842, Jones 21376—Smith by 7466 votes. These are the outcomes clearly suggested by the data. The relevant question is whether it is statistically appropriate and rationally supported to apply these pragmatic observations against the available data to come to the conclusions noted above. It is the purpose of this paper, then, to examine this question and display the results. As we believe the following tests will show, the data support the conclusions that a personal appearance by Smith in a precinct resulted in a favorable vote and, had she been able to appear in all precincts, she would have won the election by a greater margin than that by which she lost.

The Data

Table 9-2 is a simple tabulation of the election results in the area in the 1980 General Election. Column 11 indicates whether or not Smith made a personal appearance in the indicated precinct. Table 9-3 summarizes the data from Table 9-2. These constitute the entire body of data evaluated in this study. The numbers are derived directly from official election reports and records.

The Analysis

Given the data on Tables 9-2 and 9-3, the project was divided into two phases. Phase 1 consisted of discovering what the data contained. Phase 2 consisted of determining whether any one or more of the findings was, in statistical terms, significant. That is, does it mean anything?

Summary of Phase 1. Table 9-3 is the first product of this phase. It clearly shows that Smith won the majority of the walk-in votes, 21313 to 19236. Although she lost the combined absentee votes, it is interesting to note the very slight margin of her loss on the split ticket absentee ballot count, 2188 to 2293. The probability that the 105 vote

Table 9-2. Regional Voting Results (1980 General Election).

	Precinct	Number Registered Voters	Number Voting	Straight Republican Votes	Straight Democrat Votes	For Jones	For Smith	Total Votes	For Reagan	For Carter	Walked
1	114	1972	940	--	--	61	783	844	111	799	Yes
2	117	2011	1101	--	--	102	892	994	174	888	Yes
3	136	1343	811	--	--	305	457	762	431	342	No
4	215	1933	935	33	636	91	799	890	119	761	No
5	227	1693	952	76	378	201	727	928	283	637	Yes
6	228	2373	1253	269	157	657	535	1729	753	392	No
7	233	2854	1585	349	133	865	654	1519	1085	375	No
8	234	2964	1749	409	178	978	715	1693	1175	456	No
9	235	647	431	78	35	213	195	408	273	123	No
10	237	2600	1732	422	171	944	735	1679	1120	479	No
11	238	1094	632	196	60	384	231	615	434	152	Yes
12	239	1909	1118	279	176	615	456	1071	687	347	No
13	240	873	558	130	55	313	230	543	381	142	Yes
14	241	2886	1959	558	144	1128	751	1879	1343	472	Yes
15	242	3130	1909	342	341	730	1126	1856	1135	671	Yes
16	243	2483	1501	229	334	533	926	1459	813	624	No
17	247	1034	644	215	67	396	211	607	470	143	No
18	249	1571	755	38	372	90	598	688	136	565	No
19	250	1573	896	127	230	287	594	881	489	407	No
20	251	1801	1084	152	236	353	698	1051	566	440	Yes
21	252	70	42	7	4	15	23	38	22	16	No
22	253	132	71	23	5	49	19	68	50	16	No
23	254	2694	1590	343	157	896	626	1522	1030	446	No
24	255	1710	1111	237	91	688	400	1088	784	269	No
25	260	2166	1212	144	354	382	770	1152	493	639	No
26	263	915	452	109	65	261	163	424	310	122	No
27	264	2383	1360	326	94	806	483	1289	956	316	Yes
28	265	1400	824	165	150	410	391	801	479	288	No
29	266	1678	964	238	116	530	388	918	621	260	No
30	267	890	549	116	72	278	239	517	322	191	No
31	268	2113	1289	268	159	734	524	1258	834	389	No
32	269	2921	1873	375	285	838	964	1802	1155	622	Yes
33	270	1902	973	31	615	822	65	887	106	797	No
34	273	1572	917	112	246	295	577	872	426	446	No
35	274	4324	2556	506	309	1324	1141	2465	1618	768	Yes
36	275	1534	937	118	349	263	645	908	408	466	Yes
37	334	2673	1409	500	82	984	385	1369	1124	225	No
38	352/370	2003	1299	379	50	877	361	1238	1013	228	No
39	382	618	410	--	--	295	97	392	321	69	No
Absentee	--	n/a	9932	4278	1173	6571	3361	9932	6571	3361	n/a
Totals 39	Prec.	72442	52324	12177	8079	25807	24674	50481	30621	19149	12 Precincts

180

Table 9-3. Detailed Analysis of Voting Results.

		Smith			Jones			Line Total
	Straight	Split	Total	Straight	Split	Total	
Actual Vote								
Absentee	1173	2188	3361	4278	2293	6571	9932
Walk-in	6906	14407	21313	7899	11337	19236	40549
Total	8079	16595	24674	12177	13630	25807	50481
Percent of Total Vote								
Absentee	2.324%	4.334%	6.658%	8.474%	4.542%	13.017%	19.675%
Walk-in	13.680	28.539	42.220	15.647	22.458	38.105	80.325
Total	16.004	32.874	48.878	24.122	27.000	51.122	100.000
Percent of Total Personal Vote								
Absentee	4.754%	8.868%	13.622%	16.577%	8.885%	25.462%	19.675%
Walk-in	27.989	58.389	86.378	30.608	43.930	74.538	80.325
Total	32.743	67.257	100.000	47.185	52.815	100.000	100.000

difference means anything other than chance variation is very slight. On the other hand, note the large difference between the absentee results on the straight ticket votes, 1173 to 4278. Since this was a general election where a first-term incumbent president was voted out of office, we believe it more likely that the straight ticket vote Jones received was much more an expression for Reagan (or against Carter) than a vote against Smith in favor of Jones. A large number of the absentee voters are governmental employees assigned out of the country. That a significant number of these voters would be following the particulars of the local aspects of the political campaign is very unlikely. Without submitting the data to rigorous test and examination (since this matter is not the issue in question), we would like the reader to share our perception that the absentee vote is really a reflection of the outcome of the national election issues and not significantly related to the campaigning efforts of either Smith or Jones. Rather, we propose that if Smith had been able to properly campaign in the area, she would have won the election on walk-in votes in spite of the absentee ballot; she would have influenced and obtained the support of at least 567 additional votes out of the 50481 cast for the local candidates.

Estimating Potential Votes. We begin with the assumption that if Smith had walked all of the 39 precincts as she did twelve, she would have received a larger share of the vote. How much larger? The simplest estimate is obtained by applying her advantage in the twelve precincts against the total vote. 40549 votes were cast in the local race. In the twelve walked precincts Smith's percentage was 56.0714%. This equates to 22736 votes for Smith and 17813 for Jones. Even if the absentee ballots are added in, the outcome is Smith 26097 and Jones 24384. At this point a series of curve-fitting computer routines were applied to the data. This is a statistical effort to define the elements of standard curve equations that provide an estimate of the vote based on some variable. We found the highest correlation or "goodness of fit" when the actual votes were compared with the number of registered voters in a given precinct. The four major curves used in this type of analysis are: linear, exponential, logarithmic, and power.

Tables 9-4 to 9-7 summarize the results of the data being processed against various dependent and

Table 9-4. Curve Fitting, Number of Registered Voters Versus Number of Votes for Smith.

Input

X	Y	X	Y	X	Y	X	Y
1972	763	2011	892	1693	727	2854	654
1909	456	2886	751	3130	1126	1801	698
2383	483	2921	964	4324	1141	1534	645

Output

	A	B	R	t-Test	Equations
Linear	324.087	.183934	.670688	2.85936	Y = A + BX
Exponential	437.199	2.1812E-04	.604895	2.40215	Y = EXP(LOG A + BK)
Logarithmic	−2762.12	455.844	.636209	2.60768	Y = A + B LOG X
Power	11.3396	.539572	.572739	2.20944	Y = EXP(LOG A+B LOG X)

Table 9-5. Curve Fitting, Number Voting Versus Number of Votes for Smith.

Input

X	Y	X	Y	X	Y	X	Y
940	763	1101	892	952	727	1584	654
1118	456	1959	751	1909	1126	1084	698
1360	483	1873	964	2556	1141	937	645

Output

	A	B	R	t-Test	Equations
Linear	377.349	.274668	.654783	2.73956	Y = A + BX
Exponential	464.586	3.2738E-04	.593561	2.33229	Y = EXP(LOG A + BX)
Logarithmic	−2030.77	388.531	.608196	2.42292	Y = A + B LOG X
Power	27.0872	.459192	.546684	2.0646	Y = EXP(LOG A + B LOG X)

Table 9-6. Curve Fitting, Number of Registered Votes Versus Number of Votes for Jones.

Input

X	Y	X	Y	X	Y	X	Y
1972	61	2011	102	1693	201	2854	865
1909	615	2886	1128	3130	730	1801	353
2383	806	2921	838	4324	1324	1534	263

Output

	A	B	R	t-Test	Equations
Linear	−469.868	.439337	.858182	5.28652	Y = A + BX
Exponential	55.3842	8.40416E-04	.685501	2.97738	Y = EXP(LOG A + BX)
Logarithmic	−8364.51	1156.22	.864461	5.43796	Y = A + B LOG X
Power	1.2373E-05	2.23913	.699065	3.09155	Y = EXP(LOG A + B LOG X)

Table 9-7. Curve Fitting, Number of Registered Voters Versus Number Actually Voting.

Input

X	Y	X	Y	X	Y	X	Y
1972	940	2011	1101	1693	952	2854	1585
1909	1118	2886	1959	3130	1909	1801	1084
2383	1360	2921	1873	4324	2556	1534	937

Output

	A	B	R	t-Test	Equations
Linear	− 115.198	.637582	.975191	13.9308	Y = A + BX
Exponential	499.709	4.10977E-04	.95719	10.4571	Y = EXP(LOG A + BX)
Logarithmic	− 11279.1	1653.06	.967756	12.1495	Y = A + B LOG X
Power	.296735	1.08724	.969238	12.4531	Y = EXP(LOG A + B LOGX)

independent variables. The value R is the correlation of one variable to the other. Its range is from −1 to 1. A value at either end of the range means the equation is a good predictor. The closer the value approaches zero, the less reliably the equation will predict Y. The t-Test is an additional test of the equation and gives an indication of the reliability of the R value. Its value range is theoretically unlimited (that is, to infinity, plus or minus), and its interpretation is beyond the scope of this paper. Nonetheless, if the value is less than −1.796 or greater than +1.796, the R value is considered very reliable. The portion labeled "INPUT" contains the values entered for processing.

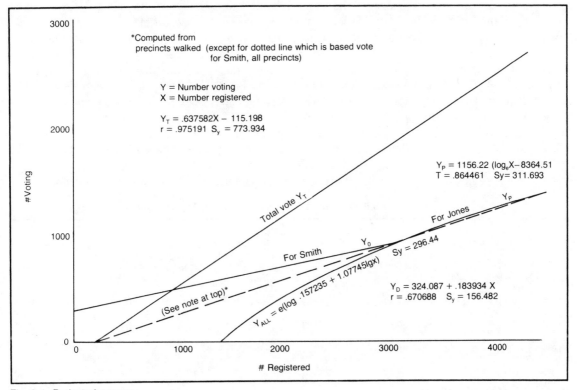

Fig. 9-1. Projected curves.

Figure 9-1 illustrates the lines or curves resulting from the foregoing tables. In all cases, the independent (horizontal) variable is the number of registered voters in a precinct and the dependent variable (vertical) is the number voting. Each line or curve is labeled to show for whom they are voting. The line Y_t confirms common wisdom: the larger the precinct, the larger the number of voters going to the polls. The line Y_d shows the larger the precinct the larger the number of people voting for Smith. It would be misleading, however, not to mention that as the precincts get larger, the vote for Smith (both actual and predicted) gets smaller when expressed as a percentage of the total vote. The foregoing is based on the data of the 12 precincts Smith walked. The dotted line (Y_{all}) is based on the data from all 39 precincts and, for the range of precinct sizes that actually exist, follows the previous example: the larger the precinct the smaller the percentage voting for Smith. Finally, the curved line Y_p is based on the vote for Jones. Interestingly enough, the same fate awaits Jones with the larger precincts. With all curves, the S_y expression is the standard error of the (Y) estimate. While the equation computes the estimate of the Y-variable as a function of the value of the X-variable, it must be understood that the real data upon which these lines are computed will deviate from this prediction. The standard error indicates the limits (plus and minus) within which the bulk of the data points will appear when plotted against the estimate at any given point. Therefore, while we compute that the expected vote for Jones in a precinct with 2000 registered voters will be about 692, the standard error suggests this value could and probably will vary by as much as 156+ votes, or from 536 to 848 votes. Although specific data points will vary from the prediction, those points below the estimate will be balanced out by about the same number above the estimate. We know the real data will vary to a degree from the predictions. The standard error gives us an estimate of how great a variation is still normal.

Significance of the Data

The observations just given have been computed with a great deal of precision. They clearly show a difference in the voter preference in the precincts Smith walked as opposed to those she didn't. We apply both the simple percentage difference and the curve-fitting estimates to the different precincts and find that had the patterns noted in the 12 walked precincts been applied and effective in the non-walked precincts, Smith should have won the election handily. The pivotal question, then, is whether these observations are statistically valid. That is, to what degree are the observed differences simply the result of chance deviation and circumstance, and to what extent are the differences not explained by random voter behavior? The differences repeatedly support the notion that observed differences are significant, that is, not the result of chance or random error. There were a number of tests conducted leading to this conclusion.

The first test was a Monte Carlo experiment.

Table 9-8. Comparative Statistics, 1978 to 1980.

| Election Type/Year | 12 Precincts Walked | | | Remaining Precincts | | | Test Results | |
	Total Vote	Candidate* Vote	Percent	Total Vote	Candidate* Vote	Percent	Standard Error	Z-Score
1978 General	8337	4700	56.3746%	11379	5960	52.3772%	.0364715	1.09603
1980 Primary	2142	1425	66.5266	2493	1585	63.5780	.0412833	.714234
1980 Runoff	2543	1772	69.6815	3226	2167	67.1730	.0281058	.892525
1980 General	16586	9300	56.0714	23963	12013	50.1315	.0297854	1.994250

*Winning Candidate

Table 9-9. Point-Biserial Correlation, 1980 Election.

PCT 0	# Regist. 1	# Voting 2	Smith 3	Jones 4	Walked 5
114	1972	940	763	61	4
117	2011	1101	892	102	2
227	1693	952	727	201	5
233	2854	1585	654	865	5
239	1909	1118	456	615	3
241	2886	1959	751	1128	1
242	3130	1909	1126	730	3
251	1801	1084	698	353	5
264	2383	1360	483	806	2
269	2921	1873	964	838	1
274	4324	2556	1141	1324	4
275	1534	937	645	263	5
136	1343	811	457	305	0
215	1933	935	799	91	0
228	2373	1253	535	657	0
234	2964	1749	715	978	0
235	647	431	195	213	0
237	2600	1732	735	944	0
238	1094	632	231	384	0
240	873	558	230	313	0
243	2483	1501	926	533	0
247	1034	644	211	396	0
249	1571	755	598	90	0
250	1573	896	594	287	0
252	70	42	23	15	0
253	132	71	19	49	0
254	2694	1590	626	896	0
255	1710	1111	400	688	0
260	2166	1212	770	382	0
263	915	452	163	261	0
265	1400	824	391	410	0
266	1678	964	388	530	0
267	890	549	239	278	0
268	2113	1298	524	734	0
270	1902	973	822	65	0
273	1572	917	577	295	0
344	2673	1409	385	984	0
352	2003	1299	363	877	0
382	618	410	97	295	0

1 = .4567
Point-biserial correlation of column 2 = .455595
Point-biserial correlation of column 3 = .536778
Point-biserial correlation of column 4 = .224276

There are 3,910,797,436 different and unique combinations of 12 precincts out of a total of 39. Even at the rate of one complete computation per second, it would take nearly 124 years to actually check out all three billion plus combinations. Instead, a computer simulation was developed to select 12 precincts at random, total the vote and compute the percentage voting for Smith. After 21746 trial combinations, we find the percentage of precinct combinations giving a vote for Smith better than the actual result to be about 4.244%. That is, if you picked any 12 precincts at random, there is a 95.756% chance that the vote for Smith would be less than 56%. Smith was asked to name the precincts in which she had made personal appearances. Immediately she named the 12 picked in the study, referring only to the data shown in Table 9-2, and looking only at the precinct numbers. This took about 30 seconds. The probability she chose the 12 at random, yet happened to select 12 that would lead us to the conclusions in her favor is .0424446. Not very likely she did it at random. Rather, we conclude, the selections were based on reality and the subsequent findings are significant and valid.

Table 9-8, summarizes the data resulting from a "Differences Between Proportions" test. The question implied was: Don't these 12 particular precincts usually favor the Democratic candidate more than the other 27 precincts? The Z-Score in the right-hand column is a measure of dispersion of one data set from another. Only if the score is greater than 1.6449 are the data considered to be better than 95% chance-free. Only in the 1980 general election does there appear to be a significant difference between the two sets of precincts.

Table 9-9 is the summary of a "Point-Biserial

Table 9-10. Comparison Between Precincts Walked Versus Those not Walked (One-Way Anova).

Source	SS	DF	MS	F	P
Total	10874300.00	38			
Between	2257050.00	1	%2257050.00	9.69	0.003800
Within	8617220.00	37	%232878.00		

Variations noted are likely to be the result of the treatment.

Input Values

Group 1	Group 2	
940	811	
1101	935	
952	1253	
1585	1749	
1118	431	
1959	1732	
1909	632	
1084	558	
1360	1501	
1873	644	
2556	755	
937	896	
	42	
	71	
	1590	
	1111	
	1212	
	452	
	824	
	964	
	549	
	1298	
	973	
	917	
	1409	
	1299	
	410	
17374	25018	Sum
1447.83	926.593	Average

Table 9-11. Comparison Between Precincts Walked Versus Those not Walked, Registered Voters (One-Way Anova).

Source	SS	DF	MS	F	P
Total	29323300.00	38			
Between	6116080.00	1	%6116080.00	9.75	0.003700
Within	23207200.00	37	%627223.00		

Variations noted are likely to be the result of the treatment.

Input values

Walked	Didn't Walk
Group 1	**Group 2**
1972	1343
2011	1933
1693	2373
2854	2964
1909	647
2886	2600
3130	1094
1801	873
2383	2483
2921	1034
4324	1571
1534	70
	132
	2694
	1710
	2166
	915
	1400
	1678
	890
	2113
	1902
	1572
	2673
	2003
	618
	1573
29418	43024 Sum
2451.5	1593.48 Average

Correlation" test. This test evaluates the relationship between some more or less continuous data (votes for a candidate) with some dichotomous criterion (in this study, walked versus didn't walk). Note that the greatest correlation between whether or not a precinct was walked and some continuous data set was with the vote for Smith (.536778). We conclude from this there is a meaningful significance in the observed differences.

Tables 9-10-12 display the outcome of several tests in the statistical family of analysis of variance. The test assumes that the test subjects (voters) are otherwise identical in personal makeup and disposition but have been divided into two or

Table 9-12. Comparison of Votes Considering Votes for the Candidates and Whether Precincts Were Walked (Two Way Anova)

Source		SS	DF	MS	F	P	
Total		7670000.00	77				
	Column	55282.00	1	%55282.00	0.63	0.564600	Smith vs. Jones
	Row	1016320.00	1	%1016320.00	11.60	0.001400	Walk vs Didn't Walk
	Row X col	113806.00	1	%113806.00	1.30	0.257000	
	Error	6484590.00	74	%87629.60			

Significant findings:
    Row effects are significant

Input variables

Cell Group 1 1 :	763	892	727	654	456	751	1126
698	483	964	1141	645			
Cell Group 1 2 :	61	102	201	865	615	1128	730
353	806	838	1324	263			
Cell Group 2 1 :	457	799	535	715	195	735	231
230	926	211	598	594	23	19	626
400	770	163	391	388	239	524	822
577	385	363	97				
Cell Group 2 2 :	305	91	657	978	213	944	384
313	533	396	90	287	15	49	896
688	382	261	410	530	278	734	65
295	984	877	295				

more groups. Each group has received a different degree of treatment (being walked, personal appearance of the candidate). Table 9-10 and Table 9-11 tend to confirm the observation that Smith walked significantly larger precincts. Table 9-12 shows the results of a "Two-Way Analysis of Variance Test" and actually tests two questions simultaneously: Is there a significant difference in the vote for Smith depending on whether or not she walked a precinct, and in a specific kind of precinct

Table 9-13. Chi-Square Analysis of Votes.

1.	Walked	Didn't	Total
# Registered	29418	43024	73342
# Voting	17374	25018	42392
Total	46792	68042	114834

Chi-Square = 1.54303 with 3 Degrees of Freedom
Density Function = .229104

2.	Walked	Didn't	Total
For Smith	9300	12013	21313
For Jones	7286	11950	19236
Total	16586	23963	40549

Chi-Square = 138.459 with 3 Degrees of Freedom
Density Function = 4.03227E-30

Table 9-14. Projected Voting Results.

Item	Precinct	Registered	Smith	12-Precinct	Difference	All precincts	Difference
1	114	1972	763	686.805	76.1951	558.058	204.942
2	117	2011	892	693.978	198.022	569.958	322.042
3	227	1693	727	635.487	91.5128	473.476	253.524
4	233	2854	654	849.035	195.035	831.117	177.117
5	239	1909	456	675.217	219.217	538.872	82.8724
6	241	2886	751	854.921	103.921	841.162	90.1623
7	242	3130	1126	899.8	226.2	918.032	207.968
8	251	1801	698	655.352	42.6479	506.098	191.902
9	264	2383	483	762.402	279.402	684.329	201.329
10	269	2921	964	861.358	102.642	852.159	111.841
11	274	4324	1141	1119.42	21.5824	1300.38	159.38
12	275	1534	645	606.242	38.7582	425.744	219.256
13	136	1343	457	571.11	114.11	368.915	88.0855
14	215	1933	799	679.631	119.369	546.176	252.824
15	228	2373	535	760.562	225.562	681.236	146.236
16	234	2964	715	869.267	154.267	865.683	150.683
17	235	647	195	443.092	248.092	167.952	27.0478
18	237	2600	735	802.315	67.3154	751.703	16.7025
19	238	1094	231	525.311	294.311	295.78	64.7797
20	240	873	230	484.661	254.661	231.939	1.93925
21	243	2483	926	780.795	145.205	715.32	210.68
22	247	1034	211	514.275	303.275	278.339	67.3391
23	249	1571	598	613.047	15.0473	436.819	161.182
24	250	1573	594	613.415	19.4152	437.418	156.582
25	252	70	23	336.962	313.962	15.2957	7.70433
26	253	132	19	348.366	329.366	30.2958	11.2958
27	254	2694	626	819.605	193.605	781.026	155.026
28	255	1710	400	638.614	238.614	478.6	78.6002
29	260	2166	770	722.488	47.512	617.43	152.57
30	263	915	163	492.387	329.387	243.984	80.9843
31	265	1400	391	581.595	190.595	385.812	5.18793
32	266	1678	388	632.728	244.728	468.958	60.9575
33	267	890	239	487.788	248.788	236.809	2.19072
34	268	2113	524	712.74	188.74	601.167	77.1671
35	270	1902	822	673.929	148.071	536.744	285.256
36	273	1572	577	613.231	36.2313	437.118	139.882
37	344	2673	385	815.743	430.743	774.467	389.467
38	352	2003	363	692.507	329.507	567.516	204.516
39	382	618	97	437.758	340.758	159.856	62.8555

(walked versus walked) are there significant differences in voter preference? From the output data we conclude that the probability that walking a precinct results in a favorable vote for Smith is about .9860.

Table 9-13 gives the results from another series of statistical tests in the chi-square family. The purpose and outcome of these tests are the same as the analysis of variance. From section 1 we conclude walking a precinct had only a slight (.770896) influence on voter turnout whereas, section 2, there is an extremely significant difference in voter preference between Smith and Jones related to whether Smith walked a given precinct.

Table 9-14 shows the impact of applying the voting estimate from Table 9-2 on each precinct. The column labeled "12-Precinct" is the estimate of the vote from that precinct had Smith campaigned there.

Whether the reader would come to the same conclusions as we did is unknown. We believe the data support the conclusions as well as possible. Limiting the study was the fact that nearly a year had past since the election when we were retained to do the study. While the election results were not perishable, we believed that the research could have been improved by a survey of the voters im-

189

mediately after the election to see if there was any candidate recognition or attitudinal differences measurable in the precincts that we could attribute to the presence or absence of the client in the precinct during the campaign. Unfortunately, too much time had passed and other (favorable) public events involving our client had appeared in the local press. We were fearful that such study could be successfully challenged by the defense. As a consequence, we had to predict an alternative history based on a "what-if" analysis.

SUGGESTED READING

Backstrom, C. H. and G. D. Hursh, 1963. *Survey Research*. Minneapolis: Northwestern University Press.

Dixon, W. J. and F. J. Massey, 1951. *Introduction to Statistical Analysis*. New York: McGraw-Hill.

Festinger, L. and D. Katz (eds.), 1953. *Research Methods in the Behavioral Sciences*. New York: Dryden Press.

Selltiz, C. et al., 1965. *Research Methods in Social Relations (Revised)*. New York: Holt, Rinehart and Winston.

Chapter 10

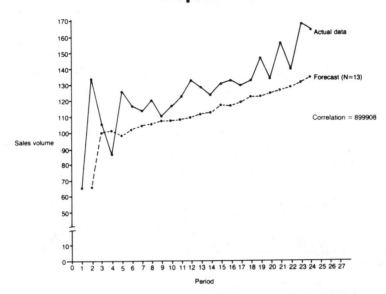

Economic Forecasting

Economic forecasting is one of the nation's favorite pastimes. Those of us longer on imagination than investment capital often "pick a stock," invest some play money, and watch our fortunes grow. The number of people who've made a fortune with "funny money" in a simulation, then have lost a fortune in real cash playing the same stock in real life, is unknown, but it must be considerable. The difficulty in accurately forecasting market behavior is illustrated in the following routine. (A graph of the results is shown in Fig. 10-1).

The pattern generated is purely random, yet it suggests a convincing portrait of the stock market sales volume or prices. A number of different techniques have been applied to the analysis of stock market behavior by some very sophisticated analysts using powerful computers—all to little avail. If anyone has really found a universal stock market

Listing 10-1. Drunkard's Walk

```
1  '**********************************************
2  'DRUNKARD'S WALK                             *
3  'LISTING 10-1                                *
4  '**********************************************
5  '
10 CLS:RANDOM
20 PRINT@0,"";:INPUT"VARIABLE";V:Y=23:CLS
30 FOR X=0TO127
40    A=RND(0):IF A<.5THEN B=-1 ELSE B=1
50    Y=Y+(B*V):IF Y>47 THEN Y=47
60    IFY<0 THEN Y=0
70    SET(X,47-Y)
80 NEXT
90 GOTO20
```

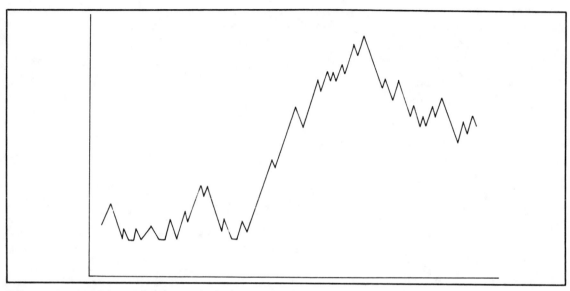

Fig. 10-1. Graph of the "Drunkard's Walk."

predictor, they're not talking. While there are analysts and counsellors who have enjoyed a certain period of fame and fortune as a consequence of their forecasting, the only ones who have survived from decade to decade are those who employ well-known and more conservative approaches to the market. The lesson of their lives is to use a number of different analytical techniques, and combine that forecast with a lot of good common sense. Accordingly, this book does not support any global approach to forecasting the stock market, although it examines a few, but puts forth some of the more specialized tools for market analysis. The reader will have to supply the common sense evaluation of the analysis. In addition to the stock market, this chapter also deals with a number of business-related forecasting and estimating techniques. In all cases, the programs and equations used are believed to be correct and accurate for the purposes for which they are composed. Nonetheless, neither the author nor the publisher can assume any responsibility or liability for the consequences of investment decisions based on these routines.

STOCK MARKET ANALYSIS

Stock market analysis breaks down into two basic tasks, each of which has two subsets. The first aspect is total market forecasting. The assumption is that as a whole market goes, so goes individual stocks. The second aspect is individual stock forecasting. In each of these approaches is the concept of long and short-term forecasting. The techniques used to do a short-term forecast are not necessarily those used for the long-term forecast, and vice-versa. From a proper historical perspective, we can see long-term growth in both market and individual stock values, yet, within that overall pattern, a more microscopic analysis reveals hectic periods of heart-stopping plunges in price and volume. A technique that reliably gives forecasts one or two hundred years in advance is useful only in corporate and estate planning. To the individual with an expected adult economic life of only forty years or so century-long cycles are only of nominal interest. Within the foregoing framework, then, here are some techniques that may be useful.

Long-Term Market Analysis

Figure 10-2 illustrates the composite market behavior for the last 160 years based on several governmental sources. The overall impression is one of long-term growth, which is the objective of a healthy capitalist economy. Without growth there is little incentive for investment, the basis of the market, and with too much growth per unit of time, values become unrealistic and investment risky beyond an acceptable level. Conservative economists generally agree a growth rate of 4 to 6 percent annually results in comfortable and workable market conditions. A rough evaluation of the data in Fig. 10-2 suggests a long-term growth, since 1800, of about 46566.67 percent. Assuming there will be no further historical surprises, such as a world war or total loss of petroleum supplies, it is not unreasonable to conclude that the trend line of the overall market performance will continue the pattern established in the past few decades. The distance between this rather presumptious observation and a wise investment strategy is incredibly long, however. The only utility of such a trend line is to suggest the direction or level the market might seek at a point in time, provided there are no other more significant market forces or predictors operating. It is a level to which the market will

eventually float, but only after some rather dramatic exceptions to the trend.

Virtually every budding market analyst has approached the problem of analyzing these data for the purpose of discovering the underlying cycles that may be present in the long-term trend. They assume that all significant market purchases are based on rational analysis (assuming the volume of investments made by the insane and irrational are insignificant) of commonly-held information, and therefore, that the market behavior will vary in direct proportion to the natural variations in the underlying forces to which the market responds. These forces include weather patterns, population growth, technological innovations, and so forth. While it is probably true that investors tend to look at such things for guidance, it is clear that interpretations as to the significance of each of these components vary as widely as the number of analysts. As a result, one analyst will panic and sell at the

Fig. 10-2. Generalized market performance, 1800-1950.

same time another analyst is mortgaging his home to raise investment capital. The net effect, frequently, is a confusing pattern similar to the Drunkard's Walk in Listing 10-1. The basic principle, however, is to select a period of time, compute the basic trend line for the included data, and use this line as the level to which the market will move. The difference between the poor and the rich, in this effort, is the skill and accuracy with which one selects the period to be analyzed. It is for such an effort the smoothing and decomposition techniques in Chapter 6 are useful. While we will avoid recommending a specific period for analysis, we think it prudent to consider data in some historical perspective. That is, it is probably counterproductive to compute a two-hundred-year trend line. First of all, there is no single source of indexed or standardized data. Second, the technologies driving the industrial component of the market no longer compete in the same relationships. For example, the demand for leather for buggy whips has given way to the demand for plastics for steering wheels. Third, political realities, both national and global, have altered economic forces. The current level of foreign aid spending creates a market influence that just didn't exist in the year 1800. Fourth, while we can compute some sort of index, as we did in Fig. 10-2, it is really more of a "guesstimate" than a precise measure. One method of index pricing is the *market basket* technique in which a specified set of commodities is periodically priced. If the price of bread and milk doubles in ten years, the theory goes, so has everything else. While the actual components of the basket are actually much more extensive than bread and milk, the shortcomings of the technique remain: the production factors to produce the components are not consistent, nor is the relative utility of the components to each other. When the price of a given commodity changes, does it reflect a basic change in the overall market or just in a limited aspect of it? When the price of bread goes up, is that due to an inflationary increase through out the economy, or is it due to a crop failure? These questions are difficult enough within a fifty-year period, let alone in a period lasting a couple of centuries.

Nonetheless, there are a broad variety of statistical and mathematical techniques with which we may evaluate short and long term economic trends and events. Before proceeding, however, we need to examine some basic mathematics considerations relevant to economics.

BUSINESS MATHEMATICS

There is a whole branch of mathematics that frequently gets poor coverage in standard math courses in our public schools: business mathematics. The mainline courses avoid deep study of the subject as a biology teacher might avoid woodworking during the study of trees. Even in business math courses the concentration is on accounting practices and the routines below remain relatively neglected. So, this section is for those readers who went to the same school the author did or one like it. It covers the areas of interest, annuities, amortization, bond values, return on investment, selling price, goodwill, and breakeven points—all essential components in the forecasting of business trends and decision making.

Interest

At the heart of many of the routines involving time and money is the simple expression: $(1 + r)^n$. We commonly see this in the equation for compound interest: $A = P(1 + 4)^n$, where A is the future total of an account that starts with the principal amount, P and has an interest rate of r paid to it in each of n periods. This section deals with the various forms of the expression and the wide variety of applications to which it can be put.

The first task is to compute the remaining terms of the compound interest equation. By simple division, the equation is solved to P as $P = A/(1 + r)^n$. To solve for n is a little more tedious, but it becomes

$$n = \frac{\text{Log}(A/P)}{\text{Log}(1 + R)}$$

The solution for r becomes

$$r = \sqrt[n]{A/P} - 1.$$

The basic equation for simple interest is:

$A = P(1 + nr)$. The solution for the various parts of this form are straight forward and avoid some of the problems of the exponential math of compound interest. The following equations summarize the procedures used to deal with interest.

Interest Equations

Compound	Simple
1. $A = P(1 + r)^r$	$A = P(1 + nr)$
2. $P = A/(1 + r)^n$	$P = A/(1 + nr)$
3. $n = Log(A/P)/Log(1 + r)$	$n = (A/P - 1)/r$
4. $r = \sqrt[n]{A/P} - 1$	$r = (A/P - 1)/n$

Annuities

An annuity is the payment of a fixed sum of money over a period of time. This can be a payment into a savings or investment account, a payment received from a bank or investment account, or a combination of both. The compound interest equations above might be taken as a special case of an annuity with one payment. If an item we want to buy costs $200.00 and we have $100.00, how long must we wait to accumulate $200.00 in a savings account paying seven percent interest? $A = 200$, $P = 100$, $r = 7/(12 \times 100) = .0058333$:

$$n = \log(A/P)/\log(1 + r)$$
$$= \log(200/200)/\log(1.0058333)$$
$$= .693147 / .005816$$
$$= 119.1714686 \text{ or } 119 \text{ months, } 5+ \text{ days}$$

The only problem is that we don't want to wait nearly twenty years to buy the item, and the seller will not guarantee the price for more than twelve months. Since the bank won't budge on the interest rate, what amount must we deposit in order to accumulate the $200.00 within twelve months? $A = 200$, $r = .0058333$, $n = 12$:

$$P = A / (1 + r)^n$$
$$= 200 / 1.0058333^n$$
$$= 200 / 1.0722897$$
$$= 186.52$$

This is still no good: we don't have the $186.52, either. We do have, however, a steady income and can put a little into savings. The question now is how much must we put into the bank each month so that it accumulates to the needed $200.00? This is the amount of the annuity. The fund that is built is called a *sinking fund*, an amount established or accumulated for a special future purpose. The purpose is based on the basic equations:

$$A = S\left(\frac{(1 + r)^n - 1}{r}\right) \qquad S = A\left(\frac{r}{(1 + r)^n - 1}\right)$$

In these equations, A is the amount accumulated after n payments of S each have been paid into an account paying r interest. Continuing the example above, $A = 200$, $r = .0058333$, $n = 12$.

$$S = A\left(\frac{r}{(1 + r)^n - 1}\right)$$
$$= 200\left(\frac{.005833}{1.005833^n - 1}\right)$$
$$= 200 \,(.005833 / .0722858)$$
$$= 200 \times .0806934 = 16.13868$$

Since payments must be either $16.13 or $16.14, we should compute eleven payments and subtract this sum from $200.00 to compute the last payment: $n = 11$, $S = 16.14$, $r = .0058333$.

$$A = S\left(\frac{(1 + r)^n - 1}{r}\right)$$
$$= 16.14\left(\frac{1.0058333^n - 1}{.0058333}\right)$$
$$= 16.14 \,(.0660674 / .0058333)$$
$$= 16.14 \times 11.325912 = 182.80022$$

The last payment, then, is equal to 200.00 less 182.80 plus the interest on 182.80 for the twelfth month

$$LP = 200 - (182.80 \times 1.005833) = 200 - 183.87$$
$$= 16.13$$

So, if we can afford to put away $16.14 for eleven months and make a final payment of $16.13. we can have the $200.00 item within twelve months. If we can afford to put the $100.00 we have on hand into the account at the beginning, the adjusted equation becomes:

$$S = (A - (P (1 + r)^n))\left(\frac{r}{(1 + r)^n - 1}\right)$$
$$= (200 - (100 \times 1.005833^n))\left(\frac{.005833}{1.005833^n - 1}\right)$$

$= (200 - (100 \times 1.0722897)) \, (.005833/.0722897)$
$= (200 - 107.22897) \times .0806934 = 7.49$

So, for a total investment of $189.88 (100 + 12 × 7.49), or so, we can buy a $200.00 item. These computations have led us through the evaluation of the amount of an annuity. There is another side to annuities in which our concern is not with putting money into an account, but in periodic withdrawals from an account. These lead us into the present values of annuities.

We are most familiar with this type of annuities from pension programs. At a certain moment, we begin receiving a certain amount of money from an account and will receive this sum either until we die (from a perpetual account) or for a specified number of payments, such a series of hospitalization payments received from an insurance company for a limited time. With the advent of IRA retirement accounts, more and more people will find these equations useful for computing relevant data. For example, we want to establish a retirement account that will pay us a certain amount (S) for 25 years, assuming that will be sufficient for our retired years (we also disregard inflation for the time being). We need to compute how large an account is required to support 300 (12 × 25) payments of S each, starting N months from now. The equations for the present value of an annuity are

$$A = S \left(\frac{1 - (1 + r)^{-n}}{r} \right) \quad S = A \left(\frac{r}{1 - (1 + r)^{-n}} \right)$$

If we want a monthly annuity of $1000, and our bank pays seven percent annual interest, the amount we need to start our retirement fund with is

$$A = S \left(\frac{1 - (1 + r)^{-n}}{r} \right)$$

$$= 1000 \left(\frac{1 - 1.005833^{-n}}{.005833} \right)$$

$$= 1000 \left(\frac{1 - .1745771}{.005833} \right) = 1000 \left(\frac{.8253229}{.005833} \right)$$

$$= 1000 \times 141.4847349 = 141484.73$$

$141,484.73! Wow, that's a lot of cash! Or is it? The answer depends on how much time we have to accumulate it. If we're 64 and plan to retire at 65, then it is probably a tough problem. On the other hand, we have thirty or forty years, then it probably is possible to achieve. Let's see. A = 141484.75, r = .005833, n = 420 (12 × 35). From the amount of an annuity

$$S = A \left(\frac{r}{(1 + r)^n - 1} \right)$$

$$= 141484.73 \left(\frac{.005833}{1.005833^n - 1} \right)$$

$$= 141484.73 \left(\frac{.005833}{10.50599} \right)$$

$$= 14184.73 \times .0005552355 = 78.55734$$

There it is: 420 monthly payments of $78.56 each will provide a retirement account of a least $141,484.73 from which 300 monthly annuity payments of $1000.00 can be paid.

Now, for purpose of example, let's assume that $78.56 is just too much, that all we can afford is $50.00 a month. Using the basic equation, this will yield a retirement account of $90,051.87. To determine the pension annuity available, we use these values and the second equation: A = 90051.87, n = 300, r = .005833

$$S = A \left(\frac{r}{1 - (1 + r)^{-n}} \right)$$

$$= 90051.87 \left(\frac{.0058333}{1 - 1.0058333^{-n}} \right)$$

$$= 90051.87 \left(\frac{.0058333}{.82533853} \right)$$

$$= 90051.87 \times .0070674 = 636.43$$

It is now for you to decide whether $636.43 is sufficient for your needs and if not, whether you can find a better savings interest rate or increase the dollar amount of the investment annuity. The task of determining the interest rate necessary to yield the desired $141,484.73 is more complicated than the preceding procedures. There is no straightforward equation that says, given S, n, and A, r = ... Rather, r must be approximated by a trial and error method that, eventually, causes one of the equations to yield the desired values. The basic algorithm is:

1. Establish the values for S, A, and n.
2. Establish a trial value for r and delta r.
3. Compute a trial value for A (AX) using one of the appropriate annuity equations.
4. If the value of AX is less than A, then go to step 5a, otherwise, go to step 5b.
5a. Add delta r to r. Go to step 3.
5b. Subtract delta r from r. Reduce the size of delta r by dividing by 2 or some similar number. If delta r is smaller than, for example, .000001, then go to step 6, otherwise, go to step 5a.
6. The current value of r is a reasonable approximation of the true r yielding the desired values. Proceed with balance of work.

To improve the accuracy of r, simply make the delta r limit factor in step 5b smaller. Using the algorithm above, the retirement problem is recomputed to determine the interest rate required to yield a retirement account equal to $141,484.73, S = 50, n = 420, r = .005, delta r(dr) = .001.

$$AX = 50 \left(\frac{2.006^n - 1}{.006} \right)$$

AX = 94461.35: too small. Increase r
r = r + dr = .006 + .001 = .007

$$AX = 50 \left(\frac{1.007^n - 1}{.007} \right)$$

AX = 126593.53: still too small. Increase r
r = .008

$$AX = 50 \left(\frac{1.008^n - 1}{.008} \right)$$

AX = 171292.98: too large. Reduce r and dr
r = r − dr + (dr/2) and dr = dr/2
r = .0075 dr = .0005

Continue with this process until dr is smaller than .000001 and r has approached .007373 (8.8456 annual interest rate).

So, if we can find a bank or an investment opportunity that will guarantee us an annual interest rate of at least 8.8456 percent per year, payable monthly, then we can still achieve our objective.

The worst case would be when no such interest rate can be found. Then we need to readjust our retirement date so that we can increase the number of $50.00 payments into the account that pays at seven percent. The period of an annuity, n, can be found from:

$$n = \frac{\log (1 + (r(A/S)))}{\log (1 + r)}$$

Using A = 141484.73, S = 50, r = .0058333

$$n = \frac{\log (1 + (.005833 (141484.73/50)))}{\log 1.0058333}$$

$$= \frac{\log 27.506458}{\log 1.0058333} = 492.158977 \text{ months}$$

This result means that a savings period of better than 492 months, or 42 years is required. Starting age thirty, retirement must be put off until age seventy-one. There is a fallacy here though. At the beginning of this example, we made the assumption that allowing for twenty-five years of retirement would be sufficient. Although we have control over a number of the variables in such a routine, life-expectancy is not an easily controlled variable. We should stay with the expectation of death at or before age 90. Accordingly, at age seventy-one, the amount required for the retirement account is not $141,484.73, but $126,648.58. By reducing the amount required, we also reduce the time necessary to accumulate it—in this case, to 474.26 months, 39 years and 6+ MONTHS. And so on. What we have established as constants are the variables S, which is equal to 50, and r, which is equal to .0058333, and the total number of periods for investment and retirement, which is equal to 720. As with interest rates, we must go through an iterative process to compute the number of periods of investment necessary to reach an amount sufficient to support the desired pension annuity. The process to do this is based on this equation:

$$Si = Sa \left(\frac{1 - (1+r)^{-n_2}}{r} \right) \left(\frac{r}{(1+r)^n - 1} \right)$$

This equation is written as part of an iterative process in which a trial value of n is varied until the

197

value of Si that is equal to or less than the periodic investment ceiling is obtained.

A similar set of problems can be resolved with a set of equations known as *double annuities*. They are:

$$S' = S'' \left(\frac{(1 + r1)^n - 1}{1 - (1 + r2)^{-n}} \right)$$

$$S'' = S' \left(\frac{1 - (1 + r2)^{-n2}}{(1 + r1)^n - 1} \right)$$

where S' is the payment for the investment and S'' is the annuity returned from the account.

Perpetual annuities are those that continue without a termination point, n2 = infinity. This is the same as living on the interest earned on a principal amount A. If r is the available interest, then $S'' = A \times r$ and $A = S''/r$. Also, $S'' = S'' ((1 + r1)^r - 1)$

Amortization

The process of computing amortization figures is very similar to annuities, especially amortizations such as those used in computing mortgage payments, car payments, and the like. The three basic equations involved in this process are:

1. $S = \dfrac{P r (1 + r)^n}{(1 + r)^n - 1}$

2. $A = \dfrac{S((1 + r)^n - 1)}{r (1 + r)^n}$

3. $n = \log (S/(S - (A \times r))) / \log (1 + r)$ where P is the amount to be financed.

The value of the interest rate, given the values for n, A, and S, is determined through an iterative process. From these equations we can also compute the sum of payments from $n \times S$, total interest paid from $(n \times S) - P$, and so forth.

To demonstrate these equations, let's compute the monthly payments on a car where P = 10000, n = 36, and r = .011667 (14% annually):

$$S = \frac{P r (1 + r)^n}{(1 + r)^n - 1}$$

$$S = \frac{10000 \times .0116667 \times 1.0116667^n}{1.0116667^n - 1}$$

$$S = \frac{116.667 \times 1.518267795}{.518267795} = 341.7765$$

The car payment is $341.78. If this value is too high, it can be reduced by either extending the number of payments, n, or reducing the amount financed, P, or the interest rate, r, or a combination of these actions.

A principle of the foregoing procedure is that the interest due and payable is computed on the current unpaid balance of the principal. As the unpaid balance declines, the amount paid in interest declines. For this reason, the first few years of ownership of a car or house are the most fruitful for tax purposes since most of the payment will go against the tax-deductable interest payment. In the later years, the situation is reversed. While the payment is the same, the larger part of the payment goes against the unpaid balance and the smaller is paid on the interest due.

To compute the unpaid balance (B) after k payments, we use:

$$B = S \frac{1 - (1 - r)^{-x}}{r}$$

where $x = n - k$

The kth payment at which B is a specified amount is given in:

$$K = \frac{\log S - \log (S - (B \times r))}{\log (1 + r)}$$

In addition to the procedure just described, there are at least three other ways to amortize notes or loans. Two of them, not commonly used these days, are the *add-on* and *discount* notes. The third is the popular *revolving* or *declining balance* approach.

Add-on and Discount Notes. The names of these notes refer to the point in the loan transaction when the interest fee is added to the principal. In the add-on technique, the interest is computed and added to the principal before the payment amount is computed. As a consequence, each monthly payment contains a constant amount for interest and principal. In the discount technique, the interest is computed and subtracted from the principal prior to the computation of the monthly payment. Payments, therefore, are made against the principal only; the interest having been paid in advance. The equations used in these approaches are

Add-on Notes	**Discount Notes**
1. $S = \dfrac{P\,r\,n + P}{n}$	$S = \dfrac{P - P\,r}{n}$
2. $n = \dfrac{P}{S - P\,r}$	$n = \dfrac{P - P\,r}{S}$
3. $P = \dfrac{S\,n}{r\,n + 1}$	$P = \dfrac{S\,n}{1 - r}$
4. $r = \dfrac{S\,n - P}{P\,n}$	$r = 1 - \dfrac{S\,n}{P}$
5. $C = P$	$C = P - P\,r$

Where S = monthly payment, P = principal, n = number of payments, r = interest rate per payment, and C = cash advanced to customer.

Declining Balance Method. This is the technique used in most revolving credit systems in which the monthly payment is a percentage of the current unpaid balance. The unpaid balance is normally the unpaid principal plus the amount of interest on this principal. If r_1 is the interest rate and r_2 is the payment percentage, the payment due (S) on a starting balance of P is:

$$S = r_2\,(P\,(1 + r_1))$$

If n is the number of payments that have been made on a regular basis, the current unpaid balance (B) is:

$$B = P\,((1 + r_1) - r_2)^n$$

There are a number of amortization routines available and the following is one more. It's a routine that facilitates an amortization schedule of a house loan as easily as that of a car. It makes provisions for depreciation (or appreciation) of the asset, as well as down payments. The input values include: sales price (include tax), down payment, life span of asset in years, interest rate, and number of monthly payments. The printed output of the program includes the monthly mortgage payment, the sum of the payments, total interest paid, current depreciated (appreciated) value, net equity, and unpaid balance on loan until paid off. It includes a graphic display of the unpaid balance, current value, and net equity.

The depreciation routine used is the *Variable Rate Declining Balance* method expressed in the equation:

$$V = P\left(1 - \frac{R}{L}\right)^k$$

where V = value, P = original value, R = depreciation (appreciation) factor, L = life span of asset, and k = current age of asset (in same units as L).

If the asset depreciates, as in most automobiles, use a positive value for R. For cars, a value between .50 and 1.75 is about right. For assets which appreciate in value, use a negative value. If you think you know how much the asset should be (V) after a certain number of years (k), you can estimate R from

$$R = L(1 - V / P)$$

We use this method for computing depreciation (appreciation) because it seems to present the most realistic curves. Straight line depreciation is the easiest to compute, but has few real-life counterparts. If the depreciation figures are to be used in an effort to evaluate tax options, it is suggested you use IRS-approved life spans for the given asset and the depreciation factors identified in official IRS documents.

Bonds

Bonds are a means by which a corporation raises capital. They are, in effect, fancy promissory notes, normally issued in multiples of $1000 each and are designed to be marketable for resale. For the life of the bond, anywhere from a few months to as long as fifty years or more, interest on the bond will be paid periodically, usually every six months. At the maturity of the bond, the face value or principal is paid. Frequently, the bond contains a provision which gives the seller the right to *call* the bond prior to the normal maturity date at some agreed upon price.

Buyers of bonds are primarily concerned with the return on investment or *yield to maturity* (YTM) of their bonds or that of bonds offered for sale. There are two ways to compute YTM. An approximation is quickly computed from:

1. $$C = \frac{1000X}{M}$$

2. $$YTM = \frac{2C}{P+M} + \frac{M^n}{P} - 1$$

Where X is the total annual interest income, M is the maturity value of the bond, P is the selling price of the bond, and n is the life of the bond in years.

There is a more accurate way to compute the YTM. In the algorithm below, the iteration makes an estimate of the selling price as a function of the maturity value and the annual interest rate. The iteration continues until the estimate closely matches the actual selling price. The assumption is that the value of r used to compute the estimate is equal to the yield.

1. Set r and delta r (dr) equal to some arbitrary value, normally .01.
2. Compute X, the estimate of price, from.

$$X = \frac{M}{(1+r)^n} + C\,\frac{(1+r)^n - 1}{r\,(1+r)^n}$$

3. If X is larger than P, go to step 4b, otherwise, go to step 4a.
4a. r = r + dr, go to step 2.
4b. r = r − dr.   dr = dr/2.   if dr is greater than .0000001, got to step 4a, otherwide, go to step 5.

5. r is approximately equal to YTM.

Additional bond-related equations include:

Present value: $A1 = M\,(1+r)^n$
Present value of interest payments:

$$A2 = r\,M\,\frac{1 - (1+r)^{-n}}{r}$$

Value of bond: $V = A1 + A2$
Listing 10-2 deals with bond values and equations.

Listing 10-2. Bond Values

```
1  '********************************************
2  'BOND VALUES                               *
3  'LISTING 10-2                              *
4  '********************************************
5  '
10 CLS
20 INPUT"WHAT IS THE CURRENT PRICE OF THE BOND";
     P
30 INPUT"WHAT IS THE MATURITY VALUE OF THE BOND"
     ;M
40 INPUT"WHAT IS THE AMOUNT OF THE ANNUAL INTERE
     ST PAYMENT";X
50 C=X/(M/1000):INPUT"FOR HOW MANY YEARS IS THE
     BOND";N
60 Y=((2*C)/(P+M))+((M/P)[(1/N))-1
70 PRINT"THE APPROXIMATE YIELD TO MATURITY (YTM)
      = ";Y*100;" %"
80 PRINT:R=.01:DR=.01
90 X=(M/((1+R)[N))+(C*((((1+R)[N)-1)/(R*((1+R)[N
     ))))
100 IFP>XTHEN120
```

200

```
110 R=R+DR:GOTO90
120 R=R-DR:DR=DR/2:IFDR>.000001THEN110
130 PRINT"COMPUTED YTM = ";R*100;" %":PRINT:GOTO
    20
```

GOODWILL

The procedures to compute goodwill are as varied and as many as there are accountants pouring over corporate financial statements. Nonetheless, the basic function of goodwill is as a component in evaluating the worth of a company, especially when the company is being sold. The computation, regardless of the process, is an effort to estimate the difference between two otherwise equally established businesses. For example, Joe and Sam both establish a produce store on the same street with the same amount of capital investment, more or less. Several years later, Joe's store earns a gross income of $93,500 annually, while Sam's store grosses $87,200. All other things being equal, we would say Joe enjoys $6,300 worth of goodwill. In real life, things are not quite that neat. A portion of Joe's superior profits may be more due to a superior location than his sparkling personality. In any event, one procedure for computing goodwill is found in:

$$G = \frac{E - A\,r}{R}$$

where E = estimated annual future earning, A = fair market value of assets exclusive of goodwill, r = normal industry rate of return on net assets, and R = 1/number of years earnings have been in excess of the industry norm.

Use the following values for the example above: both men have about $25,000 in net assets; Joe has earned an excess above the industry norm for the last three years and Sam, for the last two; the industry return on net assets is 3.25. The goodwill for the two stores can thus be computed from

$$Joe = \frac{93200 - (25000 \times 3.25)}{1\,/\,3}$$

$$= \frac{93200 - 81250}{.333333}$$

$$= \$35,850.00$$

$$Sam = \frac{87500 - (25000 \times 3.25)}{1\,/\,2}$$

$$= \frac{87500 - 81250}{.500}$$

$$= \$12,500.00$$

Joe's $35,850 is a composite of his personality and location, to the extent all other characteristics are normal. What part is location and what part is Joe is hard to determine. Only if Joe and Sam swap stories could we begin to sort out the answer. In any event, bankers are reluctant to loan significant sums on goodwill alone, especially in the event of the sale of a property in which the owner/manager (Joe) will not stay on to perpetuate the goodwill. It is, nonetheless, an acceptable measure of the health of a business. It is easily computed for small businesses with a single location and limited staff. In an event of major corporations with multinational facilities and operations, there are many other statistical tools for evaluation.

Return on Investment (ROI)

Investors use ROI to gauge how well an investment is proceeding or how likely a potential investment will prove worthwhile. It is a rate of return as a percentage of the amount invested. Corporations also use ROI as a measure of their success (or failure) in the market place. A simple approach is to compute ROI from

ROI = 100 ((A/P) − 1)

in which A represents the proceeds from a sale and P is the cost of the asset sold.

For example, if John buys a house for $69,500 and sells it at a later date for $81,000, the ROI is 16.5468 percent. An alternative approach is to use the amount of interest equation reviewed earlier in this section, $r = A\,/\,P - 1$, from $A = P\,(1 + r)^n$, where r is the ROI. Using the same data, and assuming John owned the house one year, the ROI is computed to be the same 16.5468. On the other hand, if he held the house four years, n = 4, and the ROI is computed to be only 3.9023 percent. The first approach gives John an estimate of the growth of his investment. Conversely, with a given investment amount (P), the user can compute the maximum length of time to hold an asset and still maintain an acceptable profit margin from: n = (log A/P)/(log(1 + 4)). The second approach allows him to compare the house investment with other investment options.

In a corporate setting the variables are much more complex and ROI is more easily computed as

$$ROI = \frac{Sales - Related\ Expenses}{(((N1 - L1) + (N2 - L2))\ /\ 2)}$$

where N and L are assets and liabilities, N1 meaning the beginning assets and L2 the end of period liabilities.

This approach is, in effect, a method to determine the ratio between net sales revenue to average net worth.

Selling Price

The following equations are useful in the computation of selling prices (s):

1. $S = C\ (1 + R)$ Markup on cost

2. $S = \dfrac{C}{1 - R}$ Markup based on price

3. $S = \dfrac{C}{1 = (R + r)}$ Markup on price w/ comm.

4. $S = \dfrac{C\ (1 + R)}{(1 - r)}$ Markup on cost w/ comm.

where R is the markup percentage, r is the salesman's commission, and C is the item cost.

For example, Harry's Furniture store has a policy of marking prices up 60% over wholesale (R = .60). At the beginning of the year, Harry decides to put his sales staff on a straight commission basis, paying 15% (r = .15). A new line of chairs has been delivered which have a $50.00 wholesale price. What price must Harry charge to maintain his normal margin? Using equation number 4,

$$S = \frac{C\ (1 + R)}{1 - r}$$

$$= \frac{50 \times 1.60}{.85} = 112.9411765$$

Harry will normally price the $50.00 chair (wholesale) at $112.94. So long as he keeps the actual selling price at C/(1-r) or in this case $58.82, or more, he will at least break even on the sale. In the long run he must do better than that to meet other expenses related to the operation of the store, but on individual sales he has the $54.11 margin to bargain with.

Breakeven Points

Many business ventures begin with a rosy glow of adventure and big profits. At the end of the first bill-paying session, however, the owners start looking for ways to avoid bankruptcy. In well-managed businesses, new ventures begin with estimates of sales volumes necessary to meet all expenses related to the starting up of the new venture and those related to the sale of the product. Another phase in the preliminary planning is an estimate of the market for the product. If the breakeven point is determined to be 100 units and market analysis can only support optimism for the sale of 25 units, the wise (or conservative) business will terminate development of the new product. We believe this is an area where considerable fortunes are made and lost (it also forms a large part of the justification for this book!) In real life the breakeven requirement is likely to be more like 3945 units while the market analysis suggests a market demand of something like 3925 or 3965. That one-half percent sampling error can make or break a struggling new company (and some long-established ones, too) and give executives a lot of gray hair.

There are two equations available for the determination of breakeven points. They both require the input to be in dollars (or other monetary units). The first produces a breakeven point in dollars (or other monetary units), while the second gives the point in units of the item to be sold. One is essentially equivalent to the other. The user selects the one which is more useful.

1. $B = \dfrac{\text{Total fixed costs}}{1 - \dfrac{\text{Total variable costs}}{\text{Corresponding sales volume}}}$

2. $B = \dfrac{\text{Total fixed costs}}{\text{Selling price - variable cost per unit}}$

For example, Harry has constant annual expenses totaling $75,000. These include the wages of the warehouse crew and the secretarial staff, plus rent and utilities. If he sells only those ugly $50 chairs, his breakeven analysis looks like this:

$B = \dfrac{\text{Total fixed costs}}{\text{Selling price - variable cost per unit}}$

$= \dfrac{75000}{112.94 - 50}$

$= 75000 / 62.94 = 1191.6111058$ chairs

Harry must sell at least 1192 chairs (no fractional chairs, please) to break even. If his own income is included in the $75,000, then he will survive the year; otherwise, Harry will have to sell some more chairs.

Total fixed costs consist of all the costs associated with the project that are not unit item-related; that is, plant construction and tooling costs, design costs, and other similar investments. Variable costs are unit item-related. These include the cost of materials, labor, transportation of the product, and administrative costs directly related to each item sale. Whether a cost is fixed or variable is determined by the answer to the question: does the amount vary with the number of units sold? That is, is the cost (Y) a function of the number of units sold (X) as in: $Y = A + B X$? If so, then the cost is a variable cost, not fixed.

METHODS OF STOCK MARKET ANALYSIS

As noted in the beginning of this chapter, Fig. 10-2 illustrates a generalized summary of market prices or their rough equivalent since 1800. Visual inspection suggests, and mathematical analysis confirms, that the data conform to a logarithmic trend. Based on the data in Fig. 10-2, 1900 to 1970, the equation takes on the form:

$\text{Log } Y = 3.839093 + .341027 X$

$r = .924022$

$X = \text{year}$

By projecting ahead, we can forecast the average industrial average to be 1000 in the year 1979, 2000 in the year 2000, 4000 in the year 2020, and so forth. But what does all this mean?

If the average stock price does continue to follow the pattern suggested by historical data, we must also note that wages and investment income, the primary means by which we purchase stocks, will rise to keep some sort of pace with the prices. If they don't, it is inevitable that prices would rise above a point where anyone could purchase the stocks. At that point the stocks become valueless! A thing is worth only what people can and will pay for them. Artwork may rise in value to a point beyond which most of us can afford. Some artwork may even become so esteemed that no meaningful value can be attributed to the object and no one, then, has the means to purchase the object. Stocks, on the other hand, however handsome their certificates may be, are not works of art to be held in awe and at a distance, but are the fundamental tools of the market place. A dynamic capitalist marketplace requires that the prices of stocks (partial ownership in business and the source of new capital) must remain within a certain relationship to the means to acquire these stocks. No sale of stocks yields no new capital, and therefore, no new growth. As economic growth slows, the ability of businesses to pay wages or dividends also decreases. As a consequence, there will be fewer resources available for stock purchases. Prices, therefore, should increase by some identifiable rate. Failure to maintain this relationship ultimately leads to a situation in which prices are high, relative to income, but sales volumes are very low. It seems logical, then, that wages can be expected to rise according to some exponential rate and that prices will rise ahead of wages/income for a period, until they have exceeded some market threshold, stabilize for a time, until income rises to a point where the price/income ratio is again "reasonable," then the prices will again begin to rise, and the cycle will repeat.

Left unattended, one might expect this model

to develop to a point where actual prices are stated in such large terms as to be unwieldly; e.g., in the tens of thousands of dollars for an average share of stock. At that point it might be prudent to issue new currency, restating the new monetary unit as a fraction of the old. $1.00 new would buy what $1,000 old did, but the computations would be much simpler. After one year growth at 10 percent, $1,000 would grow to $1,100. After revaluation, the price would grow from $1.00 to $1.10. The rate of growth is the same, 10 percent, but the numerical expression is easier to handle, mathematically. Politically, it may be more difficult to coax the population into believing $1 now is still the same as $1,000, but that's not the concern of the forecaster.

The primary significance of this long-term analysis is to predict where income and prices will ultimately head. It is understood that there will be periods of uncertain duration where both prices and income will deviate significantly from the long-term trend. The computed trend line is, however, not preordained, but simply a function of available historical data. As each day passes, that day's data becomes a part of the data base upon which such computations are based. A more accurate approach will make a provision for the inclusion of new data. Listing 10-3 is a routine to compute least squares trend lines, much like the programs in Chapter 5. The difference is that the routine begins with the accumulated historical data, then continues by a daily input of new data. At each entry point the trend line is recomputed and new forecasts made.

Listing 10-3. Economic Curve Fitting

```
1    '**********************************************
2    'ECONOMIC CURVE FITTING                       *
3    'LISTING 10-3                                 *
4    '**********************************************
5    '
10   CLS:@CLEAR
20   PRINT"******    CURVE FITTING    ******"
30   PRINT:PRINT"THIS ROUTINE ACCEPTS THE DATA IN
         PAIRED X,Y FORMAT AND ATTEMPTS TO   IDENTIFY
          THE BEST LINEAR OR CURVE FIT.  IT ALSO PRO
         VIDES AN ESTIMATE OF THE COEFFICIENT OF COR
         RELATION.":PRINT
40   @OPEN3
50   @INPUT N:PRINTN
60   PRINT:INPUT"ENTER NUMBER OF NEW PAIRS:";P:DIM
         XY(N+P),XX(N+P),YY(N+P):PRINT
70   FORI=1TO4
80      @INPUT E(I),F(I),G(I),H(I),J(I),K(I)
90   NEXT
100  @CLOSE
110  FORI=N+1TOP:INPUT"ENTER NEW X & Y VALUES:";X
         X(I),YY(I):NEXTI
120  CLS:PRINT"# ";"X ";"Y ","# ";"X ";"Y ","# ";
         "X ";"Y ","# ";"X ";"Y":FORI=1TOP:PRINTI;XX
         (I);YY(I),:NEXTI:PRINT
130  PRINT:PRINT"ARE THESE VALUES CORRECT?   (Y/N)
         "
140  QQ$=INKEY$:IFQQ$=""THEN140
150  IFQQ$="Y"THEN170
160  INPUT"ENTER ITEM NUMBER, NEW X VALUE, NEW Y
         VALUE:";I,XX(I),YY(I):GOTO130
170  CLS:PRINT@512,"PLEASE BE PATIENT, COMPUTING"

180  FORI=N+1TOP
190       X=XX(I):Y=(YY(I)):E(1)=E(1)+(X*Y):E(2)=
```

```
          E(2)+(X*LOG(Y))
200       IFXX(I)>LXTHENLX=XX(I)
210       E(3)=E(3)+(Y*LOG(X)):E(4)=E(4)+(LOG(X)*L
      OG(Y))
220       IFXX(I)<SXTHENSX=XX(I)
230       F(1)=F(1)+X:F(2)=F(1):F(3)=F(3)+LOG(X):F
      (4)=F(3)
240       IFYY(I)>LYTHENLY=YY(I)
250       G(1)=G(1)+Y:G(3)=G(1):G(2)=G(2)+LOG(Y):G
      (4)=G(2)
260       IFYY(I)<SYTHENSY=YY(I)
270       H(1)=H(1)+X[2:H(2)=H(1):H(3)=H(3)+LOG(X)
      [2:H(4)=H(3)
280       I(1)=F(1)[2:I(2)=I(1):I(3)=F(3)[2:I(4)=I
      (3)
290       J(1)=J(1)+Y[2:J(3)=J(1):J(2)=J(2)+LOG(Y)
      [2:J(4)=J(2)
300       K(1)=G(1)[2:K(3)=K(1):K(2)=G(2)[2:K(4)=K
      (2)
310       PRINT@640,"I =";I;
320 NEXTI
330 P=P+N
340 FORM=1TO4
350       B(M)=(E(M)-(F(M)*G(M))/P)/(H(M)-I(M)/P)
360       A(M)=(G(M)-B(M)*F(M))/P
370       R(M)=SQR((E(M)-F(M)*G(M)/P)[2/((H(M)-I(M
      )/P)*(J(M)-K(M)/P)))
380       PRINT@704,"M =";M;
390 NEXTM
400 CLS:PRINT"","A","B","R":PRINT"LINEAR:",A(1),
    B(1),R(1):PRINT"EXPONENTIAL:",EXP(A(2)),B(2
    ),R(2):PRINT"LOGARITHMIC:",A(3),B(3),R(3):P
    RINT"POWER:",EXP(A(4)),B(4),R(4):A(4)=EXP(A
    (4)):A(2)=EXP(A(2))
410 FORI=1TO6:R(I)=ABS(R(I)):NEXTI
420 IFR(1)>R(2)THEN460
430 IFR(2)>R(3)THEN480
440 IFR(3)>R(4)THEN510
450 M=4:GOTO520
460 IFR(1)<R(3)THEN440
470 IFR(1)>R(4)THEN490     ELSE450
480 IFR(2)>R(4)THEN500     ELSE450
490 M=1:GOTO520
500 M=2:GOTO520
510 M=3
520 PRINT
530 F$(1)="LINEAR":F$(2)="EXPONENTIAL":F$(3)="LO
    GARITHMIC":F$(4)="POWER":E$(1)="Y = A + BX"
    :E$(2)="Y = EXP(LOG A + BX)":E$(3)="Y = A +
     B LOG X":E$(4)="Y = EXP(LOG A + B LOG X)"
540 PRINT"THE BEST CURVE FIT IS ";F$(M):PRINT"TH
    E EQUATION IS: ";E$(M):PRINT"A =";A(M);"
    B =";B(M);"   R =";R(M):PRINT:PRINT"DO YOU
    WANT TO COMPUTE A TERM?  (Y/N)"
550 IFSX=>0ANDSY=>0THEN570
560 ZZ=1:PRINT:PRINT"(DATA INCLUDES NEGATIVE VAL
    UES, ONLY THE LINEAR EQUATION IS
```

Listing 10-3. Economic Curve Fitting (continued from page 205)

```
VALID.   IF ANOTHER FORM IS RECOMMENDED, PROGRAM
     WILL DISREGARD
AND COMPUTE LINEAR.)"
570 QZ$=INKEY$:IFQZ$=""THEN570
580 CLS
590 IFQZ$="N"THEN880
600 PRINT@960,"ENTER '@' TO STOP:";
610 PRINT@512,"WHICH VALUE (X OR Y) WILL BE ENTE
     RED?";:PRINT@576,"                    ";
620 QX$=INKEY$:IFQX$=""THEN620
630 IFQX$="Y"THEN680
640 IFQX$="@"THEN880
650 PRINT:INPUT"ENTER X-VALUE";X
660 ONMGOSUB710 ,760 ,800 ,840
670 GOTO700
680 PRINT:INPUT"ENTER Y-VALUE";Y
690 ONMGOSUB730 ,780 ,820 ,860
700 CLS:PRINT@384,"X =";X;"      Y =";Y:PRINT:GOT
     O590
710 Y=A(1)+B(1)*X
720 RETURN
730 X=(Y-(A(1))/B(1)
740 RETURN
750 RETURN
760 Y=EXP(LOG(A(2))+B(2)*X)
770 RETURN
780 X=(LOG(Y)-LOG(A(2)))/B(2)
790 RETURN
800 Y=A(3)+B(3)*LOG(X)
810 RETURN
820 X=EXP((Y-A(3))/B(3)
830 RETURN
840 Y=A(4)*(X[B(4))
850 RETURN
860 X=(Y/A(4))[(1/B(4))
870 RETURN
880 @OPEN3
890 @PRINT F
900 FORI=1TO4
910    @PRINT E(I),F(I),G(I),H(I),J(I),K(I)
920 NEXTI
930 @CLOSE
940 END
```

An alternative to this approach are the routines found in Chapter 6 for moving averages, exponential smoothing, and other time-series analysis.

Kondratieff Long Waves

Nicholai D. Kondratieff was a Russian economist who developed a number of economic theories regarding the behavior of capitalist economies. While his motives may have been less than friendly, his observations regarding Wall Street behavior bear some examination.

In Fig. 10-2, the upper data stream is a representation of the wholesale price index from 1800 to 1960. His analysis of such data led him to postulate a theory of long-term economic behavior in which prices fluctuate more or less according to the general wave form shown in Fig. 10-3.

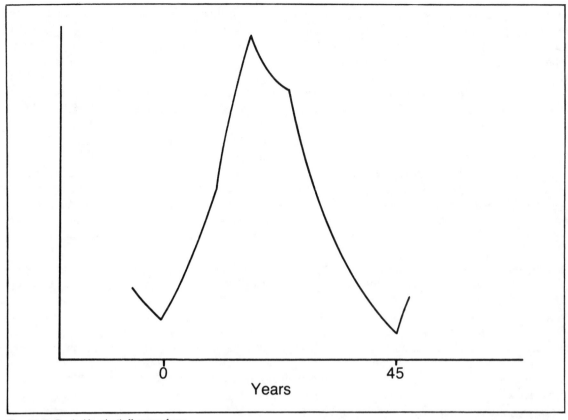

Fig. 10-3. Basic Kondratieff curve form.

This wave consists of three parts, according to Kondratieff.

A — A fairly long (25 years) period of strong growth.

B — A shorter length (8 years) plateau, marked at the start by a recessionary period.

C — A depressionary period of some 20 to 30 years.

If we superimpose the Kondratieff waves over the data from 1800 to about 1945, (Fig. 10-2) there is considerable conformity. Beyond that point, however, there is a significant deviation from the theory. Remember, also, that the illustration is drawn on a logarithmic chart in which changes in direction appear less dramatic than they really are. That is, slight deviations on a logarithmic chart are actually major changes on a linear chart (Fig. 10-5). The reader may want to adapt this theory for current data and track the market for the next few years to see if the market returns to the form predicted by the Kondratieff wave.

The original premise remains: the trend line, based on market averages, simply points to the general market mean. Individual stock prices can and will frequently deviate from the market trend. The market value of a given stock will vary as much as a function of specific industry conditions as it will as a function of the general market trend. During a period of generally healthy market, most stocks will reflect the health and growth of the market. A few stocks, however, will wither and die as the management of the particular firms make lethal errors, or as advances in technology make the particular industry obsolete. Likewise, technological advances or shrewd new managers may bring into being other businesses which bloom and experience a growth spurt at a rate far in excess of the general market trend. No simple computational procedure exists to foretell the birth of new investment opportunities. Technological forecasting (see Chapter 11) can provide indications of areas where new technology may encourage growth, but the specifics will remain generally unknown until the last moment. For these reasons, the potential investor is well-advised to retain the services of an experienced and skilled broker or investment counselor. By maintaining close watch over existing businesses, the investor may sometimes be able to spot signs of impending failure, but not always. Witness the Tylenol scare of 1982. Here was a superb product the value of which would remain a constant asset to the business and a prudent investment for the investor. Without warning, however, the poisoning done by one deranged individual devastated the market value of the parent company. We are still too close, however, to the event to say whether the firm can revise the manufacturing process sufficiently to overcome consumer fears and recover their share of market sales, thus restoring the market value of the company stocks. Many other businesses are similarly vulnerable to attack by insane individuals or terrorists. Where the acts of a madman can have an adverse impact on a decentralized industry across the nation, severe weather phenomena can have a similar unexpected impact on smaller businesses. Imagine what a large-scale earthquake or equivalent natural phenomenon in the Silcon Valley area of central California would do to the computer chip industry. While it would devastate the stock of the companies whose plant resources were destroyed, it would give an unnatural boost to the stock of the few companies in the industry located inside of the region. A secondary consequence is that those industries that depend upon integrated circuits (computers, microprocessors, etc.) would be unable to keep pace with their production orders and their stock value would also drop.

The market averages announced every evening on the radio, television, and newspapers are the averages of the sum of all the experiences each of the businesses in the market have experienced or are expected to experience in the near future. Some of the businesses have done well, perhaps in spite of common wisdom. Some of the businesses have done worse than one would expect.

Long-term analysis and forecasting of the market place suggests a generally upward trend. This means that, as a society, we are continuing to develop ways to sustain and improve our quality and quantity of life. We can even compute a fairly precise estimate of the direction and magnitude of this growth. Translating this information into a viable stock investment strategy is something else. The best and most obvious strategy is given in the quotation: "Buy low, sell high." Knowing when the bottom has been reached for buying or when the ceiling has been reached for selling is quite another matter, and requires considerable skill in evaluating the specific markets or business. It is for this reason that we encourage the reader to use the services of a professional investment counselor, and that we offer no super program with which to beat the market. The best we can do is offer those routines to help those interested to track the available data. For those seriously interested in stock market tracking, we recommend *Playing the Stock & Bond Markets with Your Personal Computer*, by L. R. Schmeltz (Tab Book No. 1251). His book contains several fine programs for microcomputer application.

A routine that might aid stock market analysis, in the meantime, is given in the Market Evaluator, Listing 10-4.

Listing 10-4. Market Evaluator

```
1  '***********************************************
2  'MARKET EVALUATOR                              *
3  'LISTING 10-4                                  *
4  '***********************************************
5  '
10 CLS:@CLEAR:CLEAR(768):PRINT"MARKET EVALUATOR"
      :PRINT:PRINT
20 PRINT"(USES ESF DATA I/O FORMAT TAPES)":PRINT
      :PRINT
```

```
30 PRINT"PROGRAM TO INPUT MOST RECENT DATA AND E
      VALUATE
MARKET TRENDS.":PRINT
40 PRINT"WILL THE LINE PRINTER BE USED?   (Y/N)
      ";:GOSUB990
50 IFQ$="Y"THENLP=1ELSELP=0
60 GOSUB830  :GOSUB1010
70 PRINT:PRINT"OPTIONS:":PRINT:PRINT
80 PRINT"          1  ----   TREND LINE WITH MEAN AN
     D STADARD DEVIATION
          2   ----   CORRELATION
          3   ---   MOVING AVERAGE
          4   ----   FINISH
SELECT   ";
90 GOSUB990
100 IFQ$="4"THEN1130
110 PRINT:PRINT"YOU HAVE";F;"PERIODS OF DATA, IN
      CLUDING THE";X;"NEW
PERIODS JUST ADDED.   ";:INPUT"ENTER THE NUMBER O
      F THE STARTING
PERIOD";S1:INPUT"ENTER THE ENDING PERIOD";S2:M=(
      S2-S1)+1
120 TX=0:TY=0:X2=0:Y2=0:XY=0
130 ONVAL(Q$)GOTO140  ,360  ,490
140 PRINT:INPUT"ENTER THE NUMBER OF THE FILE TO
      BE ANALYZED";F
150 CLS:PRINT"COMPUTING TREND LINE FOR ";N$(F)
160 FORI=S1TOS2
170    X=I:Y=M(F,I):TX=TX+X:TY=TY+Y:X2=X2+(X[2):Y
     2=Y2+(Y[2):XY=XY+(X*Y)
180 NEXTI
190 A=(XY-((TX*TY)/M))/(X2-((TX[2)/M))
200 B=(TY/M)-(A*(TX/M))
210 R=((M*XY)-(TX*TY))/SQR(((M*X2)-(TX[2))*((M*Y
     2)-(TY[2)))
220 AV=TY/M:SD=SQR((Y2-((TY[2)/M))/(M-1))
230 SE=SQR(ABS(((Y2-(A*TY)-(B*XY))/(M-2))))
240 SA=SQR(ABS((X2/(M*(X2-((TX[2)/M))))))*SE
250 SB=SE/SQR(ABS(X2-((TX[2)/M)))
260 PRINT:PRINT"LINEAR TREND FOR THIS PERIOD IS:
      Y = ";
270 IFA<0THEN310
280 IFB<0THEN300
290 PRINTA;" + ";B;"X":GOTO320
300 PRINTA;" ";B;"X":GOTO320
310 PRINTB;"X ";A
320 PRINT:PRINT"THE CORRELATION IS ";R:PRINT"THE
      MEAN OF THE DATA IS ";AV:PRINT"THE STANDAR
     D DEVIATION IS ";SD
330 PRINT"","STANDARD ERRORS":PRINT"OF ESTIMATE"
     ,SE:PRINT"OF A",SA:PRINT"OF B",SB
340 IFLP=1THENGOSUB1250
350 LPRINT"":PRINT:GOTO80
360 PRINT:INPUT"ENTER THE NUMBER OF THE FIRST FI
     LE";F1:INPUT"ENTER THE NUMBER OF SECOND FIL
     E";F2
370 CLS:PRINT"COMPUTING THE CORRELATION BETWEEN
      ";N$(F1);" AND ";N$(F2)
```

Listing 10-4. Market Evaluator (continued from page 209)

```
380 FORI=S1TOS2
390    X=M(F1,I):Y=M(F2,I)
400    TX=TX+X:TY=TY+Y:X2=X2+(X[2):Y2=Y2+(Y[2):XY
       =XY+(X*Y)
410 NEXTI
420 A1=TX/M:A2=TY/M:D1=SQR((X2-((TX[2)/M))/(M-1)
       ):D2=SQR((Y2-((TY[2)/M))/(M-1))
430 R=((M*XY)-(TX*TY))/SQR(((M*X2)-(TX[2))*((M*Y
       2)-(TY[2)))
440 PRINT:PRINT"THE CORRELATION IS ";R:PRINT
450 PRINT"FILE","MEAN","STANDARD DEVIATION"
460 PRINTN$(F1),A1,D1:PRINTN$(F2),A2,D2
470 IFLP=1THENGOSUB1250
480 PRINT:GOTO80
490 PRINT:INPUT"ENTER THE NUMBER OF THE FILE TO
       BE ANALYZED";F
500 CLS:PRINT"PERIOD","DATA","MOVING AVERAGE"
510 IFLP=1THENLPRINT"PERIOD","DATA","MOVING AVER
       AGE"
520 INPUT"ENTER PERIOD OF AVERAGE";A
530 FORI=S1TOS2
540    T=T+M(F,I):IF(S1-I)<(A-1)THEN580
550    PRINTI,M(F,I),T/A
560 IFLP=1THENLPRINTI,M(F,I),T/A
570    T=T-M(F,I-A):GOTO600
580    PRINTI,M(F,I),T/I
590 IFLP=1THENLPRINTI,M(F,I),T/I
600 NEXTI
610 IFLP=1THENLPRINT"PERIOD OF AVERAGE = ";A
620 GOTO80
630 PRINT"NUMBER OF FILES =";N,"NUMBER OF PERIOD
       S =";P
640 PRINT"FILE #","NAME","COMMENT"
650 FORI=1TON
660    @INPUTN$(I),C$(I):PRINTI,N$(I),C$(I)
670    FORJ=1TOP
680       @INPUTM(I,J)
690    NEXTJ
700 NEXTI
710 @INPUTFC$:PRINT:PRINTFC$:PRINT
720 @CLOSE
730 P=P+X:NF=X:RETURN
740 PRINT:PRINT"ALL DATA ENTERED CORRECT?  (Y/N)
       ";:GOSUB990
750 IFQ$="Y"THEN820
760 PRINT"CORRECT (N)AME  (C)OMMENT  (D)ATA   ";
       :GOSUB990
770 IFQ$="C"THEN790  ELSEIFQ$="D"THEN800  ELSEIF
       Q$<>"N"THEN760
780 INPUT"ENTER CORRECT NAME";N$(I):GOTO740
790 INPUT"ENTER CORRECT COMMENT";C$(I):GOTO740
800 INPUT"ENTER NUMBER OF PERIOD FOR CORRECTION"
       ;Y
810 INPUT"ENTER CORRECT VALUE";M(I,Y):GOTO740
820 RETURN
```

```
830 FC$=""
840 @OPEN3
850 @INPUT N,P
860 PRINT"THERE ARE";N;"FILES CURRENTLY ESTABLIS
    HED,
EACH WITH";P;"DATA ENTRIES.  HOW MANY
ADDITIONAL PERIODS TO BE ADDED",:INPUTX
870 DIM N$(N),M(N,P+X),C$(N)
880 GOSUB630
890 PRINT"ADD NEW DATA":PRINT
900 FORI=1TON
910   PRINTN$(I)
920   PRINT"IF DATA IS UNKNOWN, ENTER 0.   IF DAT
    A IS ZERO, ENTER .00001"
930   FORJ=P-X+1TOP
940     PRINT"ENTER DATA FOR PERIOD #";J,:INPUTM
    (I,J)
950   NEXTJ
960   GOSUB740
970 NEXTI
980 RETURN
990 Q$=""+INKEY$:IFQ$=""THEN990
1000 PRINTQ$:PRINT:RETURN
1010 FORI=1TON
1020   FORJ=1TOP
1030     IFJ=1THEN1100
1040     IFM(I,J)<>0THEN1100
1050     FORK=1TOP
1060       IFM(I,J+K)<>0THEN1090
1070     NEXTK
1080     M(I,J)=.00001:GOTO1100
1090     M(I,J)=(M(I,J+K)-M(I,J-1))/(K+1)
1100   NEXTJ
1110 NEXTI
1120 RETURN
1130 @OPEN3
1140 @PRINT N
1150 @PRINT P
1160 FORI=1TON
1170   @PRINTN$(I),C$(I)
1180   FORJ=1TOP
1190     @PRINTM(I,J)
1200   NEXTJ
1210 NEXTI
1220 @PRINTFC$:@CLOSE
1230 PRINT:PRINT"ALL DATA SAVED."
1240 END
1250 FORRC=0TO12
1260   FORCC=0TO63
1270     Z=PEEK(15360+(RC*64)+CC)
1280     IFZ<32THENZ=Z+64
1290     LPRINTCHR$(Z);
1300   NEXTCC
1310   LPRINT""
1320 NEXTRC
1330 LPRINT""
1340 RETURN
```

A useful feature of this program is the option to change or offset the relative phasing of the data. The user can experiment with various options to evaluate leading or lagging indicators, as well as concurrent indicators. For example, we know that unemployment is a *lagging indicator*, that is, the general state of the economy will usually improve a number of weeks (around 15) before we see an improvement in employment. We use this sort of indicator to validate market trends. That is, noting an improvement in the economy, we may want to examine the unemployment rate some 12 to 20 weeks later. If the offset rate shows a similar increase, we may accept the improvement as valid. On the other hand, if the lagging indicator reveals a downward trend, we may want to conclude the current trend is a fluke or nominal deviation.

OTHER BUSINESS AND ECONOMIC PROGRAMS

Many other tools exist to aid the small businessman in the conduct of his work. We offer a few of them here as useful applications of the microcomputer. Among them are: market sales price analysis, economic order quantity, lease/purchase evaluator, funds programming, investment amortization, and a useful spreadsheet routine.

Market Sales Price Analysis

In the Business Math section of this chapter we presented several equations to compute selling prices based on cost or selling price, with modifications for sales commissions. What the equations fail to do is to help the manager select an optimum sales price relative to the relevant market. What the selling price and breakeven equations do are to point to minimum prices necessary to survive. We need some other basis to help select optimum price levels.

Sales volume is a function of many variables, among them: location, advertising, sales team, local demand for the product (we presume it is harder to sell air conditioning in Nome, Alaska, than in Dallas, Texas), and price. If we own the only store in town for a given product or service, our price structure is more a function of our own needs than in locations with heavy competition. Seldom, however, do businesses operate without some competition. In a competitive environment, we must consider our price structure relative to the competition. If we truly have a superior product (or a lot of nerve), we might survive and prosper by charging a superior fee. If, on the other hand, our products or services (especially services) are roughly comparable, price needs close attention. All other things being equal, we assume that if our price is zero, or close to it, demand will be very great, perhaps close to 100 percent. Our profit, however, is really a loss. (Profit = Sales Income − (Expenses + Cost of Product). (Sales Income = Number of Units Sold times Selling Price.) At the other end of the spectrum, we know that even at a price significantly above the local price norm someone will buy the item. Although the income per unit sold increases, net profit again falls into a condition of net loss. A generalized illustration of this concept is shown in Fig. 10-4.

Given the number of competitors in a market area, we can compute fair market share simply by dividing the total number of potential customers by the total number of stores selling the same product or service and superimpose this value as a horizontal line across the figure. Sales above this line signify that we are doing something right and getting more than our fair share of the market, and, hopefully, making a profit. Sales volume, under any circumstance, below the fair market share is an indication that something is wrong. If the selling price is lower than the market norm, it is quite possible that some factor other than price is the villian. If your prices are significantly above the competition, perhaps you need to become more competitive. In any event, the program developed in Listing 10-5 helps evaluate your price structure in this context. It is difficult to specify just how sales volume will vary as a function of price in a given situation. Accordingly, we assume that sales volume will follow a generalized ogive or reverse S=curve pattern like the one in Fig. 10-5. An easy way to simulate an ogive curve is to use a variation of the arctangent curve where Y = ATN X. The program operates on the assumption that the curve is symmetrical about the normal price to the extent that the predicted sales volume will equal the market share, based on the specified number of competitors, when the sales price equals the market norm.

Using the market size, as well as the retail and wholesale prices, the program computes profit/loss as a function of the predicted sales volume (SV) (as a function of the ogive curve) times the retail price (RP) less the wholesale price (WP): Y = SV (RP – WP). It goes on to locate the maximum total profit and displays all the relevant data. Finally, it delivers a copy of the output to the printer.

Listing 10-5. Market Sales Price Analysis

```
1  '******************************************
2  'MARKET SALES PRICE ANALYSIS              *
3  'LISTING 10-5                             *
4  '******************************************
5  '
10 CLS:F1=-.08:F2=15
20 INPUT"ENTER ESTIMATED MARKET SIZE";MS
30 INPUT"ENTER NUMBER OF COMPETITORS IN MARKET A
     REA";NC
40 INPUT"ENTER THE RETAIL PRICE OF THE PRODUCT";
     RP
50 INPUT"ENTER THE WHOLESALE COST OF THE PRODUCT
     ";WP
60 CLS:AN=(RP*MS*(1/(NC+1)))-(WP*MS*(1/(NC+1)))
70 FORY=0TO43:SET(17,Y):NEXTY
80 FORX=17TO127:SET(X,43):NEXTX
90 Y=43-INT(43*(1/(1+NC)))
100 FORX=17TO127STEP3:SET(X,Y):NEXT
110 PRINT@0," 100 %";:PRINT@896,"   0 %";:SM=Y
120 PRINT@(64*INT(SM/3)),"S O M";
130 FORY=0TO43STEP2:SET(72,Y):NEXT
140 PRINT@993,"RETAIL = $";USING"####.##";RP;:PR
     INT" PER UNIT";
150 X=INT(55*(WP/RP))+17
160 FORY=0TO43STEP2:SET(X,Y):NEXT
170 PRINT@960+INT(X/2),"COST";
180 GOSUB320
190 FORX=17TO127
200   A=F1*(X+B-64):Y=23+(F2*ATN(A)):IFY>0ANDY<=
      43SET(X,43-Y)
210   AP=RP*((X-17)/55):SH=Y/43:NP=(MS*SH*AP)-(M
      S*SH*WP)
220   Y2=43*(NP/AN):IFY2>0ANDY2<=43SET(X,43-Y2)
230   IFNP<LGTHEN250
240   LG=NP:SP=AP
250 NEXTX
260 PRINT@422,"SELL AT $";USING"####.##";SP;:PRI
     NT" PER UNIT";:PRINT@486,"PROFIT = $";USING
     "#########.##";LG;
270 PRINT@614,"(S)UMMARY  (N)EW";
280 Q$=""+INKEY$:IFQ$=""THEN280
290 IFQ$="S"THEN390
300 IFQ$="N"THEN480
310 RESUMENEXT
320 FORB=NC*-5TONC*5
330   A=F1*(8+B):Y=23+(15*ATN(A))
340     PRINT@38,B;
```

213

Listing 10-5. Market Sales, Price Analysis (continued from page 213)

```
350   IF(43-Y)<SMTHEN370
360    PRINT@38,"    ",:RETURN
370 NEXTB
380 RETURN
390 LPRINT"MARKET SIZE =";MS,"WHOLESALE PRICE =
     $";WP,"AVERAGE RETAIL PRICE = $";RP:LPRINT"
     "
400 LPRINT"ACTUAL PRICE","EST. MARKET","INCOME",
     "COST","NET PROFIT","% OF AVE. NET":LPRINT"
     "
410 FORX=17TO127STEP2
420    A=F1*(X+B-64):Y=23+(F2*ATN(A))
430    AP=RP*((X-17)/55):SH=Y/43:NP=(MS*SH*AP)-(M
    S*SH*WP)
440    LPRINTUSING"####.##";AP,:LPRINTINT(MS*SH),
    MS*SH*AP,MS*SH*WP,NP,100*(NP/AN)
450 NEXT
460 LPRINT""
470 LPRINT"BEST MARKET PRICE ESTIMATED TO BE $";
     USING"####.##";SP
480 RUN
```

Economic Order Size

Whether a retail business acquires inventory on consignment or borrowed funds, or cash payment in full, it is faced with the problem of knowing how many of an item to order at a given moment. Even if there is no direct cost (consignment), there are associated costs in obtaining the items such as the cost of placing the order (phone bills, preparing order forms, filing, etc.) and receiving the items (stockroom labor), and the floorspace costs for storing the items until the time of sale. When the items are obtained on terms (borrowed money), there is the added cost of the money itself (interest paid). Paying cash in full ties up capital until the time of sale. In addition, that capital cost should include not only the capital itself, but the return on investment that capital could have earned if it had not been tied up in stock. The prudent businessman wants to have sufficient numbers of an item in stock so that, under normal conditions, there will be at least one available for sale when a customer wants one. On the other hand, he doesn't want to have any more on hand than are absolutely necessary tying up capital and warehouse space. In this area, there are four questions confronting him:

1. What is the maximum inventory (I2) that should be maintained?
2. What is the minimum inventory (I1) that can be allowed?
3. At what inventory level (P) should new stock be ordered?
4. What is the optimum order size (Q)?

The answers to these questions can be computed from the following relationships:

$D = T + 1$ — where T = number of days required to fill an order.

$I1 = D \, V$ — where V is maximum normal daily sales volume.

$P = T \, V + I1$ optimum order point.

$I2 = 0 + P$ — where 0 is the standard order size.

$$Q = \frac{2 \, C \, N}{M + A}$$ where A is the annual carrying cost per unit item and C is the cost to place an order.

Listing 10-6 implements these relationships, asking only that the user have available the five variables: T, V, O, C, and A. The program computes the remaining values, D, $I1$, P, $I2$, and Q and then recomputes $I2$ based on an assumption that O will be adjusted to equal Q. In circumstances where the wholesaler allows odd lot orders, this is a useful option. Lines 103-107 are available in the case where the items are obtained on interest-bearing terms. Even if the items are paid for in cash, one should use lines 103-107, using for R the available return on investment rate for investment capital.

Listing 10-6. Economic Order Quantity

```
1  '*********************************************
2  'ECONOMIC ORDER QUANTITY                     *
3  'LISTING 10-6                                *
4  '*********************************************
5  '
10 DEFFNA(A,B)=(116*(A/B-INT(A/B)))+11
20 DEF FNB(B,C)=43-(43*(B/C)-INT(B/C))
30 CLS
40 INPUT"ACTUAL UNIT REQUIREMENTS";N
50 INPUT"MAXIMUM DAILY REQUIREMENT";U
60 INPUT"NUMBER OF DAYS FOR SUPPLIER TO FILL ORD
      ER";T:D=T+1
70 I1=D*U:P=(T*U)+I1:PRINT"MINIMUM INVENTORY = "
      ;I1
80 INPUT"ENTER STANDARD ORDER";O
90 INPUT"COST TO PLACE ORDER";C:INPUT"UNIT COST
      OF ITEM";M
100 INPUT"ANNUAL CARRYING COST PER UNIT";A
103 'SECTION FOR CREDIT EVALUATION
104 PRINT"DO YOU FINANCE PURCHASES?   (Y/N)   ";
105 Q$=""+INKEY$:PRINTQ$:IFQ$="N"THEN107
106 INPUT"ENTER ANNUAL COST OF MONEY  (5%=5)";R:
      R=R/36525:RF=(R*((1+R)[(T/2)))/(((1+R)[(T/2
      ))-1):GOTO110
107 RF=1
110 A=A+(M*(1+RF))-M:I2=O+P:Q=INT(SQR((2*C*N)/(M
      +A)))+1
120 PRINT"MAXIMUM INVENTORY = ";I2:PRINT"ORDER P
      OINT = ";P
130 PRINT"OPTIMUM ORDER SIZE = ";Q
140 OA=Q:IA=OA+P:PRINT"ADJUSTED MAXIMUM INVENTOR
      Y BASED ON E.O.Q. =";IA
150 PRINT"AVERAGE INVENTORY PERIOD (ORDER TO ORD
      ER) =";365.25/(N/Q);"DAYS"
160 PRINT@960,"(G)RAPHIC DISPLAY    (P)RINTOUT";
170 Q$=""+INKEY$:IFQ$=""THEN170   ELSEIFQ$="G"THE
      N190   ELSEIFQ$="P"THEN350   ELSE170
180 RUN2
190 CLS:FORX=10TO127:SET(X,43):NEXT:FORY=0TO44:S
      ET(10,Y):NEXT
200 FORX=15TO127STEP5:SET(X,44):NEXT
210 MN=((N/Q)*C)+(Q*A):MX=(N*C)+(I*A):PRINT@0,MX
      ;:PRINT@898,O;:PRINT@963,O;:PRINT@1015,7*Q;
      :SM=MN:NQ=Q
220 FORI=1TO(7*Q)
230    OC=(N/I)*C:CC=I*A:TC=OC+CC
240    X=FNA(I,7*Q):Y=FNB(OC,MX):SET(X,Y)
250    Y=FNB(CC,MX):SET(X,Y)
260    Y=FNB(TC,MX):SET(X,Y)
270    PRINT@30,I,TC;:IFI<>QTHEN300
```

Listing 10-6. Economic Order Quantity (continued from page 215)

```
280    FORY=4TO43STEP2:SET(X,Y):NEXT:PRINT@(X/2),
       "Q";
290    PRINT@959+(X/2),Q;
300    IFTC>SMTHEN320
310    SM=TC:NQ=I
320 NEXT
330 IFSM=MNTHEN160
340 PRINT@0,"COMPUTED E.O.Q IS";NQ;".   NOW RECOM
       PUTING":Q=NQ:GOTO130
350 LPRINT"":LPRINT"ANNUAL REQUIREMENT = ";N;"UN
       ITS","MAXIMUM DAILY REQUIREMENT = ";U,"DAYS
       TO FILL ORDER = ";T
360 LPRINT"COST TO PLACE AN ORDER = $";C,:LPRINT
       "UNIT COST = $";M,"STANDARD ORDER = ";O;"UN
       ITS",
370 LPRINT"MINIMUM INVENTORY = ";I1;"UNITS","MAX
       IMUM INVENTORY =";I2;"UNITS","ORDER POINT =
       ";P;"UNITS"
380 LPRINT"OPTIMUM ORDER SIZE (E.O.Q.) = ";Q
390 PRINT:RUN10
```

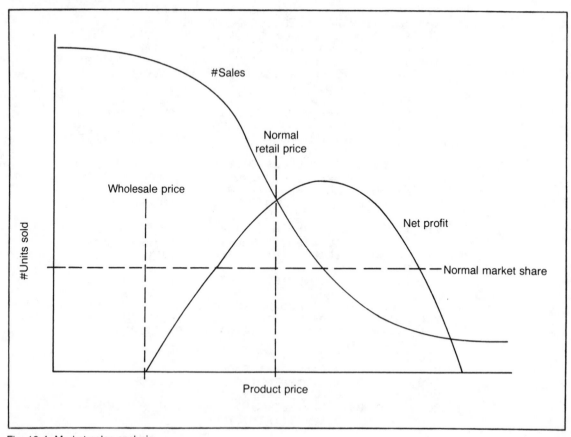

Fig. 10-4. Market sales analysis.

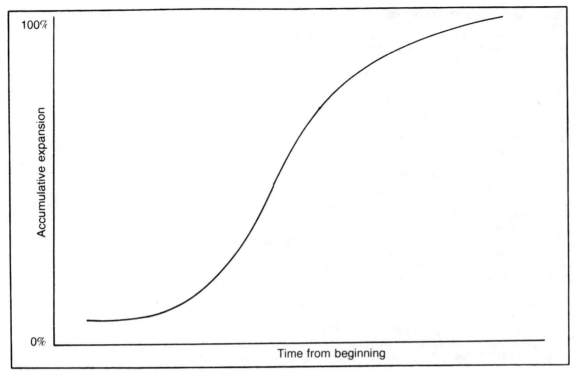

Fig. 10-5. Typical sales expansion record.

Lease-Purchase Evaluator

Businesses are often confronted with the choice of purchasing equipment or leasing it. The basic argument for leasing is that it lets the business hang on to the majority of its available capital for investment in machinery and goods that cannot be leased. For example, if a weaving machine costs $10,000, materials cost $10,000 (for a minimum run), and labor, for the minimum six-month run, costs $6,000, the cost to buy the equipment and pay for the minimum run is $26,000. If the owner has less than $26,000 available, the operation cannot even begin. If the weaving machine can be leased, however, at a cost of $300.00 a month, the cash requirement to open shop and run it for six months is $17,800. That's a 31.54 percent reduction in start-up capital required. In addition, the entire monthly payment of $300 is deductible as a business expense. If the machine were purchased, only the depreciation would be deducted. If the useful life of the machine is five years, the straight-line depreciation would be $166.67. Over the six months, the

difference is $800 (300 × 6 − 166.67 × 6).

Unfortunately, as with many things in real life, things aren't always that simple. There may be investment tax credits; the lease payment might be considerably higher; there may be security deposits required; or the effective interest rate on the lease could make the long-term cost of the equipment excessive. For example, a lease for 36 months, based on 24 percent, could result in payments of $392.33, or a total cost of $14,123.83, with nothing to show for it at the end. Listing 10-7 is a routine to compute the related factors in a lease/purchase situation leading to a comparison of both options in terms of long-term costs and benefits.

Investment Evaluator

This program is related to the previous routine in that it enables the comparison of two or more investment options in terms of long-term costs and benefits. With it the user can forecast likely return on investment and associated costs.

217

Listing 10-7. Lease-Purchase Evaluator

```
1  '************************************************
2  'LEASE-PURCHASE EVALUATOR                        *
3  'LISTING 10-7                                    *
4  '************************************************
5  '
10 CLS:PRINTCHR$(210);"****   COST ANALYSIS   ****
   ":PRINT:PRINT
20 PRINT"SYSTEM DESIRED:":PRINT:PRINT:PRINT
30 PRINT"              A  --    LEASE/PURCHASE EVA
   LUATOR
              B  --    ANNUITIES":PRINT:PRINT
40 PRINT"ENTER CHOICE";
50 Q$=""+INKEY$:IFQ$=""THEN50
60 IFQ$="A"THEN70    ELSE710
70 DIMA(50)
80 A$="#######.##        ######.##"
90 CLS:PRINTCHR$(212);"****   LEASE/PURCHASE EVAL
   UATOR   ****":PRINT:PRINT
100 INPUT"WHAT IS THE NAME OF THE ITEM";N$
110 PRINT"WHAT IS THE PURCHASE PRICE OF ";N$;::IN
    PUTPP:A(1)=PP
120 PRINT"DO YOU HAVE $";PP;"AVAILABLE IN CASH?
    (Y/N)",
130 Q1$=""+INKEY$:IFQ1$=""THEN130
140 IFQ1$="Y"THEN190
150 PRINTQ1$:INPUT"HOW MUCH CASH IS AVAILABLE";C
    A
160 CB=PP-CA:A(3)=CB:PRINT"CAN YOU BORROW/RAISE
    $";CB;"?   (Y/N)",
170 Q2$=""+INKEY$:IFQ2$=""THEN170
180 IFQ2$<>"Y"ANDQ2$<>"N"THEN160   ELSE200
190 CA=PP
200 A(2)=CA:PRINTQ2$:INPUT"BEST ANNUAL RATE OF R
    ETURN AVAILABLE ON INVESTMENTS   (5%=5)";X:I
    R=X/1200:INPUT"BEST INTEREST RATE AVAILABLE
    ON LOANS   (5%=5)";Y:LR=Y/1200
210 A(4)=IR:A(5)=LR
220 IFQ2$="Y"THEN250
230 N=LOG(PP/CA)/LOG(1+IR):A(6)=N
240 PRINT"YOU MUST INVEST THE AVAILABLE $";CA;"A
    T";IR*1200;"% FOR AT LEAST
";N;"MONTHS TO ACCUMULATE $";PP
250 INPUT"NUMBER OF PAYMENTS AVAILABLE IN TIME P
    URCHASE";LP
260 INPUT"AMOUNT OF DOWN PAYMENT REQUIRED IN EVE
    NT OF TIME-PURCHASE";DP
270 IFDP<=CATHEN290
280 N2=LOG(DP/CA)/LOG(1+IR):A(20)=N2
290 INPUT"ESTIMATED ECONOMIC LIFE IN YEARS";EL:E
    L=EL*12:A(8)=EL
300 INPUT"MONTHLY LEASE COST";ML:A(7)=ML
310 SV=.01*PP:PRINT"ESTIMATED SALVAGE VALUE (DEF
    AULT =";SV;")";::INPUTSV:A(9)=SV
320 INPUT"ESTIMATED TAX BRACKET (35%=35)";TB:TB=
    TB/100:A(10)=TB
```

```
330 CLS:PRINT"","","GROSS","AFTER-TAX NET"
340 CL=(EL*ML)-SV:A(11)=CL:A(12)=CL*(1-TB):PRINT
    "COST OF LEASING","",USINGA$;A(11);A(12)
350 A(13)=CL/EL:A(14)=A(12)/EL:PRINT"MONTHLY LEA
    SE COST",USINGA$;A(13);A(14)
360 A=PP-DP:MP=(A*LR*((1+LR)[LP))/(((1+LR)[LP)-1
    ):A(21)=MP:TP=DP+(MP*LP):A(22)=TP:A(23)=TP-
    ((1-TB)*(TP-A)):A(24)=A(23)/LP
370 PRINT"TIME PURCHASE COSTS",USINGA$;A(22);A(2
    3)
380 PRINT"MONTHLY TIME COSTS",USINGA$;A(21);A(24
    )
390 I1=CA*((1+IR)[EL):A(15)=I1:A(16)=I1-(TB*(I1-
    CA)):PRINT"INVESTMENT RETURN",USINGA$;A(15)
    ;A(16)
400 B=CA-DP:I2=B*((1+IR)[EL):A(30)=I2:A(31)=I2-(
    TB*(I2-B))
410 PRINT" LESS DOWN PAYMENT",USINGA$;A(30);A(31
    )
420 PRINT"   OPTION ADVANTAGES:"
430 IFCA<PPTHEN480
440 A(17)=A(15)-A(11):A(18)=A(16)-A(12):PRINT"LE
    ASE VS. PURCHASE",USINGA$;A(17);A(18)
450 A(25)=A(30)-A(22):A(26)=A(31)-A(23)
460 IFCA<PPTHEN480
470 PRINT"TIME PURCHASE VS. CASH",USINGA$;A(25);
    A(26)
480 A(27)=A(11)-A(22):A(28)=A(12)-A(23)
490 PRINT"TIME PURCHASE VS. LEASE",USINGA$;A(27)
    ;A(28)
500 GOSUB610
510 CLS:IFCA>=PPTHEN710
520 IFQ2$="N"THEN710
530 PRINT"YOU NEED $";CB;"TO COMPLETE A CASH PUR
    CHASE"
540 X=LOG(PP/CA)/LOG(1+IR):PRINT"IT WILL TAKE AT
    LEAST";X;"MONTHS TO SAVE THIS AT";1200*IR;
    " %"
550 IFX<LPTHEN710
560 F=CB:AP=F/(1.005*(((1.005[LP)-1)/.005))
570 Y=(CB*LR*((1+LR)[LP))/(((1+LR)[LP)-1):PRINT"
    THIS CAN BE SHORTENED TO";LP;"MONTHS THROUG
    H A LOAN"
580 PRINT"WITH PAYMENTS OF $";Y;"EACH.   INSTEAD
    OF A LOAN, A SINKING
FUND CAN BE CREATED WITH";LP;"PAYMENTS OF $";AP;
    "INTO
AN ACCOUNT PAYING AT A RATE OF 6% PER YEAR."
590 GOSUB610
600 RUN10
610 PRINT:PRINT"PRINTOUT DESIRED (Y/N)";
620 Z$=""+INKEY$:IFZ$=""THEN620
630 IFZ$="N"THEN700
640 FORI=0TO15
650   FORC=0TO63
660     LPRINTCHR$(PEEK(15360+(I*64)+C));
670   NEXTC
```

Listing 10-7. Lease-Purchase Evaluator (continued from page 219)

```
680    LPRINT""
690 NEXTI
700 RETURN
710 CLS:PRINTCHR$(210);"****   ANNUITIES & SINKIN
    G FUNDS  ****":PRINT:PRINT
720 PRINT"A SINKING FUND IS ONE WHERE A PERIOD P
    AYMENT IS PAID INTOAN
INTEREST-PAYING ACCOUNT FOR A SPECIFIED NUMBER O
    F PERIODS.   AT
THE END, THE ACCOUNT BALANCE WILL EQUAL THE DESI
    RED AMOUNT."
730 PRINT:PRINT"ENTER KNOW VALUES, USE 0 FOR UNK
    NOWN":PRINT
740 INPUT"AMOUNT OF FUTURE VALUE, DESIRED AMOUNT
    ";F:F1=F
750 INPUT"AMOUNT OF PERIODIC PAYMENT";P
760 INPUT"NUMBER OF PERIODS";N
770 INPUT"INTEREST RATE PER YEAR   (5%=5)";R:R=R/
    1200:RX=R
780 IFF=0THEN900
790 PRINT"TO BE ADJUSTED FOR INFLATION   (Y/N)";
800 Q$=""+INKEY$:IFQ$=""THEN800
810 IFQ$="N"THEN860
820 PRINT:INPUT"ENTER ANNUAL INFLATION RATE (5%=
    5)";I:I=I/1200
830 IFN=0THEN860
840 F=F*((1+I)[N)
850 PRINT"FUTURE VALUE ADJUSTED FOR INFLATION =
    $";F
860 IFP=0THEN930
870 IFN=0THEN910
880 IFR=0THEN940
890 PRINT:PRINT"ONE VALUE MUST BE = 0":GOTO740

900 F=P*(1+R)*((((1+R)[N)-1)/R):GOTO1000
910 IFQ$="Y"THEN1070
920 N=LOG(((F/P)*R)+(1+R))/(LOG(1+R)-1):GOTO1000

930 P=F/((1+R)*((((1+R)[N)-1)/R)):GOTO1000
940 DR=.01:RX=DR
950 FX=P*(1+RX)*((((1+RX)[N)-1)/RX)
960 PRINT@960,FX,RX,
970 IFFX<FTHEN990
980 RX=RX-DR:DR=DR/2:RX=RX+DR:IFDR<.0000001THEN1
    000 ELSE950
990 RX=RX+DR:GOTO950
1000 PRINT:PRINT"FUTURE VALUE            =   $";F
1010 PRINT"PAYMENT                =   $";P
1020 PRINT"NUMBER OF PAYMENTS      =   ";N
1030 PRINT"INTEREST RATE           =   ";RX*1200;
    " % PER YEAR"
1040 PRINT:INPUT"'ENTER' TO CONTINUE";ZZ
1050 RUN10
1060 END
```

```
1070 DN=1:N=F/P
1080 FX=F*((1+1)[N)
1090 PRINT@960,N,FX,
1100 PX=FX/((1+R)*((((1+R)[N)-1)/R))
1110 IFPX>PTHEN1130
1120 N=N-DN:DN=DN/2:N=N+DN:IFDN<.001THEN1140    EL
     SE1080
1130 N=N+DN:GOTO1080
1140 F=FX:GOTO1000
```

Listing 10-8. Investment Evaluator

```
1   '*********************************************
2   'INVESTMENT EVALUATOR                        *
3   'LISTING 10-8                                *
4   '*********************************************
5   '
6   'THIS PROGRAM ASSUMES THAT SOME ASSET WILL BE
        PURCHASED, EITHER FOR CASH, BORROWED FUNDS,
        OR COMBINATION OF BOTH, THEN PUT TO
SOME ECONOMIC FUNCTION RESULTING IN MONTHLY INCO
        ME.  THE PROGRAM HELPS EVALUATE THE NECESSA
        RY MATRIX OF VALUES TO
7   'ACHIEVE SPECIFIED OBJECTIVES.
8   '
10  CLS:A$="###,###.##"
20  N=0:PP=0:INPUT"PURCHASE PRICE OF ITEM";PP:P1=
        PP:IFPP=0THENN=1
30  TB=0:INPUT"APPLICABLE TAX BRACKET   (5%=5)";TB
        :TB=TB/100:IFTB=0THENN=N+1
40  IFPP=0THEN90
50  PRINT"WILL YOU FINANCE ANY PART OF $";PP;"  (
        Y/N)";
60  Q$=""+INKEY$:IFQ$=""THEN60    ELSEIFQ$="N"THEN
        90
70  PRINT:INPUT"   AMOUNT TO BE FINANCED";AF:INPU
        T"    INTEREST RATE (5%=5)";IR:RF=IR/1200:IN
        PUT"    TERM OF NOTE (# MONTHLY PAYMENTS)";T

80  P=AF*((RF*((1+RF)[T))/(((1+RF)[T)-1)):PRINT"
        THERE WILL BE";T;"PAYMENTS OF $";USINGA$;
        P:PP=(PP-AF)+(T*P)-(TB*((T*P)-AF)):PRINT"
        NEW PURCHASE PRICE = $";PP;
90  PRINT:UL=0:INPUT"USEFUL LIFE (YEARS)";UL:IFUL
        =0THENN=N+1
100 NI=PP*(1-TB)
110 LF=0:INPUT"ANTICIPATED LEASE FEE (MONTHLY)";
        LF:AI=12*LF:IFLF=0THENN=N+1
120 RI=0:INPUT"DESIRED RETURN ON INVESTMENT   (5%
        =5)";RI:R=RI/100:IFRI=0THENN=N+1
130 INPUT"SALVAGE/RESALE VALUE";SV
140 INPUT"TOTAL OF ALL COSTS INCIDENTAL TO PURCH
        ASE, LEASE AND RESALE";IC:SV=SV-IC
150 IFN=1THEN180
160 PRINT:PRINT"SORRY....ONLY ONE UNKNOWN":PRINT
        :GOTO20
```

Listing 10-8. Investment Evaluator (continued from page 221)

```
170 PRINT:PRINT"SORRY....CAN'T FIND UNKNOWN":PRI
    NT:GOTO020
180 SI=SV*(1-TB):NI=NI-SI
190 N=UL:IFPP=0THEN250
200 IFUL=0THEN260
210 IFTB=0THEN270
220 IFLF=0THEN280
230 IFRI=0THEN290
240 GOTO170
250 NI=NI+(AI/((R*((1+R)[N))/(((1+R)[N)-1)))):PP=
    NI/(1-TB):GOTO350
260 S=AI/NI:N=LOG(S/(S-R))/LOG(1+R):GOTO350
270 NI=NI+(AI/((R*((1+R)[N))/(((1+R)[N)-1)))):TB=
    (NI/PP)-1:GOTO350
280 S=(R*((1+R)[N))/(((1+R)[N)-1):AI=S*NI:LF=AI/
    12:GOTO350
290 R=.01:DR=.1:S=AI/NI
300 SX=(R*((1+R)[N))/(((1+R)[N)-1)
310 PRINT@896,"COMPUTING.... R =";R,
320 IFSX=STHEN350
330 IFSX>STHEN360
340 R=R+DR:GOTO300
350 SI=SV*(1-TB):N=UL
360 R=R-DR:DR=DR/2:IFDR>.000001THEN340
370 CLS:PRINT"PURCHASE PRICE = $";USINGA$;PP;:PR
    INT@29,"NET SALVAGE      = $";USINGA$;SV
    :PRINT@64,"USEFUL LIFE =";USING"###.##";N;:
    PRINT" YEARS";:PRINT@93,"ANNUAL DEPRECIATIO
    N = $";USINGA$;P1/N:PRINT@128,"TAX BRACKET
    =";TB*100;" %";
380 PRINT@157,"DEPRECIATED COST   = $";USINGA$;
    PP-(P1*TB)
390 IFP=0THEN410
400 PRINT"$";AF;"LOAN W/";T;"PAYM'TS @ $";USINGA
    $;P;:PRINT" EACH.":PRINT:GOTO420
410 PRINT:PRINT
420 PRINTTAB(24);"LEASE INCOME"
430 PRINT"","   MONTHLY","    ANNUAL","    TOTA
    L"
440 PRINT"GROSS";:PRINT@464,USINGA$;LF,:PRINT@48
    0,USINGA$;AI,:PRINT@496,USINGA$;N*AI
450 N2=N*AI*(1-TB):PRINT"NET",:PRINT@528,USINGA$
    ;LF*(1-TB),:PRINT@544,USINGA$;AI*(1-TB),:PR
    INT@560,USINGA$;N2
460 PRINT@607,"+ NET SALVAGE = $";USINGA$;SI
470 PRINT@671,"- ACTUAL COST = $";USINGA$;PP-(P1
    *TB)
480 PRINT@737,"NET INCOME  = $";USINGA$;SI+(N*AI
    *(1-TB))-(PP-(P1*TB))
490 PRINT"ANNUAL RETURN ON INVESTMENT = ";R*100;
    " %":PRINT"TOTAL RETURN ON INVESTMENT = ";1
    00*(((N2+SI)/(PP-(P1*TB)))-1);" %"
500 PRINT"DO YOU WANT A PRINT OUT OF THESE DATA?
    (Y/N)";
```

```
510 Q$=""+INKEY$:IFQ$=""THEN510   ELSEIFQ$="Y"THE
     N530
520 RUN10
530 LPRINT"ORIGINAL PURCHASE PRICE = $";USINGA$;
     P1
540 FORR=0TO13
550   FORC=0TO63
560     LPRINTCHR$(PEEK(15360+(64*R)+C));
570   NEXTC
580   LPRINT""
590 NEXTR
600 IFP=0THEN520
610 LPRINT"":LPRINT"LOAN SCHEDULE:":LPRINT"    AM
     OUNT FINANCED = $";USINGA$;AF:LPRINT"   ";T;
     "PAYMENTS OF ";USINGA$;P,:LPRINT"        TOTAL
      = $";USINGA$;T*P,:LPRINT"        INTEREST PAI
     D = $";USINGA$;(T*P)-AF
620 LPRINT"TAX-ADJUSTED MONTHLY COST =";USINGA$;
     (PP-(P1*TB))/T
630 LPRINT"":LPRINT"":RUN10
```

Funds Programming

This program is designed to aid program managers who have to manage several projects within a fixed budget. The characteristics of this kind of a problem include a matrix consisting of one or more project lines to be funded over one or more periods.

(The one program/one period condition is essentially a trivial problem, but the routine could accommodate it if necessary.) The program allows the user to specify the various initial matrix values and then permits modifications and adjustments to meet changing circumstances.

Listing 10-9. Funds Programming

```
1 '*****************************************
2 'FUNDS PROGRAMMING                       *
3 'LISTING 10-9                            *
4 '*****************************************
5 '
10 CLS:CLEAR500
20 PRINT"FUNDS PROGRAMMING":PRINT:PRINT
30 PRINT"THIS VERSION IS DESIGNED TO ALLOW THE U
     SER TO PRGRAM FUNDS OVER
A FIVE-PERIOD SPAN, WHETHER MONTHS, QUARTERS, OR
     YEARS.  IT WILLACCOMODATE UP TO 9 LINE ITE
     MS.  AT THIS POINT, INDICATE THE
NUMBER OF LINE ITEMS DESIRED:",
40 X$=""+INKEY$:IFX$=""THEN40    ELSEN=VAL(X$)
50 IF0<NANDN<10THEN60    ELSE10
60 A$="####.## ####.## ####.## ####.## ####.##
     ####.##"
70 PRINTN:PRINT:DIMLI(N,6),C(6),R(N),N$(N),CV(5)
     ,RV(N)
80 FORI=1TO5
90   PRINT"IS THERE IS CEILING LIMIT TO PERIOD #
     ";I;"?   (Y/N)";
100   R$=""+INKEY$:IFR$=""THEN100
110   PRINT"  ";R$:IFR$="N"THEN130
120   INPUT"ENTER CEILING";CV(I)
```

Listing 10-9. Funds Programming (continued from page 223)

```
130 NEXTI
140 FORI=1TON
150   PRINT:PRINT"ENTER NAME OF LINE ITEM #";I;:I
      NPUTQ$
160   N$(I)=LEFT$(Q$,12)
170   PRINT"IS THERE A CEILING LIMIT TO ";Q$;"?
      (Y/N)"
180   X$=""+INKEY$:IFX$=""THEN180
190   IFX$="N"THEN210
200   INPUT"ENTER CEILING VALUE";RV(I)
210   FORJ=1TO5
220    A=0:PRINT"ENTER BUDGET VALUE FOR PERIOD #"
      ;J;:INPUTA
230    IFCV(J)=0THEN290
240    IF(C(J)+A)<=CV(J)THEN290
250    PRINTA;"CAUSES THE PERIOD CEILING VALUE TO
       BE EXCEEDED BY";(C(J)+A)-CV(J);".
IS THIS ACCEPTABLE?   (CEILING WILL BE ADJUSTED.)
       (Y/N)"
260     X$=""+INKEY$:IFX$=""THEN260
270     IFX$="N"THEN220
280     CV(J)=C(J)+A
290     IFRV(I)=0THEN350
300     IF(R(I)+A)<=RV(I)THEN350
310     PRINTA;"CAUSES THE CEILING VALUE TO BE EX
      CEEDED BY";(R(I)+A)-RV(I);".
IS THIS ACCEPTABLE? (CEILING WILL BE ADJUSTED.)
       (Y/N)";
320     X$=""+INKEY$:IFX$=""THEN320
330     IFX$="N"THEN220
340     RV(I)=R(I)+A
350     LI(I,J)=A:R(I)=R(I)+A:C(J)=C(J)+A:TT=TT+A

360   NEXTJ
370 NEXTI
380 PRINT:INPUT"ENTER NAME OF OVERALL SYSTEM BEI
    NG PROGRAMMED";S$
390 PRINT"1 - DAILY  2 - WEEKLY  3 - MONTHLY  4
    - QUARTERLY  5 - YEARLY";
400 Z$=""+INKEY$:IFZ$=""THEN400   ELSEZ=VAL(Z$)
410 B$(1)="DAILY":B$(2)="WEEKLY":B$(3)="MONTHLY"
    :B$(4)="QUARTERLY":B$(5)="YEARLY"
420 P$(1)="DAY":P$(2)="WEEK":P$(3)="MONTH":P$(4)
    ="QUARTER":P$(5)="YEAR"
430 CLS:PRINT@33,P$(2);:PRINT@59,"ROW";
440 F=1:IFTT<10000THEN460
450 F=10[(INT(LOG(TT)/2.30259)-3)
460 IFF<>1THENPRINT@0,"SCALE = VALUES /";F;
470 PRINT@65,"#      ITEM";:PRINT@84,"1       2
            3         4        5       TOTAL";
480 FORX=0TO127:SET(X,7):NEXT
490 FORY=3TO11+((N+1)*3):SET(31,Y):NEXT
500 FORI=1TON
510   PRINT@128+(64*I),I;N$(I);:PRINT@128+(I*64)
```

```
          +16,USINGA$;LI(I,1)/F;LI(I,2)/F;LI(I,3)/F;L
          I(I,4)/F;LI(I,5)/F;R(I)/F;
 520 NEXTI
 530 FORX=0TO127:SET(X,3+((I+1)*3)):NEXT
 540 PRINT@128+(64*(I+1))+2,"COLUMN TOTAL";
 550 PRINT@128+(64*(I+1))+16,USINGA$;C(1)/F;C(2)/
          F;C(3)/F;C(4)/F;C(5)/F;TT/F;
 560 FORY=3TO11+(I*3):SET(112,Y):NEXT
 570 PRINT@896,"ARE THESE DATA ACCEPTABLE?   (Y/N)
          ";
 580 Q$=""+INKEY$:IFQ$=""THEN580
 590 IFQ$="Y"THEN760
 600 PRINT@896,CHR$(253);:PRINT@896,"ENTER THE CO
          RRECT VALUE, ROW, AND COLUM TO BE ENTERED";
          :INPUTX,R,C
 610 A=LI(R,C)
 620 IFCV(C)=0THEN680
 630 IF(C(C)+X-A)<=CV(C)THEN680
 640 PRINT@896,CHR$(253);:PRINT@896,X;"CAUSES THE
           PERIOD CEILING TO BE EXCEEDED.  OK?  (Y/N)
          ";
 650 Q$=""+INKEY$:IFQ$=""THEN650
 660 IFQ$="N"THEN600
 670 CV(C)=CV(C)+X-A
 680 IFRV(R)=0THEN740
 690 IF(R(R)+X-A)<=RV(R)THEN740
 700 PRINT@896,CHR$(253);:PRINT@896,X;"CAUSES THE
           LINE CEILING TO BE EXCEEDED. OK?  (Y/N)";
 710 Q$=""+INKEY$:IFQ$=""THEN710
 720 IFQ$="N"THEN600
 730 RV(R)=RV(R)+X-A
 740 TT=TT+X-A:C(C)=C(C)+X-A:R(R)=R(R)+X-A:LI(R,C
          )=X
 750 GOTO430
 760 PRINT@896,CHR$(253);:PRINT@896,"PRINTOUT DES
          IRED?  (Y/N)";
 770 Q$=""+INKEY$:IFQ$=""THEN770
 780 IFQ$="Y"THEN820
 790 PRINT@896,"TOUCH ANY KEY FOR ANOTHER COMPUTA
          TION";
 800 Q$=""+INKEY$:IFQ$=""THEN800
 810 RUN
 820 FORR=0TON+4
 830   FORC=0TO63
 840     A=PEEK(15360+(R*64)+C)
 850     IFA>31ANDA<91THEN870
 860     LPRINT" ";:GOTO880
 870     LPRINTCHR$(A);
 880   NEXTC
 890   LPRINT""
 900 NEXTR
 910 LPRINT"":LPRINTB$(2);" BUDGET PROGRAM FOR ";
          S$:LPRINT""
 920 GOTO790
```

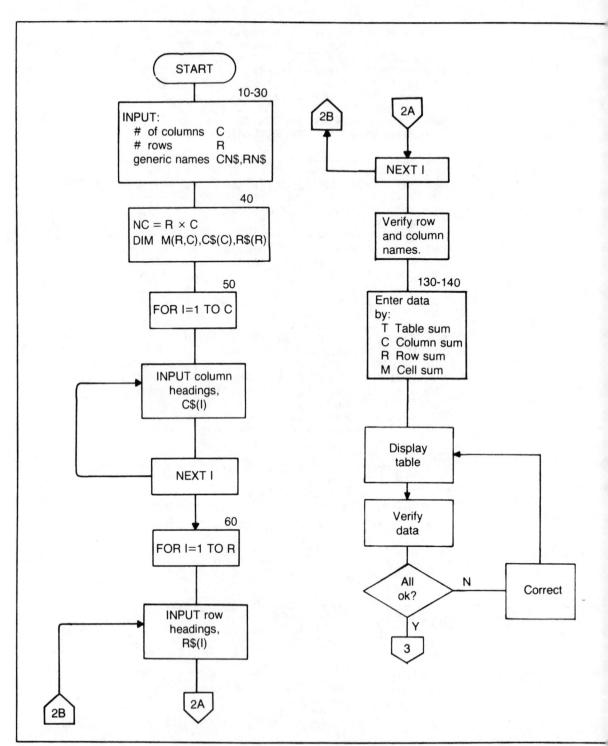

Fig. 10-6. Flowchart of Listing 10-10.

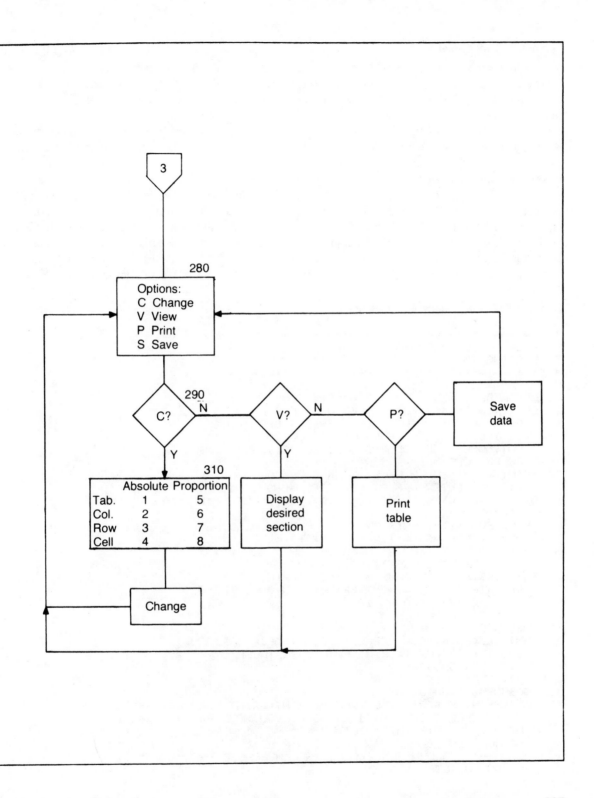

Poorman's Spreadsheet

An outgrowth of the previous program, this routine provides an inexpensive, but useful version of a number of ledger-sheet computational routines. The basic design as shown in Fig. 10-6 is simple. The user defines the name and number of rows (R) and columns (C) that will constitute the worksheet. Then, the matrix values can be entered in several different modes. In the first mode, the user specifies the table total (T) from which the computer calculates $(N = R \times C)$ cell values as an equal fraction of the total $(M = T/N)$. In the second mode, the user specifies either the column or row totals for each row or column, then the computer enters the appropriate fractional values. In the third mode, the user may specify each of the cell values individually. The computer then computes row, column, and table totals. At this point, the user can vary cell values by any one of the three modes just used to establish the initial array. Having selected the mode, the user then selects the manner of adjustment. This can be either an additive process or a multiplicative process. In the additive process the adjustment factor can be either positive or negative (creating a subtractive process). In the multiplicative process an input number greater than one results in a multiplication of the specified cells. If the input factor is less than one, a division process is created. This processing can be repeated as necessary until the desired relationships are achieved.

Listing 10-10. Poor Man's Spreadsheet

```
1   '*****************************************
2   'POOR MAN'S SPREADSHEET                 *
3   'LISTING 10-10                          *
4   '*****************************************
5   '
10  CLEAR500:A$="%     %   ":B$="####.##   ":C$=B$
20  CLS:PRINTCHR$(212);"SPREADSHEET FORECASTING":
    PRINT:PRINT:PRINT"(NOTE: THE PROGRAM AUTOMA
    TICALLY CREATES ROW AND COLUMN TOTALS)":IN
    PUT"NUMBER OF COLUMNS DESIRED";C:INPUT"NUMB
    ER OF ROWS DESIRED";R
30  PRINT:INPUT"ENTER GENERIC NAME OF COLUMNS";CN
    $:INPUT"ENTER GENERIC NAME OF ROWS";RN$
40  DIM M(R,C),C$(C),R$(R):NC=R*C:C$(0)="TOTAL":R
    $(0)="TOTAL"
50  PRINT:FORI=1TOC:PRINT"NAME OF COLUMN HEADING
    #";I,:INPUTV$:C$(I)=LEFT$(V$,6):NEXT
60  PRINT:FORI=1TOR:PRINT"NAME OF ROW LABEL #";I,
    :INPUTV$:R$(I)=LEFT$(V$,6):NEXT
70  F=-1:CLS:PRINT"COLUMN HEADINGS":PRINT:FORI=1T
    OC:PRINTI;C$(I),:NEXT:PRINT:PRINT"ARE THESE
    OK?  (Y/N)";:GOSUB910
80  IFQ$="Y"THEN100
90  GOSUB950  :GOTO70
100 F=1:CLS:PRINT"ROW LABELS":PRINT:FORI=1TOR:PR
    INTI;R$(I),:NEXT:PRINT:PRINT"ARE THESE OK?
    (Y/N)";:GOSUB910
110 IFQ$="Y"THEN130
120 GOSUB950  :GOTO100
130 CLS:PRINTCHR$(212);"OPTIONS":PRINT:PRINT:PRI
    NT"TO CREATE THE INITIAL TABLE, YOU HAVE FO
    UR OPTIONS:":PRINT:PRINT:PRINT"    1    --
    TABLE SUM
    2    --    COLUMN SUM   (CELLS ARE AVERAGED FR
    OM COLUM TOTAL)"
```

228

```
140 PRINT"      3  --   ROW SUM  (CELLS ARE AVER
    AGED FROM ROW TOTAL)
          4  --    EACH CELL FILLED INDIVIDUALLY":PRI
    NT:PRINT:PRINT"SELECT OPTION":GOSUB910
150 ONVAL(Q$)GOTO160 ,190 ,230 ,250
160 CLS:PRINTCHR$(212);"TOTAL SUM FILL PROCESS":
    PRINT:PRINT:INPUT"ENTER THE SUM OF ALL VALU
    ES OF THE TABLE.";TS:CV=TS/NC:PRINT:PRINT"T
    HANK YOU.    THIS WILL CAUSE THE VALUE";CV;"

TO BE ENTERED THROUGHOUT THE MATRIX.    NOW LOADIN
    G...":PRINT
170 FORI=1TOR:FORJ=1TOC:M(I,J)=CV:NEXTJ:NEXTI
180 GOTO270
190 CLS:PRINTCHR$(212);"COLUMN SUM FILL PROCESS"
    :PRINT:PRINT
200 FORI=1TOC:PRINT"ENTER THE SUM OF THE";R;"CEL
    LS IN COLUMN";I,:INPUTX:M(0,I)=X:FORJ=1TOR:
    M(0,0)=M(0,0)+X/R:M(J,I)=X/R:NEXTJ:NEXTI:PR
    INT
210 PRINT"THE TABLE TOTAL IS";M(0,0)
220 GOTO270
230 CLS:PRINTCHR$(212);"ROW SUM FILL PROCESS":PR
    INT:PRINT
240 FORI=1TOR:PRINT"ENTER THE SUM OF THE";C;"CEL
    LS IN ROW";I,:INPUTX:M(I,0)=X:FORJ=1TOC:M(I
    ,J)=X/C:M(0,0)=M(0,0)+(X/R):NEXTJ:NEXTI:PRI
    NT:GOTO210
250 CLS:PRINTCHR$(212);"INDIVIDUAL CELL FILL PRO
    CESS":PRINT:PRINT
260 FORI=1TOR:FORJ=1TOC:PRINT"ENTER VALUE FOR RO
    W #";I;", COLUMN #";J,:INPUT X:M(I,J)=X:M(I
    ,0)=M(I,0)+X:M(0,J)=M(0,J)+X:M(0,0)=M(0,0)+
    X:NEXTJ:NEXTI:GOTO210
270 GOSUB580  :PRINT:PRINT"THE TABLE IS FILLED W
    ITH THE INITIAL DATA SET."
280 PRINT"YOU NOW HAVE THESE OPTIONS:":PRINT:PRI
    NT"(C)HANGE  (V)IEW  (P)RINT  (T)ABLE PRINT
       (N)EW":PRINT:PRINT"SELECT",:GOSUB910
290 IFQ$="C"THEN310  ELSEIFQ$="V"THEN680     ELSE
    IFQ$="P"THEN690  ELSEIFQ$="T"THEN970        E
    LSEIFQ$<>"N"GOSUB910

300 RUN
310 CLS:PRINTCHR$(212);"CHANGE OPTIONS":PRINT:PR
    INT"YOU MAY CHANGE THE TABLE VALUES BY AN A
    BSOLUTE OR PROPORTIONATE VALUE.   AS WITH TH
    E INITIAL DATA ENTRY, CHANGES MAY BE MADE F
    OR THE TABLE, COLUMN OR ROW.   FROM THE TABL
    E BELOW, SELECT YOUR     OPTION:"
320 PRINT:PRINT"","ABSOLUTE","PROPORTIONATE":PRI
    NT"TABLE","  1","  5":PRINT"COLUMN","  2","
      6":PRINT"ROW","  3","  7":PRINT"CELL","
    4","  8":GOSUB910
330 IFQ$>"4"THEN540
340 PRINT:INPUT"ENTER THE DESIRED ABSOLUTE VALUE
    ";U
350 PRINT"(A)DD                 (M)ULTIPLY",:GOSUB930
```

Listing 10-10. Poor Man's Spreadsheet (continued from page 229)

```
360 IFZ$="A"THEN370  ELSE380
370 ONVAL(Q$)GOTO390  ,410  ,450  ,490
380 ONVAL(Q$)GOTO400  ,430  ,470  ,490
390 FORI=1TOR:FORJ=1TOC:M(I,J)=M(I,J)+(V/NC):NEX
    T:NEXT:GOTO570
400 FORI=1TOR:FORJ=1TOC:M(I,J)=M(I,J)*V:NEXT:NEX
    T:GOTO570
410 INPUT"ENTER COLUMN NUMBER";C1
420 FORI=1TOR:M(I,C1)=M(I,C1)+(V/R):NEXT:GOTO570

430 INPUT"ENTER COLUMN NUMBER";C1
440 FORI=1TOR:M(I,C1)=M(I,C1)*V:NEXT:GOTO570
450 INPUT"ROW NUMBER";R1
460 FORI=1TOC:M(R1,I)=M(R1,I)+V:NEXT:GOTO570
470 INPUT"ENTER ROW NUMBER";R1
480 FORI=1TOC:M(R1,I)=M(R1,I)*V:NEXT:GOTO570
490 INPUT"ENTER CELL ROW/COLUMN COORDINATES, AND
     VALUE";X,Y,V
500 ONVAL(Z$)GOTO510  ,520
510 M(X,Y)=M(X,Y)+V:GOTO570
520 M(X,Y)=M(X,Y)*V:GOTO570
530 GOTO570
540 PRINT:INPUT"ENTER DESIRED PERCENTAGE CHANGE
    (5%=5)";V:V=V/100
550 ONVAL(Q$)-4GOTO400  ,430  ,470  ,560
560 INPUT"ENTER CELL ROW, COLUMN NUMBER";X,Y:GOT
    O520
570 '
580 M(0,0)=0:FORI=0TOC:M(0,I)=0:NEXTI:FORI=0TOR:
    M(I,0)=0:NEXT:FORI=0TOR:FORJ=0TOC:M(0,0)=M(
    0,0)+M(I,J):M(0,J)=M(0,J)+M(I,J):M(I,0)=M(I
    ,0)+M(I,J):NEXTJ:NEXTI
590 LG=M(1,1):SM=M(1,1)
600 FORI=1TOR:FORJ=1TOC
610   IFM(I,J)<=LGTHEN630
620   LG=M(I,J)
630   IFSM<=M(I,J)THEN650
640   SM=M(I,J)
650 NEXTJ:NEXTI
660 F=INT(LOG(LG)/LOG(10))-1:IFF=-1THENF=0
670 GOTO280
680 PRINT:INPUT"ENTER FIRST ROW AND FIRST COLUMN
     TO BE DISPLAYED";R1,C1
690 CLS:PRINT@8+((C/2)*8),CN$:PRINTUSINGA$;RN$;
700 FORI=C1TOC1+5
710   IFI>CTHEN730
720   PRINTUSINGA$;C$(I);
730 NEXT
740 PRINT"TOTAL   "
750 FORI=R1TOR1+10
760   IFI>RTHEN840
770   PRINTUSINGA$;R$(I);
780   FORJ=C1TOC1+5
790     IFJ>CTHEN810
800       PRINTUSINGB$;M(I,J)/(10[F);
```

```
810    NEXTJ
820    PRINTUSINGC$;M(I,0)
830 NEXTI
840 PRINT"TOTAL     ";
850 FORI=C1TOC1+5
860    IFI>CTHEN890
870    PRINTUSINGC$;M(0,I)/(10[F);
880 NEXT
890 PRINTUSINGC$;M(0,0)/(10[F)
900 PRINT@960,"(C)HANGE  (V)IEW  (P)RINT  (N)EW
       (T)ABLE PRINT    SELECT";:GOSUB910   :GOTO29
       0
910 Q$=""+INKEY$:IFQ$=""THEN910
920 RETURN
930 Z$=""+INKEY$:IFZ$=""THEN930
940 RETURN
950 PRINT:INPUT"ENTER NUMBER AND CORRECTED NAME"
       ;N,X$:IFF=1THENR$(N)=X$ELSEC$(N)=X$
960 RETURN
970 LPRINT"","","",C$(0):LPRINTUSINGA$;R$(0);:A=
       1:B=14
980 FORI=ATOB
990    IFI>CTHEN1020
1000    LPRINTUSINGA$;C$(I);
1010 NEXT
1020 LPRINT"TOTAL"
1030 FORI=1TOR
1040    IFI>RTHEN1120
1050    LPRINTUSINGA$;R$(I);
1060    FORJ=ATOB
1070      IFJ>CTHEN1090
1080      LPRINTUSINGB$;M(I,J)/(10[F);
1090    NEXTJ
1100    LPRINTUSINGC$;M(I,0)/(10[F)
1110 NEXTI
1120 LPRINT"TOTAL     ";
1130 A=1:B=C
1140 FORI=ATOB:LPRINTUSINGB$;M(0,I);:NEXT
1150 LPRINTUSINGC$;M(0,0)/(10[F);
1160 A=B+1:IFA>CTHEN1190
1170 B=A+13:IFB>CTHENB=C
1180 LPRINT"":GOTO970
1190 GOTO290
```

Market Trend Evaluation

Listings 10-11 and 10-12 help the user evaluate different market trends.

EXERCISES

1. Figure 10-7 shows the difference between the appreciated balance of two invest-

Listing 10-11. Market Evaluator—Data Base Manager

```
1 '*********************************************
2 'MARKET EVALUATOR -- DATA BASE MANAGER    *
3 'LISTING 10-11                             *
4 '*********************************************
5 '
```

```
10 CLS:@CLEAR:PRINT"MARKET EVALUATOR -- DATA BAS
      E MANAGER":PRINT:PRINT
20 PRINT"(USES ESF DATA I/O FORMAT TAPES)":PRINT
      :PRINT
30 PRINT"PROGRAM TO CORRECT EXISTING OR ADD NEW
      FILES.


                      1  --   CORRECT
                      2  --   ADD NEW
                      3  --   FINISH AND RECORD
SELECT  ";
40 GOSUB790
50 ONVAL(Q$)GOTO60   ,340  ,810
60 GOSUB70   :GOTO200
70 @OPEN3
80 @INPUTN,P:DIM N$(N),M(N,P),C$(N)
90 PRINT"NUMBER OF FILES =";N,"NUMBER OF PERIODS
      =";P
100 PRINT"FILE #","NAME","COMMENT"
110 FORI=1TON
120    @INPUTN$(I),C$(I):PRINTI,N$(I),C$(I)
130    FORJ=1TOP
140       @INPUTM(I,J)
150    NEXTJ
160 NEXTI
170 @INPUTFC$:PRINT:PRINTFC$:PRINT
180 @CLOSE
190 RETURN
200 PRINT:PRINT"SELECT FILE NUMBER OF ITEM TO BE
      CORRECTED   ";
210 GOSUB790
220 PRINTQ$:Q=VAL(Q$):PRINT:PRINT"WHICH AREA WIL
      L BE CORRECTED?


                      1  --   NAME
                      2  --   PERIOD REPORT
                      3  --   COMMENT
                      4  --   MASTER FILE COMMENT

SELECT   ";
230 GOSUB790
240 ONVAL(Q$)GOTO250  ,260  ,280   ,290
250 INPUT"ENTER CORRECT NAME";N$(Q):GOTO300
260 PRINT"THERE ARE";P;"PERIODS ON FILE, WHICH O
      NE DO YOU NEED
TO CORRECT   ";:INPUTX
270 PRINT"THE CURRENT VALUE IS ";M(Q,X);".   ENTE
      R CORRECT VALUE.",:INPUTM(Q,X):GOTO300
280 INPUT"ENTER NEW COMMENT";C$(Q):GOTO300
290 INPUT"ENTER NEW MASTER FILE COMMENT";FC$
300 PRINT:PRINT"                    1  --  ANOTHER F
      ILE
                  2  --  FINISH
SELECT   ";
310 GOSUB790
```

```
320 ONVAL(Q$)GOTO330  ,810
330 PRINT:FORI=1TON:PRINTI,N$(I):NEXT:GOTO200
340 PRINT:PRINT"                    1 --  CREATE NE
    W SYSTEM
                    2  --  ADD TO EXISTING SYSTEM
SELECT  ";
350 GOSUB790
360 ONVAL(Q$)GOTO370  ,630
370 CLS:PRINT"NEW SYSTEM CREATOR":PRINT:PRINT:IN
    PUT"NUMBER OF FILES TO BE BUILT";N
380 INPUT"NUMBER OF DATA PERIODS AVAILABLE";P
390 DIM N$(N),M(N,P),C$(N)
400 FORI=1TON
410   PRINT"ENTER NAME OF FILE #";I,:INPUTN$(I)
420   PRINT"IF DATA IS UNKNOWN, ENTER 0.  IF DAT
    A IS ZERO, ENTER .00001
430   FORJ=1TOP
440     PRINT"ENTER DATA FOR PERIOD #";J;:INPUTM
    (I,J)
450    NEXTJ
460    GOSUB480
470   C$(I)=" ":INPUT"ENTER FILE COMMENT, IF ANY
    ";C$(I):GOTO570
480   PRINT:PRINT"ALL DATA ENTERED CORRECT?  (Y/
    N)  ";:GOSUB790
490   IFQ$="Y"THEN560
500   PRINT"CORRECT (N)AME  (C)OMMENT  (D)ATA
    ";:GOSUB790
510   IFQ$="C"THEN530  .ELSEIFQ$="D"THEN540  ELSE
    IFQ$<>"N"THEN500
520   INPUT"ENTER CORRECT NAME";N$(I):GOTO480
530   INPUT"ENTER CORRECT COMMENT";C$(I):GOTO480

540   INPUT"ENTER NUMBER OF PERIOD FOR CORRECTIO
    N";X
550   INPUT"ENTER CORRECT VALUE";M(I,X):GOTO480

560    RETURN
570 NEXTI
580 PRINT:PRINT"DO YOU HAVE A MASTER FILE COMMEN
    T TO MAKE?  (Y/N)  ";
590 GOSUB790
600 IFQ$="N"THEN620
610 INPUT"ENTER COMMENT";FC$:GOTO810
620 FC$=""
630 @OPEN3
640 @INPUT N,P
650 PRINT"THERE ARE";N;"FILES CURRENTLY ESTABLIS
    HED,
EACH WITH";P;"DATA ENTRIES.  HOW MANY NEW FILES
    ARE TO BE ADDED",:INPUTX
660 DIM N$(N+X),M(N+X,P),C$(N+X)
670 GOSUB110
680 PRINT"ADD NEW FILES":PRINT
690 FORI=N+1TON+X
700   PRINT"ENTER NAME OF FILE #";I,:INPUTN$(I)
```

Listing 10-11. Market Evaluator—Data Base Manager (continued from page 233)

```
710    PRINT"IF DATA IS UNKNOWN, ENTER 0.   IF DAT
       A IS ZERO, ENTER .00001"
720    FORJ=1TOP
730      PRINT"ENTER DATA FOR PERIOD #";J,:INPUTM
       (I,J)
740    NEXTJ
750    GOSUB480
760    C$(I)=" ":INPUT"ENTER FILE COMMENT, IF ANY
       ";C$(I)
770 NEXTI
780 GOTO810
790 Q$=""+INKEY$:IFQ$=""THEN790
800 PRINTQ$:PRINT:RETURN
810 FORI=1TON
820    FORJ=1TOP
830      IFJ=1THEN900
840      IFM(I,J)<>0THEN900
850      FORK=1TOP
860        IFM(I,J+K)<>0THEN890
870      NEXTK
880      M(I,J)=.00001:GOTO900
890      M(I,J)=(M(I,J+K)-M(I,J-1))/(K+1)
900    NEXTJ
910 NEXTI
920 PRINT"READY TO LOAD DATA.   (C)ONTINUE   ";:GO
       SUB790
930 IFQ$<>"C"THEN920
940 @OPEN3
950 @PRINT N
960 @PRINT P
970 FORI=1TON
980    @PRINTN$(I),C$(I)
990    FORJ=1TOP
1000       @PRINTM(I,J)
1010     NEXTJ
1020 NEXTI
1030 @PRINTFC$:@CLOSE
1040 PRINT:PRINT"ALL DATA SAVED."
1050 END
```

Listing 10-12. Market Trend Evaluator

```
1  '*************************************************
2  'MARKET TREND EVALUATOR                        *
3  'LISTING 10-12                                 *
4  '*************************************************
5  '
10 CLS:@CLEAR:CLEAR(768):PRINT"MARKET EVALUATOR"
       :PRINT:PRINT
20 PRINT"(USES ESF DATA I/O FORMAT TAPES)":PRINT
       :PRINT
30 PRINT"PROGRAM TO INPUT MOST RECENT DATA AND E
       VALUATE
MARKET TRENDS.":PRINT
```

```
40 PRINT"WILL THE LINE PRINTER BE USED?   (Y/N)
      ";:GOSUB990
50 IFQ$="Y"THENLP=1ELSELP=0
60 GOSUB830  :GOSUB1010
70 PRINT:PRINT"OPTIONS:":PRINT:PRINT
80 PRINT"         1  ---    TREND LINE WITH MEAN AN
      D STADARD DEVIATION
          2  ---    CORRELATION
          3  ---    MOVING AVERAGE
          4  ---    FINISH
SELECT   ";
90 GOSUB990
100 IFQ$="4"THEN1130
110 PRINT:PRINT"YOU HAVE";P;"PERIODS OF DATA, IN
      CLUDING THE";X;"NEW
PERIODS JUST ADDED.   ";:INPUT"ENTER THE NUMBER O
      F THE STARTING
PERIOD";S1:INPUT"ENTER THE ENDING PERIOD";S2:M=(
      S2-S1)+1
120 TX=0:TY=0:X2=0:Y2=0:XY=0
130 ONVAL(Q$)GOTO140  ,360  ,490
140 PRINT:INPUT"ENTER THE NUMBER OF THE FILE TO
      BE ANALYZED";F
150 CLS:PRINT"COMPUTING TREND LINE FOR ";N$(F)
160 FORI=S1TOS2
170    X=I:Y=M(F,I):TX=TX+X:TY=TY+Y:X2=X2+(X[2):Y
      2=Y2+(Y[2):XY=XY+(X*Y)
180 NEXTI
190 A=(XY-((TX*TY)/M))/(X2-((TX[2)/M))
200 B=(TY/M)-(A*(TX/M))
210 R=((M*XY)-(TX*TY))/SQR(((M*X2)-(TX[2))*((M*Y
      2)-(TY[2)))
220 AV=TY/M:SD=SQR((Y2-((TY[2)/M))/(M-1))
230 SE=SQR(ABS(((Y2-(A*TY)-(B*XY))/(M-2))))
240 SA=SQR(ABS((X2/(M*(X2-((TX[2)/M)))))))*SE
250 SB=SE/SQR(ABS((X2-((TX[2)/M))))
260 PRINT:PRINT"LINEAR TREND FOR THIS PERIOD IS:
      Y = ";
270 IFA<0THEN310
280 IFB<0THEN300
290 PRINTA;" + ";B;"X":GOTO320
300 PRINTA;" ";B;"X":GOTO320
310 PRINTB;"X ";A
320 PRINT:PRINT"THE CORRELATION IS ";R:PRINT"THE
       MEAN OF THE DATA IS ";AV:PRINT"THE STANDAR
      D DEVIATION IS ";SD
330 PRINT"","STANDARD ERRORS":PRINT"OF ESTIMATE"
      ,SE:PRINT"OF A",SA:PRINT"OF B",SB
340 IFLP=1THENGOSUB1250
350 LPRINT"":PRINT:GOTO80
360 PRINT:INPUT"ENTER THE NUMBER OF THE FIRST FI
      LE";F1:INPUT"ENTER THE NUMBER OF SECOND FIL
      E";F2
370 CLS:PRINT"COMPUTING THE CORRELATION BETWEEN
      ";N$(F1);" AND ";N$(F2)
380 FORI=S1TOS2
390    X=M(F1,I):Y=M(F2,I)
```

Listing 10-12. Market Trend Evaluator (continued from page 235)

```
400    TX=TX+X:TY=TY+Y:X2=X2+(X[2):Y2=Y2+(Y[2):XY
       =XY+(X*Y)
410 NEXTI
420 A1=TX/M:A2=TY/M:D1=SQR((X2-((TX[2)/M))/(M-1)
       ):D2=SQR((Y2-((TY[2)/M))/(M-1))
430 R=((M*XY)-(TX*TY))/SQR(((M*X2)-(TX[2))*((M*Y
       2)-(TY[2)))
440 PRINT:PRINT"THE CORRELATION IS ";R:PRINT
450 PRINT"FILE","MEAN","STANDARD DEVIATION"
460 PRINTN$(F1),A1,D1:PRINTN$(F2),A2,D2
470 IFLP=1THENGOSUB1250
480 PRINT:GOTO80
490 PRINT:INPUT"ENTER THE NUMBER OF THE FILE TO
       BE ANALYZED";F
500 CLS:PRINT"PERIOD","DATA","MOVING AVERAGE"
510 IFLP=1THENLPRINT"PERIOD","DATA","MOVING AVER
       AGE"
520 INPUT"ENTER PERIOD OF AVERAGE";A
530 FORI=S1TOS2
540    T=T+M(F,I):IF(S1-I)<(A-1)THEN580
550    PRINTI,M(F,I),T/A
560 IFLP=1THENLPRINTI,M(F,I),T/A
570    T=T-M(F,I-A):GOTO600
580    PRINTI,M(F,I),T/I
590 IFLP=1THENLPRINTI,M(F,I),T/I
600 NEXTI
610 IFLP=1THENLPRINT"PERIOD OF AVERAGE = ";A
620 GOTO80
630 PRINT"NUMBER OF FILES =";N,"NUMBER OF PERIOD
       S =";P
640 PRINT"FILE #","NAME","COMMENT"
650 FORI=1TON
660    @INPUTN$(I),C$(I):PRINTI,N$(I),C$(I)
670    FORJ=1TOP
680       @INPUTM(I,J)
690    NEXTJ
700 NEXTI
710 @INPUTFC$:PRINT:PRINTFC$:PRINT
720 @CLOSE
730 P=P+X:NF=X:RETURN
740 PRINT:PRINT"ALL DATA ENTERED CORRECT?   (Y/N)
       ";:GOSUB990
750 IFQ$="Y"THEN820
760 PRINT"CORRECT  (N)AME   (C)OMMENT   (D)ATA    ";
       :GOSUB990
770 IFQ$="C"THEN790   ELSEIFQ$="D"THEN800   ELSEIF
       Q$<>"N"THEN760
780 INPUT"ENTER CORRECT NAME";N$(I):GOTO740
790 INPUT"ENTER CORRECT COMMENT";C$(I):GOTO740
800 INPUT"ENTER NUMBER OF PERIOD FOR CORRECTION"
       ;Y
810 INPUT"ENTER CORRECT VALUE";M(I,Y):GOTO740
820 RETURN
830 FC$=""
840 @OPEN3
```

```
850 @INPUT N,P
860 PRINT"THERE ARE";N;"FILES CURRENTLY ESTABLIS
     HED,
EACH WITH";P;"DATA ENTRIES.  HOW MANY
ADDITIONAL PERIODS TO BE ADDED",:INPUTX
870 DIM N$(N),M(N,P+X),C$(N)
880 GOSUB630
890 PRINT"ADD NEW DATA":PRINT
900 FORI=1TON
910    PRINTN$(I)
920    PRINT"IF DATA IS UNKNOWN, ENTER 0.  IF DAT
     A IS ZERO, ENTER .00001"
930    FORJ=P-X+1TOP
940      PRINT"ENTER DATA FOR PERIOD #";J,:INPUTM
     (I,J)
950    NEXTJ
960    GOSUB740
970 NEXTI
980 RETURN
990 Q$=""+INKEY$:IFQ$=""THEN990
1000 PRINTQ$:PRINT:RETURN
1010 FORI=1TON
1020    FORJ=1TOP
1030      IFJ=1THEN1100
1040      IFM(I,J)<>0THEN1100
1050      FORK=1TOP
1060        IFM(I,J+K)<>0THEN1090
1070      NEXTK
1080      M(I,J)=.00001:GOTO1100
1090      M(I,J)=(M(I,J+K)-M(I,J-1))/(K+1)
1100    NEXTJ
1110 NEXTI
1120 RETURN
1130 @OPEN3
1140 @PRINT N
1150 @PRINT P
1160 FORI=1TON
1170    @PRINTN$(I),C$(I)
1180    FORJ=1TOP
1190      @PRINTM(I,J)
1200    NEXTJ
1210 NEXTI
1220 @PRINTFC$:@CLOSE
1230 PRINT:PRINT"ALL DATA SAVED."
1240 END
1250 FORRC=0TO12
1260    FORCC=0TO63
1270      Z=PEEK(15360+(RC*64)+CC)
1280      IFZ<32THENZ=Z+64
1290      LPRINTCHR$(Z);
1300    NEXTCC
1310    LPRINT""
1320 NEXTRC
1330 LPRINT""
1340 RETURN
```

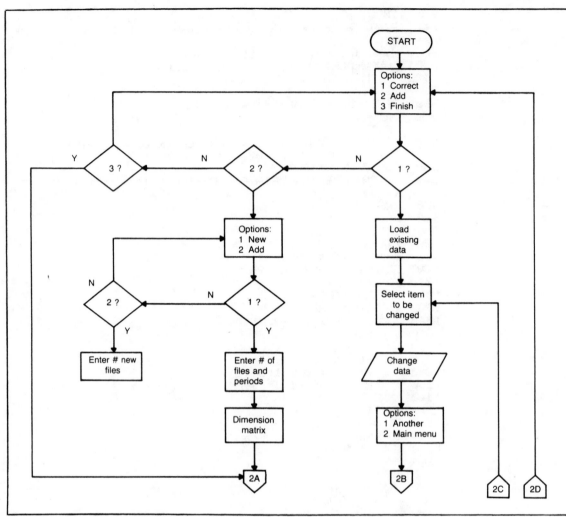

Fig. 10-7. Flowchart for Listing 10-11.

ments, one appreciating at 10 percent per year and the other at 5 percent.

Assume that the upper curve represents the asking price of a home and lower line represents the median family income in a given community. The dashed line is approximately twice the value of the lower, 5 percent, line. Whether the bottom line is 5 percent or 7.5, whether the top line is 8, 10, or 15 percent, is really immaterial. The point of this figure is that median family income normally increases at one rate and the median price for a home in the same

community rises at another rate. For the purposes of granting loans, a rule of thumb often used is that families can afford a home the price of which is no more than twice the family income. Notice, however, that at about the 13th year the median price rises to a level greater than twice the median family income. The significance of this is that more than half the population can no longer afford to buy a home. During the 10 to 15-year period ending sometime in 1980, real estate sales people were touting the purchase of homes as an obviously wise

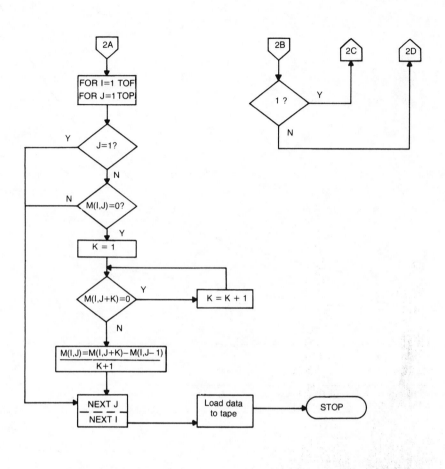

investment. The median price of homes was exceeding the annual inflation rate by almost a factor of two to one. "How could one lose?" they would ask. Some even went so far as to suggest that this incredible rate differential would go on forever. One look at Fig. 10-7, however, tells the story. No matter what the rates are, so long as the appreciation rate for the median sales price of used or new homes is greater than the rate of increase of median family incomes, there is an inevitable point at which the sales price becomes excessive and unrealistic. Until the income level of the majority of potential home-owners increases to the point at which median income is realistically related to sales price, sales will slump and/or prices will level off.

Figure 10-8 gives what we believe is the more realistic price curve as a function of median family income. This exercise has three parts:

A. Gather used-home prices for your community for the last 25 years or so, as well as the local median family income. Plot these data more or less as shown in Fig. 10-8.

B. From these data, test the

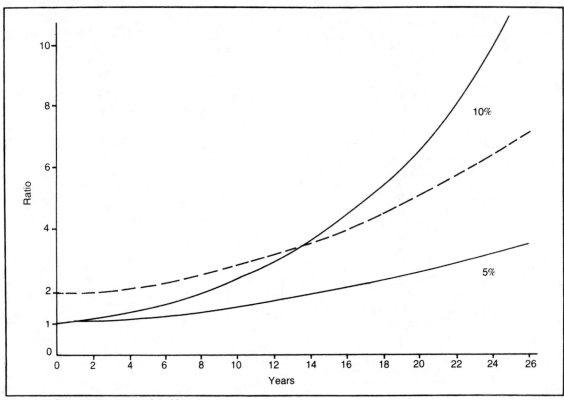

Fig. 10-8. Comparative accumulated interest curves.

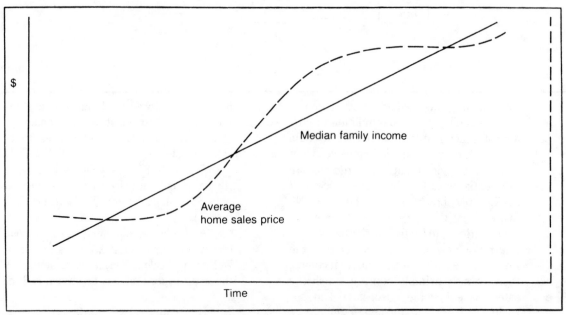

Fig. 10-9. Hypothetical relationship between median income and sales prices of homes.

hypothesis illustrated in Fig. 10-8. If the hypothesis is not sustained, go on to the next exercise, otherwise, go on to the next step.

C. Compute the interval between the beginning and the end of a rising price cycle. Compute the mean length of the price plateau period. We suspect the ratio of the rising time to plateau time to be roughly 10 to 1. That is, prices will rise steadily for about ten years, and then level off for a year or so until income rises to meet the minimum levels for significant major purchases. Develop the data and the procedure to sustain or revise this hypothesis.

2. Collect stock market data for a month. Use the drunkard's walk, decomposition, and regression techniques to forecast the subsequent 30-day activity record. Which technique gives the most satisfying results? Why?

SUGGESTED READING

Edwards, R. D. and J. Magee, 1976. *Technical Analysis of Stock Trends*. Springfield, MA: John Magee & Associates.

Hardy, C. C., 1978, *Investors Guide to Technical Analysis*. New York: McGraw-Hill.

Hefert, E. A., 1978. *Techniques of Financial Analysis*. Homewood, IL: Dow Jones-Irwin.

Malinvaud, E., 1966. *Statistical Methods of Econometrics*. Amsterdam: North Holland Publishing Co.

Chapter 11

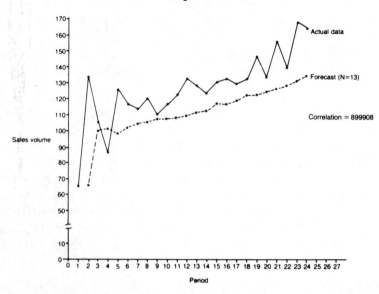

Technological Forecasting

Although Leonardo da Vinci did a remarkable job of forecasting a wide variety of technological innovations (among them, the helicopter and submarine), technological forecasting (or TF) was not developed as a coherent art or craft until the 1960s. The reasons for the disinterest in TF until then, and the reasons for the dramatic change in corporate attitudes are many. Perhaps one of the more significant factors is the rate of growth in technological capability. That is, in da Vinci's time decades might pass between technological innovations that might advance a capability in one order of magnitude. For example, in 1400 AD a pump may drain a field at the rate of ten gallons an hour, and it might be another century until a better pump can remove one hundred gallons per hour. Today, on the other hand, technological developments are advancing faster than we can design and market the finished product. Airplanes, for example, are often technologically obsolete before they take their maiden flight for certification. In computer science the growth rate is chilling. (See Fig. 11-1.) In 1944, the processing speed of the Harvard Mark I computer was .403 operations per second. By 1946, the Eniac computer could rush along at 44.65 operations per second—an improvement of some 10979.40 percent. By 1964, the CDC 6600 operated at a rate of 4,091,293 operations per second—an improvement of over one billion percent from 1944! While not all aspects of the twentieth century are rushing along at that rate and while there are upper limits to many technological systems, the fact remains that the rate of technological advance in general is increasing to the point where we have to pay close attention to developments to insure, from a corporate viewpoint, that we are not overrun by the competition, and, from a social viewpoint, that technology does not devastate our lives, but is exploited effectively to improve the quality of life. This chapter reviews some of the major technological forecasting techniques, identifies those suitable for application on or to microcomputers, and provides programs and algorithms useful in forecasting technology.

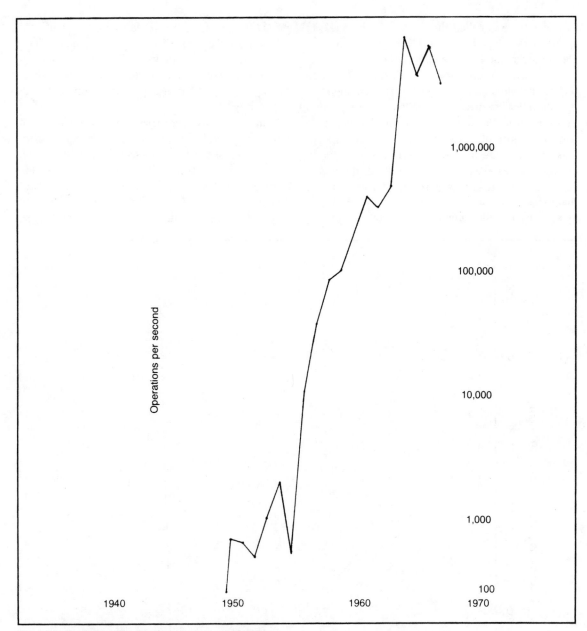

Fig. 11-1. Operating speeds of computers, 1940-1970.

TECHNOLOGICAL FORECASTING TECHNIQUES

Emerging from the scientific and management literature of the last 15 to 20 years are a number of forecasting techniques, each with some advantage and utility. Among them are: intuitive forecasting, goal-oriented forecasting, dynamic modeling, and trend extrapolation methods.

Intuitive Forecasting

This is an approach based on informed or expert opinion. One of the more notable examples of this technique is called the Delphi Technique. An approach developed by the RAND Corporation, the Delphi technique exploits informed or expert opinion concerning future events or developments. The technique relies on three characteristics: anonymity, statistical analysis, and feedback of reasoning. In brief, a panel of experts are given a list of anticipated events or future technologies and are asked to make an estimate of when each item will actually occur. The responses are then evaluated statistically, and the results are returned to the panel members for comment. If a member's own estimate is significantly different from the concensus, the member is asked either to defend the exceptional position or to conform to the group standard. The comment, statistical analysis, and feedback process is repeated two to four times. In the end the forecasting team has a chart somewhat similar to the one in Fig. 11-2.

In reality, in order to preserve the advantage of anonymity, the panel never meets in conference, but is addressed as individuals, none of whom know who the other members are. The reasoning for this feature is that good (perhaps the more accurate) response may come from those on the panel with only very modest credentials. It is felt that if these

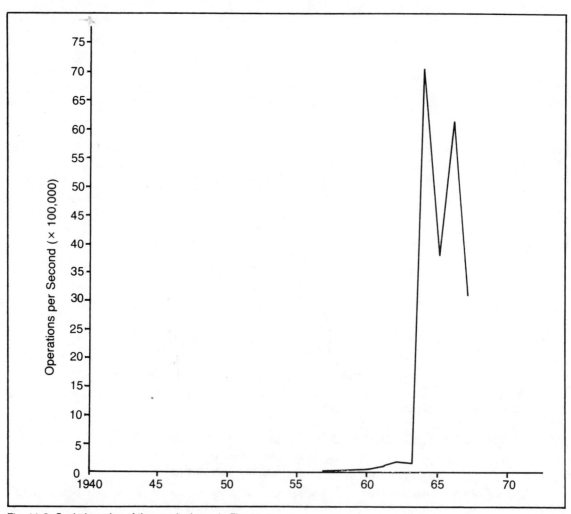

Fig. 11-2. Scaled version of the graph shown in Fig. 11-1.

people were to know that some distinguished and recognized world authority was on the panel and that that person was taking issue with the lesser figure's estimate, the first person might back off and concede the position more because of reputation than because of fact or reason. Conversely, the technique forces the responsible world expert to rely upon reason and fact in defense of his position rather than depending on reputation to support his credability. Those using this technique hope that the interaction of experts will elicit meaningful estimates of future events or technologies.

The technique is not without some difficulties. This approach is time-consuming for all involved. The staff must prepare and cull out hundreds of items prior to beginning the test and then spend considerable time in the computation of the statistics after each round. The technique rests on the assumption that the experts will spend a responsible amount of time considering each of the options presented them. An adequate response may take days, if not weeks, for each expert to consider and prepare. The greater the stature of the expert, the more difficult it is to spare the kind of time required, not to mention the difficulty keeping the panel members motivated during each subsequent round. Having evaluated a subject two or three times, and having settled on a firm estimate, it is most demanding to expect the expert to review the material the fourth or fifth time with the same enthusiasm as the first time. As a consequence, more recent Delphi experiments have modified the approach by shortening the list of topics and by limiting the reappraisals to only two or three iterations.

A difficult aspect of the Delphi technique is the framing of the items to be evaluated. One approach is to brainstorm a number of technologies that appear to have some chance of coming into being sometime in the future—no matter how distant. Another approach might be to present the panel members with a scenario or protocol within which they generate the list of topics or future developments. For example, each member could be asked to: "Identify ten sources of electrical energy not currently available, five modes of transportation not yet developed." These lists are then consolidated into a master list, eliminating redundant items.

Regardless of the technique selected, each item must be clearly stated and not ambiguous; that is, each item must be limited to one topic, one distinct technology, or one event. Further, as a technical consideration, the number of panelists must be large enough to produce meaningful statistics. It is most often pointless, for example, to compute standard deviations on a sample consisting of fewer than 15 to 20 items (read panelists). Fifty, to several hundred panelists are even better if you can round them up. We know of one study that involved several thousand panelists. However, don't abandon an experiment with the Delphi process if you can only collect a dozen or two panelists, or if your list only has several items. Previous chapters have referred to the principle of central tendency in research statistics. Even the opinion of one panelist will ordinarily fall somewhere in the range of the median or concensus view. Two or three such opinions will definitely begin to highlight the concensus.

In any event, it is beyond the scope of this book to really aid you in the selection of panelists or the selection of the survey items, although the microcomputer can be used to keep track of the panel participants in a mailing list file or the survey items in a word-processing system. Rather, the program found in Listing 11-1 computes the statistical data required to summarize the responses of the panelists. It also identifies those panelists who, because of significant departure from the norm, will be required to explain or defend their positions, or to conform to the majority view. Listing 11-1 depends on Listing 11-2, which is a short program that allows you to save your data concerning the events. This data is reloaded and used by the program in Listing 11-1.

Goal-Oriented Forecasting

This technique is based on the assumption that technology develops to satisfy the needs of society: "Necessity is the mother of invention." To forecast the future technology, one makes the best possible projection of social needs and extropolates from these technologies that must be created to

Listing 11-1. Delphi Analysis

```
1   '**************************************************
2   'DELPHI ANALYSIS                                  *
3   'LISTING 11-1                                     *
4   '**************************************************
5   '
10  CLS:@CLEAR:CLEAR1000:PRINTCHR$(210);"DELPHI S
    UPPORT":PRINT:PRINT:GOSUB820   :T$(1)="EARLI
    EST":T$(2)="PROBABLE":T$(3)="LATEST"
20  INPUT"CURRENT YEAR";Y
30  FORI=1TON
40    PRINT"PANELIST NUMBER";I
50    FORJ=1TOM
60      PRINT"EVENT:   ";N$(J)
70      PRINT"ENTER EARLIEST TIME FOR EVENT",:INP
    UT T(1,I,J)
80      PRINT"ENTER PROBABLE TIME FOR EVENT",:INP
    UT T(2,I,J)
90      PRINT"ENTER LATEST TIME FOR EVENT",:INPUT
    T(3,I,J):PRINT
100   NEXTJ
110   PRINT
120 NEXTI
130 PRINT:PRINT"ALL TIMES CORRECT?   (Y/N)";
140 Q$=""+INKEY$:IFQ$=""THEN140
150 PRINTQ$:IFQ$="Y"THEN200
160 PRINT:INPUT"ENTER PANELIST NUMBER, ITEM NUMB
    ER";I,J
170 PRINTN$(J):INPUT"ENTER CORRECT EARLIEST TIME
    ";T(1,I,J)
180 INPUT"ENTER CORRECT PROBABLE TIME";T(2,I,J)
190 INPUT"ENTER CORRECT LATEST TIME";T(3,I,J):GO
    TO130
200 PRINT:PRINT"PROCESSING DATA":PRINT
210 DIM M(M,3),SD(M,3),SX(M,3),X2(M,3)
220 FORI=1TON
230   FORJ=1TOM
240     FORK=1TO3
250       X=T(K,I,J)-Y:SX(J,K)=SX(J,K)+X:X2(J,K)
    =X2(J,K)+(X[2)
260     NEXTK
270   NEXTJ
280 NEXTI
290 FORI=1TOM
300   FORJ=1TO3
310     M(I,J)=Y+SX(M,J)/N:SD(I,J)=SQR((X2(I,J)-
    ((SX(I,J)[2)/N))/(N-1))
320   NEXTJ
330 NEXTI
340 LPRINT"EVENT #","NAME","MEAN","S.D.":LPRINT"
    "
350 PRINT"#","NAME","MEAN","S.D"
360 FORI=1TOM
370   LPRINTI,N$(I)
380   PRINTI,N$(I)
390   FORJ=1TO3
```

```
400      LPRINT"  ";T$(J),M(I,J),SD(I,J)
410        PRINTT$(J),M(I,J),SD(I,J)
420    NEXTJ
430 NEXTI
440 PRINT"THE FOLLOWING INDIVIDUALS HAVE FORECAS
     T EVENT TIMES
SIGNIFICANTLY DIFFERENT FROM THE MEAN.    THEY SH
     OULD EITHER
CHANGE THEIR TIMES OR EXPLAIN THE DEVIATION:":PR
     INT
450 FORI=1TOM
460    FORJ=1TON
470      FORK=1TO3
480        IF T(K,J,I)>(M(I,K)-(3*SD(I,K)))AND T(
     K,J,I)<((M(I,K)+(3*SD(I,K)))THEN510
490        PRINT"PANELIST #";J,N$(I),T$(K)
500        LPRINT"PANELIST #";J,N$(I),T$(K)
510      NEXTK
520    NEXTJ
530 NEXTI
540 CLS
550 FORX=0TO125:SET(X,40):NEXT
560 FORX=10TO120STEP10:SET(X,41):NEXT
570 I=10+Y:FORX=899TO954STEP5:PRINT@X,I;:I=I+10:
     NEXT
580 FORI=1TOM
590    PRINT@0,N$(I)
600    FORJ=1TON
610      FORK=1TO3
620        X=T(K,J,I)-Y:Y=39
630        IFPOINT(X,Y)THEN640
640        SET(X,Y):GOTO660
650        Y=Y-1:GOTO630
660      NEXTK
670    NEXTJ
680    LPRINTN$(I):LPRINT""
690    FORR=3TO41
700      FORC=0TO125
710        IFPOINT(C,R)LPRINT"*";ELSELPRINT" ";
720      NEXTC
730      LPRINT""
740    NEXTR
750    FORJ=0TO125STEP5
760      IF(J/10)<>INT(J/10)THEN780
770      LPRINTJ+Y+" ";:GOTO790
780      LPRINT"     ";
790    NEXTJ
800 NEXTI
810 END
820 PRINT:PRINT"LOADING DATA"
830 @OPEN3
840 @INPUT N,M:DIM T(3,N,M),N$(M)
850 FORI=1TOM:@INPUT N$(M):NEXT
860 @CLOSE
870 RETURN
```

Listing 11-2. Delphi Support

```
1   '*******************************************
2   'DELPHI SUPPORT                            *
3   'LISTING 11-2                              *
4   '*******************************************
5   '
10  CLS:@CLEAR:CLEAR1000:PRINTCHR$(210);"DELPHI S
      UPPORT":PRINT:PRINT
20  INPUT"ENTER NUMBER OF PANELISTS";N
30  INPUT"ENTER NUMBER OF EVENTS";M
40  DIMN$(M):PRINT
50  FORI=1TOM
60    PRINT"ENTER NAME OF EVENT # ";I,:INPUTN$(I)

70  NEXTI
80  FORI=1TOM:PRINTI;N$(M),:NEXT
90  PRINT:PRINT"ALL ENTRIES CORRECT?  (Y/N)   ";
100 Q$=""+INKEY$:IFQ$=""THEN100
110 IFQ$="Y"THEN130
120 PRINT:INPUT"ENTER ITEM NUMBER AND CORRECT NA
      ME";X,N$(X):CLS:GOTO80
130 PRINT:PRINT"LOADING DATA"
140 @OPEN3
150 @PRINT N,M
160 FORI=1TOM:@PRINT N$(M):NEXT
170 @CLOSE
180 END
```

satisfy those social needs. In the very early 1960s, President Kennedy announced the objective of putting a man on the moon by the end of the decade. At the time of the announcement, the technologies required to achieve that goal did not exist. As the American people embraced the concept and accepted it as a political and social objective, it was possible to forecast a number of technologies that would emerge in subsequent years. Many such forecasts were valid and those who attended to them became quite wealthy. Except for recommending a Delphi approach for forecasting what social needs might exist at some point in the future, this book will pursue goal-oriented forecasting no farther, however.

Dynamic Modeling Method

The user of this technique specifies the subject or limits of the study and begins seeking some starting point estimates or limits that can be quantified. Using these values, the data are allowed to run to a logical conclusion, which becomes the forecast. A simple example might be a model designed to forecast the supply of petroleum through the next ten to twenty years. The forecaster carefully attempts to construct a model of the region under study that includes all factors affecting the demand and production of oil during the period in question. Certainly, population studies are important, as are forecasts of the future of various oil-consuming equipment and industries. These, and other identifiable variables are built into the model. When all factors have been entered, the computer follows the limits prescribed and generates a forecast.

Often, however, many of the forecasts upon which the model is built are far from precise and unique values. Rather, the forecasts fall within some specified range of values. Seldom can we certify that the population of a region will be exactly X people, but we must say the population will range between this value and that. The model and subsequent forecast often become complicated, especially if there are a large number of input variables, each of which has a range of possible values. In such an instance, the user of this technique can elect to use one of the three options. The first makes the

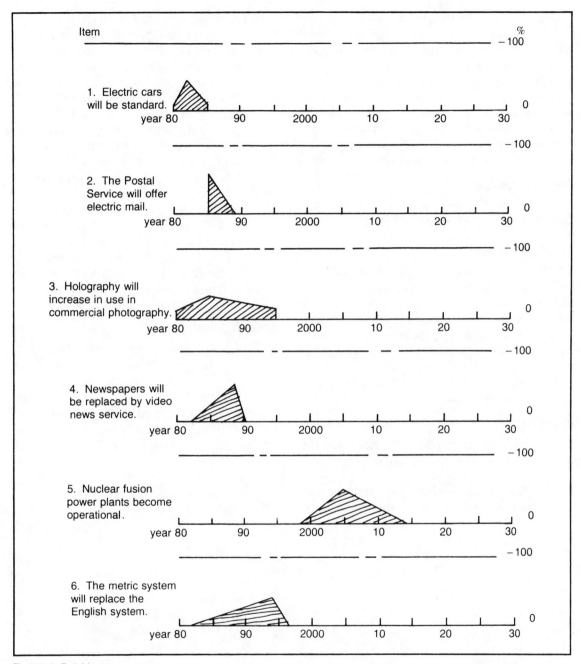

Fig. 11-3. Delphi summary page.

computer generate a forecast based on all possible combinations of all the input variables. Even with the most sophisticated computers a serious task of any significant scope would take an extraordinary length of time to complete. An alternative is to use an expert to interact with the computer in selecting several sets of parameters that intuitively seem correct or more appropriate. A third approach is to assign probabilities to the probabilities and use only the more probable. For example, while the regional population may be estimated to vary from 1,000,000 to 3,000,000, the extremes will only be realized under very improbable circumstances, and the most probable population projection is for the population to range from 1,760,340 to 1,890,000. Instead of sending the computer through the entire two million person range, we limit it to the range of 130 thousand or so it is most likely to have to handle.

Trend Extrapolation

This technique exploits the mathematical trend line and regression analysis tools.

Trend Line Analysis

To make an estimate of the future, the trend line analyst simply looks at the historical data, computes a best-fit trend, and projects it some distance into the future. If the population growth rate is 5 percent a year and the population of the United States in a given year is 200 million, we can project that ten years later, the population will be about 325,778,925 people. Chapter 13 deals in greater detail with population estimates.

EXERCISES

1. Run a Delphi exercise in your class to make an estimate of ten technological advances likely to occur.
2. The S or ogive-curve is frequently the best description of the accumulative expansion of an innovation in a given technological or economic environment. Research the sources of sales information concerning microcomputers. Collect total sales volume (number of units) sold each year from 1965 to the present. Develop a routine to fit an S-curve to these data. On the basis of your work, forecast the approximate date microcomputer sales will reach a natural plateau. What is the annual sales volume at this point? [A microcomputer herein is considered to be a computing system using a high language (BASIC, FORTRAN, COBOL, or the like, with no more than 64K of RAM, and costing no more than $3000 for a fully operational unit. This definition is certainly open to challenge. It simply attempts to focus on the type of device we commonly view as a *microcomputer*.]

SUGGESTED READING

Blohm, H. and K. Steinbuch, eds., 1973. *Technological Forecasting in Practice*. London: Saxon House.

Bright, J. R., 1980. *Practical Technological Forecasting*. Austin, TX: Technologies Futures, Inc.

Cetron, M. J., ed., 1971: *Industrial Applications of Technology Forecasting*. New York: John Wiley and Sons.

Martino, J. P., 1972. *Technological Forecasting for Decision Making*. New York: American Elsevier Publishing Company.

Chapter 12

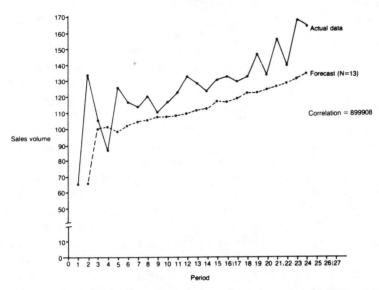

Astronomical Applications

The stars appear at both ends of the forecasting spectrum. At one extreme, the positions of the stars have been thought to hold the fates of all living creatures. It is believed that Adolph Hitler made major decisions concerning the conduct of the German offensives during World War II based on astrological advice. But, despite bizarre extents to which the advocates of astrology may have taken their beliefs, we owe a great debt to generations of mystics for their preoccupations with the positions of the planets and the stars. From them we have remarkably long and accurate records from which we can reconstruct any number of useful and helpful pieces of astronomical information.

Today's star-gazers may have more practical applications in mind, but the task of forecasting astronomical phenomena remains a dark and tedious science. Our national and global economies rise and fall, based in part on the ability of astronomers and astrophysicists to accurately control the orbits of earth resources satellites. That task requires skill in determining the positions of not only the spacecraft itself, but also of the stars and the planets for reference points. In the quest for knowledge and scientific advancement, we must also be able to chart the courses, which will enable us to safely land equipment and eventually people on these planets.

While this chapter cannot offer detailed solutions to all the astronomical problems, it can offer a starting point. In this chapter we will sort out some of the problems in telling time and the seasons both through ancient techniques devised by those who built Stonehenge and through systems used by NASA to compute courses to the planets. Since weather forecasting is a science the complexity of which normally exceeds the capabilities of the microcomputer, we feel unable to adequately devote a chapter to the subject. Nonetheless, since weather is a function of the natural universe and greatly influenced by astronomical phenomena, the chapter does include weather-related forecasting routines. The bibliography recommends advanced reading for those whose interest in weather forecasting remains unabated.

CALENDARS AND TELLING TIME

Ancient man must have noticed at least two natural phenomena: the cycle of day and night, and the passage of the seasons from summer to winter to summer again.

Somewhere in these beginnings there must have been a useful purpose in learning how to count. While the concept of zero or nullity is a relatively recent Arab invention, man has been counting beans, eggs, days, months, and years for as long as we have any recorded history. Indeed, many of the original artifacts we have as evidence of man's emergence are inventory or shipping records containing numbers. The length of the year in days must have been one of man's original constants. As we became more aware of the function of smaller fractions of time as useful tools in estimating things like the distance we have sailed in open seas, the more important became the task of dividing the day into meaningful portions such as hours, minutes, and seconds. With the coming of the second, the wiser among us became aware that the year was not precisely 365 days, but a touch longer. So long as the best clocks were only accurate to the nearest hour or so, and navigation was still mainly coastal, people were satisfied with exactly 24 hours in a day, and minutes and seconds being one-sixtieth of the larger value. Since then, we become a bit more precise. A second, now, is roughly the interval of time it takes for 9,192,631,770 cycles of the radiation corresponding to the transition of the caesium-133 atom. Try counting to over nine billion between the tick and the tock of the clock—that's a second! Sixty of those make a minute, sixty of which make an hour, twenty-four of which, more or less, make a day. Beyond a day the relationships cease to exist. It's true that years (a set of days) and centuries are computed in the course of astronomical work, but years are not precise functions of days. Some years contain more days than others, and the number of days in a given year work out to a very odd number. Depending on the type of year one is referring to, a year contains either 365.2564 or 365.24215 days, each of which actually consisting of 23 hours, 56 minutes and 4.09 seconds—at last count. Why the difference? Well, it takes one tropical year for the earth to complete its 360 degree course around the sun, and that is equal to 365.24215 days or so. However, if you were to gaze out at a particular star at midnight on the first of January one year, you would have to wait until about 12.20.52 AM a year later to see the same star in the same position. This illustrates differences between the tropical and sidereal time.

Stonehenge

Sometime during the second millenia B.C. a group of ambitious stonecutters cut and dragged massive 30-ton sandstone blocks from up to 135 miles away to the Salisbury Plain and there constructed that circular monument to man's obsession with solar and lunar phenomena; Stonehenge. While many of the larger stones in the center of the arrangement are now lying in disarray, it is possible to confirm that many of them were used to foretell the positions of the sun and the moon at significant moments, such as the summer soltice, the vernal equinox, and so forth. Surrounding the central ring of stones is an equally interesting, if less obvious, set of holes. Numbering 56, they are called the Aubrey holes. It wasn't until 1963 that British astronomer Gerald Hawkins used a computer to support a hypothesis that the holes can be and probably were, used to determine the position of the moon and sun, as well as the likelihood of lunar and solar eclipses. For the purposes of this kind of solar astronomy, it is acceptable and perhaps easier to accept the original convention that the sun moves about the earth in an orbit as the planets revolve about the sun. Figure 12-1 is a rough representation of such an orbit, as well as the actual orbit of the moon. Notice that the orbit of the moon is inclined somewhat in relationship to the "orbit" of the sun. The two points where the orbit of the moon crosses that of the sun are the *nodes* of the moon's orbit. These points, relative to an observer on earth, are not stationary, but revolve slowly in a clockwise direction. If a full moon occurs when the moon is at one of the nodes, there will be a lunar eclipse. If the moon is new and at one of the nodes, there will be a solar eclipse.

Using four stones, the ancient Britons could

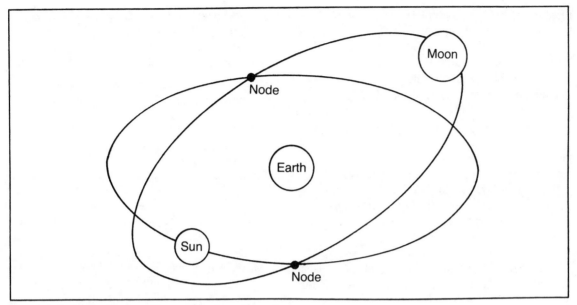

Fig. 12-1. Conceptual notion of lunar and solar nodes.

predict a number of phenomena. One stone is marked to represent the moon and another, the sun, and the remaining two are marked and placed to represent the two nodes, one opposite the other. By observing the following rules the priests could make their forecasts:

1. Move the moon's marker one hole counterclockwise twice a day, at morning and evening.
2. Move the sun's marker one hole counterclockwise every 6.5 days.
3. Move the node markers one hole clockwise 3 times a year.

When the moon's marker falls into a hole occupied by one of the node markers, there is a possibility of an eclipse, depending on the position of the sun. If the sun is very close to being on the opposite side of the ring, the moon will be full and a lunar eclipse is likely. If both the moon and sun markers are close to each other, a solar eclipse is possible, but dependent on the time of day and the actual relative positions.

Out of all these combinations of orbits and cycles comes another interesting feature, the *saros*. It happens that if we know the date and time of an eclipse, we can very quickly predict the date and time of the last and the next eclipse of the same type simply by adding or subtracting 6585 days and approximately seven hours to the date and time of the known eclipse. This period is also equal to exactly 223 full moons. This is the saros.

We leave it to your imagination to figure out how people who left behind no trace of a written language or artifacts of civilization other than Stonehenge itself could make the necessary long-term observations and computations in order to develop the 56-hole arrangement. The truth may be that they moved the stones and dug the holes according to some much simple protocol, but as an idiot-savant reaches astounding conclusions, inadvertently constructed their clever machine.

Modern Calendars

During the reign of Julius Caesar a calendar routine was established the features of which persist to a large degree to this date. A fundamental characteristic of the Julian calendar was the concept of the 365.25-day solar year contrasted with the 365-day civil year. The compensation used, until the 1500s was to simply increase the length of a month one day once every four years. Because of the slight, but eventually significant disparity between the 365.24215-day year and the 365.25-day year, the calendar drifted so that the seasons were no longer in step with the calendar. Upon the recommentation of his learned staff, Pope Gregory instituted a minor, but profoundly effective, change in the rule. Leap years would continue to be implemented once every four years except for century years, those ending in 00 (1900, 2000, 21000), unless the century year was also evenly divisable by 400 (such as 2000). This modification keeps the years even with the seasons for a significantly long period. The calendar scheme we now use in the western world is the Gregorian calendar.

A vestige of the older calendar is the sequential numbering of the days from January 1 each year. Thus, the Julian date refers not to the older protocol, but simply the place a date has in the year. In most years, May 29 is the 149th day of the civil year (150th in Leap Years).

It is frequently useful or even necessary to be able to compute the number of days between two dates and to determine the day of the week given a date. In astronomy it is essential to be able to compute the number of days between a benchmark date, called the *epoch*, and any other date.

If we specify a date by Y = year, M = month (January = 1), and D = day of month, the first step is to convert this to a standardized day number form. This is done with the following algorithm:

1. If M is larger than 2, make X = 0; otherwise make X = 1.
2. Let C = the integer part of $\dfrac{Y - X}{100}$.
3. Let N = D plus the integer part of 365 × $\dfrac{M - 2}{12}$ + X plus the integer part of the 365.25 × (Y − X − .75 × C).
4. The day of the week (Sunday = 0) = the integer part of 7 × (N/7 − integer part of N/7)
5. The Julian date is computed from N − 336 plus the integer part of the integer part of 365.25 × (Y − 1) less .75 × C)

By computing the basic N for two dates, the number of days between those dates can be computed by simple subtraction. Steps 4 and 5 in the algorithm yield the day of the week of a given date and the Julian date of the date. A number of computer programs supporting accounting activities, banking transactions, or any other time-based event often use Julian dates as part of the file identifiers.

Listing 12-1. Basic Calendar

```
1  '*****************************************************
2  'BASIC CALENDAR                                    *
3  'LISTING 12-1                                      *
4  '*****************************************************
5  '
10 DEFDBLN,J
20 CLS:PRINT"CALENDAR":PRINT:PRINT
30 DW$(0)="SUNDAY":DW$(1)="MONDAY":DW$(2)="TUESD
   AY":DW$(3)="WEDNESDAY":DW$(4)="THURSDAY":DW
   $(5)="FRIDAY":DW$(6)="SATURDAY"
40 DIMM$(12):MM$="JANFEBMARAPRMAYJUNJULAUGSEPOCT
   NOVDEC":FORI=1TO12:M$(I)=MID$(MM$,((I-1)*3)
   +1,3):NEXTI
50 DIMMD(12):D$="312831303130313130313031":FORI=
   1TO12:MD(I)=VAL(MID$(D$,((I-1)*2)+1,2)):NEX
   T
60 PRINT"A    --    JULIAN DATE, GIVEN DAY, MONTH,
   AND YEAR

B    --    DAY, MONTH, AND YEAR, GIV
```

```
                    EN JULIAN DATE":PRINT:PRINT"ENTER CHOICE   "
                    ;
70  Q$=""+INKEY$:IFQ$=""THEN70     ELSEIFQ$="B"THEN
        310
80  PRINT:INPUT"ENTER DATE DESIRED   (DD,MM,YYYY)"
        ;D,M,Y
90  GOSUB130
100 PRINT:PRINT"THE JULIAN DATE OF ";M$(M);D;","
        ;Y;", IS ";
110 PRINTN;".
THE DAY IS ";DW$(DW);" AND IS DAY #
        ";JD;"OF THE YEAR. "
120 END
130 IFM>2THEX=0ELSEX=1
140 'COMPUTE CENTURY
150 C=INT((Y-X)/100)
160 'CHECK FOR LEAP YEAR
170 IF(Y/4)<>INT(Y/4)THEN210
180 IF(Y/100)<>INT(Y/100)THEN200
190 IF(Y/400)<>INT(Y/400)THEN210
200 LY=1:GOTO220
210 LY=0
220 IFFL=0THEN250
230 RETURN
240 'COMPUTE JULIAN NUMBER
250 N=D+INT(367*(((M-2)/12)+X))+INT(INT(365.25*(
        Y-X))-(.75*C))
260 'COMPUTE DAY OF WEEK
270 DW=INT(7*((N/7)-INT(N/7)))
280 'COMPUTE ANNUAL JULIAN DATE
290 JD=N-(336+INT(INT(365.25*(Y-1))-(.75*C)))
300 RETURN
310 PRINT:FL=1:INPUT"ENTER JULIAN DATE (LONG FOR
        M:  1/1/1900 = 693932)";N
320 Y=1950
330 A=N-712193:M=1:D=1
340 GOSUB170   :IFLY=1THEN390
350 IFA<=365THEN400
360 A=A-365:Y=Y+1:PRINT@640,Y;
370 GOSUB170   :IFLY=0THEN350
380 A=A-1:GOTO340
390 IFA>366THEN360
400 MD(2)=MD(2)+LY
410 IFA<=MD(M)THEN430
420 A=A-MD(M):M=M+1:PRINT@650,M;:GOTO410
430 D=A:FL=0:GOSUB130
440 GOTO100
```

Listing 12-1 implements these basic rules. It also allows the user to input the time of day and expresses the day of the week by its name.

It is also possible to reverse the process and convert the base day number back into a recognizable date. The process to accomplish this is:

1. Let N = the notional

Julian date   N = 2445210.45

2. Let I be the integer and F   I = 2445210
   the fractional part of N   F = .45

3. If I is greater than 2299160, then do step 3A, otherwise, do step 3B

3A. A = integer part
(I-1867216.25)/36524.25   A = 15
B = I + A + 1 − integer
part (A/4)   B = 2445223
3B. A = 1
4. C = B + 1524   C = 2446747
5. D = integer part
(C − 122.1)/365.25   D = 6698
6. E = integer part
365.25 × D   E = 2446444
7. G = integer part (C −
E)/30.6001   G = 9
8. Compute the day of the
month from d = C + F −

E − integer part
30.6001. × G   d = 28
9. If G is less than 13.5 then
M = G − 1 else M = G −
13. This is the month
number   M = 8
10. If M is greater than 2.5,
then Y = D − 4716 else Y
= D − 4715. This is the
year.   Y = 1982

Thus the day number 2445210.45 converts to August 28, 1982. The fractional portion, .45, converts to 10.48 AM.

A routine to implement this conversion is found in Listing 12-2.

Listing 12-2. Julian Calendar Date

```
1   '*****************************************
2   'JULIAN TO CALENDAR DATE              *
3   'LISTING 12-2                         *
4   '*****************************************
5   '
10  CLS
20  INPUT"ENTER JULIAN DATE";N
30  I=INT(N):F=N-I
40  IF I>2299160 THEN 60
50  A=I:GOTO70
60  A=INT((I-1867216.25)/36524.25):B=I+A+1-INT(A/
    4)
70  C=B+1524
80  D=INT((C-122.1)/365.25)
90  E=INT(365.25*D)
100 G=INT((C-E)/30.6001)
110 DM=C+F-E-INT(30.6001*G)
120 IFG<13.5 THEN M=G-1 ELSE M=G-13
130 IFM>2.5 THEN Y=D-4716 ELSE Y=D-4715
140 PRINT:PRINT"JULIAN DATE";N;"IS EQUIVALENT TO
    ";M;"/";INT(DM);"/";Y
150 PRINT:PRINT:GOTO20
```

These routines are simple and straightforward tools that can be used in a number of different routines. Listing 12-3 can be used in a number of different routines. It is a full-blown calendar routine. It calls out the days by their names as it does the months. In addition, it permits the computation of a date by either the Julian (old style) or Gregorian protocols, and gives the phase of the moon. It computes the number of days between two dates and prints out actual calendar pages. Finally, given any three of the four calendar features, (day, day of week, month, or year), it computes all those dates (between a specified starting and stopping date) that satisfy the three criteria. For example, if we need to compute what years Friday the 13th occurs in October, between 1969 and 1990. The program computes that these conditions exist in 1972, 1978, and 1989.

Listing 12-3. Super Calendar

```
1  '*****************************************
2  'SUPER CALENDAR                          *
3  'LISTING 12-3                            *
4  '*****************************************
5  '
10 DEFDBLA-H,K-Y:CLS:D$(0)="SUNDAY":D$(1)="MONDA
   Y":D$(2)="TUESDAY":D$(3)="WEDNESDAY":D$(4)=
   "THURSDAY":D$(5)="FRIDAY":D$(6)="SATURDAY"
20 DIMM$(12),ML(12):M$(1)="JANUARY":ML(1)=31:M$(
   2)="FEBRUARY":M$(3)="MARCH":ML(3)=31:M$(4)=
   "APRIL":ML(4)=30:M$(5)="MAY":ML(5)=31:M$(6)
   ="JUNE":ML(6)=30:M$(7)="JULY":ML(7)=31:M$(8
   )="AUGUST":ML(8)=31:M$(9)="SEPTEMBER":ML(9)
   =30
30 M$(10)="OCTOBER":ML(10)=31:M$(11)="NOVEMBER":
   ML(11)=30:M$(12)="DECEMBER":ML(12)=31:CLS:F
   L=0:PRINTCHR$(212);"****    CALENDAR   ****":P
   RINT:PRINT
40 PRINT"1  --   ADVANCED CALENDER
2   --   CALENDAR OF MONTH
3   --   # DAYS BETWEEN TWO DATES
4   --   DATE, GIVEN # DAYS BETWEEN
5   --   OPEN CONDITIONS":PRINT:PRINT"ENTER CHOICE
   ";
50 Q$=""+INKEY$:IFQ$=""THEN50    ELSEONVAL(Q$)GOT
   O60   ,420  ,590  ,620  ,900
60 CLS:PRINT"          ********   ADVANCED CALEND
   AR   ********":PRINT:PRINT:PRINT"THIS ROUTIN
   E COMPUTES THE NUMBER OF DAYS SINCE 1 FEB 0
   AD IN
EITHER THE JULIAN OR GREGORIAN CALENDAR SYSTEMS.
    IT ALSO
COMPUTES THE JULIAN DATE OF THE DAY OF THE CURRE
   NT YEAR,";
70 PRINT"THE DAY OF THE WEEK, AND THE PHASE OF T
   HE MOON FOR THAT DATE.":PRINT:PRINT:INPUT"E
   NTER YEAR, MONTH, DATE (YYYY,MM,DD)";Y,M,D:
   PRINT
80 PRINT"GREGORIAN CALENDAR (NEW) -- 1
JULIAN CALENDAR (OLD)     -- 0",
90 S$=""+INKEY$:IFS$=""THEN90    ELSES=VAL(S$)
100 PRINTS:PRINT:IFS>1THEN80    ELSEGOSUB120
110 GOSUB230  :INPUT"'ENTER' TO RETURN TO MAIN P
    ROGRAM";ZZ:RUN
120 IFM>2THENX=0ELSEX=1
130 IFS=0THENC=2ELSEC=INT((Y-X)/100)
140 IF(Y/4)<>INT(Y/4)THEN180
150 IF(Y/100)<>INT(Y/100)THEN170
160 IF(Y/400)<>INT(Y/400)THEN180
170 LY=1:GOTO190
180 LY=0
190 N=D+INT(367*(((M-2)/12)+X))+INT(INT(365.25*(
    Y-X))-(.75*C))
```

Listing 12-3. Super Calendar (continued from page 257)

```
200 P=N/29.53059:P=P-INT(P):DW=INT(7*((N/7)-INT(
    N/7)))
210 JD=N-(336+INT(INT(365.25*(Y-1))-(.75*C)))
220 IFLY=1THENML(2)=29ELSEML(2)=28:RETURN
230 PRINT@(F2*448),"";:PRINTM$(M),D,Y:PRINT"DAY
    NUMBER (SINCE 1 FEB 0 AD) =";N
240 IFLY=0THEN260
250 PRINTY;"IS A LEAP YEAR"
260 PRINT"JULIAN DATE WITHIN YEAR        =";JD
270 PRINT"DAY OF WEEK :              ";D$(D
    W)
280 PRINT"PHASE OF MOON               =";P
290 PRINT"(0 = 1ST QTR   .25 = FULL   .50 = 3RD
    QTR   .75 = NEW MOON)"
300 RETURN
310 'PRINT ROUTINE
320 PRINT:PRINT"DO YOU WANT TO SEE A PRINTOUT?
    (Y/N)";
330 Q$=""+INKEY$:IFQ$=""THEN330   ELSEIFQ$="N"THE
    N410
340 PRINTQ$:LPRINT"","",D;M;Y,"",:IFFL=1THENLPRI
    NTDD;MM;YYELSELPRINT""
350 LPRINT""
360 LPRINT"DAY NUMBER (SINCE 1 JAN 4713 BC) =";
    N,"",:IFFL=1THENLPRINTN1ELSELPRINT""
370 LPRINT"JULIAN DATE WITHIN YEAR        =";
    JD,"",:IFFL=1THENLPRINTJ1ELSELPRINT""
380 LPRINT"DAY OF WEEK :                    "
    ;D$(DW),"",:IFFL=1THENLPRINTD$(D1)ELSELPRIN
    T""
390 LPRINT"PHASE OF MOON               =";
    P,:IFFL=1THENLPRINTP1ELSELPRINT""
400 LPRINT"":IFFL=1THENLPRINT"DIFFERENCE BETWEEN
    THESE TWO DATES IS";ABS(N1-N);"DAYS."
410 LPRINTSTRING$(2,10):FL=0:RUN10
420 'CALENDAR OF MONTH
430 CLS:PRINTCHR$(212);"**   CALENDAR OF MONTH   *
    *":PRINT:PRINT:INPUT"ENTER YEAR AND MONTH (
    JANUARY = 1)";Y,M:D=1:S=1:GOSUB120
440 IFDW<7THEN450   ELSEDW=0
450 IFM<>2THEN470
460 IFLY=1THENML(2)=29ELSEML(2)=28
470 L=INT((LEN(M$(M))+6)/2):CLS:PRINT@32-L,M$(M)
    ;Y;
480 FORI=0TO6:PRINT@130+(I*9),LEFT$(D$(I),3);:NE
    XTI
490 WK=1:DT=1:DX=DW
500 PRINT@130+(DW*9)+(64*WK),DT;:DW=DW+1
510 IFDW<7THEN530
520 DW=0:WK=WK+1
530 DT=DT+1:IFDT<=ML(M)THEN500
540 PRINT@704,"HARDCOPY DESIRED?   (Y/N)";
550 Q$=""+INKEY$:IFQ$=""THEN550
560 IFQ$="Y"THEN580
570 RUN10
```

```
580 FORI=0TO10:FORJ=0TO63:LPRINTCHR$(PEEK(15360+
    (64*I)+J));:NEXTJ:LPRINT"":NEXTI:RUN10
590 '# DAYS BETWEEN TWO DATES
600 CLS:PRINTCHR$(212);"**  # DAYS BETWEEN TWO D
    ATES  **":PRINT:PRINT:S=1:INPUT"ENTER FIRST
    DATE (YYYY,MM,DD)";Y,M,D:GOSUB120  :CLS:GO
    SUB230  :FL=1:N1=N:INPUT"ENTER SECOND DATE
    (YYYY,MM,DD)";Y,M,D:GOSUB120  :F2=1:GOSUB23
    0
610 PRINT"THE DIFFERENCE BETWEEN THE TWO DATES I
    S";ABS(N1-N);"DAYS":GOTO110
620 CLS:PRINTCHR$(212);"**  DATE, GIVEN # DAYS B
    ETWEEN  **":PRINT:PRINT:S=1
630 PRINT"A --  DATE PRIOR TO SPECIFIED START
B   --  DATE SUBSEQUENT TO SPECIFIED START":PRINT
    :PRINT"ENTER CHOICE";
640 Q$=""+INKEY$:IFQ$=""THEN640
650 PRINT:INPUT"START DATE (YYYY,MM,DD)";Y,M,D:G
    OSUB120  :CLS:GOSUB230  :N1=N:PRINT:PRINT:I
    NPUT"NUMBER OF DAYS DIFFERENCE";ND
660 IFQ$="A"THEN680
670 NX=N1+ND:GOTO690
680 NX=N1-ND
690 Q=INT((ND-(INT(ND/365.25)*365.25))/30.4375):
    IFNX<N1THEN720
700 Y=Y+INT(ND/365.25):M=M+Q:IFM<13THEN740
710 M=1:Y=Y+1:GOTO740
720 Y=Y-INT(ND/365.25):M=M-Q:IFM>0THEN740
730 M=12:Y=Y-1
740 GOSUB120  :PRINT@50,ABS(N1-N);
750 IFN<NXTHEN830
760 IFN=NXTHEN890
770 D=D-1
780 IFD>0THEN740
790 M=M-1
800 IFM=0THEN820
810 D=ML(M):GOTO740
820 M=12:Y=Y-1:GOTO810
830 D=D+1
840 IFD>ML(M)THEN860
850 GOTO740
860 M=M+1:D=1
870 IFM<13THEN740
880 M=1:Y=Y+1:GOTO740
890 F2=1:GOSUB230  :PRINT@960,"'ENTER' TO CONTIN
    UE";:INPUTZZ:RUN
900 CLS:S=1:PRINTCHR$(212);"** OPEN CONDITIONS
    **":PRINT:PRINT
910 PRINT"THIS ROUTINE ALLOWS YOU TO SPECIFY THR
    EE OF THE FOUR VALUES
BELOW.  USE '0' FOR THE UNKNOWN.  THE PROGRAM FI
    NDS THE ANSWER.":PRINT
920 PRINT"     YEAR (ANY POSITIVE VALUE)
    MONTH (1-12)
    DATE (1-31)
    DAY OF WEEK (1-7)  (SUNDAY = 1)"
930 PRINT@960,"USE '0' FOR UNKNOWN VALUE";:PRINT
```

Listing 12-3. Super Calendar (continued from page 259)

```
      @704,"ENTER YEAR":INPUTXY:IFXY>0THEN950
940 PRINT@704,"SEARCH BEGINS IN WHAT YEAR":INPUT
    FY:PRINT@704,"SEARCH ENDS IN WHAT YEAR  ":I
    NPUTYL:Y=FY-1:PRINT@704,"
                 ";
950 PRINT@424,XY;:PRINT@704,"ENTER MONTH":INPUTX
    M:PRINT@488,M$(XM);:PRINT@704,"ENTER DATE "
    :INPUTXD:PRINT@552,XD;:PRINT@704,"ENTER DAY
     OF WEEK":INPUTXW:XW=XW-1:IFXW=>0THENPRINT@
    616,D$(XW)
960 PRINT:PRINT:IFXY=0THEN1030
970 IFXM=0THEN1040
980 IFXD=0THEN1050
990 IFXW=-1THEN1060
1000 PRINT"NO UNKNOWNS?   (Y/N)";
1010 Q$=""+INKEY$:IFQ$=""THEN1010 ELSEIFQ$="Y"TH
     EN900
1020 RUN
1030 M=XM:D=XD:GOTO1070
1040 Y=XY:D=XD:GOTO1110
1050 Y=XY:M=XM:GOTO1160
1060 Y=XY:M=XM:D=XD:GOTO1210
1070 Y=Y+1:GOSUB130
1080 IFY>YLTHEN1240
1090 IFDW<>XWTHEN1070
1100 GOSUB1250 :GOTO1070
1110 M=1
1120 GOSUB130
1130 IFDW<>XWTHEN1150
1140 GOSUB1250
1150 M=M+1:IFM=13THEN1240 ELSE1120
1160 D=1
1170 GOSUB130
1180 IFDW<>XWTHEN1200
1190 GOSUB1250
1200 D=D+1:IFD>ML(M)THEN1240 ELSE1170
1210 CLS:GOSUB120
1220 GOSUB230
1230 PRINT:GOTO110
1240 PRINT:PRINT"THAT CONCLUDES THE SURVEY OF AV
     AILABLE DATA":PRINT:GOTO110
1250 PRINT@896,Y,M$(M),D,D$(DW):LPRINTY,M$(M),D,
     D$(DW):RETURN
```

Easter

Unlike many holidays and religious periods which have standard dates or easily computed periods (Christmas = December 25, Thanksgiving = fourth Thursday in November, etc.), Easter is a movable date defined as the first Sunday March 21. The routine given in Listing 12-4 relies heavily on modular math. That is, $2000_{\text{mod}19} = 19 \times (2000/19 - $ integer part of $(2000/19)) = 5$. The algorithm for computing the date of Easter, given the year Y, is:

1. $A = Y_{\text{mod}19}$
2. $B = $ integer part $Y/100$ $\quad C = Y_{\text{mod}100}$
3. $D = $ integer part $B/4$ $\quad E = B_{\text{mod}4}$
4. $F = $ integer part $\dfrac{B + 8}{25}$

5. $G = $ integer part $\dfrac{B - F + 1}{3}$

6. $H = (19A + B - D - G + 15)_{mod30}$

7. $I = $ integer part $C/4$ $K = C_{mod4}$

8. $L = (32 + 2E + 2I - H - K)_{mod\,7}$

9. $M = $ integer part $\dfrac{A + 11H + 22L}{451}$

10. $N = $ integer part $\dfrac{H + L - 7M + 114}{31}$

$P = (H + L - 7M + 114)_{mod31}$

11. The day of the month on which Easter falls is $= P + 1$

12. The month of Easter is $= N$ (January $= 1$)

Listing 12-4. The Date of Easter

```
1  '***********************************************
2  'THE DATE OF EASTER                           *
3  'LISTING 12-4                                 *
4  '***********************************************
5  '
10 CLS
20 M$(2)="FEBRUARY":M$(3)="MARCH":M$(4)="APRIL":
   M$(5)="MAY"
30 DEF FNM(X,Y)=Y*(X/Y-INT(X/Y))
40 INPUT"ENTER YEAR (YYYY)";Y
50 A=FNM(Y,19)
60 B=INT(Y/100):C=FNM(Y,100)
70 D=INT(B/4):E=FNM(B,4)
80 F=INT((B+8)/25):G=INT((B-F+1)/3)
90 H=FNM((19*A)+B-D-G+15,30)
100 I=INT(C/4):K=FNM(C,4)
110 L=FNM(32+(2*E)+(2*I)-H-K,7)
120 M=INT((A+(11*H)+(22*L))/451)
130 Z=H+L-(7*M)+114:N=INT(Z/31):P=FNM((H+L-(7*M)
    +114),31)
140 PRINT:PRINT"EASTER SUNDAY";Y;"FALLS ON";P+1;
    M$(N):PRINT
150 PRINT:RUN20
```

COMPUTING PLANETARY POSITIONS

On January 1, 1980 the nine planets of the solar system were positioned as shown in Fig. 12-2. This chart is useful if one is interested in planetary positions for the first of January, 1980. A difference of only a day, one way or the other, makes the chart totally inadequate and inaccurate. Books are available (see the bibliography under "Astronomy") that give planetary positions, but only for a sampling of days. For example, one resource consulted in this work lists the positions of the planets in increments of forty days. The routines that follow facilitate the computation of planetary positions for any given day in any specified year.

The primary concern of the users of these routines will be the precision of the forecast. Precision in astronomical forecasting carries a heavy price in complexity of programs and the consumption of memory. If the purpose of the effort is simply to determine the position of the planets relative to signs of the zodiac for astrological reference, the first program to follow should be sufficient. On the other hand, those using this volume to develop programs to accurately position and aim powerful telescopes will have to use the second routine as a starting point or foundation program for a yet more precise and complicated program.

The first program is based on several assumptions known to be false from the outset. Among these are the assumptions that the orbits of the planets are circular, that the center of the orbit is at the center of the sun, that the mean distances and

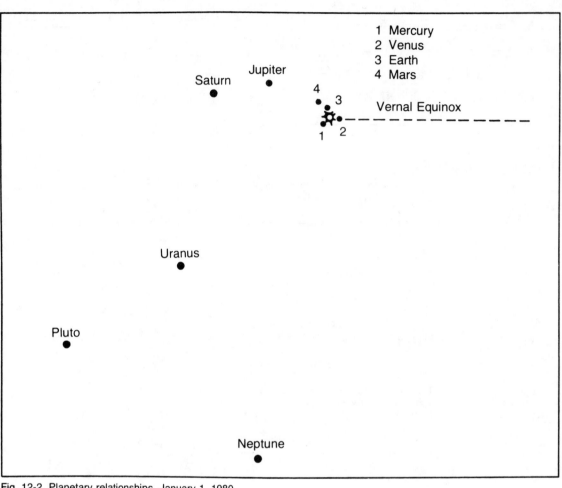

Fig. 12-2. Planetary relationships, January 1, 1980.

Table 12-1. Planetary Positions, January 1, 1980.

Planet	Distance From Sun AU's	Distance From Sun 10⁶Km	Sidereal Period Years	Days	Mean Orbital Velocity Km/Sec	Mean Daily Angular Motion Seconds of Arc	Position 1-1-1980 Degrees
Mercury	.3871	57.91	.24085	87.97	47.9	14731.9608	196.5770
Venus	.7233	108.21	.61521	224.70	35.0	5767.4497	356.3670
Earth	1.000	149.60	1.000039	365.26	29.8	3548.0544	99.3364
Mars	1.5237	227.90	1.88089	686.98	24.1	1886.4435	131.0189
Jupiter	5.2037	778.30	11.8653		13.1	298.9930	150.6210
Saturn	9.5803	1428.00	29.6501		9.6	119.7180	170.7233
Uranus	19.1410	2872.00	83.7445		6.8	41.9780	231.4843
Neptune	30.1982	4498.00	165.9510		5.4	21.4930	259.9150
Pluto	39.4387	5910.00	247.6870		4.7	14.1160	198.4410

mean angular motions of the planets are constant, and that the planes of all the orbits are coincidental; that is, they are all in one plane. We accept these assumptions to the extent the results are sufficiently accurate for our purposes due to the ease and speed of computation.

Table 12-1 gives the fairly precise locations of the planets as of January 1, 1980, plus the mean distances from the sun, and the mean daily angular motion. It is from these data the positions for Fig. 12-2 were computed.

The first stage in computing planetary positions is the conversion of the desired date into a Julian date. From the Julian date, the number of days to the reference date (January 1, 1980) are computed by subtraction. It is then a simple matter of multiplying this value times the mean daily angular motion and adding the result to the reference position. In the case of dates prior to the reference date, the product of the number of days (which will be a negative value) and the angular motion will be a negative value which, when "added" to the reference point will automatically yield the correct position. Listing 12-5 contains the program for the first planetary position routine. A sample run is shown in Fig. 12-3.

Listing 12-5. Simple Planetary Position

```
1  '*****************************************
2  'SIMPLE PLANETARY POSITION               *
3  'LISTING 12-5                            *
4  '*****************************************
5  '
10 CLS:RESTORE:DEFDBL A-H,M-Y:DIMMO$(12)
20 DEFFNM(A,B)=B*((A/B)-INT(A/B))
30 RD=.01745329277777778
40 GOSUB180
50 FORI=1TO9:READZ$(I),D(I),M(I),P(I):NEXT
60 D1=ND:T=D1/36525:D2=D1/10000:PM=N/29.53059:PM
   =360*(PM-INT(PM))
70 SR=180+((JD+103.62893)*.985626):IFSR>360THENS
   R=SR-360
80 MR=SR+PM:IFMR>360THENMR=MR-360
90 PRINT"R.A. OF SUN = ";SR:PRINT"R.A. OF MOON =
   ";MR
100 PRINT:PRINT"PLANET","POSITION  (DEGREES FROM
    VERNAL EQUINOX)"
110 FORI=1TO9
120   P1(I)=ABS(P(I)+((D1*M(I))/3600))
130   IFP1(I)<=360THEN150
140   P1(I)=P1(I)-360:GOTO130
150   PRINTUSING"%               %     ###.######
    ";Z$(I);P1(I)
160 NEXT
170 PRINT:RUN10
180 DW$(0)="SUNDAY":DW$(1)="MONDAY":DW$(2)="TUES
    DAY":DW$(3)="WEDNESDAY":DW$(4)="THURSDAY":D
    W$(5)="FRIDAY":DW$(6)="SATURDAY"
190 J$="JANFEBMARAPRMAYJUNJULAUGSEPOCTNOVDEC":FO
    RI=1TO12:MO$(I)=MID$(J$,(3*(I-1))+1,3):NEXT

200 INPUT"ENTER DATE DESIRED  (DD,MM,YYYY)";D,M,
    Y:M0=M:D0=D:GOSUB280
210 INPUT"ENTER GREENWICH TIME DESIRED  (24-HOUR
    CLOCK: HHMM)";T
```

Listing 12-5. Simple Planetary Position (continued from page 263)

```
220 TH=INT(T/100):DM=((T/100)-TH)/.6:T=((12+TH+D
    M)/24)-.5:ND=N+T-2444239
230 PRINT"JULIAN DATE =";N:PRINT"ADJUSTED FOR TI
    ME =";N+T:PRINT"DAY OF WEEK = ";DW$(DW):PRI
    NT"JULIAN DATE WITHIN YEAR =";JD:PRINT"NUMB
    ER OF DAYS SINCE EPOCH (NOON, 31 DEC 1979)
    = ";ND
240 IFLY=0THEN260
250 PRINTY;"IS A LEAP YEAR"
260 PRINT:RETURN
270 D1=N-2415020+T:T=D1/36525:D2=D1/10000
280 IFM>2THEX=0ELSEX=1
290 C=INT((Y-X)/100)
300 IF(Y/4)<>INT(Y/4)THEN340
310 IF(Y/100)<>INT(Y/100)THEN330
320 IF(Y/400)<>INT(Y/400)THEN340
330 LY=1:GOTO350
340 LY=0
350 N=D+INT(367*(((M-2)/12)+X))+INT(INT(365.25*(
    Y-X))-(.75*C))+1721088.5
360 W=N-1721088.5:DW=INT(7*((W/7)-INT(W/7)))
370 JD=N-(336+INT(INT(365.25*(Y-1))-(.75*C)))-17
    21088.5
380 RETURN
390 DATA MERCURY,.3871,14732.42,196.577
400 DATA VENUS,.7233,5767.668,356.367
410 DATA EARTH,1,3548.192,99.3364
420 DATA MARS,1.5237,1886.4435,131.0189
430 DATA JUPITER,5.2037,298.993,150.621
440 DATA SATURN,9.5803,119.718,170.7233
450 DATA URANUS,19.141,41.978,231.4843
460 DATA NEPTUNE,30.1982,21.493,259.915
470 DATA PLUTO,39.4387,14.116,198.441
```

The algorithm used in this program is very simple and straightforward:

1. Compute the number of days from January 1, 1980 (N).
2. For each planet, multiply this value times the mean daily angular motion, M_x and add the product to the planet's longitude as of 1/1/1980, L_x: $L_x' = L_x + (N * M_x)$.

Due to the eliptical nature of each planet's orbits, however, this routine produces incorrect results. Whether the results are acceptable or not is a function of the use to which they are put. They are adequate to obtain a general notion of the direction of a planet relative to the sun and, deduced from that, relative to the position of the earth.

For those in need of greater precision, there are several routines that yield the accuracy desired but require considerably more computation. The following several algorithms provide fairly accurate locational data for the sun, moon, and the nine planets of the solar system.

Orbits

As noted above, celestial orbits are eliptical in shape, instead of circular. The basic form is shown in Fig. 12-4. The sun is colocated with one of the two *foci* (F,F'). The point along the major axis, $\overline{AB}$, at which the plane comes closest to the sun is called the *perihelion* and the farthest point is called the *aphelion*. One-half of the distance from A to B is called the *semi-major* axis and is frequently used in orbital computations.

```
ENTER DATE DESIRED   (DD,MM,YYYY)? 1,9,01982
ENTER GREENWICH TIME DESIRED   (24-HOUR CLOCK: HHMM)? 1200
JULIAN DATE = 2445213.5
ADJUSTED FOR TIME = 2445214
DAY OF WEEK = WEDNESDAY
JULIAN DATE WITHIN YEAR = 244
NUMBER OF DAYS SINCE EPOCH (NOON, 31 DEC 1979) =  975

R.A. OF SUN =  162.6321263220745

R.A. OF MOON =  65.73370904728675

PLANET          POSITION  (DEGREES FROM VERNAL EQUINOX)
MERCURY           226.607417
VENUS             118.443750
EARTH             340.305067
MARS              281.930681
JUPITER           231.598271
SATURN            203.146925
URANUS            242.853342
NEPTUNE           265.736021
PLUTO             202.264033
```

Fig. 12-3. Results of Listing 12-5.

To the ancient astronomers, and to casual present day observers, the sun appears to revolve around the earth instead of the other way around. The following routine leads to the computation of the sun's location along an imaginary orbit around the earth against a background of stars and constellations. This value is called the *right ascension* of the sun and is illustrated in Fig. 12-5. A detailed dia-

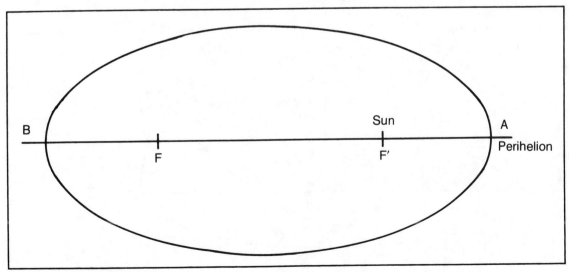

Fig. 12-4. Standard eliptical orbit.

265

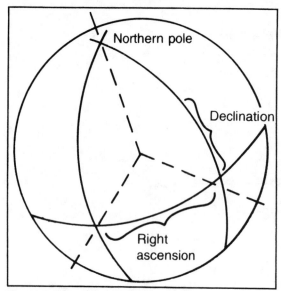

Fig. 12-5. Celestial relationships.

gram of celestial relationships is shown in Fig. 12-6.

The algorithm to compute the sun's position on a given date is:

1. Compute the number of days, D, from the beginning of 1980: January 0.0, 1980.

2. Calculate $N = \dfrac{360}{365.2422} \times D$. This is equal to: $N = .985648 \times D$.

3. Add or substract multiples of 360 until $0 < = N < = 360$.

4. Calculate $M = N - 3.762863$. If the result is less than zero, add 360.

5. Calculate $E = \dfrac{360}{\pi} e \sin M$. This is equal to: $E = 1.91574 \sin M$.

6. Calculate $L = N + E + 278.83354$. If the result is greater than 360, subtract 360. This is the sun's geocentric (earth-centered) ecliptic longitude.

7. Calculate $T = \dfrac{N - 2415020}{36525}$

8. Calculate $OE = 23°27'08.26'' - 46.845''T - .0059''T^2 + .00181''T^3$

9. Calculate $RA = \tan^{-1}\left[\dfrac{\sin L \cos OE}{\cos L}\right]$. This is the right ascension of the sun.

10. Calculate $DE = \sin^{-1}[\sin OE \sin L]$. This is the declination of the sum (see Figs. 12-4 and 12-5).

11. During the computation of RA, the use of

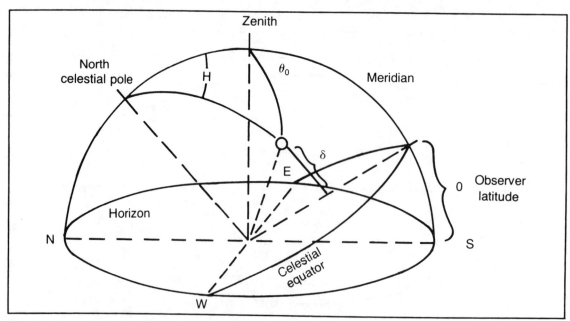

Fig. 12-6. Detailed celestial relationships.

266

the arc tangent function can introduce an ambiguity of a multiple of 180°. It is sometimes necessary to add or subtract 180° to bring RA into the correct quadrant. Use this subalgorithum for this:

a. $X = \cos L$
b. $Y = \sin L \cos OE$

	Y positive	Y negative
X positive	$\emptyset <= RA <= 90$	$270 <= RA <= 360$
X negative	$90 <= RA < 180$	$180 <= RA <= 270$

12. Convert RA to hours by $RA = 24 \dfrac{RA}{360}$

13. Convert the decimal hours to hours, minutes, and seconds. ($32.34° = 2.156h = 2h\ 09'21.6'$)

14. The declination can be converted from decimal degrees to degrees, minutes, and seconds, but this step is not necessary.

As a check on your implementation of this algorithm, the location of the sun, on July 27, 1980, should be:

$$RA = 08h\ 25'\ 44''$$
$$DE = 19°\ 13'\ 53''$$

In step 4 of the previous algorithm we calculated the value M, which is the mean anomaly, reasonably accurately. There is an alternative process that can be used to improve the accuracy of M. Having found M, we compute the eccentric anomaly, E, from:

$$E = e \sin E = M/57.29577$$

where E is expressed in radians, and e is the eccentricity, .016718.

This relationship requires an iterative solution to find E.

1. $E = M$
2. $X = E - .016718 \sin E - M$
3. If $X = .0000001$, go to step 6.
4. $E = E - \dfrac{X}{1 - .016718 \cos E}$
5. Go to step 2.
6. Go to the computation of the *true anomaly*

The true anomaly is found from

$$V = 2 \tan^{-1}\left(1.01686 \tan \dfrac{E}{2}\right)$$

L, then is computed from

$$L = (57.29577\ V) + 282.596403$$

The processing then continues from the second half of step 6 in the main algorithm. Using this procedure should lead to a revised location where

$$RA = 08h\ 23'\ 46''$$
$$DE = 19°\ 20'\ 38''$$

The distance to the sun and its angular diameter, using the data just computed, is found from

$$R = \dfrac{-9.55792 \times 10^8}{(1 + 2.7828 \cos V)}$$

$$TH = .533128 \dfrac{(1 + 2.7828 \cos V)}{-6.39905}$$

R will be the distance of the sun from the earth in kilometers. TH is the apparent angular diameter of the sun. Solving from the data for July 27, 1980

$$R = 1.519196 \times 10^8 \text{ kilometers}$$
$$TH = 0°\ 31'\ 30''\ (.525°)$$

Sunrise and Sunset. Closely related to computing the location of the sun at a given instant is the task of determining the time of sunrise and sunset. The algorithm for this process is:

1. Input the month and day of the year, MO and DY.
2. Input the latitude and longitude of the observer, LA and LO.
3. Determine TD: $TD = (LO - INT(L))/15$
4. If daylight savings time is in effect, $DL = 1$, else $DL = \emptyset$.
5. Let $J =$ the Julian date within the year.
6. $X = \dfrac{J}{7}$ and $PL = .120831\ (\pi/26)$
7. Calculate:
   a. $D = .456 - 22.915*\cos(2*PL*X) - 43*\cos(2*PL*X) - .156*\cos(3*PL*X) + 3.82\sin(PL*X) + .06*\sin(2*PL*X) - .082*\sin(3*PL*X)$

(This is approximately equal to the declination of the sun).

   b. $E = .008 + .51*\cos(PL*X) - 3.197*\cos(2*PL*X) - .106*\cos(3*PL*X) - .15*\cos(4*PL*X) - 7.317*\sin(PL*X) - 9.471*$

sin(2*PL*X)−.391*sin(3*PL*X)−.242*
sin(4*PL*X)

(This is the "equation of time" (see below)).

    c. Convert LA, D to radians. (Divide by 57.29577)

    d. If the absolute value of (sinD/cos LA) is less than 1, go to sub-step f.

    e. There is no sunrise or sunset, observer is in polar region. Go to step 1.

    f. Y = (sin D /cos LA)

    g. $Z1 = 90 - (\tan^{-1}(Y/ \sqrt{1-Y^2}))$ *57.29577

    h. Z2 = 360 − Z1

8. The azimuth of sunrise is Z1. The azimuth of sunset is Z2.

9. Convert Z1 to radians: Z = Z1/57.29577

10. Compute ST − sin Z/cos D

11. If the absolute value of ST is equal to or greater than 1, then T = 6 and TT = 6; go to step 15.

12. $CT = \sqrt{1 - ST^2}$

13. $T = \dfrac{57.29577}{15*\text{arc tan }(ST/CT)}$

14. TT = T

15. If D is greater then zero, go to step 17.

16. TT = 12, T = T + TD − E/60 −.04

17. Compute time of sunrise:

    a. T1 = INT(T) = The hour of sunrise

    b. T2 = T−T1

    c. T2 = INT(T2*600 + 5)/10) = minutes after the hour

18. Compute the time of sunset:

    a. T = 12 − TT and T = TD − E/60 + .04

    b. T1 = INT(T) = The hour of sunset

    c. T2 = T − T1

    d. T2 = INT((T2*600 + 5)/10) − minutes.

Equation of Time. In step 7b just above we computed the value E and called it the equation of time. The rate at which the sun moves through the sky is not as nearly constant as we would think, due to the elliptic nature of the earth's orbit and the inclination of the earth on its axis. The equation of time is the difference between the time computed from the average rate of the sun's motion and the time determined from the sun's actual position. The value E is added to the time estimate (mean sun time) to arrive at the real sun time. Listing 12-7 includes the algorithms to compute the equation of time and the times of sunrise and sunset.

Planetary Positions. Listing 12-6 is a major routine to compute the positions of the planets in both heliocentric (sun-centered) and geocentric modes with a fair degree of precision. Figure 12-7 shows a flowchart of the program, and Fig. 12-8 shows the references and variables for the program. Figure 12-9 shows a sample run through the program. Routines to obtain a degree of precision significantly greater than given here quickly become quite extensive and tedious both for the programmer and the computer. That which is given here should be sufficient for most purposes.

Listing 12-6. Complex Planetary Positions

```
1  '**********************************************
2  'COMPLEX PLANETARY POSITIONS                 *
3  'LISTING 12-6                                *
4  '**********************************************
5  '
10 CLS:RD=.017453292777777778:EE=RD*23.441884:M$=
   "%     %     ###.######        ###.######
       ###.######"
20 DEFFNA(X)=ATN(X/SQR(-X*X+1)):DEFFNM(A,B)=B*(A
   /B-INT(A/B))
30 GOSUB1010
40 PRINT"LOADING DATA FOR:":PRINT
50 RESTORE:FORI=1TO9:READZ$(I),P(I),LE(I),LP(I),
   EC(I),RA(I),OI(I),LO(I),AD(I),AB(I):PRINT@7
```

```
         28,Z$(I);"    ";::NEXT
60  GOSUB1450 :CLS:GOSUB1520
70  A$="####.####  %        %":D$="DEGREES"
80  FORI=1TO9
90     PRINT@(30-(LEN(Z$(I))/2)),"   ";Z$(I);"      "
       ;:Q=I
100    NP=.985695*ND/P(I):NF=FNM(NP,360):M=NP+LE(
       I)-LP(I):M=FNM(M,360):PRINT@165,USINGA$;M;D
       $;:M=M*RD
110    HL=NP+(114.5915573*EC(I)*SIN(M))+LE(I):IFH
       L<0THENHL=HL+360ELSEIFHL>360THENHL=HL-360EL
       SEHL=HL
120    PRINT@229,USINGA$;HL;D$;
130    V(I)=(HL-LP(I))*RD:GOTO140
140    PRINT@293,USINGA$;V(I)/RD;D$;
150    L(I)=(V(I)/RD)+LP(I):L(I)=FNM(L(I),360):R(
       I)=(RA(I)*(1-(EC(I)[2)))/(1+(EC(I)*COS(V(I)
       )))
160    PRINT@357,USINGA$;L(I);D$;:PRINT@421,USING
       A$;R(I);"AU'S";
170    X=SIN((L(I)-LO(I))*RD)*SIN(OI(I)*RD):PS(I)
       =FNA(X)/RD
180    PRINT@485,USINGA$;PS(I);D$;
190    A=(L(Q)-LO(Q))*RD:Y=SIN(A)*COS(OI(Q)*RD):X
       =COS(A)
200    A=ATN(Y/X)/RD:GOSUB750
210    L1=A+LO(Q):R1=R(Q)*COS(PS(Q)*RD):Z=(L(3)-L
       1)*RD:ZZ=(L1-L(3))*RD
220    IFI<3THEN250
230    IFI=3THEN360
240    A=((ATN((R(3)*SIN(ZZ))/(R1-(R(3)*COS(ZZ)))
       ))/RD)+L1:L2=A:GOTO270
250    A=ATN((R1*SIN(Z))/(R(3)-(R1*COS(Z))))/RD
260    L2=180+L(3)+A
270    L2=FNM(L2,360)
280    B=ATN((R1*TAN(PS(Q)*RD)*SIN((L2-L1)*RD))/(
       R(3)*SIN((L1-L(3))*RD))):GOSUB950  :AS(Q)=L
       2:DE(Q)=TH
290    PRINT@549,USINGA$;AS(Q);"HOURS";:PRINT@613
       ,USINGA$;DE(Q);D$;
300    RH(Q)=SQR(ABS((R(3)[2)+(R(Q)[2)-(2*R(3)*R(
       Q)*COS((L(Q)-L(3))*RD))))
310    PRINT@677,USINGA$;RH(Q);"AU'S";
320    TT(Q)=8.316*RH(Q):TH(Q)=AD(Q)/RH(Q):PRINT@
       741,USINGA$;TT(Q);"MINUTES";:PRINT@805,USIN
       GA$;TH(Q);"";
330    F(Q)=.5*(1+COS((L(Q)-L(3))*RD)):PRINT@869,
       USINGA$;F(Q);"";
340    Z=(R(Q)*RH(Q))/(AB(Q)*SQR(F(Q))):L2=LOG(Z)
       /LOG(10)
350    M(Q)=(5*LZ)-26.7:PRINT@933,USINGA$;M(Q);""
       ;
360    PRINT@970,"(P)RINT    ANY OTHER KEY TO CONT
       INUE";
370    Q$=""+INKEY$:IFQ$=""THEN370
380    IFQ$<>"P"THEN400
390    GOSUB1350
```

Listing 12-6. Complex Planetary Positions (continued from page 269)

```
400    PRINT@970,"
            ";
410 NEXTI
420 CLS:PRINTCHR$(212);"GEOCENTRIC POSITIONS":PR
    INT"        RT ASCEN.   DECL.     DISTANCE   TI
    ME   DIAM.   BRIGHT.  PHASE":PRINT"PLANET      (H
    OURS)    (DEG.)     AU'S    MIN.    ARCSEC":P
    RINT
430 M$="%       % ###.#### ###.#### ###.#### ###.#
    ### ###.#### ##.# #.##"
440 FORQ=1TO9
450    IFQ=3THEN470
460    PRINTUSINGM$;Z$(Q);AS(Q);DE(Q);RH(Q);TT(Q)
    ;TH(Q);M(Q);F(Q)
470 NEXTQ
480 N=.9856473*ND:N=FNM(N,360)
490 M=N-3.76286:IFM<0THENM=M+360
500 M=M*RD:E=M
510 EX=E-(.016718*SIN(E))-M
520 IFABS(EX)<.000001THEN540
530 E=E-(EX/(1-(.016718*COS(E)))):GOTO510
540 V1=1.01686*TAN(E/2):V=2*ATN(V1)
550 L0=(V/RD)+282.596403:L0=FNM(L0,360)
560 PRINT:L2=L0:B=0:GOSUB950
570 R=1.495985E+08/149.6E+6:T=8.316*R:TA=.533128
    /R
580 PRINTUSINGM$;"SUN";L2;TH;R;T;TA;0;0
590 N=(360/365.2422)*ND:N=FNM(N,360)
600 M=(N-284.40761):IFM<0THENM=M+360:M=M*RD
610 E=6.291076591*SIN(M)
620 L2=N+E+64.975464:IFL2>360THENL2=L2-360
630 L1=(13.176396*D)+64.975464:L1=FNM(L1,360)
640 MM=L1-(.111404*D)-349.383063:MM=FNM(MM,360)
650 N=151.950429-(.052953*D):N=FNM(N,360)
660 EV=1.2739*SIN(((2*(L1-L2))-MM)*RD):AE=.1858*
    SIN(M):A3=.37*(M):M1=(MM*RD)+EV-AE-A3:EC=6.
    2886*SIN(M1):A4=.214*SIN(2*M1):LL=(L1*RD)+E
    V+EC-AE+A4:V=.6583*SIN(2*(LL-L2)*RD):LT=LL+
    V
670 N1=(N*RD)-(.16*SIN(M)):V=SIN(LT-N1)*.99597
680 X=COS(LT-N1):A=(ATN(V/X))/RD:GOSUB750
690 L2=A+(N1/RD):X=SIN(LT-N1)*.0896834:B=FNA(X)
700 GOSUB950
710 D=LT-(L2*RD):PH=.5*(1-COS(D)):R=.996986/(1+(
    .0549*COS((MM*RD)+EC))):R=(R*384401)/149.6E
    +6:T=8.316*R:TA=.5181/R:BR=0:D=(LT-(L2*RD))
    :PH=.5*(1+COS(D))
720 PRINTUSINGM$;"MOON";L2,TH;R;T;TA;BR;PH:A=0:B
    =8
730 GOSUB1350
740 END
750 IFY=>0ANDX=>0THEN820
760 IFY<0ANDX=>0THEN860
770 IFY=>0ANDX<0THEN900
780 IF180<=AANDA<=270THEN940
```

```
790 IFA<180THENA=A+180
800 IFA>270THENA=A-180
810 GOTO780
820 IF0<=AANDA<=90THEN940
830 IFA<0THENA=A+180
840 IFA>90THENA=A-180
850 GOTO820
860 IF270<=AANDA<=360THEN940
870 IFA<270THENA=A+180
880 IF360<ATHENA=A-180
890 GOTO860
900 IF90<=AANDA<=180THEN940
910 IFA<90THENA=A+180
920 IF180<ATHENA=A-180
930 GOTO900
940 RETURN
950 L=L2*RD
960 X=(SIN(B)*COS(EE))+(COS(B)*SIN(EE)*SIN(L)):T
    H=FNA(X)/RD
970 Y=(SIN(L)*COS(EE))-(TAN(B)*SIN(EE)):X=COS(L)

980 A=ATN(Y/X)/RD:GOSUB750
990 L2=A/15:RETURN
1000 END
1010 DW$(0)="SUNDAY":DW$(1)="MONDAY":DW$(2)="TUE
     SDAY":DW$(3)="WEDNESDAY":DW$(4)="THURSDAY":
     DW$(5)="FRIDAY":DW$(6)="SATURDAY"
1020 J$="JANFEBMARAPRMAYJUNJULAUGSEPOCTNOVDEC":D
     IMMO$(12):FORI=1TO12:MO$(I)=MID$(J$,(3*(I-1
     ))+1,3):NEXT
1030 INPUT"ENTER DATE DESIRED   (DD,MM,YYYY)";D,M
     ,Y:M0=M:D0=D:GOSUB1150
1040 INPUT"ENTER GREENWICH TIME DESIRED   (24-HOU
     R CLOCK: HHMM)";T
1050 TH=INT(T/100):DM=((T/100)-TH)/.6:T=((12+TH+
     DM)/24)-.5:ND=N+T-2444239
1060 PRINT"JULIAN DATE =";N:PRINT"ADJUSTED FOR T
     IME =";N+T:PRINT"DAY OF WEEK = ";DW$(DW):PR
     INT"JULIAN DATE WITHIN YEAR =";JD:PRINT"NUM
     BER OF DAYS SINCE EPOCH (NOON, 31 DEC 1979)
      = ";ND
1070 IFLY=0THEN1090
1080 PRINTY;"IS A LEAP YEAR"
1090 LPRINTDW$(DW);",";D0;MO$(M);",";Y,T*2400;"H
     OURS"
1100 ´
1110 LPRINT"JULIAN DATE = ";JD,"DAYS SINCE 0.0 J
     AN 1980 = ";ND
1120 LPRINT""
1130 PRINT:RETURN
1140 ´
1150 IFM>2THEX=0ELSEX=1
1160 C=INT((Y-X)/100)
1170 IF(Y/4)<>INT(Y/4)THEN1210
1180 IF(Y/100)<>INT(Y/100)THEN1200
1190 IF(Y/400)<>INT(Y/400)THEN1210
1200 LY=1:GOTO1220
```

Listing 12-6. Complex Planetary Positions (continued from page 271)

```
1210 LY=0
1220 N=D+INT(367*(((M-2)/12)+X))+INT(INT(365.25*
     (Y-X))-(.75*C))+1721088.5
1230 W=N-1721088.5:DW=INT(7*((W/7)-INT(W/7)))
1240 JD=N-(336+INT(INT(365.25*(Y-1))-(.75*C)))-1
     721088.5
1250 RETURN
1260 DATA "MERCURY",.24085,231.2973,77.1442128,.
     2056306,.3870986,7.0043579,48.0941733,6.74,
     1.918E-06
1270 DATA VENUS,.61521,355.73352,131.2895792,.00
     67826,.7233316,3.394435,76.4997524,16.92,1.
     721E-06
1280 DATA EARTH,1.00004,98.83354,102.596403,.016
     718,1,0,0,0,0
1290 DATA MARS,1.88089,126.30783,335.6908166,.09
     33865,1.5236883,1.8498011,49.4032001,9.36,4
     .539E-06
1300 DATA JUPITER,11.86224,146.966365,14.0095493
     ,.0484658,5.202561,1.3041819,100.2520175,19
     6.74,1.994E-04
1310 DATA SATURN,29.45771,165.322242,92.6653974,
     .0556155,9.554747,2.4893741,113.4888341,165
     .6,1.74E-04
1320 DATA URANUS,84.01247,228.0708551,172.736328
     8,.0463232,19.21814,.7729895,73.8768642,65.
     8,7.768E-05
1330 DATA NEPTUNE,164.79558,260.3578998,47.86721
     48,.0090021,30.10957,1.7716017,131.5606494,
     62.2,7.597E-05
1340 DATA PLUTO,250.9,209.439,222.972,.25387,39.
     78459,17.137,109.941,8.2,4.073E-06
1350 FORR=0TO14
1360   FORC=0TO63
1370     Z=PEEK(15360+(64*R)+C)
1380     IFZ<32THENZ=Z+64
1390     LPRINTCHR$(Z);
1400   NEXTC
1410   LPRINT""
1420 NEXTR
1430 LPRINT"":LPRINT""
1440 RETURN
1450 NE=.9856473*ND/1.00004:NE=FNM(NE,360):ME=NE
     -3.763857
1460 ME=FNM(ME,360)*RD
1470 LE=NE+(1.915742*SIN(ME))+98.83354:LE=FNM(LE
     ,360)
1480 V(3)=(LE-102.596403)*RD
1490 L(3)=(V(3)/RD)+102.596403:L(3)=FNM(L(3),360
     )
1500 R(3)=(1-(EC(3)[2]))/(1+(EC(3)*COS(V(3)))):PS
     (3)=0
1510 RETURN
1520 PRINT@128,"MEAN ANOMOLY = ";:PRINT@192,"HEL
     IOCENTRIC LONGITUDE = ";:PRINT@256,"TRUE AN
```

```
       OMOLY = ";:PRINT@320,"CORRECTED HELIOCENTRI
       C LONGITUDE = ";:PRINT@384,"RADIUS VECTOR =
       ";:PRINT@448,"HELIOCENTRIC LATITUDE = "
1530  PRINT@512,"RIGHT ASCENSION = ";:PRINT@576,"
      DECLINATION = ";
1540  PRINT@640,"DISTANCE FROM EARTH = ";:PRINT@7
      04,"TIME (LIGHT SPEED) = ";:PRINT@768,"APPA
      RENT DIAMETER = ";:PRINT@832,"PHASE = ";:PR
      INT@896,"BRIGHTNESS = ";
1550  RETURN
```

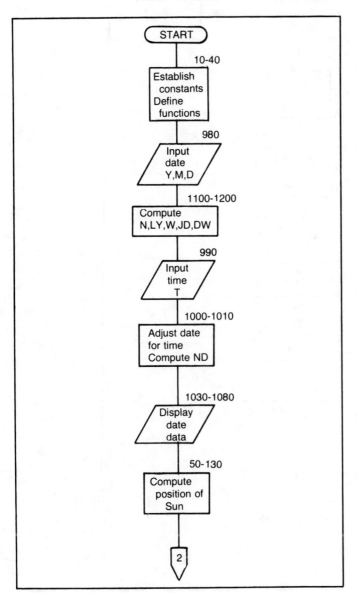

Fig. 12-7. Flowchart of Listing 12-6.

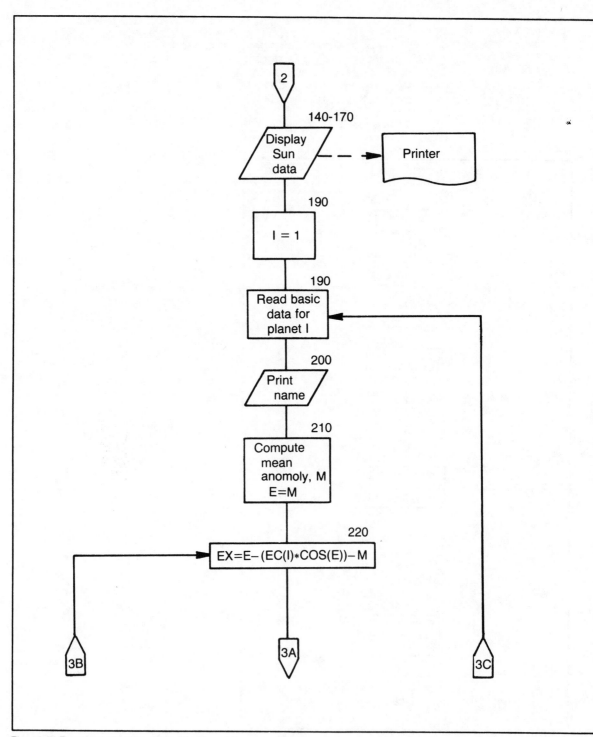

Fig. 12-7. Flowchart of Listing 12-6. (Continued from page 273.)

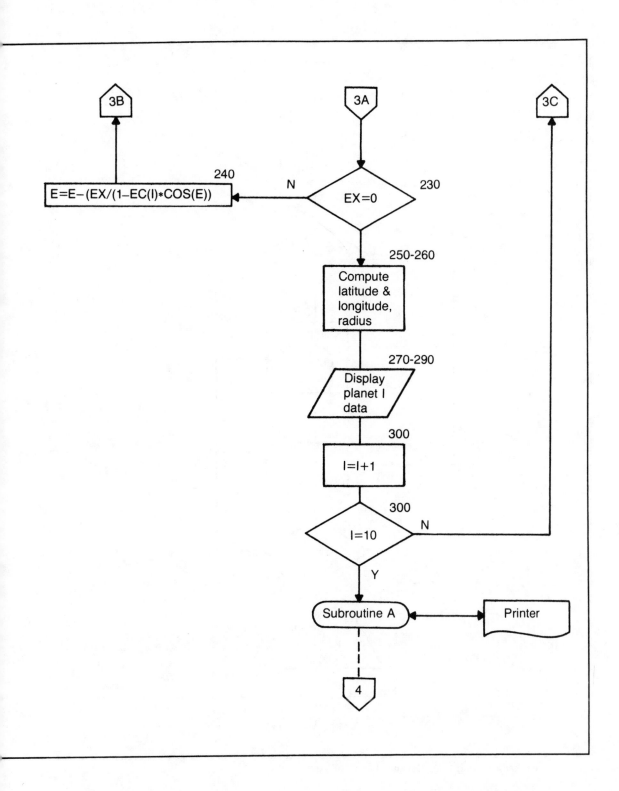

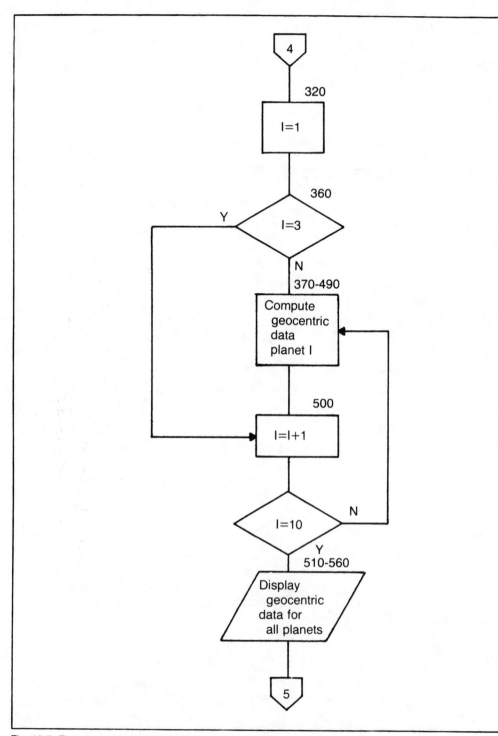

Fig. 12-7. Flowchart of Listing 12-6. (Continued from page 275.)

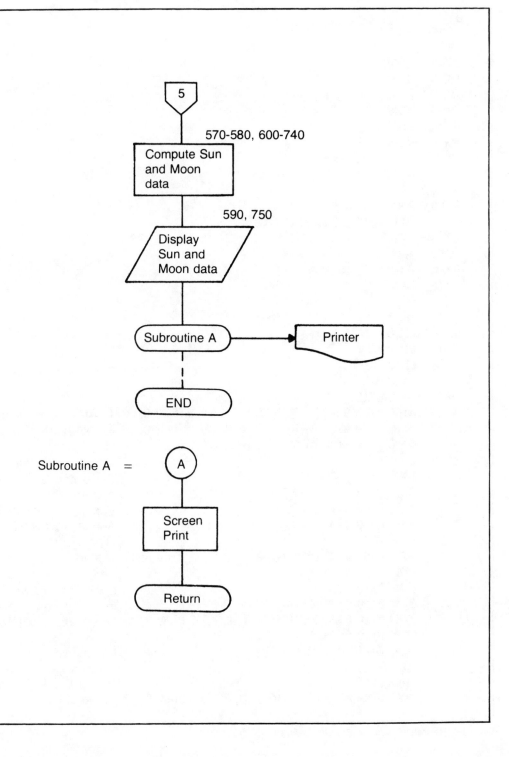

5

570-580, 600-740

Compute Sun and Moon data

590, 750

Display Sun and Moon data

Subroutine A → Printer

END

Subroutine A = (A)

Screen Print

Return

```
LINE     REFERENCES
00100    00120
00130    00110
00220    00240
00250    00230
00500    00360
00560    00540
00620    00630
00640    00620
00780    00390 00710 00930
00820    00780
00830    00790
00840    00800
00850    00810 00820 00830 00870 00880
00880    00860
00890    00850
00900    00440 00570 00730
00950    00040
01040    01020
01100    00980
01150    01130
01160    01120 01140
01170    01150
01310    00330 00760
VARIABLE REFERENCES
A        00010 00030 00030 00030 00030 00070 00150 00380 00380    1. Angular diameter of Sun.
         00380 00390 00400 00410 00420 00710 00720 00720 00850    2. Intermediate variable (380)
         00850 00860 00870 00870 00880 00880 00910 00930 00940
A3       00690 00690                                              Correction factor #3 (moon)
A4       00690 00690                                              Correction factor #4 (moon)
AB       00190 00430                                              Apparent brightness, planet
AD       00190 00460                                              Apparent diameter, planet
AE       00690 00690 00690                                        Annual equation, moon
AS       00440 00550                                              Right Ascension, planet
B        00030 00030 00030 00030 00440 00570 00720 00910 00910    Latitude
         00920
BR       00740 00750                                              Brightness, moon
C        00810 00820 00830 00840 00850 00960 01110 01170 01190    Intermediate variable
D        00600 00600 00660 00670 00690 00740 00740 00740 00740    Intermediate variable
         00990 00990 01170
DE       00090 00440 00550 00610                                  Intermediate variable
DM       01000 01000                                              Minutes
DW       01010 01040 01180                                        Day of Week
DW$      00960 00960 00960 00960 00960 00960 00960 01010 01040    Name of the Day
```

Fig. 12-8. References and variables for Listing 12-6.

Variable	Line references	Description
E	00090 00090 00100 00100 00120 00120 00120 00130 00210 00220 00220 00240 00240 00240 00250 00580 00610 00610 00620 00620 00630 00630 00630 00640 00740	True anomoly
EC	00070 00100 00120 00130 00130 00150 00150 00190 00220 00240 00250 00250 00260 00260 00690 00690 00740	Eccentricity of orbit
EE	00020 00910 00910 00920 00920	Intermediate variable
V	00690 00690 00690	Correction for evection
EX	00100 00110 00120 00220 00230 00240	Trial value for anomoly
F	00150 00150 00150 00470 00430 00550	Intermediate value
H	00010	Intermediate value
I	00190 00190 00190 00190 00190 00190 00190 00200 00220 00240 00250 00250 00250 00260 00260 00260 00260 00260 00260 00260 00260 00260 00270 00270 00280 00280 00280 00290 00290 00300 00320 00320 00320 00320 00320 00350 00360 00370 00380 00380 00380 00400 00400 00400 00440 00440 00440 00450 00450 00450 00450 00460 00460 00460 00460 00460 00470 00470 00480 00480 00480 00480 00490 00500 00530 00540 00550 00550 00550 00550 00550 00550 00550 00550 00970 00970 00970 01310 01330 01380	Loop counter, intermediate value.
J	01320 01330 01360	Loop counter
J$	00970 00970	Month string
JD	01010 01060 01190	Julian Date
L	00260 00260 00260 00260 00270 00280 00320 00380 00400 00420 00440 00450 00450 00470 00470 00900 00910 00920 00920	Intermediate variable
L0	00140 00140 00140 00140 00140 00570	Intermediate variable
L1	00400 00400 00440 00440 00660 00660 00660 00670 00690 00690	Intermediate variable
L2	00420 00423 00420 00420 00430 00430 00430 00440 00440 00570 00590 00650 00650 00650 00690 00690 00720 00740 00740 00750 00900 00940	Intermediate variable
L3	00040 01050	Intermediate variable
L4	00040 01050	Intermediate variable
LE	00070 00090 00190 00210	Solar longitude at epoch
LL	00690 00690 00690	Intermediate variable
LO	00190 00280 00380 00400	Longitude, ascending node, planet
LP	00070 00090 00140 00190 00210 00260	Solar longitude at perigee
LT	00690 00700 00710 00720 00740 00740	Intermediate variable
LY	01020 01150 01160	Leap Year flag
LZ	00430 00490	Log of Z to base e, line 480
M	00010 00030 00030 00030 00030 00030 00090 00090 00090 00100 00210 00210 00210 00210 00220 00490 00550 00610 00610 00620 00650 00660 00670 00690 00690 00690 00700	Mean anomoly

279

	00010 00020 00030 00040 00050 00080 00090 01040 01100 01170	
M$	00220 00320 00520 00550 00590 00750	String definition
MO	00090	Month
M1	00690 00690 00690	Intermediate variable
MM	00570 00570 00670 00690 00690 00740	Moon's corrected anomoly
MO$	00970 00970 01040	Name of month
N	00050 00050 00050 00060 00090 00600 00600 00600 00600 00610 00630 00630 00630 00700 01000 01010 01010 01090 01170 01130 01190	Number of degrees since epoch
N$	00070	String
N1	00700 00700 00710 00720 00720	Intermediate variable
ND	00050 00210 00600 01000 01010 01050	Number of days since epoch
OI	00190 00280 00330	Orbital inclination, planet
P	00190 00210	Intermediate variable
PH	00740 00740 00750	Phase of moon
PS	00230 00290 00320 00400 00440	Heliocentric latitude
R	00070 00150 00190 00260 00260 00270 00320 00400 00410 00440 00450 150 00450 00450 00490 00580 00580 00580 00590 00740 00740 00740 00740 00740 00750	Radius
RC	00150 00160 00580	Radius
R1	00400 00410 00410 00440	Intermediate variable
RD	00020 00020 00090 00140 00210 00260 00280 00280 00280 00390 00390 00390 00400 00400 00410 00440 00440 00440 00450 00470 3610 00650 00690 00690 00690 00690 00700 00710 00720 00740 00740 00740 00900 00910 00930	Radian conversion factor
PH	00450 00460 00460 00490 00550	Planetary radius
T	00590 00590 00740 00750 00990 01000 01000 01000 01000 01010 01040 01090 01090	Time
TA	00580 00590 00740 00750	Time required for light travel
TH	00150 00170 00440 00460 00550 00590 00750 00910 01000 01000 01000	Time, hours
TT	00460 00550	Apparent diameter
U	00130 00140 00150 00250 00260 00260 00640 00650 00690 00690	Intermediate variable
U1	00130 00130 00250 00250 00640 00640	Intermediate variable
W	01180 01180 01180	Intermediate variable
X	00030 00030 00030 00030 00280 00280 00280 00280 00380 00390 00620 00620 00630 00710 00710 00720 00720 00780 00900 00910 00910 00920 00930 01100 01110 01170 01170	Intermediate variable
Y	00010 00390 00390 00700 00710 00730 00920 00930 00980 01030 01040 01110 01120 01120 01130 01130 01140 01140 01170 01190	Intermediate variable

Fig. 12-8. References and variables for Listing 12-6. (Continued from page 279.)

```
Z        00400 00410 00410 00430 00430 00730 00730 00790 01330        Intermediate variable
         01340 01340 01340 01350
Z$       00190 00200 00320 00370 00550                                String
END OF LIST - RESTART?
```

```
SATURDAY, 22 NOV, 1980              1200 HOURS
JULIAN DATE =  327                  DAYS SINCE 0.0 JAN 1980 =   327


                          MERCURY

MEAN ANOMOLY =                           52.4229   DEGREES
HELIOCENTRIC LONGITUDE =                148.2420   DEGREES
TRUE ANOMOLY =                           71.0978   DEGREES
CORRECTED HELIOCENTRIC LONGITUDE =      148.2420   DEGREES
RADIUS VECTOR =                           0.3476   AU'S
HELIOCENTRIC LATITUDE =                   6.8942   DEGREES
RIGHT ASCENSION =                        14.5840   HOURS
DECLINATION =                           -12.7648   DEGREES
DISTANCE FROM EARTH =                     1.0377   AU'S
TIME (LIGHT SPEED) =                      8.6294   MINUTES
APPARENT DIAMETER =                       6.4952
PHASE =                                   0.5141
BRIGHTNESS =                              0.3937
          (P)RINT   ANY OTHER KEY TO CONTINUE


                 GEOCENTRIC POSITIONS
          RT ASCEN.   DECL.    DISTANCE   TIME   DIAM.   BRIGHT. PHASE
PLANET    (HOURS)     (DEG.)    AU'S      MIN.   ARCSEC

MERCURY   14.5840  -12.7648    1.0377    8.6294    6.4952   0.4 0.51
VENUS     13.7450   -8.8623    1.3202   10.9791   12.8159   3.0 0.41
MARS      18.0257  -24.5013    2.1757   18.0929    4.3021   4.3 0.19
JUPITER   12.3123   -0.7672    5.9429   49.4215   33.1048   0.7 0.28
SATURN    12.5051   -0.8834   10.0927   83.9308   16.4079   3.6 0.23
URANUS    15.6258  -19.1922   19.7775  164.4700    3.3270  14.3 0.00
NEPTUNE   17.3584  -21.8301   31.2527  259.8970    1.9902  12.4 0.04
PLUTO     13.9989    5.5284   30.8067  256.1890    0.2662  17.7 0.09

SUN       15.8443  -20.1211    1.0000    8.3159    0.5331   0.0 0.00
MOON       6.0871   19.0825    0.0027    0.0225  191.3040   0.0 0.54


SATURDAY, 22 NOV, 1980              1200 HOURS
JULIAN DATE =  327                  DAYS SINCE 0.0 JAN 1980 =   327
```

Fig. 12-9. Results of Listing 12-6.

```
NAME OF LOCATION? WASHINGTON D.C.
LATITUDE OF WASHINGTON D.C. (DD,MM)? 39,54
LONGITUDE OF WASHINGTON D.C. (DDD,MM)? 77,01
TIME ZONE (E, C, M, P) E
IS DAYLIGHT SAVINGS TIME IN EFFECT? (Y/N)
ENTER MONTH (JAN =1) AND DAY? 9,1
DECLINATION OF SUN =    8.21 DEGREES
EQUATION OF TIME =    0.03 MINUTES
AZIMUTH OF SUNRISE =   79.42 DEGREES
AZIMUTH OF SUNSET =  280.58 DEGREES
TIME OF SUNRISE =     6:33  AM S.T.
TIME OF SUNSET =     7:37  PM S.T.

ANOTHER DATE? (Y/N)
```

Fig. 12-10. Results of Listing 12-7.

Figure 12-10 shows a sample run through Listing 12-7, the Sunrise/Sunset program.

Table 12-2 contains the essential elements for computing the planetary positions, based on the epoch of January 0.0, 1980. These data are included in the data section of the program at line 1210.

The algorithm for determining planetary positions, in general, is:

1. Compute the number of days since epoch, D.
2. Compute the mean anomaly, M from

$$M = .985648 \frac{D}{T_p} + LE - LP$$

where T_p is the orbital period of the planet in tropical years; LE is the longitude at epoch; and LP is the longitude at perihelion.

Listing 12-7. Sunrise/Sunset

```
1  '*********************************************
2  'SUNRISE/SUNSET                              *
3  'LISTING 12-7                                *
4  '*********************************************
5  '
10 CLS:DIMN(12):PL=3.141593/26:RD=57.29577:A$="#
   ###.## %         %"
20 FORI=1TO12:READN(I):NEXT
30 LINE INPUT"NAME OF LOCATION?   ";N$
40 PRINT"LATITUDE OF ";N$;"  (DD,MM)";:INPUTD,M:
   LA=D+M/60
50 PRINT"LONGITUDE OF ";N$;"  (DDD,MM)";:INPUTD,M
   :LO=D+M/60
60 LO=75+((INT(LO/15)-5)*15)
70 PRINT"IS DAYLIGHT SAVINGS TIME IN EFFECT?  (Y
   /N)"
80 Q$=""+INKEY$:IFQ$=""THEN80   ELSEIFQ$="Y"THEN
   DL=1ELSEDL=0
90 TD=(D+M/60-LO)/15:INPUT"ENTER MONTH (JAN=1) A
   ND DAY";M,DA
100 X=(N(M)+DA)/7:D=.456-22.915*COS(PL*X)-.430*C
```

```
         OS(2*PL*X)-.156*COS(3*PL*X)+3.830*SIN(PL*X)
         +.060*SIN(2*PL*X)-.082*SIN(3*PL*X):PRINT
110 PRINT"DECLINATION OF SUN = ";USINGA$;D;"DEGR
    EES"
120 E=.008+.51*COS(PL*X)-3.197*COS(2*PL*X)-.106*
    COS(3*PL*X)-.15*COS(4*PL*X)-7.317*SIN(PL*X)
    -9.471*SIN(2*PL*X)-.391*SIN(3*PL*X)-.242*SI
    N(4*PL*X)
130 PRINT"EQUATION OF TIME =    ";USINGA$;E;"MINU
    TES"
140 CL=COS(LA/RD):SD=SIN(D/RD):CD=COS(D/RD):Y=SD
    /CL:IFABS(Y)=>1THENPRINT"NO SUNRISE OR SUNS
    ET":PRINT:GOTO230
150 Z=90-RD*ATN(Y/SQR(1-Y*Y)):PRINT"AZIMUTH OF S
    UNRISE = ";USINGA$;Z;"DEGREES"
160 PRINT"AZIMUTH OF SUNSET =    ";USINGA$;360-Z;"
    DEGREES"
170 ST=SIN(Z/RD)/CD:IFABS(ST)=>1THENT=6:TT=6:GOT
    O190
180 CT=SQR(1-ST*ST):T=RD/15*ATN(ST/CT):TT=T
190 IFD<0THENT=12-T:TT=T:T=T+TD-E/60-.04
200 GOSUB270
210 PRINT"TIME OF SUNRISE =      ";T1$;":";T2$;"
    ";T$;"AM S.T.":T=12-TT:T=T+TD-E/60+.04:GOS
    UB270
220 PRINT"TIME OF SUNSET =      ";T1$;":";T2$;"
    ";T$;"PM S.T.":PRINT:PRINT
230 PRINT"ANOTHER DATE?  (Y/N)";
240 Q$=""+INKEY$:IFQ$=""THEN240   ELSEIFQ$="N"THE
    N260   ELSEIFQ$<>"Y"THEN240
250 RUN
260 END
270 T1=INT(T):T2=T-T1:T1$=STR$(T1+DL):T2=INT((T2
    *600+5)/10):T2$=STR$(T2):T2$=RIGHT$(T2$,LEN
    (T2$)-1):IFINT(T2)<10THENT2$="0"+T2$
280 RETURN
290 DATA0,31,59,90,120,151,181,212,243,273,304,3
    34
```

Table 12-2. Planetary Ephemeral Data, January 1, 1980.

Planet	Period, T (tropical years)	Longitude at epoch (degrees)	Longitude perihel. (degrees)	Eccent. of orbit	Semi-major axis (AUs)	Inclinat. of orbit	Longitude of ascen. node	Angular size at 1 AU	Brightness factor A
Mercury	.24085	231.2973	77.14421	.2056306	.387099	7.004358	48.09417	6.74	1.918×10^{-6}
Venus	.61521	355.7335	131.28958	.0067826	.723332	3.394435	76.49975	16.92	1.721×10^{-5}
Earth	1.00004	98.8335	102.59640	.0167180	1.000000	---	---	---	---
Mars	1.88089	126.3078	335.69082	.0933865	1.523688	1.849801	49.40320	9.36	4.539×10^{-6}
Jupiter	11.86224	146.9664	14.00955	.0484658	5.202561	1.304182	100.25202	196.74	1.994×10^{-4}
Saturn	29.45771	165.3222	92.66540	.0556153	9.554747	2.489374	113.48883	165.60	1.740×10^{-4}
Uranus	84.01247	228.0709	172.73633	.0453232	19.218140	.772990	73.87686	65.80	7.768×10^{-5}
Neptune	164.79558	260.3579	47.86721	.0090021	30.109570	1.771602	131.56065	62.20	7.597×10^{-5}
Pluto	250.90000	209.4390	222.97200	.0253870	39.784590	17.137000	109.94100	8.20	4.073×10^{-6}

3. Then compute $V = M + 114.49155 \; EC_p \sin M$ (degrees) (solved iteratively.) V is the "true anomaly." EC_p is the eccentricity of the planet's orbit.

4. Compute $L_p = V + LP$. This is the heliocentric longitude.

5. Compute the distance of the planet from the sun, the *radius vector*,

$$R_p = \frac{R(1 - EC_p{}^2)}{1 + EC_p \cos V}$$

where R is the semimajor axis.

6. The heliocentric latitude of the planet is found from

$$PS = \text{arc sin } (\sin (L_p - LO_p) \sin OI_p)$$

where LO_p is the longitude of the ascending node and OI_p is the orbital inclination.

These six steps have led to the computation of a planet's celestial latitude and longitude relative to the sun. Often, however, it is very useful to compute these positions relative to the earth to make the task of locating the planet easier for observers and astronomers. To do this the following steps are given:

1. Compute:
   a. $A = L_p - LO_p$
   b. $Y = \sin A \cos OI_p$
   c. $X = \cos A$
   d. $A = \tan^{-1} (Y/X)$ (Be sure to resolve the arc tan ambiguity.)
   e. $L1 = A + LO_p$
   f. $R1 = R_p \cos PS_p$
   g. $Z = L_3 - L1$
   h. $A = \tan^{-1} ((R1 \sin Z)/(R_3 - R1 \cos Z))$
   i. $L2 = 180 + L_3 + A$ (Adjust to keep within 360°.)
   j. $B = \tan^{-1} (R1 \tan PS_p \sin (L2 - L1))/(R_3 \sin (L1 - L_3))$
   k. $L = L2$ converted to radians
   l. $X = (\sin B \cos EE) + (\cos B \sin EE \sin L)$
   m. $TH = \tan^{-1} X$
   n. $Y = (\sin L \cos EE) - (\tan B \sin EE)$
   o. $X = \cos L$

p. $AS_p = \dfrac{\tan^{-1} (Y/X)}{15}$

2. AS_p is the right ascension.
3. TH is the declination.

ASTROLOGICAL SIGNS

For those interested in astrology, the sign of the zodiac in which you will find the sun, your sun sign, is given in the equation

$$Z = INT(JD - 79)/30.4375) + 1$$

If $Z \leq 0$, then $Z = 13 - Z$

where Z = zodiac number and $Z = 1 = $ Aries.

Alternatively, the sign of the zodiac for the sun and any of the planets can be found by dividing the right ascension in the geocentric mode by 2 and adding 1 to the integer value. That is

$$Z = INT(RA/2) + 1$$

WEATHER AND THE COMPUTER

While picnics can be very important events in our lives, our interest in weather has a practical foundation that justifies our interest far beyond pleasant outings. A little precaution can save us millions of dollars in crop and property damages. By knowing when bad weather is going to strike, we can adjust our plans and prevent loss. What is bad weather? During the few days before and after planting a crop rain is a "bad" thing. The farmer doesn't want to plow in a field of mud, nor does he want to see the fresh seed wash down to the river. After the planting, a little rain, just enough to nurture the crop, is acceptable. Even when the crop has rooted and sprung from the soil, a heavy rain can still destroy many crops, either from the physical beating of the plants or from subsequent rotting of the plant sitting in the saturated soil. On the other hand, we certainly can't do without rain somewhere in the world. While we can irrigate deserts and bring forth crops, that irrigation water was at some point rain. In a general sense, what we want is some rain, not too much, at the right time.

In a similar fashion, we have an ambivalent

attitude toward wind. A little wind at the right time can be put to good service. We used to use it to drive cargo ships from continent to continent. We use it today to generate electricity in remote locations. We use it to pump subsurface water to irrigate our crops. Too much wind, on the other hand, can literally blow away everything we own, starting with the crops in the field. Combine a severe wind with a severe rain (or the frozen form, snow) and we have disaster of great dimension. While foreknowledge of a storm does nothing to help us prevent the storm, we can take defensive measures. We can put off planting the crop; we can board up the windows on the beach house; we can place sand bags along the river banks, and so forth. But, what does this have to do with microcomputers?

Modern meteorologists use computers in two main ways: forecasting and display. Every evening we are treated to grand demonstrations of the power of the computer as the television weather reporters dazzle us with computer-generated maps of the nation, the state, or the local area. They superimpose radar returns from thunderstorms. They animate the short-range weather pattern so we can see the course of the weather through the day. The graphic displays of the map sections are well within the reach of the microcomputer and are available in a number of commercial packages and published map routines. The remaining functions require access to the basic data and radar systems. Unfortunately, for our purposes, long-range forecasting requires access to vast amounts of current and accurate weather conditions throughout the world. Without special knowledge of the forecasting equations involved and access to the current weather data base, weather forecasting on a modern-scale is generally not within the range of the microcomputer owner. In this book we offer several routines to be used to help predict tides, and to compare current weather with historic weather, but with one modest exception, we make no real attempt to turn your micro into a home version of the National Weather Service.

Timing the Tides

Tides, the movement of large masses of water,

are the result of the gravitational forces exerted by the sun and moon, and are influenced by the rotation of the earth on its axis. Normally where there is a very large lake, sea, or ocean, there will be four tides every day, two high tides and two low tides. Between the two high (and the two low) tide peaks there is normally an interval of 12 hours 25 minutes, although this can vary from 6 hours to over 24 hours, depending on local bottom and shore conditions. The height or magnitude of the tides is a function of the relative position of the sun and the moon, and the shape of the particular coast. Coastlines that are generally smooth with open expanses of sandy beaches and shallow bottoms that extend far out into the sea will generally experience undramatic tides of little consequence. The Mediterranean has regions where the tides are measured in inches. At the other extreme, harbors located at the upper regions of long, narrow channels leading to the sea may experience dramatic tidal actions. The Bay of Fundy is said to have normal tides on the order of 53 feet. Where the channel to the sea is intersected by one or more other channels to the same or other large bodies of water, the tidal action and timing can get quite complicated. The program that follows, Listing 12-8, offers a routine to predict the times of low and high tides based on recent tidal time data. It assumes that the period between tides is a linear constant and simply computes a linear line of regression based on the known times of high and low tides. Due to inherent inaccuracies of this approach, it is best used with fairly current data and is not to be projected too far in the future—at least not until it can be further validated by the user. The program, based on the normal tidal conditions in the Washington, D.C. area, which consist of two high and low tides, separated by about 13 hours 7 minutes, can easily be adapted for conditions throughout the world. In regions where there are more or less than two high tides daily, the program can be adjusted in lines 20, 80-110, 130, 230, 290, 310 by simply changing 4 to the actual number of daily tides. In line 240, we compute and display the mean period between tides, and the standard error of this value. Theoretically, though unlikely, the actual

Listing 12-8. Tidal Timer

```
1  '****************************************************
2  'TIDAL TIMER 1                                     *
3  'LISTING 12-8                                      *
4  '****************************************************
5  '
10 CLS:PRINT"TIDE TIMER":PRINT:PRINT
20 INPUT"FOR HOW MANY DAYS DO YOU HAVE DATA";D:D
     IM DN(D),TT(D,2)
30 PRINT:PRINT
40 FORI=1TOD
50    INPUT"ENTER DAY NUMBER";DN(I)
60    INPUT"TIME OF FIRST HIGH TIDE";T:GOSUB350
70    TT(I,1)=T:INPUT"TIME OF SECOND HIGH TIDE";T
     :GOSUB350
80    TT(I,2)=T
90    PRINT
100 NEXTI
110 FORI=1TO2
120    TX=0:TY=0:X2=0:Y2=0:XY=0
130    FORJ=1TOD
140       X=DN(J):Y=TT(J,I)
150       TX=TX+X:TY=TY+Y:X2=X2+(X[2):Y2=Y2+(Y[2):
     XY=XY+(X*Y)
160    NEXTJ
170    B(I)=(XY-(D*((TX/D)*(TY/D))))/(X2-(D*((TX/
     D)[2)))
180    A(I)=(TY/D)-(B(I)*(TX/D))
190    R(I)=((D*XY)-(TX*TY))/SQR(((D*X2)-(TX[2))*
     ((D*Y2)-(TY[2)))
200 NEXTI
210 T=(A(2)+B(2))-(A(1)+B(1)):T1=T/100:GOSUB360
     :PRINT"MEAN TIME BETWEEN TIDES = ";H;"HOUR
     S";M;"MINUTES.
STANDARD ERROR = +/- ";:T=SQR((X2-((XY[2)/Y2))/(
     D-2)):GOSUB360   :PRINTH;":";M
220 PRINT:PRINT"TIDE","ALPHA","BETA","CORRELATIO
     N"
230 PRINT"HIGH # 1",A(1),B(1),R(1):PRINT"HIGH #
     2",A(2),B(2),R(2)
240 PRINT:PRINT"(G)RAPHIC       (D)ATE ";
250 Q$=""+INKEY$:IFQ$=""THEN250
260 IFQ$="G"THEN380
270 IFQ$<>"D"THEN240
280 T$(1)="FIRST HIGH TIDE":T$(2)="SECOND HIGH T
     IDE"
290 PRINT:PRINT:INPUT"ENTER DAY NUMBER DESIRED";
     N
300 FORI=1TO2
310    T=A(I)+(B(I)*N):GOSUB360
320    PRINTT$(I);" WILL OCCUR AT ",H;M
330 NEXTI
340 PRINT:GOTO240
350 H=INT(T):M=(H-INT(H))/.6:T=INT(H)+M:RETURN
360 H=INT(T/100):M=INT(60*((T/100)-H)):IF H>23 T
```

```
     HEN H=H-24
370 RETURN
380 CLS
390 INPUT"STARTING DAY (FROM BASE)";ND:CLS
400 T2=(A(1)+(B(1)*ND))/100
410 FORX=0TO127:SET(X,23):NEXT
420 FORC=448TO511STEP2:PRINT@C,".";:NEXT
430 FORI=0TO127
440     IFJ<>48THEN460
450     FORY=0TO47STEP2:SET(X,Y):NEXT:J=0
460     P=1.570763*((I+T2)/T1):J=J+1
470     X=I:Y=20*SIN(P):SET(X,23-Y)
480 NEXT
490 GOTO490
```

time of a tide could deviate from the forecast by as much as the number of days ahead of actual data multiplied by the standard error. That is, if the standard error is 8.5 minutes, a forecast for a high tide 20 days ahead could be off by as much as 2 hours 49.6 minutes, plus or minus. The standard error can be reduced by increasing the number of days of data used. The program in Listing 12-9 is used to compute tidal times from known periods.

As noted before, the height of the tides is a function of changing factors (the position of the sun and the moon) and the geological structure of the local region. While we can compute a nominal tidal magnitude from the relative positions of the sun and the moon, there is no routine available from which we can accurately forecast tidal magnitude without having available a good model of the local geological structure. The deviations between the hypothetical

Listing 12-9. Tidal Timer 2

```
1  '*******************************************
2  'TIDAL TIMER 2                           *
3  'LISTING 12-9                            *
4  '*******************************************
5  '
10 CLS:PRINT"TIDE TIMER":PRINT:PRINT
20 INPUT"ENTER ALPHA AND BETA COEFFICIENTS";A,B
30 INPUT"ENTER MEAN TIME BETWEEN TIDES";T:GOSUB1
       80
40 T2=T:T1=(A+B)/100
50 PRINT:PRINT"(G)RAPHIC       (D)ATE ";
60 Q$=""+INKEY$:IFQ$=""THEN60
70 IFQ$="G"THEN190
80 IFQ$<>"D"THEN30
90 T$(1)="FIRST HIGH TIDE":T$(2)="SECOND HIGH TI
       DE"
100 PRINT:PRINT:INPUT"ENTER DAY NUMBER DESIRED";
       N
110 FORI=1TO2
120     T=A(I)+(B(I)*N):GOSUB170
130     PRINTT$(I);" WILL OCCUR AT ",H;M
140 NEXTI
150 PRINT:GOTO30
160 H=INT(T):M=(H-INT(H))/.6:T=INT(H)+M:RETURN
```

```
170 H=INT(T/100):M=INT(60*((T/100)-H)):IF H>23 T
     HEN H=H-24
180 RETURN
190 CLS
200 INPUT"STARTING DAY (FROM BASE)";ND:CLS
210 T2=(A(1)+(B(1)*ND))/100
220 FORX=0TO127:SET(X,23):NEXT
230 FORC=448TO511STEP2:PRINT@C,".";:NEXT
240 FORI=0TO127
250    IFJ<>48THEN270
260    FORY=0TO47STEP2:SET(X,Y):NEXT:J=0
270    P=1.570763*((1+T2)/T1):J=J+1
280    X=I:Y=20*SIN(P):SET(X,23-Y)
290 NEXT
300 GOTO300
```

(sun/moon) and actual tidal magnitudes are often so great that we make no effort here to develop such a routine. It might be interesting, however, for the reader to develop such a program to track the actual times and heights of tides in a region. The graph of regional tidal actions are often quite elegant.

Annual Temperatures

Listing 12-10 is a brief routine used to compare current temperatures with historic records for a given locality. The user enters in the mean, high,

and low temperatures for each month of the year, as well as the temperature for a given recent day. The computer then displays the annual record in graphic form and highlights the current temperature against these curves so the user can get an impression of whether the current weather is warmer or colder than the established norms.

The Great Seattle Weather Machine

There are nearly as many ways to forecast the weather as there are television studios broadcast-

Listing 12-10. Annual Temperatures

```
1  '*****************************************
2  'ANNUAL TEMPERATURES                     *
3  'LISTING 12-10                           *
4  '*****************************************
5  '
10 CLS:DIM M$(12),M(12),MX(12),MN(12)
20 FORI=1TO12
30    READ M$(I):PRINT:PRINT"ENTER MEAN TEMPERATU
      RE FOR ";M$(I),:INPUT M(I)
40    INPUT"MAXIMUM TEMPERATURE";MX(I):INPUT"MINI
      MUM TEMPERTURE";MN(I)
50 NEXT
60 CLS:SM=M(1):LG=M(1)
70 PRINT"MONTH","MEAN","MAXIMUM","MINIMUM"
80 FORI=1TO12:PRINTI;M$(I),M(I),MX(I),MN(I):NEXT

90 FORI=1TO12
100    TN=TN+MN(I):TX=TX+MX(I):TM=TM+M(I)
110    IFSM<MN(I)THEN130
120    SM=MN(I)
130    IFMX(I)<LGTHEN150
140    LG=MX(I)
```

```
150 NEXT
160 PRINT:PRINT"MEAN",TM/12,TX/12,TN/12:R=LG-SM:
    L=SM:H=LG:M=H-(R/2)
170 PRINT@960,"ENTER JULIAN DATE, MONTH, AND TEM
    PERATURE   ";:INPUTJD,MO,TT
180 SD=(MX(MO)-MN(MO))/6:Z=(TT-M(MO))/SD:PRINT"C
    URRENT TEMPERATURE Z-SCORE = ";Z;::INPUT" 'E
    NTER' TO CONTINUE";ZZ
190 CLS:PRINT@0,LG;:PRINT@448,M;:PRINT@960,SM;
200 FORX=17TO127STEP3:SET(X,22):NEXT
210 FORI=1TO12
220    X=(I*10)+7
230    PRINT@452+(I*4.5),LEFT$(M$(I),1);
240    Y=47-(46.9*(M(I)-L)/R)
250    SET(X,Y):Y=47-(46.9*(MX(I)-L)/R)
260    SET(X,Y):Y=47-(46.9*(MN(I)-L)/R)
270    SET(X,Y)
280 NEXT
290 X=16+(111*(JD/365)):FORY=0TO47STEP2:SET(X,Y)
    :NEXT
300 Y1=47-(46.9*(TT-L)/R):SET(X,Y1)
310 FORXX=X-6TOX+6STEP2:SET(XX,Y1):NEXT:S1=M(1):
    L1=M(1):M1=1
320 Y=INT(Y1/3)*64:PRINT@Y,TT;
330 GOTO330
340 DATAJAN,FEB,MAR,APR,MAY,JUN,JUL,AUG,SEP,OCT,
    NOV,DEC
```

ing evening weather forecasts. While many of them depend upon the National Weather Service for their background information and long range forecasts, a handful of independent forecasters use a curious batch of homemade or secret techniques. The routines of the publishers of the *Old Farmer's Almanac* are said to be nearly as old as the country itself, yet they are rather reliable, as long range (more than five days in the future) forecasts go. One routine, developed in a university setting and relied upon by millions of viewers of one of the major morning news broadcasts, is based in part on an observation that the major weather patterns of the United States move from west to east in six-day intervals. That is, occasional disruptions notwith-standing, a weather pattern occurring in Seattle on Sunday is likely to drift eastward and hit the Atlantic coast sometime on Friday or Saturday. The leading exponents of this technique are quick to add that they temper their forecasts in consideration of sunspot cycles, volcanic eruptions, and other such phenomena. The short program in Listing 12-11 incorporates the six-day concept. The user specifies his location and the weather in Seattle for any given day. The computer then computes the angular distance between the two locations and from that the time required for the weather to drift eastward at the rate of about 7.6 degrees a day. It adds this time to the starting date and displays the forecast.

Listing 12-11. Seattle Weather Machine

```
1 '*********************************************
2 'SEATTLE WEATHER MACHINE                     *
3 'LISTING 12-11                               *
4 '*********************************************
5 '
```

Listing 12-11. Seattle Weather Machine (continued from page 289)

```
10 CLS:PRINT"SEATTLE WEATHER MACHINE":PRINT:PRIN
   T
20 INPUT"ENTER YOUR LONGITUDE";LO:LP=122.5
30 ND=(LP-LO)/7.583333
40 INPUT"WHAT IS THE WEATHER IN SEATTLE TODAY";W
   $
50 INPUT"WHAT IS TODAY'S DATE, MONTH  (DD,MM)";D
   ,M
60 M$="JANFEBMARAPRMAYJUNJULAUGSEPOCTNOVDEC"
70 D$="312831303130313130313031"
80 MO$=MID$(M$,((M-1)*3)+1,3)
90 DV=VAL(MID$(D$,((M-1)*2)+1,2))
100 WD=D+ND:IFWD<=DVTHEN120
110 M=M+1:D=D-DV:GOTO80
120 PRINT"ON";WD;MO$;" THERE WILL BE ";W$;" IN Y
    OUR LOCATION"
130 END
```

Storm Probabilities

While denying any superstitious tendencies, the author prefers to end this chapter with a fourteenth program. We overheard a conversation recently in which two otherwise intelligent people were moaning about the fact it had been nearly ten years since the last bad storm had struck a portion of the Atlantic. The essence of their observation was that prior to the current period, severe storms had struck the coast on the average of once every five years. On this basis, they concluded, the probability of a major storm in a given year was: $P = 1/5 = .20000$.

The fact of the matter is that the expectation must include current history. The would-be forecasters had based their prediction concerning the probability of a storm on the average of the number of storms per year for the entire length of the record. The key is the word *entire*. The erstwhile prognosticators had disregarded the last ten years. If the previous weather record consisted of 100 years and 20 storms, more or less evenly distributed over that period, the mean time between storms is indeed five years, give or take a few months; and the standard deviation would be something in the neighborhood of three to six months. However, the most recent experience of the ten-year storm-free period now lowers the probability to $P = 20/110 = .191198$, raises the mean time between storms several months, and increases the standard deviation to something over 13 months.

The program in Listing 12-12 computes the actual probability of a major storm. If you have the actual storm frequency data, the program will accept these data, computing the mean and standard deviation of the time between storms. If you don't have these data, but you do have a general idea (e.g., one storm every so many years), the computer will process this information and assume a standard deviation of one-third of the mean time. The consideration behind this approach is that if it has been a long time since the last disaster, perhaps nature has changed its pattern and the region is becoming more storm-free. Please don't rush out and buy beach-front property on the basis of the output of this program alone, but do give it a try.

EXERCISES

1. Modify the program in Listing 12-6 to identify dates of lunar and solar eclipses.
2. We have been taught that the number of sunspots in a year vary from high to low over what appears to be an eleven-year cycle. Numerical analysis of the number of sunspots occurring annually, however, has led scientists to conclude that the cyclic nature of sunspots is best represented by a composite wave of six cycles with the respective periods of 5.5, 8.1, 9.7, 11.2, 100, and 180 years. Write a program which in-

Listing 12-12. Storm Predictor

```
1  '*****************************************
2  'STORM PREDICTOR                        *
3  'LISTING 12-12                          *
4  '*****************************************
5  '
10 CLS:PRINT"STORM PREDICTOR":PRINT:PRINT
20 PRINT"A  --  WEATHER RECORD AVAILABLE":PRINT:
     PRINT"B  --  AVERAGE AVAILABLE":PRINT:PRINT
     "SELECT      ";
30 Q$=""+INKEY$:IFQ$=""THEN30    ELSEIFQ$="A"THEN
     120
40 CLS:INPUT"ENTER AVERAGE NUMBER OF STORMS PER
     YEAR";AS
50 INPUT"NUMBER OF YEARS FOR WHICH RECORD IS VAL
     ID";RL
60 INPUT"NUMBER OF MONTHS SINCE LAST STORM";LS
70 TS=RL*AS:T=RL+(LS/12):TA=TS/T:SD=TA/3
80 PRINT"THE TRUE AVERAGE IS";TA;"STORMS PER YEA
     R"
90 PRINT"STANDARD DEVIATION = ";SD
100 PRINT"THE PROBABILITY OF A STORM WITHIN ONE
     MONTH = ";TA/12
110 PRINT:GOTO20
120 CLS:INPUT"YEAR RECORD BEGINS";Y1
130 INPUT"CURRENT YEAR";Y3:INPUT"CURRENT MONTH";
     CM
140 RL=Y3-Y1-1:Y2=Y3-1
150 FORI=Y1TOY2
160    PRINT"ENTER NUMBER OF STORMS IN";I,:INPUTN
     S
170    TS=TS+NS:S2=S2+(NS[2):N=N+1
180    IFNS=0THENX=12ELSEX=12/NS
190    TX=TX+X:X2=X2+(X[2):NX=NX+1
200 NEXT
210 SD=SQR((S2-((TS[2]/N))/(N-1))
220 INPUT"NUMBER OF STORMS SO FAR THIS YEAR";NS
230 IFNS=0THENX=CM
240 TX=TX+X:X2=X2+(X[2):NX=NX+1
250 TA=(TS+NS)/((RL*12)+CM)
260 SX=SQR((X2-((TX[2]/NX))/(NX-1))
270 PRINT"THE TRUE AVERAGE NUMBER OF STORMS PER
     YEAR IS ";12*TA
280 PRINT"THE AVERAGE UP TO THE BEGINNING OF";Y3
     ;"WAS ";TS/RL
290 PRINT"THE STANDARD DEVIATION WAS ";SD
300 PRINT"THE AVERAGE NUMBER OF MONTHS BETWEEN S
     TORMS IS ";TX/(TS+NS)
310 PRINT"THE STANDARD DEVIATION IS ";SX
320 PRINT"THE PROBABILITY OF A STORM WITHIN ONE
     MONTH IS = ";TS/((12*RL)+CM)
330 PRINT:GOTO20
```

corporates this information and generates a forecast of the sunspot sequence.

3. Use a microcomputer to attempt to determine the total length, if there is one, of the entire cycle of these six sub-cycles. If there is such a complete period, attempt to locate the current date along that scale. (Detailed sunspot data may be obtained from the World Data Center in Boulder, Colorado.) If there does not seem to be an overall cycle, develop a program to overlay actual recent data over an extended version of the model to determine a pragmatic best fit.

4. Chapter 7 in the Heman-Goldberg book listed below contains an extensive table of correlations between sunspot activity and a number of terrestrial atmospheric and meteorological phenomena. Obtain a copy of the table and devise experiments to validate one or more of the correlations as they pertain to your location.

SUGGESTED READING

Abell, G. 1963. *Exploration of the Universe.* New York: Holt, Rinehart, and Winston.

Duffett-Smith, P., 1981. *Practical Astronomy with Your Calculator.* Cambridge, England: Cambridge University Press.

Herman, J. R. and R. A. Goldberg, 1978. *Sun, Weather, and Climate.* Washington, DC: NASA.

Chapter 13

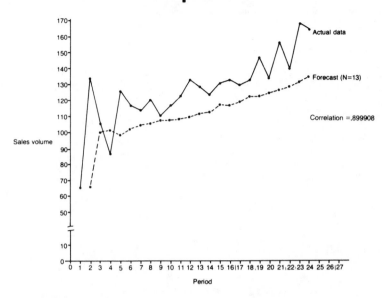

Population Estimates

Making population estimates is one of the more practical aspects of forecasting. It is essential to know what the population of a school, city, state, nation, or the world is going to be at some point in the future for one level of planning or another. Prudent resource management requires that we make strategic purchases of goods and materials at optimum times with regard not only to price, but to the expected degree of demand. Demand, we believe, is partially a function of population.

A second aspect to population estimation is found in a variety of natural or environmental sciences, such as biology or animal management. In these areas the task is as much to determine what the current population is, from a sample, as it is to forecast what it will be sometime in the future.

The tools we have available include nearly all the basic techniques that have been presented so far in this book. Successful population estimates have been made using curve fitting techniques, modeling and simulations, numerical analysis, and probabilistic approaches. In the final analysis, the technique of choice will be that which consistently provides the most reliable forecast. Nonetheless, each of the techniques, given a particular forecasting task, have their own advantages or benefits, as well as liabilities. In this chapter we shall examine some of the more common techniques, highlighting their contributions and limitations.

FORECASTING SOCIAL POPULATIONS

The very nature of living populations, their reproductive and changing aspects, suggest a series of applicable techniques. As with modeling techniques, the approaches all begin with a determination of the current or baseline population. Secondly, we must know the rate at which the population reproduces and increases as well as the rate at which the same population decreases through deaths of its members. Listing 13-1 is a short routine based on the population factors of birth and death rate.

This routine has only limited utility. Of all of

293

Listing 13-1. Population Estimator I

```
1  '************************************************
2  'POPULATION ESTIMATOR I                       *
3  'LISTING 13-1                                 *
4  '************************************************
5  '
10 CLS:DEFDBLB,D,E,N,P
20 INPUT"ENTER CURRENT POPULATION";P:P1=P
30 INPUT"POPULATION YEAR";Y
40 INPUT"NUMBER OF LIVE BIRTHS PER 1000 POPULATI
      ON";B:B=B/1000
50 INPUT"NUMBER DEATHS PER 1000 POPULATION";D:D=
      D/1000
60 INPUT"TARGET YEAR";TY
70 PRINT"YEAR","# BIRTHS","# DEATHS","POPULATION
      "
80 FORI=1 TO (TY-Y)
90    NB=B*P:ND=D*P:P=P+NB-ND
100     PRINTY+I,INT(NB)+1,INT(ND)+1,INT(P)+1
110 NEXTI
120 EI=((P/P1)[(1/(TY-Y)))-1
130 PRINT:PRINT"EFFECTIVE ANNUAL POPULATION CHAN
      GE = ";100*EI;" %"
140 PRINT:PRINT"DO YOU WANT TO COMPUTE ANY OTHER
       POPULATION YEAR FROM THIS VALUE?   (Y/N)  "
      ;
150 Q$=""+INKEY$:IFQ$=""THEN150
160 PRINTQ$:IFQ$="N"THEN210
170 PRINT:INPUT"ENTER DESIRED YEAR";DY
180 EP=P1*((1+EI)[(DY-Y))
190 PRINT"ESTIMATED POPULATION IN";DY;"IS";INT(E
      P)+1
200 GOTO140
210 END
```

the procedures, it is the simplest to compute and manage. The user can alter the birth and death rates so that over a certain time span, the forecast based on a population of some years ago matches current reality, although this is a little risky. Nonetheless, once the effective rate of population increase (EI) is computed, it is a fairly simple matter to project future populations from:

$$P' = P (1 + EI)^n$$

References in the media to population growth rates are the same as EI. Forecasts using this measure are best limited to short-range forecasting.

There is an immediate and major defect in the foregoing technique: it disregards the migration of people in and out of an area. For this reason, it is a technique better suited for an isolated island or similar population center. Since, in normal situa-tions, migration consists of both immigration into a country or region, and emigration out of an area, the rate we are concerned with is the *net immigration*. This value is computed for a given period simply by subtracting the number of those leaving from the number of those entering. This value will be negative when those leaving outnumber those entering. For a country on the scale of the United States, net immigration is a significant factor in population forecasts. Listing 13-2 expands on the first program and makes provisions for net immigration.

This second program has broader utility and application, but it is still inadequate for major forecasting work. Among other things, the birthrate as a function of the total population is often too crude a measure, especially for forecasts over an extended period of time. A modification often made is to

Listing 13-2. Population Estimator II

```
1 '**********************************************
2 'POPULATION ESTIMATOR II                      *
3 'LISTING 13-2                                 *
4 '**********************************************
5 '
10 CLS:DEFDBLB,D,E,N,P
20 INPUT"ENTER CURRENT POPULATION";P:P1=P
30 INPUT"POPULATION YEAR";Y
40 INPUT"NUMBER OF LIVE BIRTHS PER 1000 POPULATI
      ON";B:B=B/1000
50 INPUT"NET IMMIGRATION PER 1000 POPULATION";N:
      N=N/1000
60 INPUT"NUMBER DEATHS PER 1000 POPULATION";D:D=
      D/1000
70 INPUT"TARGET YEAR";TY
80 PRINT"YEAR","# BIRTHS","# DEATHS","POPULATION
      "
90 FORI=1 TO (TY-Y)
100    NB=B*P:NI=N*P:ND=D*P:P=P+NB+NI-ND
110    PRINTY+I,INT(NB)+1,INT(ND)+1,INT(P)+1
120 NEXTI
130 EI=((P/P1)[(1/(TY-Y)))-1
140 PRINT:PRINT"EFFECTIVE ANNUAL POPULATION CHAN
      GE = ";100*EI;" %"
150 PRINT:PRINT"DO YOU WANT TO COMPUTE ANY OTHER
      POPULATION YEAR FROM THIS VALUE?   (Y/N)   "
      ;
160 Q$=""+INKEY$:IFQ$=""THEN160
170 PRINTQ$:IFQ$="N"THEN220
180 PRINT:INPUT"ENTER DESIRED YEAR";DY
190 EP=P1*((1+EI)[(DY-Y))
200 PRINT"ESTIMATED POPULATION IN";DY;"IS";INT(E
      P)+1
210 GOTO150
220 END
```

determine the birthrate as a function of the number of those females in the population normally considered to be in the primary age range for conception and delivery. Among humans in this country the practice is to consider the birthrate as a function of the number of females between 15 and 44 years of age. While there are births recorded involving women younger than 15 and older than 44, their numbers have been statistically insignificant. With the current increase in the numbers of women giving birth later in life than the previous limit of 44, and a possible decline in the number of adolescent mothers, these limits may have to be adjusted upward from, say, 15 to 16 or 17, and from 44 to 45 or 50, or at least expanded to include the range 15 to 46 or 47 years. It is just this sort of change in social behavior that will always make the process of population forecasting tedious and long-range population estimates speculative at best. In any event, Listing 13-3 includes provisions for this

Listing 13-3. Population Forecaster III

```
1 '**********************************************
2 'POPULATION FORECASTER III                    *
3 'LISTING 13-3                                 *
4 '**********************************************
5 '
```

Listing 13-2. Population Estimator II (continued from page 295)

```
10 CLS:DEFDBLB,D,E,N,P
20 INPUT"ENTER CURRENT POPULATION";P:P1=P
30 INPUT"POPULATION YEAR";Y
40 INPUT"TOTAL NUMBER OF FEMALES";TF
50 INPUT"NUMBER FEMALES, AGE 0 TO 14";F1:F2=F1/P

60 INPUT"NUMBER FEMALES, AGE 15-44";F:F3=F/P
70 INPUT"NUMBER OF LIVE BIRTHS PER 1000 FEMALES
      AGE 15-44";B:B=B/1000
80 INPUT"NET IMMIGRATION PER 1000 POPULATION";N:
      N=N/1000
90 INPUT"NUMBER DEATHS PER 1000 POPULATION";D:D=
      D/1000
100 INPUT"TARGET YEAR";TY
110 PRINT"YEAR","# BIRTHS","# DEATHS","POPULATIO
      N"
120 FORI=1 TO (TY-Y)
130    NB=B*F:NI=N*P:ND=D*P:P=P+NB+NI-ND
140    A1=(1/30)*F:A2=D*F:A3=(1/15)*F1:A5=D*F1:A6
      =NB/2:A7=NI*F3:A8=NI*F2
150    F=F-A1-A2+A3+A7:F1=F1-A3-A5+A6+A8
160    PRINTY+I,INT(NB)+1,INT(ND)+1,INT(P)+1
170 NEXTI
180 EI=((P/P1)[(1/(TY-Y)))-1
190 PRINT:PRINT"EFFECTIVE ANNUAL POPULATION CHAN
      GE = ";100*EI;" %"
200 PRINT:PRINT"DO YOU WANT TO COMPUTE ANY OTHER
       POPULATION YEAR FROM THIS VALUE?  (Y/N)  "
      ;
210 Q$=""+INKEY$:IFQ$=""THEN210
220 PRINTQ$:IFQ$="N"THEN270
230 PRINT:INPUT"ENTER DESIRED YEAR";DY
240 EP=P1*((1+EI)[(DY-Y))
250 PRINT"ESTIMATED POPULATION IN";DY;"IS";INT(E
      P)+1
260 GOTO200
270 END
```

component of population forecasting. In addition to knowing the baseline female population between 15 and 44, we must also know the population of the females 14 years and younger. Each year a portion of the younger set will become 15, and a portion of the child-bearing group will become 45 and theoretically cease child-bearing. In studies involving other than human populations, the basic technique is essentially the same, only the year brackets will change according to the particular animal involved. Population studies aimed at determining the total animal population of an area, such as a national forest, require combining the separate population for each species.

The analyst can expand the population program to include an input of the current or baseline population for each age group in the population, as well as the birth and death rates. It is also useful to include data on race and sex as well. Each level of detail, of course, increases the workload and computer memory requirements, as well as increasing the accuracy of the forecast.

There is an alternative theory that suggests that it is as simple and as meaningful to apply numerical techniques to the task, especially in studies of large populations. These include curve fitting techniques, multivariate correlations, and polynomial evaluations.

Curve Fitting Techniques

Using the technique of least squares analysis and curve fitting, the period is represented by the X variable and the population of record the Y variable. We can use either the actual year (e.g., 1978) or apply an arbitrary measure (e.g., 1978 = 1, 1979 = 2, 1980 = 3, etc.). The only restriction on using the arbitrary measure is that the intervals must be properly labeled in proportion to the interval. That is, if 1960 = 1, and 1970 = 2, then 1985 must be 3.5, not 4. Further, it is possible and advisable to truncate the population data to a more manageable form. For example, the U.S. population in 1950 was estimated to be 151,325,798 (U.S. Census Bureau). Algebraically, it doesn't matter if that number is expressed in the full form as above, or as: 151.325798, or 15.1325798, or whatever multiple.

dividing by one million, then we must multiply the output by the same amount to obtain the actual forecast. Listing 13-4 provides a routine to accept period population data and to perform least squares curve fitting analysis. The user of this routine may input the total population estimates for several known periods or may do several subsets of these data if available. That is, the first run may consist of computing a curve for the male component, while the second consists of the curve for the female component. The total forecast, then, is the sum of the two subsets.

ESTIMATING ANIMAL POPULATIONS

Listing 13-5 is a short routine useful in estimating wild animal populations. The basic approach is to collect a sample (A) of creatures under study and mark them in some fashion, such as with a

Listing 13-4. Population Estimate From Sample

```
1  '************************************************
2  'POPULATION ESTIMATE FROM SAMPLE              *
3  'LISTING 13-4                                 *
4  '************************************************
5  '
10 CLS:A(1)=1.96:A(2)=2.33:A(3)=2.58:A(4)=3.3
20 INPUT"ENTER NUMBER OF ORGANISMS MARKED AND
RELEASED IN THE GENERAL POPULATION";A
30 PRINT:INPUT"ENTER NUMBER OF ORGANISMS COLLECT
    ED
IN SUBSEQUENT ACTIVITY";B
40 PRINT:INPUT"ENTER NUMBER OF ORGANISMS
IN SECOND COLLECTION THAT ARE MARKED";M
50 PRINT:PRINT"1 -- 95 %    2 -- 98 %    3 -- 99 %
        4 -- 99.9 %":PRINT
60 PRINT"CONFIDENCE LEVEL DESIRED    ";
70 Q$=""+INKEY$:IFQ$=""THEN70
80 PRINTQ$:Z=A(VAL(Q$)):P=M/B:Q=(B-M)/B
90 P1=A/(P-(Z*SQR((P*Q)/B))):P2=A/(P+(Z*SQR((P*Q
    )/B)))
100 PRINT:PRINT"THE TOTAL POPULATION IS ESTIMATE
    D TO BE
ABOUT ";INT((A*B)/M)+1;
110 PRINT", RANGING FROM ";INT(P2)+1;"TO ";INT(P
    1)+1
120 END
```

As a practical matter, it is often easier for the computer to munch away at the truncated numbers than the expanded form. Having made the forecast, the only consideration is to remember to expand the forecast results. That is, if we truncate the input by

dye mark, ear tags, or some other nondestructive device. The animals are then released and allowed to mingle for a reasonable period of time: sufficient to become randomly redistributed among their own species.

After this period of time, another sample (B) of animals is collected with no special effort to select the marked animals. The animals are counted. Those with the marking from the first sample are also noted (M). The general estimate of the actual local population is found from:

$$P = INT\left(\frac{A \times B}{M}\right) + 1$$

The program includes a subroutine to compute the probable limits on either side of this estimate as a function of a normally distributed population.

Listing 13-5. Population Curve Fitting

```
1  '**********************************************
2  'POPULATION CURVE-FITTING                      *
3  'LISTING 13-5                                  *
4  '**********************************************
5  '
10 CLS:CLEAR250:DEFDBL A-H,N-Z
20 PRINT:PRINT"THIS ROUTINE ACCEPTS POPULATION D
     ATA IN PAIRED X,Y FORMAT AND   ATTEMPTS TO
        IDENTIFY THE BEST LINEAR OR CURVE FIT.   IT
     ALSO    PROVIDES AN ESTIMATE OF THE COEFFI
     CIENT OF CORRELATION.":PRINT
30 PRINT"YOU MAY USE ANY INTERVAL (YEARS, DECADE
     S, CENTURIES, ETC.), BUT THE INTERVAL MUST
     BE CONSTANT, WITH NO GAPS IN THE DATA.   DO
     NOTUSE THE YEAR, BUT, INSTEAD, NUMBER EACH
     INTERVAL FROM 1 TO N.":PRINT
40 PRINT:INPUT"ENTER NUMBER OF PAIRS:";P:DIM XX(
     30),XX(P),YY(P):PRINT
50 FORI=1TOP:PRINT"ENTER POPULATION FOR PERIOD #
       ";I,:INPUT YY(I):XX(I)=I:NEXTI
60 A$=" ####   ####.###       "
70 CLS:PRINT"PERIOD   POPUL.     PERIOD    POPUL.
         PERIOD    POPUL."
80 FORI=1TOP
90    PRINTUSINGA$;I;YY(I);
100   IF(I/3)<>INT(I/3)THEN120
110   PRINT
120 NEXT
130 PRINT:PRINT"ARE THESE VALUES CORRECT?   (Y/N)
     "
140 QQ$=INKEY$:IFQQ$=""THEN140
150 IFQQ$="Y"THEN170
160 INPUT"ENTER PERIOD AND CORRECT POPULATION";I
     ,YY(I):GOTO70
170 CLS:PRINT@512,"PLEASE BE PATIENT, COMPUTING"
180 FORI=1TOP
190 GOTO210
200     ONERRORGOTO1430
210     X=XX(I):Y=(YY(I)):E(1)=E(1)+(X*Y):E(2)=E
     (2)+(X*LOG(Y))
220     IFXX(I)>LXTHENLX=XX(I)
230     E(3)=E(3)+(Y*LOG(X)):E(4)=E(4)+(LOG(X)*L
     OG(Y))
240     IFXX(I)<SXTHENSX=XX(I)
250     F(1)=F(1)+X:F(3)=F(3)+LOG(X)
260     IFYY(I)>LYTHENLY=YY(I)
270     G(1)=G(1)+Y:G(2)=G(2)+LOG(Y)
```

```
280      IFYY(I)<SYTHENSY=YY(I)
290      H(1)=H(1)+X[2:H(3)=H(3)+LOG(X)[2
300      I(1)=F(1)[2:I(3)=F(3)[2
310      J(1)=J(1)+Y[2:J(2)=J(2)+LOG(Y)[2
320      K(1)=G(1)[2:K(2)=G(2)[2
330      PRINT@640,"I =";I;
340 NEXTI
350 F(2)=F(1):F(4)=F(3):G(3)=G(1):G(4)=G(2):H(2)
    =H(1):H(4)=H(3):I(2)=I(1):I(4)=I(3):J(3)=J(
    1):J(4)=J(2):K(3)=K(1):K(4)=K(2)
360 FORM=1TO4
370      B(M)=(E(M)-(F(M)*G(M))/P)/(H(M)-I(M)/P)
380      A(M)=(G(M)-B(M)*F(M))/P
390      R(M)=SQR((E(M)-F(M)*G(M)/P)[2/((H(M)-I(M
    )/P)*(J(M)-K(M)/P)))
400      PRINT@704,"M =";M;
410 NEXTM
420 B$="%          %  ####.####     ####.####
        ##.######"
430 CLS:PRINT"","A","B","R":PRINTUSINGB$;"LINEAR
    :";A(1);B(1);R(1):PRINTUSINGB$;"EXPONENTIAL
    :";EXP(A(2));B(2);R(2):PRINTUSINGB$;"LOGARI
    THMIC:";A(3);B(3);R(3):PRINTUSINGB$;"POWER:
    ";EXP(A(4));B(4);R(4):A(4)=EXP(A(4)):A(2)=E
    XP(A(2))
440 FORI=1TO6:R(I)=ABS(R(I)):NEXTI
450 IFR(1)>R(2)THEN490
460 IFR(2)>R(3)THEN510
470 IFR(3)>R(4)THEN540
480 M=4:GOTO550
490 IFR(1)<R(3)THEN470
500 IFR(1)>R(4)THEN520   ELSE480
510 IFR(2)>R(4)THEN530   ELSE480
520 M=1:GOTO550
530 M=2:GOTO550
540 M=3
550 PRINT
560 F$(1)="LINEAR":F$(2)="EXPONENTIAL":F$(3)="LO
    GARITHMIC":F$(4)="POWER":F$(5)="PARABOLIC":
    E$(1)="Y = A + BX":E$(2)="Y = EXP(LOG A + B
    X)":E$(3)="Y = A + B LOG X":E$(4)="Y = EXP(
    LOG A + B LOG X)":E$(5)="Y = A0 + A1 X + A2
    X[2"
570 C$="#####.######"
580 PRINT"THE BEST CURVE FIT IS ";F$(M):PRINT"TH
    E EQUATION IS: ";E$(M):PRINT"A =";USINGC$;A
    (M);:PRINT"   B =";USINGC$;B(M);:PRINT"   R
    =";USINGC$;R(M):PRINT:PRINT"DO YOU WANT TO
    COMPUTE A TERM?   (Y/N)"
590 IFSX=>0ANDSY=>0THEN610
600 ZZ=1:PRINT:PRINT"(DATA INCLUDES NEGATIVE VAL
    UES. ONLY THE LINEAR EQUATION IS
VALID.  IF ANOTHER FORM IS RECOMMENDED, PROGRAM
    WILL DISREGARD
AND COMPUTE LINEAR.)"
610 QZ$=INKEY$:IFQZ$=""THEN610
620 CLS
```

Listing 13-5. Population Curve Fitting (continued from page 299)

```
630 IFQZ$="N"THEN920
640 PRINT@960,"ENTER '@' TO STOP:";
650 PRINT@512,"WHICH VALUE (X OR Y) WILL BE ENTE
    RED?";:PRINT@576,"                    ";
660 QX$=INKEY$:IFQX$=""THEN660
670 IFQX$="Y"THEN720
680 IFQX$="@"THEN920
690 PRINT:INPUT"ENTER X-VALUE";X
700 ONMGOSUB750 ,800 ,840 ,880
710 GOTO740
720 PRINT:INPUT"ENTER Y-VALUE";Y
730 ONMGOSUB770 ,820 ,860 ,900
740 CLS:PRINT@384,"X =";X;"       Y =";Y:PRINT:GOT
    O630
750 Y=A(1)+B(1)*X
760 RETURN
770 X=(Y-(A(1)))/B(1)
780 RETURN
790 RETURN
800 Y=EXP(LOG(A(2))+B(2)*X)
810 RETURN
820 X=(LOG(Y)-LOG(A(2)))/B(2)
830 RETURN
840 Y=A(3)+B(3)*LOG(X)
850 RETURN
860 X=EXP((Y-A(3))/B(3)
870 RETURN
880 Y=A(4)*(X[B(4))
890 RETURN
900 X=(Y/A(4))[(1/B(4))
910 RETURN
920 GOSUB1060
930 LPRINTSTRING$(2,10)
940 LPRINT" ":LPRINT"TABLE OF INPUT/OUTPUT VALUE
    S":LPRINT" "
950 LPRINT"INPUT":LPRINT"X","Y","X","Y","X","Y",
    "X","Y"
960 FORI=1TOP:LPRINTXX(I),YY(I),:NEXTI
970 IFRR=2THEN1040
980 LPRINT" ":LPRINT"OUTPUT":LPRINT" ","A","B","
    R","t-TEST","EQUATIONS"
990 LPRINT"LINEAR",A(1),B(1),R(1),TT(1),E$(1)
1000 LPRINT"EXPONENTIAL",A(2),B(2),R(2),TT(2),E$
     (2)
1010 LPRINT"LOGARITHMIC",A(3),B(3),R(3),TT(3),E$
     (3)
1020 LPRINT"POWER",A(4),B(4),R(4),TT(4),E$(4)
1030 LPRINTSTRING$(5,10):CLS:RUN
1040 LPRINTSTRING$(3,10)
1050 END
1060 FX=(LX-SX)/126:FY=(LY-SY)/46
1070 ZX=127*(ABS(SX)/(LX-SX)):ZY=47-(47*(ABS(SY)
     /(LY-SY)))
1080 CLS
1090 FORI=1TOP
```

```
1100        SET((XX(I)-SX)/FX,47-((YY(I)-SY)/FY))
1110 NEXTI
1120 X=ZX:FORI=0TO47:SET(X,I):NEXTI
1130 Y=ZY:FORI=0TO127:SET(I,Y):NEXTI
1140 PRINT@960+INT(ZX/2),0;:PRINT@1017,LX;:PRINT
     @64*INT(ZY/3),0;:PRINT@0,LY;
1150 IFRR=2THEN1170
1160 GOSUB1330
1170 PRINT@0,"(P)RINT    (C)ONTINUE    ";
1180 Q$=""+INKEY$:IFQ$=""THEN1180
1190 IFQ$="P"GOSUB1210
1200 RETURN
1210 LPRINT LY
1220 FORI=0TO47
1230     FORJ=0TO127
1240         IFPOINT(J,I)THENLPRINT"*";ELSELPRINT" ";
1250     NEXTJ
1260     LPRINT" "
1270 NEXTI
1280 LPRINT"0";STRING$(112," ");LX
1290 LPRINT"X-AXIS: MINIMUM =";SX;"   MAXIMUM =";
     LX;"   SCALE INTERVAL VALUE =";(LX-SX)/128
1300 LPRINT"Y-AXIS: MINIMUM =";SY;"   MAXIMUM =";
     LY;"   SCALE INTERVAL VALUE =";(LY-SY)/48
1310 LPRINTSTRING$(3,10)
1320 RETURN
1330 FORI=SXTOLXSTEP(LX/100)
1340    ONERRORGOTO1430
1350    X=I:IFRR=1THEN1400
1360    ONMGOSUB750    ,800    ,840    ,880
1370    SET((X-SX)/FX,47-((Y-SY)/FY))
1380 NEXTI
1390 RETURN
1400 X$=STR$(X):GOSUB1440
1410 GOTO1370
1420 END
1430 RESUMENEXT
1440 X=VAL(X$):P=0:FORJ=1TOD:P=P+R(J+1,D+1)*X[J: Y=P:NEXTJ:RETURN
```

EXERCISES:

1. From county record, obtain the population of your county for the last hundred years. From county health authorities obtain a reliable estimate of the birth and mortality rates for your county. From these data, compute the best estimate of the county population for the next hundred years.

2. Having conducted the research in item 1 above, contact the local branch of the Chamber of Commerce and make an appointment to discuss your findings with a business analyst. Compare your projections with the Chamber's projections. How close are they? At what point, if at all, do they diverge? Why? Are these factors you can include in your program? How do the revised projections compare?

3. Develop a routine to compute world population data for the next fifty years.

4. Develop a study which implements the major features of the Population Estimator II.

SUGGESTED READING

Makridakis, S. and S.C. Wheelwright, 1978. *Forecasting Methods & Applications*. New York: John Wiley & Sons.

Chapter 14

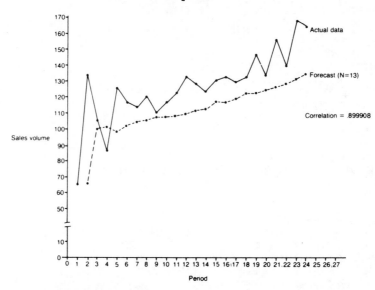

Educational Testing

It is the premise of this chapter that there is a place and a legitimate need for responsible educational testing. Opponents of testing argue that tests discriminate. By this they would imply that discrimination is inherently wrong. We would argue that only discrimination based on irrelevant factors is unfair and wrong. Tests, by their very nature, discriminate; that is, they identify differences in one or more characteristics in people.

The purpose of this chapter, however, is not to resolve social issues, but to provide the reader with sufficient information to use in microcomputer applications in testing or at least to make use of the microcomputer in a rational evaluation of testing programs. All modern testing is, or should be, precise and scientific. As with all other activities involving humans, the number of variables, and the indeterminate nature of many of them, are such that precision becomes a relative term. The primary objective of such testing, then, is that these tests be reliable and valid. In the pages that follow, we shall attempt to provide routines with which one may measure the reliability and validity of tests.

STATISTICAL BASICS

Before proceeding further, you should become familiar with the material present in Chapters 2 and 5. Among the principles presented, the key points applicable to educational testing include, but are not limited to, the concept of central tendency, measures of dispersion, and the various measures of correlation.

Central Tendency

A normal, fundamental aspect of data related to a specific characteristic is a concentration of points at or near the center of the data. For example, an easily identified characteristic of people is height. If we measure the height of a group of people chosen at random and chart the data, we will see a grouping of the data about the mean of the collection. Some people will be rather short or rather tall, but most will be of normal height. We measure central tendency by one of three characteristics: mean, mode, or median. The mean is simply the sum of each of the data points divided by the number of items. The median is the center value in an ordered list of the data. That is, if we list the data points in order of their magnitude, the median is the middle point in that list. The mode of the most frequent score. In the following list, the mode is 62:

Item #	Value	Item #	Value
1	58	6	62
2	61	7	62
3	61	8	63
4	62	9	63
5	62	10	65

The median is also 62. The computed mean is 61.7.

Measures of Dispersion

While our first concern is to determine the point about which the data seem to revolve, we are also interested in the degree to which the data deviate from the center point. The primary measures of dispersion are the range and standard deviation of the data. The range is simply the numerical distance between the smallest and the largest values in the data. In tests in which the score is a percentage, the largest score is, of course, 100. The smallest possible is zero. Regardless of the center of the data, whether 35, 50, or 60 percent, we are interested in knowing how far on either side of that point the data fall. However the test is scored, the range is useful as a first estimate of the utility of a test. If the range is small relative to the potential, there is a question of whether the test is really doing a good job of discriminating. Assume that we have a school program in which students are to be placed in one of five courses of instruction in French, depending on their starting French language facility. If all the scores on the screening test fall between 78 and 79 percent, the test has no use as a discriminator. Instead, we need another test in which, even if the mean is still 78.5, the range is at least from 76 to 81, and preferably larger. Up to a point, the wider the range, the more sure we are the test is a reliable tool. We can use the standard deviation to gauge whether the range is excessive. From the computation of the standard deviation, as well as the skew and kurtosis, we can infer the degree to which the data reflect random distribution. That is, if the range of the data is from zero to 100 percent and each possible score was achieved by more or less the same number of test subjects, the distribution is flat and suggests the test is poorly correlated to the criterion measure.

Correlation

Test items may be either positively or negatively correlated to the test criterion (see Fig. 14-1 and 14-2), but they should be correlated in some way. An alternative way of illustrating this requirement is shown in Fig. 14-3. Chapter 5 provides a detailed analysis and description of correlation computation techniques.

VALIDITY

A test is considered to be valid if it measures what it is designed to measure. There are three aspects to this concept of validity: content, criterion, and construct validity.

Content Validity

We are often concerned that a test adequately covers the total content of the course of instruction. That is, if the course involves a matrix of instruction involving economic, political, and demographic comparisons of three countries, a content valid test should have at least nine items to cover each of the topics presented. Whether they are distinct items or one or more of them covers two or more of the matrix options is immaterial. What is relevant is that the items adequately cover the material presented.

Criterion Validity

A test is, in a sense, a sampling of the information held in the minds of the subjects. We trust that a properly constructed French examination is somehow logically and reliably related to the students' fluency in the language. If, for example, a student may readily receive a perfect score on a final French examination in a course in conversational French, yet cannot carry on a conversation in French, the examination lacks criterion validity. Therefore, an aspect of criterion validity is the predictive power of the examination. Does one who does well on the test do well in the related field?

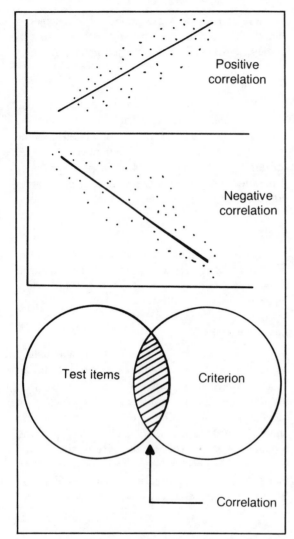

Fig. 14-1. Correlation between test items and criterion measures.

Construct Validity

This is an aspect of testing about which many of the emotional issues revolve. This aspect raises the question of the degree to which there is a causal relationship between the test or test items and the underlying theory or the attribute it seeks to measure. One portion of a screening examination for applicants for employment as firemen may include some mathematics questions involving trignometry. While such items may be shown to be somehow correlated with mental acuity and mental acuity is somehow related with success in combating fires, they may well be successfully challenged as irrelevant items lacking construct validity in the entry level screening process. On the other hand, a portion of the test which includes a measure of the amount of dead weight that the subject can lift and carry or the speed he or she can move over a specified distance may well be directly correlated (construct valid) to the tasks to be performed.

Figure 14-2 illustrates the general notion of the relationships between test scores and their validity as related to the criterion measures of the test. The sectors of the score results within the scattergram of the data are described as:

A — Valid Positives: test scores that correctly identify those who should be selected.

B — False Positives: test scores of those who passed the test but shouldn't have been selected.

C — Valid Negatives: test scores that properly identify those not capable of the task.

D — False Negatives: test scores of those who failed, but should have been selected.

In the development of any test, our objective is to maximize sectors A and C. To the extent that we are able to do this, we are more sure that a failing grade or score will be properly given to a person who actually fails to meet the basic criterion, and a passing grade is given to a capable respondent. As a rule of thumb, the better the correlation, either positive or negative, the better we have achieved the objective of minimizing sectors B and D, and maximized sectors A and C.

To the extent that we have properly stated the criterion measure, the correlation between the test score and the criterion measure is equivalent to the validity coefficient of the test.

RELIABILITY

Another way of viewing reliability is in the sense of the consistency of results. Regardless of the validity of a test, a reliable test should be con-

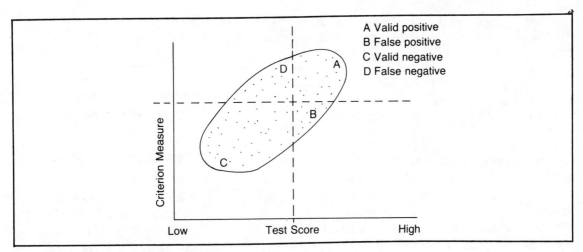

Fig. 14-2. Test scores correlated to criterion measures.

sistent each time it is given. If our test tends to identify people with high mathematics skills in one instance, it should do so in all instances. Alternatively, if the test, administered on Monday, indicates a person is skilled in a subject, it should make the same forecast in a retest on Friday. We are not concerned with what we are measuring but with how well it is measured. Figure 14-3 illustrates a key concern in the area of reliability.

The objective in improving reliability is to

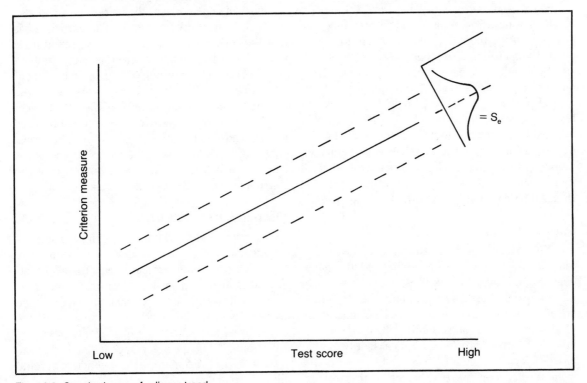

Fig. 14-3. Standard error of a linear trend.

minimize the degree of error in the distribution of test scores when charted against the criterion measure.

There are several techniques used to compute the reliability of a test. These include retesting using the same test, testing with parallel tests, using the subdivided test, and using the Kuder-Richardson estimates.

Retesting Using the Same Test

The basic approach is to administer the same test to the same subjects. The scores obtained on one test are correlated (as shown in Chapter 5) with the scores on the retest. There are two methods of using this technique. The first is to retest immediately after the first test. The second is to retest after some interval, using the same test on the same subjects. The greater the correlation the more reliable the test. The correlation, R, is often referred to as the *Coefficient of Reliability*.

Parallel Tests

On the chance or suspicion that test scores obtained using the previous technique are a function of the subject's memory, test administrators will often attempt to administer *parallel* tests, tests that are as identical to each other as possible. One method to do this is to create a large pool of test items from the material being taught or otherwise tested and then randomly selecting items for the two tests. As with the single test, the parallel tests may be administered either in close proximity in time or with an interval. The coefficient of reliability is calculated as before by computing Pearson's rho correlation between the two sets of test scores.

Subdivided Tests

Subdivided tests contain pairs of items attempting to measure the same thing with the same degree of difficulty. In this sense, the test is much like the parallel test approach, only the two tests are administered simultaneously. The computation of the coefficient of reliability, known as the Spearman-Brown prophecy formula, is a two-step process. The first step is to compute a *rho* coefficient (r) between the two halves of the test as

above. The second step is to compute the coefficient of reliability (R) from

$$R = \frac{2\,r}{1 + r}$$

If the correlation between the two halves of a test is .55, then the reliability of the test is presumed to be

$$R = \frac{2 \times .55}{1 + .55} = \frac{1.100}{1.55} = .709677$$

The shortcomings of this technique are three. First, there is no chance to test variations in the individual over time. A student may do well one day and not so well the next, or vice-versa. What we really want out of a testing situation is not how excellently or how horribly someone can do under extreme conditions, but what we can normally expect of that person over a period of time. Second, unless great care is exercised, the test items may not be as distinctly random or independent as they should be, but dependent to the extent that if the student gets one correct, the paired item will also normally be answered correctly. The third defect is that the technique is of little value in timed tests where the objective is to answer as many items as possible correctly in a limited span of time, without expecting that all items will be answered or even attempted. In selecting items to answer, the subject might not choose to answer the second of paired items. Those purchasing tests from commercial publishers should be sure the reliability measures quoted are based on either extensive use of the instrument or on parallel test measurements.

Kuder-Richardson Estimates

Leaders and innovators in testing and statistical measurements, the Kuder-Richardson team gave their names to a number of equations for test-related statistical measures. One of these, "Formula 20," is a fairly precise equation requiring the user to compute the standard deviation, s, of the test scores, the percentage of students passing a given item, P, and the percentage failing each item, Q,(Q = 1 − P). From these the coefficient of reliability is computed as

$$R = \left(\frac{N}{N-1} \right) \left(\frac{s^2 - \Sigma p\,q}{s^2} \right)$$

The second equation, "Formula 21," simplifies the process somewhat and requires only the computation of the standard deviation and the mean test score, M, for the group being tested. While the results are a bit more conservative than those obtained using Formula 20, the computation is simpler. With a microcomputer, the slight increase in complexity required when using the first equation should be no problem, but we offer the second form for those whose tasks are not as demanding. The equation is

$$R = \left(\frac{N}{N-1} \right) \left[1 - \frac{M\left(1 - \frac{M}{N}\right)}{s^2} \right]$$

Interpretation of the Coefficient of Reliability. We would like to have some method of translating the coefficients just computed into some more meaningful form. In Fig. 14-3 we noted the range of test scores around a trend line. This range is known as the standard error of measurement, s'. If we have computed the standard deviation of the test scores and have computed the coefficient of reliability, we can compute the standard error of measurement from:

$$s' = s \sqrt{1 - R}$$

Given a set of test scores from which we have computed the standard deviation to be 12 points and reliability to be .7096774, the standard error is:

$$s' = 12\sqrt{1 - .7096774} = 12\sqrt{.2903226} = 6.4658$$

Normally, better than 68 percent of the students' scores will be within 6.47 points, plus or minus, of the true score.

Effect of Length of a Test on Reliability

Common sense suggests that a test of ten items is more reliable than a test with two items. We have an equation available that gives us an estimate of how well lengthening a test improves the reliability. To use it, we must have first computed the basic coefficient of reliability of the original test and know the number of items on that test,

N_1 and the number of items proposed on the second test, N_2. From these we can compute the new reliability coefficient, R'

1. $N = N_2/N_1$

2. $R' = \dfrac{N\,R}{1 + (N - 1)\,R}$

Suppose, using the previous example (R = .7096774), there were 40 items on the first test and the proposition is to triple the length to 120 items. What is the effect on the reliability of the second test?

1. $N = 120 / 40 = 3$

2. $R' = \dfrac{3 \times .7096774}{1 + (3 - 1) \times .7096774} = .8799999$

By tripling the length, we have increased the reliability 24 percent. Even if the standard deviation remains at 12, the standard error of measurement is only plus or minus 4.156, a reduction in error by 35.7091 percent.

Reliability of Difference in Scores

Assume we have tested a group of students in a given subject using two different tests, a pretest and a final exam. The final exam scores suggest the majority of the class have improved their knowledge of the subject matter. The question we have is: how reliable are the noted differences in the scores? To answer this we need three values: R', the reliability of the first test; R'', the reliability of the second test; and r, the correlation between the two tests. The reliability of the difference score is computed from:

$$R = \frac{\dfrac{R' + R'' - r}{2}}{1 - r}$$

Using the data from the examples above, assume the pretest has a correlation with the final exam of .7856663. The reliability of the differences noted is:

$$R = \frac{\frac{.7096774 + .879999}{2} - .7856663}{1 - .7856663} = .04280966$$

The correlation is not good: this highlights a curious aspect of this kind of correlation. The closer the correlation of the two scores approaches the average of the two separate correlations, the closer the reliability of the differences approaches zero.

To improve the reliability of the difference scores, it is useful to reduce the correlation between the two screening measures and increase the reliability of the separate measures.

Listing 14-1 offers a program to handle each of the reliability measures just reviewed. You may elect to retain the entire program, or to extract from it just those sections desired.

Listing 14-1. Test Reliability Coefficients

```
1  '****************************************
2  'TEST RELIABILITY COEFFICIENTS          *
3  'LISTING 14-1                           *
4  '****************************************
5  '
10 CLS:PRINT"RELIABILITY COEFFICIENTS":PRINT:PRI
   NT
20 PRINT"1  ---   RESTESTING/PARALLEL TESTING
2  ---   SUBDIVIDED TESTS
3  ---   KUDER-RICHARDSON ESTIMATES
4  ---   STANDARD ERROR OF MEASUREMENT
5  ---   LENGTH OF TEST
6  ---   RELIABILITY OF DIFFERENCE SCORES":PRINT:
   PRINT"SELECT    ";
30 Q$=""+INKEY$:IFQ$=""THEN30   ELSEONVAL(Q$)GOT
   O40  ,160  ,280  ,570  ,680  ,760
40 CLS:PRINT"RETESTING/PARALLEL TESTING RELIABIL
   ITY":PRINT:PRINT
50 INPUT"NUMBER OF STUDENTS";N
60 PRINT
70 FORI=1TON
80    PRINT"STUDENT #";I;", ENTER SCORE TEST 1 AN
   D TEST 2";:INPUTX,Y
90 GOSUB840
100 NEXT
110 PRINT
120 GOSUB850
130 S1=SQR((X2-((TX[2)/N))/(N-1)):S2=SQR((Y2-((T
    Y[2)/N))/(N-1))
140 M1=TX/N:M2=TY/N
150 PRINT:PRINT"THE COEFFICIENT OF RELIABILITY I
    S = ";R:PRINT:PRINT"","TEST # 1","TEST # 2"
    :PRINT"MEAN SCORE",M1,M2:PRINT"STAN. DEV.",
    S1,S2:F=1:GOTO610
160 CLS:PRINT"SUBDIVIDED TESTS":PRINT:PRINT

170 INPUT"NUMBER OF ITEMS ON TEST";N
180 IF (N/2)=INT(N/2)THEN200
190 PRINT"SORRY, THERE MUST BE AN EVEN NUMBER OF
    ITEMS.":GOTO170
200 P=N/2
210 FORI=1TOP
220    PRINT"ENTER THE NUMBER CORRECT RESPONSES,
    ITEM # ";I;:INPUTX
```

```
230    INPUT"        ENTER THE NUMBER CORRECT RESPON
       SES FOR THE PAIRED ITEM";V
240    GOSUB840
250 NEXTI
260 GOSUB850
270 F=2:R=(2*R)/(1+R):GOTO130
280 CLS:PRINT"KUDER-RICHARDSON ESTIMATES":PRINT:
       PRINT
290 INPUT"ENTER NUMBER OF STUDENTS";M
300 INPUT"ENTER NUMBER OF TEST ITEMS";N
310 DIM G(M),T(N)
320 FORI=1TOM
330    PRINT:PRINT"STUDENT # ";I
340    FORJ=1TON
350      PRINT"TEST ITEM #";J;",  (C)ORRECT   (I)NC
       ORRECT  ";
360      Q$=""+INKEY$:IFQ$=""THEN360
370      PRINTQ$:IFQ$="I"THEN390
380      T(J)=T(J)+1:G(M)=G(M)+1
390    NEXTJ
400 NEXTI
410 FORI=1TOM
420    TX=TX+G(I):X2=X2+(G(I)[2)
430 NEXT
440 S2=(X2-((TX[2)/N))/(N-1):M=TX/N:S=SQR(S2)
450 FORI=1TON
460    P=T(I)/N:Q=1-P
470    SP=SP+(P*Q)
480 NEXTI
490 R1=(N/(N-1))*((S2-SP)/S2)
500 M=TX/N
510 R2=(N/(N-1))*(1-((M*(1-(M/N)))/S2))
520 PRINT:PRINT"MEAN GRADE = ";M
530 PRINT"STANDARD DEVIATION = ";SQR(S2)
540 PRINT"","FORM. 20","FORM. 21"
550 PRINT"COEF. OF REL.",R1,R2
560 F=3:GOTO610
570 CLS:PRINT"STANDARD ERROR OF MEASUREMENT":PRI
       NT:PRINT
580 INPUT"ENTER STANDARD DEVIATION";S
590 INPUT"ENTER COEFFICIENT OF RELIABILITY";R
600 GOTO640
610 IFF=3THEN640
620 S=S1:GOTO640
630 S=S2:F=0:GOTO640
640 SY=S*SQR(1-R)
650 PRINT"STANDARD ERROR OF MEASUREMENT = ";SY
660 IFF=1ORF=2THEN630
670 END
680 CLS:PRINT"LENGTH OF TEST":PRINT:PRINT
690 INPUT"ENTER LENGTH OF CURRENT TEST";M
700 INPUT"ENTER RELIABILITY OF CURRENT TEST";R1
710 INPUT"ENTER PROPOSED LENGTH OF NEW TEST";N
720 N=N/M
730 R2=(N*R1)/(1+((N-1)*R1))
740 PRINT:PRINT"RELIABILITY OF NEW TEST SHOULD B
       E = ";R2
```

Listing 14-1. Test Reliability Coefficients (continued from page 309)

```
750 END
760 CLS:PRINT"RELIABILITY OF DIFFERENCE SCORES":
    PRINT:PRINT
770 INPUT"ENTER RELIABILITY OF FIRST TEST";R1
780 INPUT"ENTER RELIABILIVT OF SECOND TEST";R2
790 INPUT"ENTER CORRELATION BETWEEN TWO TESTS";R

800 PRINT
810 RD=(((R1+R2)/2)-R)/(1-R)
820 PRINT"RELIABILITY OF DIFFERENCE SCORE = ";RD

830 END
840 TX=TX+X:TY=TY+Y:X2=X2+(X[2):Y2=Y2+(Y[2):XY=(
    X*Y):RETURN
850 R=((N*XY)-(TX*TY))/SQR(((N*X2)-(TX[2))*((N*Y
    2)-(TY[2))):RETURN
```

Student Record Book

An informal measure of the reliability of a test is the degree to which it correlates with the student's other grades in the subject being tested. Listings 14-2 and 14-3 constitute a routine for establishing and maintaining student scores and grades over an entire school year. Not a mere electronic recordbook, it computes the relevant statistics for each of the students and each of the tests recorded. The user may specify whether the output is given as the actual score, the percentage (if the score is not already in percentage form), percentiles, or a letter grade (A to E) based on a normal curve.

For each student the program computes the current grade or score average and the trend of the grades to date. With the alpha and beta coefficients final grades can be estimated, thus giving the teacher advance warning of students in need of special assistance.

Listing 14-2 is a data management program used once for each class to establish the basic data file. Listing 14-3 is the main program used to maintain the record through the year.

OTHER TESTS AND TESTING TECHNIQUES

There have been numerous tests and testing techniques developed to investigate an equally broad range of human behavior and education. What follows are some of these which may be usefully exploited with a microcomputer.

Guttmann Scalar Analysis

The long history of research into the measurement of attitudes has long been clouded by the problem of being sure that the attitude statement to which the subjects are to respond belong to the same scale. For example, one statement reads, in effect, that wars are not cost-effective even for the

Listing 14-2. Student Record Book Setup

```
1 '*********************************************
2 'STUDENT RECORD BOOK SETUP                   *
3 'LISTING 14-2                                 *
4 '*********************************************
5 '
10 CLS:CLEAR1500:@CLEAR
20 INPUT"NUMBER OF STUDENTS";N:DIM N$(N),S(N,1)
```

```
30 FORI=1TON
40    PRINT"NAME OF STUDENT # ";I,:INPUTN$(I)
50    INPUT"TEST SCORE ";S(I,1)
60 NEXT
70 INPUT"MAXIMUM TEST SCORE";MX(1)
80 PRINT:PRINT"ALL INPUTS CORRECT?  (Y/N)";
90 Q$=""+INKEY$:IFQ$=""THEN90    ELSEIFQ$="Y"THEN
      120
100 PRINT:INPUT"ENTER STUDENT NUMBER AND CORRECT
      NAME";X,N$(X)
110 GOTO80
120 PRINT:INPUT"CLASS FILE NUMBER";F:T=1
130 @OPENF:@PRINT N,T
140 FORI=1TOT
150   @PRINT MX(1)
160 NEXTI
170 FORI=1TON
180   @PRINT N$(I)
190   FORJ=1TOT
200     @PRINTS(I,J)
210   NEXTJ
220 NEXT
230 @CLOSE
240 END
```

winners, while another statement says that wars to defend oneself are legitimate while other forms of military action are not. It has been pointed out that subjective responses to these two items are not suitable for comparison because they are really measures of two different scales. In the early 1950's a technique was developed to determine the degree to which a set of statements fall upon the same scale. The theory is that if the statements are perfectly ordered and unidimensional, responses by a set of subjects can be arranged in this pattern:

Agree With Item Number

Subject	1	2	3	4	5	6	7	8	9	Score
1							X	X	X	3
2						X	X	X	X	4
3					X	X	X	X	X	5
4				X	X	X	X	X	X	6
5			X	X	X	X	X	X	X	7
6		X	X	X	X	X	X	X	X	8
7	X	X	X	X	X	X	X	X	X	9

The utility of this approach is that by scoring an attitude survey with the items so arranged, it is assumed that if the subject agrees with item number 3, the same subject will also agree with items 4 through 9. In the beginning of the analysis, we understand that the items and the respondents are not so neatly arranged. Instead, the initial distribution may appear as

Agree With Item Number

Subject	1	2	3	4	5	6	7	8	9	Score
1		X	X	X			X	X	X	6
2	X	X	X	X	X	X	X	X	X	9
3		X		X			X		X	4
4	X	X	X	X			X	X	X	7
5		X		X			X	X	X	5
6		X					X		X	3
7	X	X	X	X			X	X	X	8
Total	3	7	4	6	1	2	7	5	7	

The procedure at this point is to reorder the matrix so that either the column totals or the row totals form a numerical sequence. Ordering the row scores gives us

Agree With Item Number

Subject	1	2	3	4	5	6	7	8	9	Score
6		X					X		X	3
3		X	X				X		X	4
5		X	X				X	X	X	5
1		X	X	X			X	X	X	6

4	X X X X X X X	7
7	X X X X X X X X	8
2	X X X X X X X X	9
Total	3 7 4 6 1 2 7 5 7	

Reorder the columns in a similar fashion gives us

Subject	5 6 1 3 8 4 2 7 9	Score
6	X X X	3
3	X X X X	4
	.....	
2	X X X X X X X X X	9

(The same as the first)

We can use this technique to simplify the construction of both surveys and tests. Assume that we have a test containing 40 items, which we administer to ten students. By using an "*" to indicate an item answered incorrectly, we table the responses by the procedures noted above. The final table looks like this:

Item Numbers

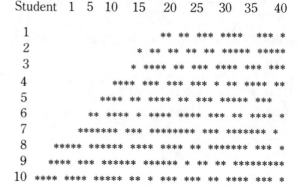

Judging from the table, items numbered 21 through 40 do not appear to add anything to the discrimination process. That is, if we review the

Listing 14-3. Student Record Book

```
1  '*****************************************
2  'STUDENT RECORD BOOK                     *
3  'LISTING 14-3                            *
4  '*****************************************
5  '
10 CLS:CLEAR1500:@CLEAR
20 INPUT"CLASS FILE NUMBER";F
30 @OPEN F:@INPUT N,T
40 DIM N$(N),S(N,T+1),RT(N),CT(T+1),SD(N),SE(N),
     A(N),B(N),ES(T+1),L(T+1),H(T+1),MX(T+1),TX(
     T+1),TY(T+1),X2(T+1),Y2(T+1),XY(T+1),P(N)
50 FORI=1TOT
60    @INPUT MX(I)
70 NEXTI
80 FORI=1TON
90    @INPUT N$(I):PRINTN$(I);
100   FORJ=1TOT
110      @INPUT S(I,J):PRINTS(I,J),
120   NEXTJ
130 NEXTI
140 @CLOSE
150 PRINT:PRINT"MAXIMUM POSSIBLE SCORE FOR TEST
    ";T+1,:INPUT MX(T+1)
160 FORI=1TON
170   PRINT"ENTER CURRENT TEST SCORE FOR ";N$(I)
    ,:INPUTS(I,T+1)
180 NEXT
```

```
190 PRINT:PRINT"ALL DATA CORRECT?  (Y/N)";
200 Q$=""+INKEY$:IFQ$=""THEN200
210 IFQ$="Y"THEN240
220 INPUT"ENTER STUDENT NUMBER AND CORRECT SCORE
    ";X,S(X,T+1)
230 GOTO190
240 T=T+1:CLS:PRINT@0,"COMPUTING ";T;" TEST SCOR
    E RESULTS":B$=" #### "
250 LPRINT"#   NAME","TEST SCORES";STRING$((T*6)-
    11," ");"SUM  MEAN     S.D.      S.E.       AL
    PHA     BETA"
260   A$="####  ###.##   ##.###   ###.###   ####.##
    #   ####.###":B$=" ### "
270 FORI=1TON
280   LPRINTI;N$(I),:PRINT N$(I);
290   TX=0:TY=0:X2=0:Y2=0:XY=0
300   FORJ=1TOT
310     X=J:Y=S(I,J):RT(I)=RT(I)+Y:TT=TT+Y:LPRIN
    TUSINGB$; Y;:PRINT Y;:TX=TX+X:TY=TY+Y:X2=X2
    +(X[2):Y2=Y2+(Y[2):XY=XY+(X*Y)
320   NEXT
330   SD(I)=SQR((Y2-((TY[2)/T))/(T-1)):SE(I)=SD(
    I)/SQR(T)
340   B(I)=(XY-(TX*(TY/T)))/(X2-(T*((TX/T)[2))):
    A(I)=(TY/T)-(B(I)*(TX/T))
350   LPRINTUSINGA$;RT(I);RT(I)/T;SD(I);SE(I);A(
    I);B(I)
360   PRINTRT(I);RT(I)/T;SD(I);SE(I);A(I);B(I)
370 NEXTI
380 C$="##.# "
390 LPRINT"TOTAL",
400 FORI=1TOT
410   FORJ=1TON
420     X=J:Y=S(J,I):CT(I)=CT(I)+Y:TX(I)=TX(I)+X
    :TY(I)=TY(I)+Y:XY(I)=XY(I)+(X*Y):X2(I)=X2(I
    )+(X[2):Y2(I)=Y2(I)+(Y[2)
430   NEXTJ
440   LPRINTUSINGB$;CT(I);
450 NEXTI
460 LPRINTTT,TT/T:LPRINT"MEAN",
470 FORJ=1TOT
480   LPRINTUSINGC$;CT(J)/N;
490 NEXTJ
500 LPRINTTT/N,(TT/N)/T:LPRINT"S. D.",
510 FORI=1TOT
520   SD(I)=SQR((Y2(I)-((TY(I)[2)/N))/(N-1)):LPR
    INTUSINGC$;SD(I);
530 NEXTI
540 LPRINT"":LPRINT"S. E.",
550 FORI=1TOT
560   S=SD(I)/SQR(N):LPRINTUSINGC$;S;
570 NEXTI
580 LPRINT"":LPRINT"COEF. OF REL.",
590 FORI=1TOT
600   LPRINTUSING" #.###";(N/(N-1))*(1-((CT(I)/N
    )*(1-((CT(I)/N)/N))/SD(I));
610 NEXTI
```

Listing 14-2. Student Record Book Setup (continued from page 313)

```
620 DIM SM(T),LG(T)
630 LPRINT"":LPRINT"LOW SCORE",
640 FORI=1TOT
650    SM(I)=1.0E+30:LG(I)=1.0E-30
660    FORJ=1TON
670      IFSM(I)<S(J,I)THEN690
680      SM(I)=S(J,I)
690      IFS(J,I)<LG(I)THEN710
700      LG(I)=S(J,I)
710    NEXTJ
720    LPRINTUSINGB$;SM(I);
730 NEXTI
740 LPRINT"":LPRINT"HIGH SCORE",
750 FORI=1TOT
760    LPRINTUSINGB$;LG(I);
770 NEXTI
780 LPRINT"":LPRINT"MAX. POSS.",
790 FORI=1TOT
800    LPRINTUSINGB$;MX(I);
810 NEXTI
820 @OPEN F
830 @PRINT N,T
840 FORI=1TOT
850    @PRINT MX(I)
860 NEXTI
870 FORI=1TON
880    @PRINT N$(I)
890    FORJ=1TOT
900      @PRINT S(I,J)
910    NEXTJ
920 NEXTI
930 @CLOSE
940 FORI=1TON
950    FORJ=1TON
960      IFJ=ITHEN990
970      IFS(I,T)<S(J,T)THEN990
980      TS=TS+1
990    NEXTJ
1000   P(I)=100*(TS/N):TS=0
1010 NEXTI
1020 CLS:PRINT"# NAME","SCORE","PER CENT","% - T
     ILE LETTER"
1030 LPRINT"":LPRINT"#","NAME","SCORE","PERCENTA
     GE","PERCENTILE","LETTER"
1040 FORI=1TON
1050   C=INT((S(I,T)-(CT(T)/N))/SD(T))+3:IFC<0TH
     ENC=0
1060   IFC>4THENC=4
1070   PRINTI;N$(I),S(I,T),S(I,T)/MX(T),P(I);CHR
     $(69-C)
1080   LPRINTI,N$(I),S(I,T),INT(10000*(S(I,T)/MX
     (T)))/100,P(I),CHR$(69-C)
1090 NEXTI
1100 END
```

responses to each of the items numbered greater than 20, we cannot identify which student made the particular set of responses. On the other hand, by reviewing the responses to items 1 through 20 (as renumbered in the rearranging process) we can identify the particular student. Additionally, by noting which item number a student first makes a mistake on, one can immediately compute a fair estimate of the total number missed. For example, if a student first misses item number 15, then we assume the remaining 25 items will also be incorrectly answered, yielding a score of 37.5 (15/40 = .375). Armed with these data, we have a rational basis for deleting from the test items 21 through 40, using only the first 20. The program in Listing 14-4 takes the drudgery out of reordering the tables of test data into the format shown above. It is up to the user to determine which of the items appear to be superfluous.

Forecasting From Entry Indicators

Educational resources are limited. Whether there is a shortage of classroom space during periods of increased student population (from previous "baby booms") or a shortage of teachers (especially technically trained teachers who have

Listing 14-4. Guttmann Scalar Analysis

```
1  '***********************************************
2  'GUTTMANN SCALAR ANALYSIS                      *
3  'LISTING 14-4                                  *
4  '***********************************************
5  '
10 CLS:INPUT"ENTER NUMBER OF TEST ITEMS";TI
20 INPUT"ENTER NUMBER OF STUDENTS";NS
30 DIMA(NS,TI),RT(NS),CT(TI),TR(NS),TC(TI)
40 CLS:PRINT@960,"1 = CORRECT      0 = WRONG"
50 FORI=1TONS
60    TR(I)=1
70    FORJ=1TOTI
80       TC(J)=J
90       PRINT@512,"STUDENT #";I;",  ITEM #";J;
100      R$=""+INKEY$:IFR$=""THEN100
110      R=VAL(R$)
120      A(I,J)=R:RT(I)=RT(I)+R:CT(J)=CT(J)+R
130   NEXTJ
140 NEXTI
150 CLS
160 GOSUB180
170 GOTO270
180 CLS
190 FORI=1TONS
200    FORJ=1TOTI
210       IFA(I,J)=1THENSET(J,I)
220    NEXTJ
230 NEXTI
240 GOSUB730
250 GOSUB620
260 RETURN
270 M=NS
280 M=M/2
290 IFINT(M)=0THEN430
300 K=NS-M:J=1
310 I=J
320 L=I+M
330 IFRT(I)<=RT(L)THEN410
340 T=RT(I):RT(I)=RT(L):RT(L)=T
```

Listing 14-4. Guttmann Scalar Analysis (continued from page 315)

```
350  T=TR(I):TR(I)=TR(L):TR(L)=T
360  FORZ=1TOTI
370  T=A(I,Z):A(I,Z)=A(L,Z):A(L,Z)=T
380  NEXTZ
390  I=I-M
400  IFI<1THEN410    ELSE320
410  J=J+1
420  IFJ>KTHEN280    ELSE310
430  GOSUB180
440  M=TI
450  M=M/2
460  IFINT(M)=0THEN600
470  K=TI-M:J=1
480  I=J
490  L=I+M
500  IFCT(I)<=CT(L)THEN580
510  T=CT(I):CT(I)=CT(L):CT(L)=T
520  T=TC(I):TC(I)=TC(L):TC(L)=T
530  FORZ=1TONS
540  T=A(Z,I):A(Z,I)=A(Z,L):A(Z,L)=T
550  NEXTZ
560  I=I-M
570  IFI<1THEN580    ELSE490
580  J=J+1
590  IFJ>KTHEN450    ELSE480
600  GOSUB180
610  GOTO810
620  C=0
630  FORI=1TONS
640     FORJ=1TOTI
650        IF(I+J)>(NS+TI)/2THEN670
660        IFA(I,J)=0THENC=C+1
670     NEXTJ
680  NEXTI
690  PRINT@1000,"C =";C;
700  LPRINT"C =";C
710  LPRINT"":FORI=1TOTI:LPRINTTC(I);:NEXT:LPRINT
     "":FORI=1TOTI:LPRINTCT(I);:NEXTI:LPRINTSTRI
     NG$(2,10)
720  RETURN
730  FORI=1TONS
740     LPRINTI;TR(I),
750     FORJ=1TOTI
760        IFA(I,J)=1THENLPRINT"*";ELSELPRINT" ";
770     NEXTJ
780     LPRINT"";RT(I)
790  NEXTI
800  RETURN
810  PRINT@960,"(R)OW,    (C)OLUMN OR (E)ND?
                      ";
820  Q$=""+INKEY$:IFQ$=""THEN820
830  IFQ$="R"THEN1010
840  IFQ$="E"THEN1080
850  Q$=""
```

```
860 PRINT@960,"ENTER COLUMN NUMBER 1 AND COLUMN
    NUMBER 2";:INPUTM,N
870 T=CT(M):CT(M)=CT(N):CT(N)=T
880 T=TC(M):TC(M)=TC(N):TC(N)=T
890 FORZ=1TONS
900   T=A(Z,M):A(Z,M)=A(Z,N):A(Z,N)=T
910 NEXTZ
920 CLS
930 FORI=1TONS
940   FORJ=1TOTI
950     IFA(I,J)=1THENSET(J,I)
960   NEXTJ
970 NEXTI
980 GOSUB730
990 GOSUB620
1000 GOTO810
1010 PRINT@960,"   ENTER ROW 1 AND ROW 2 NUMBERS
     ";:INPUTM,N
1020 T=RT(M):RT(M)=RT(N):RT(N)=T
1030 T=TR(M):TR(M)=TR(N):TR(N)=T
1040 FORZ=1TOTI
1050   T=A(M,Z):A(M,Z)=A(N,Z):A(N,Z)=T
1060 NEXTZ
1070 GOTO920
1080 RUN10
```

been lured into industry), there never seems to be a flush period where anyone desiring to learn something can be sure of finding a seat in a class where the subject is taught by the most qualified teacher.

It is prudent, then, to make an attempt to forecast the likely academic performance of an applicant before admission so that those enrolled in a course of study are those most likely to make the most effective use of the resources available. When the target program is an extension of previous training or experiences, then the screening process is simplified. For example, the study of mathematics covers a number of years. Entry into an advanced algebra course can be controlled simply by examining one's grades in the previous algebra course(s).

Problems arise when there is no precursor course or obvious indicators. One such example is in the area of language training. Numerous tests exist which identify persons on the basis of something called verbal skills, but this indicator score is only slightly correlated to proficiency in learning a number of modern languages. Even the experience of having learned one language in a high school

setting is no guarantee of success in a more intense and extensive program.

The author was, for several years, professionally involved in a major program to provide practical language training for a large organization requiring a number of people trained in a number of foreign languages. Over the years a number of screening tools had been used, and discarded, to select from the employees those to attend an intensive language program in which a full two to four-year college-level language program is compressed into four to ten months. Classic indicators of success were of little use. Several screening devices had been developed, but even these only had a correlation with the terminal criterion (success in the program) of about .45 to .55. The significance of these correlations is that a large number of students were selected who were, in the final analysis, ill-suited to the program. We were interested in identifying some other factors which might shed some light on the screening problem and improve the selection process. Failing that, could we identify students who were more inclined to experience difficulty in training? We hypothesized that if we could identify these problem-prone students in advance, we could extend an early helping hand through our counselling staff. A major deviation from previous studies, which involved a number of tests of verbal skills and other measures of intellectual functioning, was the desire to use readily noted and obvious characteristics (age, sex, height, weight, etc.) as the independent variables. What we wanted was a screening tool we could implement as the students arrived for training. In addition to the basic demographic characteristics, we also had available the employee's job grade rating (1-9), educational level, the grade-point average from previous training, as well as the scores from the basic employment screening tests and the language aptitude test. The basic plan of the study consisted of six phrases:

Phase 1. Design and develop study plan and materials. Select test variables.

Phase 2. Distribute data collection forms to the counselling staff. Brief staff on program technique and objectives.

Phase 3. Collect and tabulate data for three-month period.

Phase 4. Perform statistical analysis of data, correlating the relationships between the test variables and the periodic test grades the students receive at well-defined intervals. Identify, if possible, useful indicator variables. Brief counselling staff on outcome of studies and those students who seem to be high-risk.

Phase 5. Maintain records on academic performance of subjects through completion of course.

Phase 6. Perform final statistical analysis and prepare report.

Phase 1: The product of this phase was the program plan identified just above. In addition, we developed the data collection forms and selected the characteristics to be measured. We finally settled on eight independent variables: employment grade, age, height, weight, educational level, grade-point average, language aptitude score, and employment screening score. The dependent variable was to be the grades obtained by each student after six to nine weeks of training and after the completion of the program. Tables 14-1 through 14-3 summarizes these variables.

Phases 2 and 3. These phases were conducted as planned without exceptional incident.

Phase 4. For the analysis, we were fortunate to have access to the institution's main computer system through which we could access a remote system upon which was a powerful set of statistical programs designed to evaluate large amounts of multivariate statistical problems. Table 14-4 summarizes the simple correlations between each of the independent variables and the dependent variable.

The program used to evaluate these data was one of a large set of biomedical statistical programs resident on a large mainframe computer system. We hypothesized that the magnitude of the depen-

Table 14-1. Summary of Student Characteristics, Males.

	Grade	Age	Height	Weight	Ed Level	GPA	Job Score	Apt. Score	Test Score
Number	106	106	106	106	69	65	45	57	95
Mean	3.981	25.189	70.802	168.594	13.812	2.945	347.556	31.719	86.453
Stan. Dev.	1.648	4.957	2.579	26.980	1.365	.576	26.804	7.223	7.269
Variance	2.717	24.568	6.650	727.940	1.863	.331	718.473	52.167	52.837
Coef. of Var.	41.401	19.678	3.642	16.003	9.883	19.546	7.712	22.771	8.408
Stan. Skew	− .229	.894	.328	.515	.411	− .215	− 1.427	.606	− 1.060
Stan. Excess	− .529	.451	− .467	− .156	− .738	− .494	2.374	− .042	1.361
Smallest Entry	1	18	66	133	12	1.7	250	21	59
Largest Entry	8	42	77	245	17	4.0	380	51	99

(Male Students)

Table 14-2. Summary of Student Characteristics, Females.

	Grade	Age	Height	Weight	Ed Level	GPA	Job Score	Apt. Score	Test Score
Number	31	31	31	31	31	31	21	30	27
Mean	1.452	20.516	64.968	129.452	13.194	3.275	281.000	33.167	82.926
Stan. Dev.	.874	2.662	2.236	12.152	1.712	.456	37.677	7.979	9.189
Variance	.764	7.008	4.999	147.667	2.930	.208	1419.530	63.672	84.439
Coeff. of Var.	60.205	12.977	3.441	9.387	12.975	13.924	13.408	24.059	11.081
Stan. Skew	1.598	.802	− .117	.092	1.010	− .529	− .218	1.059	−1.229
Stan. Excess	.982	− .567	− .339	− .666	− .663	.334	− .840	1.006	.809
Smallest Entry	1	18	60	107	12	2.0	205	20	57
Largest Entry	4	26	69	157	17	4.0	346	55	94

(Female Students)

dent variable, the grade on the first (and, presumably, subsequent tests), was a function of the multivariate form

$$Y = A_0 + A_1X_1 + A_2X_2 + A_3X_3 + ... + A_nX_n$$

We knew from experience that the best (highest correlation) form of the equation is not necessarily derived from using all of the independent variables. Instead, it was likely that the best predictor of the grade might be computed by using only some of the independent variables. But, which ones? The fundamental task of the program we used was to sort through the available data and compute the correlation between the dependent and a given set of independent variables. Having computed the various correlations, the task falls back on us to select the combination that provides us the best predictor tool. The secondary function of the program was to specify the coefficients to use in the regression equation. The coefficients, A_1, A_2, A_3, etc., are computed for each of the independent variables. To these is added the residual or constant A_0. The result, for a given individual is the predicted six-week grade. The implication of these data is that, for a new female student, for example, the predicted six-week grade (Y), would be

Y = 178.02117 + 1.75139 × Age + .09345 × Job Score

− .03996 × Weight − .41554 × Aptitude Score

− .87122 × Educational Level − 1.89512 × Height

− 2.559 × GPA

Thus, age (maturity?) and something in the basic employment screening tests were positively related to success in the program, while a higher rating in any of the other areas tended to predict failure.

Table 14-3. Summary of Student Characteristics, All.

	Grade	Age	Height	Weight	Ed Level	GPA	Job Score	Apt. Score	Test Score
Number	137	137	137	137	99	102	66	87	122
Mean	3.409	24.131	69.482	159.737	13.596	3.048	326.379	32.218	85.672
Stan. Dev.	1.843	4.943	3.498	29.409	1.497	.558	43.618	7.524	7.872
Variance	3.395	24.435	12.235	864.880	2.241	.312	1902.510	56.608	61.975
Coef. of Var.	54.053	20.485	5.034	18.411	11.010	18.310	13.364	23.352	9.189
Stan. Skew	.040	1.000	− .232	.552	.564	− .406	− .917	.812	−1.209
Stan. Excess	−1.101	.750	− .208	− .200	− .858	− .295	− .030	.572	1.639
Smallest Entry	1	18	60	107	12	1.7	205	20	57
Largest Entry	8	42	77	245	17	4.0	380	55	99

(All Students)

Table 14-4. Correlations Between Characteristics.

	Grade	Age	Height	Weight	Ed Level	GPA	Job Score	Aptitude	Test Score
Grade	1.0000	.82436	.42700	.50335	.29047	−.17263	.65758	−.01235	.11713
Age		1.00000	.25512	.38580	.58706	−.19561	.46259	.11025	.07440
Height			1.00000	.72337	.07756	−.23437	.47622	−.16012	.08234
Weight				1.00000	.14018	−.28537	.41309	−.18328	.04066
Ed. Level					1.00000	−.10110	.27349	.30966	.26751
GPA						1.00000	−.04231	.24628	−.10835
Job Score							1.00000	.15661	.37971
Aptitude Score								1.00000	−.05177
First Test									1.00000

The correlation between the predicted scores and the actual test scores was: r = .57137, superior to the correlation between the aptitude test and the grades. The equation above suggests that age is the fundamental determinant of success in the program. Was this a function of maturity, or were there unmeasured variables closely related to age that were really operative? It didn't really matter. The objective was to identify the relationships, which we did. Our primary task was to see how the different variables interacted to produce a predictor tool. The limitation of this routine was that it simply rank ordered the independent variables. The processing began with the factor that seemed to have the most significant relationship to the dependent variable, and then added in, one at a time, each of the remaining variables until the least significant factor was added. At the time of the study we were told that a more sophisticated routine, one that would evaluate each combination was not available on the immediate system, and, in any event, would be a very difficult problem to handle.

We are very happy to note, however, that the microcomputer industry has made life a bit easier. Very recently, we recomputed the related data from this study on the author's microcomputer system using the Multiple Linear Regression program found in Listing 5-5. Not only did it perform the computations that, ten years ago, were beyond reach, but it completed the task in less than two hours, most of which was consumed in printing the results.

EXERCISES

1. Write the following as a mathematical formula:

   The standard error of the estimate equals the square root of the sum of the squared deviations of the predicted scores from the observed scores divided by one less than the number of observations.

2. State the following equation in words:

$$r = \frac{XY}{(N-1)S_x S_y}$$

3. Describe how you would develop a test to predict later high school dropouts from a population of junior high school students.

SUGGESTED READING

American Psychological Association, 1966. *Standards for Educational and Psychological Tests and Manuals*. Washington, D.C.: American Psychological Association.

Guilford, J.P., 1965. *Fundamental Statistics in Psychology and Education*. New York: McGraw-Hill.

Thorndike, R.L. and E. Hagen, 1969. *Measurement and Evaluation in Psychology and Education*. New York: John Wiley & Sons.

Chapter 15

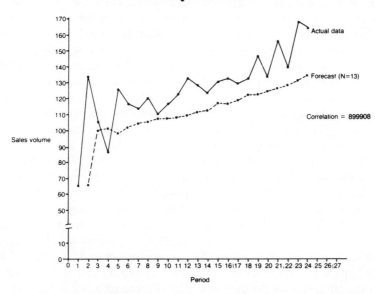

Forecasting Random Events

By definition, we ought not be able to forecast random events. After all, if we can predict an outcome of a random event, it doesn't seem to be very random does it? The truth of the matter is that while we really can't predict the exact outcome of a given random event, we can develop some generalized notions about a set of otherwise random data.

For example, dice are frequently used to determine the outcome of various games. We use dice to play craps and to determine the moves to be made in a variety of board games. Some of the more recent fantasy games employ many-sided dice having anything from 4 to 24 sides. Given the identity of a die (number of sides) we can compute probable outcomes. In craps, for instance, we use two six-sided dice. The sides are numbered consecutively from one to six. By throwing the two die concurrently, the possible sum of any two faces ranges from two to twelve. While the probability of any one side appearing is $1/6 = .166667$, there is a range of probabilities from .027778 (for 2 and 12) to .166667 (for 7) for the combined scores. We cannot pre-

determine the outcome of a particular throw of the dice, but we can determine the likely average outcome of a number of throws. From this knowledge we can develop a betting strategy designed to minimize losses and maximize winnings.

This chapter examines several common activities with randomly determined outcomes and offers some solutions to minimizing the uncertainty involved. The computing power of today's microcomputers make short work of problems that have puzzled analysts of random events for centuries. It provides a way to pragmatically identify the underlying and true game-odds of a number of activities. It certainly is a lot easier than flipping coins thousands of times. The routines involved are simply suggested solutions. This is an area where the reader can derive great enjoyment in developing alternative approaches to these problems.

THE UNIVERSAL GAME MACHINE

Winning, in its larger sense, is a national, if not global, preoccupation. We demonstrate this by noting that given a choice, most people elect to win than lose, to realize a profit from their investments of time, money, and energy. The competition is so intense, however, that the rate of return on "sure things" is usually only a nominal five to ten percent. Conservative investors are not ordinarily satisfied with just even odds; they seek opportunities where the chance of failure is virtually nonexistent. A project that offers only a five percent return on investment may go wanting for funding. Yet, a few people are making a respectable living at the gaming tables of Nevada and New Jersey. In addition to the owners of the casinos, successful gamblers are making investment decisions and winning in situations where the normal rate of return is certainly no greater than five percent and the odds of winning big are nil.

The key, of course, is not really the number of times one wins in a game where the odds are unfavorable (which is more often than not the case) but the strategy of betting one uses. To stay in a game, one must continue to bet, even though he or she frequently loses. The net profit of the professional gambler is derived by placing a significantly more sizeable wager at the appropriate moment; i.e., just before a winning play. Success depends on the limited ability to foretell the future and a workable betting strategy. These factors require an understanding of the probabilities involved and the experimental development of a betting strategy suited to the game. Until the last couple of centuries, mankind had to rely upon intuition or hunch, as well as a profound superstition, to shape their fortunes. With the development of probability theory and statistics, however, we have acquired the tools needed to handle the difficult odds situation in a rational manner. From an experimental standpoint, however, data generation and collection was a very tedious process. It was one thing to predict the outcome of a series of dice throws theoretically but quite something else to confirm the theory in a scientifically acceptable and consistent manner— especially if confirmation requires several tens of thousands of repetitions. Reference works, except those written very recently, refer to authoritative works in which conclusions are reached on the basis of three or four thousand trials. Flipping coins to a more satisfactory level of fifty or one hundred repetitions is very hard work to say the least.

With the advent of the modern computer we gained the means to examine these realms electronically. The solution of such problems, however, remained either in the domain of the private corporations that could afford a computing system or was considered too trivial by those controlling publicity owned computing resources. With microcomputers all this has changed. Indeed, the basis for this section began in 1976 with original work done by the author on hand-held programmable calculators. The project had two objectives: to develop a sense of the underlying probability of winning at games a "win" is the function of one or more conditional events (such as craps or blackjack, etc.), and to study the phenomenon of extended runs of wins or losses. It was for the latter the Universal Game Machine (UGM) was invented.

We believed that underlying all standard games of chance was some "true" underlying probability of winning, regardless of the complexity of the rules. If we adequately define the rules of the game, we would eventually be able to compute its true odds. Of greater interest at the moment, however, was the phenomenon of runs.

The professional gambler frequently laughs at the novice who insists on playing good money after bad on the presumption that some "law of averages" would intervene and permit a winning combination. The wiser gambler knows, of course, that the outcome of the toss of the dice has absolutely no bearing on the outcome of the next or any other toss of the dice—the probability of any given combination remains constant.

At the same time common sense intrudes to the extent of noting that in games where the odds are fairly even, such as coin tossing, one wins fairly frequently and the number of times one loses more than two or three times in a row is really quite rare. On the other hand, in games where the odds of winning are quite slim (lotteries, drawings, etc.), one loses with a great consistency—winning more than one raffle in a row is quite extraordinary. We took this line of reasoning one step further and

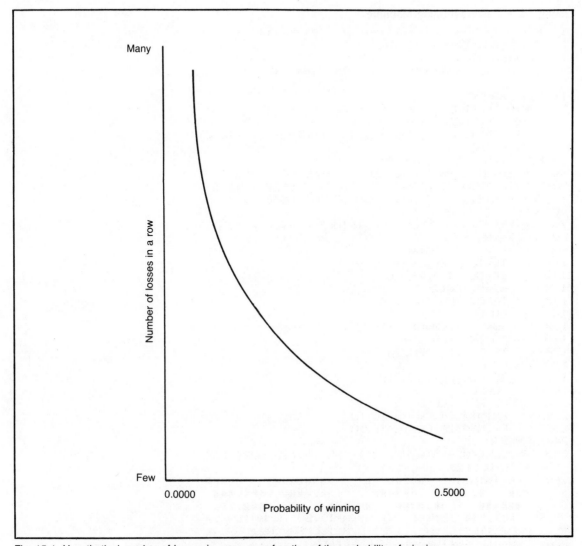

Fig. 15-1. Hypothetical number of losses in a row as a function of the probability of winning.

hypothesized that the number of times we could reasonably expect to win or lose in a row was a function of the probability of winning one trial: as the probability of losing increased, we should except the number of times we would lose in a row would increase by some rational function. The basic hypothesis is illustrated in Fig. 15-1.

The next step was to develop a process by which the actual values of the chart could be computed. The UGM serves this purpose quite well. Rather than simulating the rules of actual games, the UGM assumes there is a game in which the probability of winning is a known value, P, where $\emptyset = < = P < = 1$. For each trial the UGM generates a random number, X, in the same range. If X is found to be greater than P, we assume that a loss has happened. On the other hand, if X is less than P, we assume there has been a "win". For the purpose of our study, statistics were maintained on the number of trials, the numbers wins and losses, the record lengths of win and loss runs, and so forth. The basic UGM is specified in Listing 15-1. You

323

Listing 15-1. Universal Game Machine

```
1    '*****************************************
2    'UNIVERSAL GAME MACHINE                   *
3    'LISTING 15-1                             *
4    '*****************************************
5    '
10 CLS: RANDOM
20 LPRINT"PROBABILITY   # TRIALS    # WINS    RAT
       IO   LONGEST SET    AVERAGE    S.E.    # LOSS
       ES   RATIO   LONGEST SET    AVERAGE    S.E.
       ":LPRINT""
30 FORP=.05TO.5001STEP.05
40     PRINT@16,"PROBABILITY OF WINNING = ";P;
50     PRINT@200,"CURRENT","TOTAL","% OF # TRIALS"
       :PRINT@256,"WINS";:PRINT@320,"LOSSES",
60     FORN=1TO10000
70       PRINT@80,"NUMBER OF TRIALS PLAYED = ";N;
80       X=RND(0)
90       IF X<P THEN160
100      TL=TL+1:CL=CL+1
110      IF CL<>1 THEN220
120      W2=W2+CW[2
130      IF CW<=LW THEN150
140      LW=CW
150      NW=NW+1:CW=0:GOTO220
160      TW=TW+1:CW=CW+1
170      IF CW<>1 THEN220
180      L2=L2+CL[2
190      IF CL<=LL THEN210
200      LL=CL
210      NL=NL+1:CL=0
220      PRINT@264,CW,TW,TW/N;
230      PRINT@328,CL,TL,TL/N;
240    NEXTN
250 SW=SQR((W2-((TW/NW)[2))/(NW-1)):SL=SQR((L2-
    ((TL/NL)[2))/(NL-1))
260    LPRINTUSING" #.######    #######    ###
    ###    #.####    ######    ##.####    ###.###
    ######    #.####    ######    ###.###
    ###.###";P;N-1;TW;TW/(N-1);LW;TW/NW;SW/SQ
    R(NW);TL;TL/(N-1);LL;TL/NL;SL/SQR(NL)
270    LW=0:LL=0:TW=0:TL=0:NW=0:NL=0
280 NEXTP
```

Table 15-1. Result of Universal Game Machine Run.

Probability	#Trials	#Wins	Ratio	Longest Set	Average	S.E.	#Losses	Ratio	Longest Set	Average	S.E
0.050000	1000	45	0.0450	2	1.0000	0.152	955	0.9550	88	21.705	4.364
0.100000	1000	97	0.0970	2	1.0899	0.142	903	0.9030	45	10.146	2.578
0.150000	1000	145	0.1450	3	1.1694	0.152	855	0.8550	27	6.895	2.027
0.200000	1000	213	0.2130	5	1.2604	0.155	787	0.7870	34	4.657	1.578
0.250000	1000	225	0.2250	5	1.3554	0.197	775	0.7750	25	4.669	1.679
0.300000	1000	323	0.3230	10	1.5236	0.199	677	0.6770	17	3.193	1.347
0.350000	1000	360	0.3600	7	1.5385	0.214	640	0.6400	16	2.735	1.242
0.400000	1000	401	0.4010	7	1.6849	0.247	599	0.5990	9	2.506	1.232
0.450000	1000	431	0.4310	9	1.7737	0.280	569	0.5690	14	2.351	1.231
0.500000	1000	512	0.5120	10	2.1513	0.333	488	0.4880	10	2.050	1.262

may wish to alter it to include provisions for record-keeping based on the results on different betting strategies.

Table 15-1 summarizes the outcome of several runs of the program.

Figure 15-2 illustrates the plot of the number of record loss runs as a function of the probability of winning.

For us, the outcome of this experiment was very interesting and gratifying. (It's always gratifying to have one's suspicions proven. . . .) From the data it is clear that we can compute all we need to know about a game and our chance of making a net profit from it by simply knowing what the underlying game probability is and how much we have to bet. We can also judge whether or not we

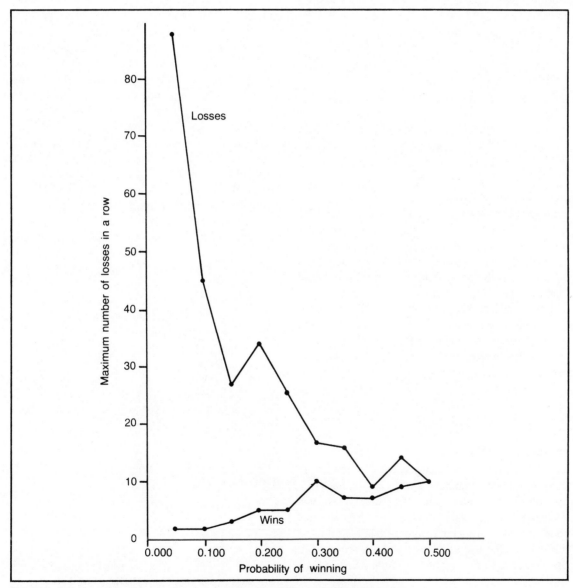

Fig. 15-2. Actual number of losses in a row as a function of the probability of winning.

should even try the game to begin with. In a simple application of the information, if we know that a losing streak of ten times in a row is not exceptional, we should be prepared to lose at least ten times, yet have sufficient funds left with which to make a bet large enough to recoup our losses to that point plus make a little profit. Examination of these data and the data obtained from previous runs of this routine have led us to the following set of relationships:

1. P = probability of winning
2. $Q = 1 - P$
3. $L_q = Q/P$ Average number of losses in a row
4. $P(L_q) = Q^{L.8}$ Probability of L_q losses in series
5. $L_y = 80.4848 \times 2.71828^{-4.379 \times P}$ Most likely number of losses in a row given P, the probability of winning.

The relationship noted in equation 5 was empirically derived from the experimental data obtained in 1976. On the basis of the data in Table 15-1 similar equations can be developed (using the curve fitting routine from Chapter 6) that can be used to predict the longest normal run of losses using the game odds as the base. While it is always possible that a player could encounter a run of bad luck longer than that computed, it would be very unlikely. Based on the most recent run of ten thousand trials for each increment of P, from .05 to .50 in steps of .05, the longest normal run of losses can be computed from.

BETTING STRATEGIES

There are about as many betting strategies as there are people who have spent two minutes in a casino or a hot poker game. To data, no one has announced a sure fire scheme—and we are not about to do so here—but if wagering is your hobby, there are some useful lessons to be learned from the UGM and from something called a *Markov Process*.

The simplest betting strategy is to make the same wager, trial after trial. If you have a good enough bankroll and if the odds are ever so slightly in your favor, you will eventually end up a winner if you stay with it long enough. On the other hand, if the odds are not in your favor, as in most games in a casino, you will, in the long run, always lose. From a special subset of the Markov Process, Markov Chains, we can derive a set of equations that tell us just about how long it will take to reach some specified profit or to lose all of a bankroll. In *Probability: An Introductory Course* by Norman R. Draper and Willard E. Lawrence, there is a comprehensive discussion of the Markov Process and an explanation of the development of the equations given below. We will leave the history of the equations to the truly curious. A Markov Chain is, in this perspective, a random walk wherein a gambler moves from a condition of a certain degree of wealth (bankroll) in a series of steps indicating wins or losses. Whether a given step will be a win or loss is unknown, but the "randomness" of the outcome is known to be influenced by the basic game odds. Such an analysis produces the following equations.

1. P = Probability of winning at each step or trial
2. $Q = 1 - P$
3. J = Starting investment of bankroll
4. V = Objective or goal
5. $L = ((Q/P)^J - (Q/P)^V)/(1 - (Q/P)^V)$ Probability of a total loss
6. $E = V - J - (V \times L) = V(1 - L) - J$ Expected loss or gain
7. $T - E/(P - Q)$ Mean time (in # of plays) to reach a loss or the objective.

Where $P = Q$ ($P = .5$), the equations become a little simpler. Rules 1-4 remain the same. The others become:

5. $L = (V - J)/V$
6. $E = \emptyset$
7. $T = J(v - J)$

Listing 15-2 is a short routine based on the foregoing equations from the Markov Process.

Listing 15-2. Markov Odds

```
1  '************************************************
2  'MARKOV ODDS                                    *
3  'LISTING 15-2                                   *
4  '************************************************
5  '
10 CLS:PRINT"WELCOME TO THE GAMBLERS' ADVISOR.":
      PRINT:PRINT:PRINT"THIS PROGRAM WILL NOT IMP
      ROVE YOUR GAMING SKILLS.   INSTEAD, IT   WILL
      SIMPLY ADVISE YOU WHAT THE REALISTIC ODDS
      ARE OF WINNING   (IF AT ALL) AND WHERE SOME
      OF THE PITFALLS MIGHT BE.":PRINT
20 PRINT"TO FACILITATE THIS VENTURE, I NEED TO K
      NOW THE PROBABILITY OF   WINNING IN THE GAM
      E YOU HAVE CHOSEN.   IF YOU KNOW WHAT THIS
          VALUE IS, SIMPLY ENTER IT BELOW.   IF YOU
      DON'T, PLEASE DUMP THISPROGRAM AND RUN A S
      IMULATION TO DETERMINE";
30 PRINT" THE TRUE GAME ODDS.   WHEN YOU HAVE IT
      , ENTER BELOW."
40 PRINT:INPUT"PROBABILITY OF WINNING THE GAME A
      T ANY RANDOM POINT";P:Q=1-P:IFP=.5THEN60

50 PL=100/LOG(Q/P)
60 INPUT"WHAT IS THE AMOUNT OF YOUR BANKROLL";BR
      :J=BR
70 INPUT"WHAT IS YOUR GOAL, HOW MUCH DO YOU WANT
      TO LEAVE WITH";G:V=G
80 IFP=>.5THEN110
90 IFV<PLTHEN110
100 V=V/10:J=J/10:GOTO90
110 CLS:PRINT"FIRST, THE SIMPLE COMPUTATIONS....
      ":PRINT:PRINT"       ASSUMING YOU BET A CON
      STANT WAGER EACH PLAY...":PRINT
120 IFP=.5THEN150
130 L=(((Q/P)[J)-((Q/P)[V))/(1-((Q/P)[V))
140 E=(V*(1-L))-J:T=E/(P-Q):GOTO160
150 L=(V-J)/V:E=0:T=J*(V-J)
160 PRINT"THE PROBABILITY OF A TOTAL LOSS (WIN)
      = ";L
170 PRINT"THE EXPECTED LOSS (GAIN) = $ ";E
180 PRINT"MEAN NUMBER OF PLAYS TO LOSS (WIN)";T
190 AL=E/T
200 PRINT"AVERAGE LOSS (GAIN) PER PLAY = $ ";AL
210 W=INT(P*100):NG=G/W
220 PRINT:PRINT"LET'S ASSUME YOU PLAY THIS GAME
      100 TIMES.   WE PREDICT YOU WILL
WIN";W;"TIMES, ON THE AVERAGE.   THIS MEANS EACH
      WIN MUST NET YOU AT LEAST $";NG;".   ";
230 IFNG<ALTHEN260
240 PRINT"YOU WILL HAVE TO ADOPT A BETTING STRAT
      EGY A BIT MORE SOPHISTICATED THAN A CONSTAN
      T BET IF YOU HOPE TO       REALIZE YOUR GOAL
      OF $";G:PRINT
250 END
260 PRINT"CONGRATULATIONS!":END
```

Another approach to betting is a routine called the Martingale system. Simply put, one begins with a unit wager. This can be one dollar, five, ten, or twenty. It doesn't matter; the first wager, whatever the amount, is the unit bet. If the first trial or game is lost, the second bet is twice the first. If the second trial or game is lost, the third bet is twice the second, and so on until either the bankroll is exhausted or a win condition is satisfied. At the point where a win is experienced, the subsequent bet is returned to one unit; the same as the first bet. Theoretically, it doesn't matter how bad the game odds are, the player will always end up winning using the Martingale system—theoretically, that is. In practice there are a couple of facts of life that diminish the utility of the Martingale system. The first is that one could lose a lot of money before winning anything. In fact, it was this aspect of the system that drove the creation of the UGM and the study to determine the length of normal loss strings. The size of a bet after N loses is equal to 2^{N-1}. After five losses the bet will be 16 times the first. After ten losses the bet will be 512 times the first. As you can see from Table 15-1, even with even odds, a string of ten losses in a row is not unusual. In the range of odds where most casino games are found ($P = .45$) loss strings of 14 or 15 are common. Bets in this range would easily be 16384 to 32768 times the first bet. Assuming a $1.00 initial bet, after 15 losses, the bet would be 32768, and the accumulated losses up to that point would be 32767. The second reality is that virtually every casino that has the resources to handle 32768 dollar bets also has bet limits, usually about five hundred or a thousand dollars. And the final fact of life is that the profit gained by using the Martingale system is exactly equal to the number of times the player wins. That is, if the unit bet is a dollar in a game where the probability of winning is .45, and a thousand games are played, the bettor will have a net profit of $450.00.

An alternative approach to Martingale system is to use a multiple other than two. You could also use 1.5, 3.76, .98, or any other value desired. If we call the multiple A, the following is true:

Bet after N losses $= A^{N-1}$

Sum of all such bets up to the Nth trial $=$

$$\frac{A^N - 1}{A - 1}$$

In the sense of a footnote, there is also a Reverse Martingale system wherein the bet is doubled every time there is a win and reduced to unity when there is a loss. Unless the game odds are strongly in your favor, you would be further ahead just giving the money to charity and taking the tax deduction.

SODA POP SIMULATION

A prominent manufacturer of a popular carbonated beverage has run a contest in which the bottle cap plays a pivotal role. Under the plastic seal on each cap is either one of the twenty-six letters of the alphabet, or a cash value of $.25, $.50, or $1.00. The letters are used to spell out designated words. Twenty-two letters appear in a normal and random distribution. Four of the letters, key to winning the major prizes, a shirt, chair, or cash of either $100 or $2000, are distributed in much smaller quantities. The promotional material provides the odds of winning the various prizes:

Prize	Probability Of Winning	Number in 2,000,000	Accumulative Total
$.25	.0400000	80,000	80,000
$.50	.0020000	4,000	84,000
$1.00	.0010000	2,000	86,000
Shirt	.0001000	200	86,200
Chair	.0000100	20	86,220
$100	.0000050	10	86,230
$2000	.0000005	1	86,231

The random function on a computer such as the TRS-80 works only within the integer range of the Z80; that is, only between 0 and 32767. That fact creates a little problem. The direct way to begin a simulation of this game would be to generate a random number in the range 1 to 2,000,000 (as in RND(2000000)), but, as we have just noted, the normal limit is 32767. To circumvent this, we use the expression: X=INT (RND(0)*2000000), trusting that the random number generator will give us a reasonably even distribution of values between 0 and 1,999,999, two million numbers in all. Having generated a number, X, the next step, is to determine whether or not it signifies a win, and, if so, what kind.

By examining the right hand column, "Accumulative Total": we can see that out of two million caps, there will be only 86,231 winning caps. Therefore, we will say that if X is greater than 86,231, then there is no win of any kind. All we do is buy another bottle (debiting our bank balance) and

try again. On the other hand, if X is less than 86232, check to determine where in the range it falls and what kind of prize it wins. Using the table of odds, we will say that if X is less than 80001, the prize is $.25. If X is in the range 80001 to 84000, then the prize is $.50, and so on. A flowchart of this process is given in Fig. 15-3.

From this flowchart the program in Listing 15-3 was developed.

One of the rules of the game is that to win you have to spell a word or a phrase from the collected letters. The program makes no provision for this

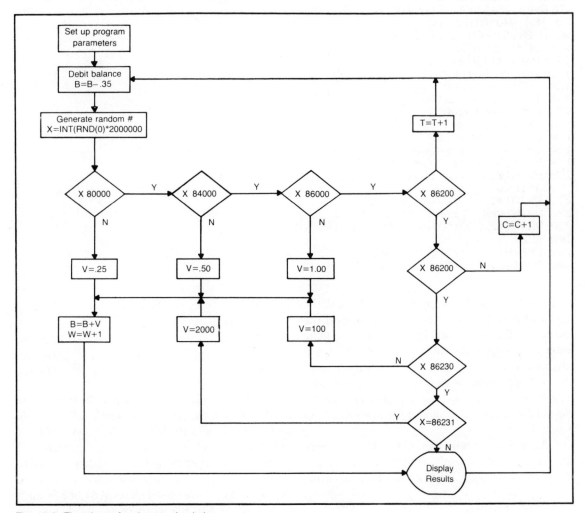

Fig. 15-3. Flowchart of soda pop simulation.

Listing 15-3. Soda Pop Simulation

```
1  '*******************************************
2  'SODA POP SIMULATION                      *
3  'LISTING 15-3                             *
4  '*******************************************
5  '
10 CLS:LPRINT"BALANCE","WON","SHIRTS","CHAIRS","

RATIO: WON TO INVESTMENT"
20 RANDOM:DEFDBLX
30 FORP=1TO650
40 B=B-.35:X=0
50 X=INT(RND(0)*2000000)
60 IFX>80000THEN80
70 B=B+.25:W=W+.25:GOTO200
80 IFX>84000THEN100
90 B=B+.5:W=W+.5:GOTO200
100 IFX>86000THEN120
110 B=B+1:W=W+1:GOTO200
120 IFX>86200THEN140
130 T=T+1:GOTO200
140 IFX>86220THEN160
150 C=C+1:GOTO200
160 IFX>86230THEN180
170 B=B+100:W=W+100:GOTO200
180 IFX<>86231THEN200
190 B=B+2000:W=W+2000:GOTO200
200 PRINT@15,P;:PRINT@30,X;:PRINT@128,"BANK = $
    ";B;
210 PRINT@158,W,W/(P*.41825);
220 PRINT@192,T;"T-SHIRTS",,T/P;
230 PRINT@256,C;"DIRECTORS' CHAIRS",C/P;
240 NEXT
250 LPRINTB,W,T,C,W/271.8625
260 B=0:W=0:T=0:C=0:GOTO30
```

aspect on the basis that better than 95.69% of all the caps will have the necessary letters to spell the balance of the words and by the time a winning letter comes up, sufficient numbers of letters will have been collected to complete the phrase. From a strictly logical point of view this is not necessarily true, but this theory is adequate to demonstrate the essential aspects of the game and the probability of winning.

Assuming one buys two million bottles, there should be approximately 86,231 winning caps. Based on the odds provided, one would end up with:

Prize	Number	Value
$.25	80,000	$20.000.00
$.50	4,000	2,000.00
$1.00	2,000	2,000.00
$100.00	10	1,000.00
$2000.00	1	2,000.00
Total Cash		$27,000.00

Since the retail price of each of the two million bottles is $.35, the total investment is $700,000.00, and the net loss is $673,000.00. Now, we still have 200 T-shirts and 20 canvas chairs. Assuming the value ratio between the shirts and chairs is equal to their numbers (e.g., a chair is worth ten shirts), to break even we have to sell shirts at $1,682.50 each and chairs at $16,825.00 each: not too likely, we think.

The contest is a pleasant diversion while consuming your favorite beverage. It is, however, a poor reason for any major investment in something you otherwise would not buy. That's our forecast.

CRAPS SIMULATION

The true age of this game is unknown, but it is not unreasonable to believe that it has very ancient roots. The computation of the odds in the game, however, has been a very tedious task. The rules of the game, from which we begin the computation, are fairly simple:

1. A player rolls two fair dice on a flat and hard surface. In casinos, this surface is marked with the various odds offered for each possible combination of points and bets.
2. If the total of the upward showing faces is seven or eleven, there is an automatic win.
3. If the total of the two faces is two, three, or twelve, there is an automatic loss.
4. If the total is some other value (i.e., four to six, or eight to ten), that value becomes the "point" and the player continues to roll the dice.
5. The player continues to roll the dice until
   a. the point value appears again
      or
   b. the player rolls a seven combination.
6. If the player rolls the "point," there is a win.
7. If the player rolls a seven there is a loss.

The computation of the odds for the first three steps is pretty straightforward. The probability of a seven is $6/36 = .166667$. The probability of an eleven is $2/36 = .055556$. The probability of winning on the first roll, then, is $P = 6/36 + 2/36 = 8/36 = .222222$ (or about once every 4.5 rolls). The probability of losing is easily computed from

$$Q = 1/36 + 2/36 + 1/36 = .111111$$

The probability of either winning and losing on the first roll is .333333, exactly once every three rolls. The implication is clear: two out of every three rolls will result in continuing the game in search of one's point. And this is where it gets difficult to compute by hand.

You could build a table of probabilities, that shows the odds of winning associated with the different points. That is, the probability of a given point value becoming the point. But, given a specific point, what is the probability of rolling the dice to a successful search for that point? If you try to build a contingency tree for each of the possible and subsequent outcomes, you will quickly note how rapidly it gets out of hand. An alternative solution is to play the game a large number of times, keeping good records along the way, and at some distant time, simply dividing the number of times you've won by the total number of games played. Not too many years ago that used to be exactly the way statisticians approached complicated probabilities. The modern programmable hand calculator and the microcomputer frees us from the task. Listing 15-4 implements the game rules for craps cited above. It keeps track of wins and losses, posting the result along with each trial. Try it yourself and find out what your chances are.

Listing 15-4. Craps Simulator

```
1  '***************************************************
2  'CRAPS SIMULATOR                                   *
3  'LISTING 15-4                                      *
4  '***************************************************
5  '
10 CLS:RANDOM
20 PRINT@25,"CRAPS SIMULATOR":PRINT:PRINT@960,"F
      OR PRINTED SUMMARY, TOUCH AND HOLD 'P'";
30 PRINT@192,"# GAMES","DIE #1","DIE #2","TOTAL"

40 PRINT@384,"# WINS","# LOSSES","WIN/LOSS RATIO
      ";
50 PRINT@588,"      1           2           3           4
      5         6";
```

Listing 15-4. Craps Simulator (continued from page 331)

```
60 PRINT@640,"DIE # 1";:PRINT@704,"DIE # 2";
70 D1=RND(6):D2=RND(6):TD=D1+D2
80 Q$=""+INKEY$:IFQ$=""THEN110
90 IFQ$<>"P"THEN110
100 GOSUB310
110 G=G+1
120 D(1,D1)=D(1,D1)+1:D(2,D2)=D(2,D2)+1
130 PRINT@258,G,D1,D2,TD
140 PRINT@645+(9*D1),D(1,D1);:PRINT@709+(9*D2),D
    (2,D2);
150 IFTD=7THEN270
160 IFTD=11THEN270
170 IFTD<4THEN280
180 IFTD=12THEN280
190 P=TD
200 D1=RND(6):D2=RND(6):TD=D1+D2
210 D(1,D1)=D(1,D1)+1:D(2,D2)=D(2,D2)+1
220 PRINT@258,G,D1,D2,TD
230 PRINT@645+(9*D1),D(1,D1);:PRINT@709+(9*D2),D
    (2,D2);
240 IFTD=7THEN280
250 IFTD=PTHEN270
260 GOTO200
270 W=W+1:WL=W/G:GOTO290
280 L=L+1:WL=W/G
290 PRINT@450,W,L,WL
300 GOTO70
310 LPRINT"SUMMARY AFTER";G;"GAMES"
320 FORR=2TO14
330   FORC=0TO63
340     X=PEEK(15360+(R*64)+C):IFX<32THENX=X+64
350     LPRINTCHR$(X);
360   NEXT
370   LPRINT""
380 NEXT
390 LPRINT"":RETURN
```

CARD GAMES

Not too long after ancient man designed dice out of pebbles, just as soon as a reliable paper technology was developed, card games came along to help fill out a television and radio-free evening. Today's card decks used for bridge, poker, blackjack, canasta, and a number of similar games consist of 52 cards each, and contain four suits (hearts, diamonds, clubs, and spades) with thirteen cards in each suit, ranging from the ace to the king. In virtually all of these games, the first step is to shuffle the cards so that the location of any given card is randomly determined. Listing 15-5 is a short routine used to shuffle one deck of cards into a random sequence. Each card is conceived to be numbered from 1 to 52. The shuffling routine creates a matrix in which these 52 numbers appear randomly.

To determine the suit to which a card belongs,

Listing 15-5. Basic Card Dealing

```
1  '*************************************************
2  'BASIC CARD DEALING                              *
3  'LISTING 15-5                                    *
4  '*************************************************
5  '
```

```
10 CLS
20 RANDOM
30 DIM A(52)
40 FOR I=1 TO 52
50    A(I)=I
60 NEXT
70 FOR I=1 TO 52
80    X=RND(52)
90    Y=RND(52)
100   H=A(X)
110   A(X)=A(Y)
120   A(Y)=H
130 NEXT
140 FOR I=1 TO 52
150   PRINTI;A(I),:LPRINT I;A(I),
160 NEXT
170 END
```

take the integer value of the card number, divide it by thirteen (and a nudge), and add one

$$\text{Suit} = \text{integer part } (C / 13.01) + 1$$

Using this approach, card number 25 is found to be in the second suit:

$$\text{Suit} = \text{INT}(25 / 13.01) + 1 = \text{INT}(1.92160) + 1 = 2$$

The determination of the value of the card is done in a similar fashion, using a modulus form

$$\text{Value} = \text{INT}((13*((C/13.01) - \text{INT}(C/13.01)))) + 1$$
$$= \text{INT}((13*((25/13.01) - \text{INT}(25/13.01)))) + 1$$

$$= \text{INT}(13*(1.922 - 1)) + 1$$
$$= \text{INT}(11.98078) + 1 = 12 \text{ (Queen)}$$

With the foundation of a procedure to shuffle the cards and an algorithm to identify the suit and value of each card, we can implement any number of routines on the microcomputer to check out card games and their outcomes. Listing 15-6 offers a short program to shuffle any number of decks of cards for subsequent dealing to a user-specified number of players. The reader can use this routine as the first step in the development of a card game evaluation program.

Listing 15-6. Card Dealer

```
1  ´*********************************************
2  ´CARD DEALER                                 *
3  ´LISTING 15-6                                *
4  ´*********************************************
5  ´
10 CLS:RANDOM:PRINT"HOW MANY DECKS?   (1 TO 9)";
20 D$=""+INKEY$:IFD$=""THEN20
30 D=VAL(D$):IFD<1ORD>9THEN20
40 NC=52*D:DIMA(NC),PC(8,12)
50 PRINTD:PRINT"NUMBER OF PLAYERS?   (1 TO 7)";
60 P$=""+INKEY$:IFP$=""THEN60
70 P=VAL(P$):IFP<1ORP>7THEN60
80 PRINTP:PRINT"YOUR POSITION AT TABLE?   (1 TO 7
   )";
90 VP$=""+INKEY$:IFVP$=""THEN90
100 VP=VAL(VP$):IFVP<1ORVP>7THEN90
110 SP=NC/2:PRINTVP:INPUT"RE-SHUFFLE AFTER HOW M
    ANY CARDS";SP
120 IFSP>NCTHEN110
```

```
130 PRINT"RE-SHUFFLE WILL OCCUR WHEN";SP;"CARDS
    HAVE BEEN DEALT":PRINT"SHUFFLING";D;"DECK(S
    ), WITH A TOTAL OF";NC;"CARDS..."
140 FOR A=1 TO NC
150   A(A)=A:PRINT@1010,A;
160 NEXT
170 FOR B=1 TO NC
180   X=RND(NC):Y=RND(NC)
190   H=A(X):A(X)=A(Y):A(Y)=H
200   PRINT@1010,B;
210 NEXT
220 S$(1)="SPADES":S$(2)="HEARTS":S$(3)="DIAMOND
    S":S$(4)="CLUBS"
230 CC$="A23456789TJQK"
240 PRINT
250 FOR I=1 TO NC
260   X=A(I):V=1+INT((13*((X/13.01)-INT(X/13.01)
    )))
270   C$=MID$(CC$,V,1)
280   V=1+INT((4*((X/4.01)-INT(X/4.01))))
290   PRINTI;" ";C$;" OF ";S$(V)
300 NEXT
310 END
```

Listing 15-7, built upon the routine in Listing 15-6, facilitates the playing of a game of blackjack or "21." This game comes about as close to a game of skill that casinos offer their customers. A number of routines have been developed and successfully applied to "beat the odds" and win significant sums. Unfortunately, many of the better systems depend on the version of the game in which only one deck of cards is used. The more decks used, the more difficult it is to compute appropriate strategies. The reason for this is that with one deck it is feasible to keep track of the number of cards of each point value, especially the 10s and face cards, which can quickly change a potential win to a loss. Knowing the number of 10s that have been played (since there are only four), it is easy to compute the probability that the next card will be a 10. Likewise, we can compute the probability of a face card (also carrying a value of ten). As the number of decks increases, however, the task of tracking the played cards quickly becomes too difficult to be a practical approach.

The most effective and recent algorithm for managing to win in multiple-deck versions of the game concentrates on evaluating the cards that can be seen face up on the playing surface, rather than trying to keep mental count of cards, many of which cannot be seen.

Listing 15-7. Blackjack Trainer

```
1  '*************************************************
2  'BLACKJACK TRAINER                              *
3  'LISTING 15-7                                   *
4  '*************************************************
5  '
10 CLS:G=1:DIMC$(13):GOTO970
20 'CARD DEALING SUBROUTINE
30 C=C+1:CD=CD+1:X=A(C):X=X-(INT(X/52)*52):V=1+I
   NT((13*((X/13.1)-INT(X/13.1)))):PRINT@1004,
   "CARD #";CD;"OF";NC;
40 M$="A23456789TJQK"
50 IFCD>SPTHEN150
60 IFV>1THEN120
70 IFI<=PTHEN90
```

```
80 C$="A":IFS(I)<=10THENS(I)=S(I)+11ELSES(I)=S(I
      )+1:GOTO180
90 PC(I,N)=1:C$="A":PRINT@76+(I*64)+(3*N),C$;:PR
      INT@704,"HOW MANY POINTS SHALL THIS ACE BE
      WORTH, (O)NE  OR  (E)LEVEN";
100 Z$=""+INKEY$:IFZ$=""THEN100  ELSEIFZ$="O"THE
      NV=1ELSEV=11
110 S(I)=S(I)+V:PRINT@704,CHR$(255);:V=1:GOTO180
120 IFV<10THEN140
130 S(I)=S(I)+10:GOTO180
140 S(I)=S(I)+V:GOTO180
150 PRINT@0,"SHUFFLING
          ";
160 GOSUB200
170 CD=0:C=0:GOTO20
180 'CARD NAMER
190 C$=MID$(M$,V,1):PC(I,N)=V:RETURN
200 'SHUFFLING SUBROUTINE
210 FORA=1TONC:A(A)=A:PRINT@1010,A;:NEXT
220 FORB=1TONC:X=RND(NC):Y=RND(NC):H=A(X):A(X)=A
      (Y):A(Y)=H:PRINT@1010,B;:NEXT:RETURN
230 'INITIAL TABLE SET-UP
240 CLS:PRINT"DEALING....GAME #";G;
250 FORI=1TOP
260    IFI<>YPTHEN280
270    PRINT@64+(I*64),"    YOU":GOTO290
280    PRINT@64+(I*64),"    ";I
290 NEXT
300 PRINT"  DEALER"
310 FORN=1TO2
320    FORI=1TOP
330       GOSUB20    :PRINT@71+(I*64),S(I);:PRINT@7
      6+(I*64)+(3*N),C$;:IFN=1THEN390
340       BJ(I)=0:IFS(I)<>11THEN360
350       IFPC(1,1)=10ORPC(1,2)=1THEN370    ELSE380
360       IFS(I)<>21THEN380
370       BJ(I)=1:PRINT@110+(I*64),"BLACKJACK";:S(
      I)=21:PRINT@71+(I*64),S(I);
380       BE(I)=1
390    NEXTI
400    GOSUB20    :PRINT@71+(I*64),S(I);:IFN=2THEN
      430
410    X$=C$
420    PRINT@76+(I*64)+3,CHR$(143);:GOTO440
430    PRINT@76+(I*64)+6,C$;
440 NEXTN
450 FORI=1TOP
460    POKE15360+(I*64),128:IFS(I)>21THEN610
470    N=2:NC(I)=2
480    N=N+1:POKE15360+((1+I)*64),143:PRINT@0,"PL
      AYER #";I;", YOUR TURN";
490 PRINT@896,"(S)TAND        (H)IT";
500    A$=""+INKEY$:IFA$=""THEN500
510    IFA$="S"THEN610
520    IFA$<>"H"THEN500    ELSE540
530    NC(I)=3:GOSUB20    :PRINT@76+(I*64)+(3*N),C
      $;:PRINT@71+(I*64),S(I);:DF(I)=1:GOTO600
```

Listing 15-7. Blacjkack Trainer (continued from page 335)

```
540    NC(I)=NC(I)+1:GOSUB20
550    PRINT@76+(I*64)+(3*N),C$;:PRINT@71+(I*64),
       S(I);:IFS(I)<22THEN480  ELSE600
560    PRINT@76+(I*64)+6," ";
570    X$=MID$(M$,PC(I,2),1)
580    PRINT@105+(I*64),X$;
590    BE(I)=2
600    IFS(I)>21PRINT@110+(I*64),"BUST";
610    IFNC(I)>2THEN650
620    IFPC(I,1)<>10RPC(I,2)<>1THEN650
630    S(I)=S(I)+10
640    PRINT@71+(I*64),S(I);
650 NEXTI
660 N=3
670 'DEALER'S PLAY RULES
680 POKE15360+(I*64),128:PRINT@0,"DEALER IS PLAY
       ING......";
690 GOTO710
700 PRINT@76+(I*64)+3,X$;
710 IFS(I)<22THEN730
720 GOTO850
730 IFPC(I,1)=1THEN760
740 IFPC(I,2)=1THEN770
750 GOTO800
760 IFPC(I,2)>10THEN790
770 IFPC(I,1)>10THEN790
780 N=N+1:GOTO800
790 BJ(I)=1
800 IFS(I)>17THEN850
810 IFS(I)<17THEN830
820 IFPC(I,1)<>1ANDPC(I,2)<>1THEN850
830 GOSUB20
840 PRINT@76+(I*64)+(3*N),C$;:PRINT@71+(I*64),S(
       I);:GOTO710
850 PRINT@76+(I*64)+(3*N),C$;:PRINT@71+(I*64),S(
       I);
860 D=P+1
870 PRINT:PRINT"ANOTHER GAME   (Y/N)";
880 Q$=""+INKEY$:IFQ$=""THEN880
890 IFQ$="N"THEN1140
900 PRINT:PRINT"SAME PLAYERS AND RULES?   (Y/N)";

910 Q$=""+INKEY$:IFQ$=""THEN910
920 IFQ$="N"THEN960
930 FORI=1TOP+1:BJ(I)=0:S(I)=0:NEXT
940 G=G+1
950 GOTO230
960 RUN10
970 'BASIC GAME DATA
980 PRINT"BLACKJACK TRAINER":PRINT:PRINT
990 RANDOM:PRINT"HOW MANY DECKS?   (1 TO 9)";
1000 D$=""+INKEY$:IFD$=""THEN1000
1010 D=VAL(D$):IFD<1ORD>9THEN1000
```

```
1020 NC=52*D:DIMA(NC),PC(8,12)
1030 PRINTD:PRINT"NUMBER OF PLAYERS?   (1 TO 7)";
1040 P$=""+INKEY$:IFP$=""THEN1040
1050 P=VAL(P$):IFP<1ORP>7THEN1040
1060 PRINTP:PRINT"YOUR POSITION AT TABLE?   (1 TO
       7)";
1070 YP$=""+INKEY$:IFYP$=""THEN1070
1080 YP=VAL(YP$):IFYP<1ORYP>7THEN1070
1090 SP=NC/2:PRINTYP:INPUT"RE-SHUFFLE AFTER HOW
       MANY CARDS";SP
1100 IFSP>NCTHEN1090
1110 PRINT"RE-SHUFFLE WILL OCCUR WHEN";SP;"CARDS
       HAVE BEEN DEALT":PRINT"SHUFFLING";D;"DECK(
       S), WITH A TOTAL OF";NC;"CARDS..."
1120 GOSUB200
1130 GOTO230
1140 END
```

MONOPOLY® SIMULATOR

A product of the Parker Brothers Company, Monopoly has long fascinated young and old alike. The program in Listing 15-8 lets the user simulate the play of a game with from one to five players. The program does not attempt to actually play the game, trading properties, paying penalties, and so forth, but is designed to determine which if any properties or locations seem to be visited by players more often than others. Knowing which ones are the more popular can help you shape a winning strategy.

Since the game uses two die, the most common value expected is seven. We might assume that over an extended play of the game those properties whose sequential numbers are multiples of seven would be more popular than the others. We've not run the program extensively enough to reach any definitive conclusions but maybe a reader will pick up the challenge and probe this mystery.

Listing 15-8. Monopoly Simulator

```
1  '*****************************************
2  'MONOPOLY SIMULATOR                       *
3  'LISTING 15-8                             *
4  '*****************************************
5  '
10 CLS:RANDOM
20 PRINT"MONOPOLY SIMULATOR":PRINT:PRINT
30 INPUT"ENTER NUMBER OF PLAYERS (1-5)";P
40 INPUT"ENTER NUMBER OF TURNS IN GAME";T
50 DIM A(5,T),L$(40),T(5)
60 FORI=1TO40:READ L$(I):NEXT
70 FORI=1TOP:A(I,J)=40:NEXT
80 CLS:PRINT"PLAYER","CURRENT POSITION";
90 FORI=1TOP:PRINT@64+(I*64),I;:NEXT
100 PRINT@960,"TURN #";
110 PRINT@980,"FOR PRINTED SUMMARY, TOUCH AND HO
      LD 'P'";
120 FORI=1TOT
130    Q$=INKEY$:IFQ$=""THEN160
140    IFQ$<>"P"THEN160
```

337

Listing 15-8. Monopoly Simulator (continued from page 337)

```
150    GOSUB280
160    PRINT@970,I;
170    FORJ=1TOP
180      D1=RND(6):D2=RND(6):TD=D1+D2
190      PP=A(J,I-1)+TD:IFPP>40THENPP=PP-40
200      IFPP=30THENPP=10
210    A(J,I)=PP:PRINT@80+(64*J),L$(PP)+"",
220   NEXTJ
230 NEXTI
240 END
250 DATAMEDITERRANEAN AVENUE,COMMUNITY CHEST,BAL
    TIC AVENUE,INCOME TAX,READING RAILROAD,ORIE
    NTAL AVENUE,CHANCE,VERMONT AVENUE,CONNECTIC
    UT AVENUE,JAIL,ST. CHARLES PLACE,ELECTRIC C
    OMPANY,STATES AVENUE,VIRGINIA AVENUE,PENNSY
    LVANIA RAILROAD
260 DATAST. JAMES PLACE,COMMUNITY CHEST,TENNESSE
    E AVENUE,NEW YORK AVENUE,FREE PARKING,KENTU
    CKY AVENUE,CHANCE,INDIANA AVENUE,ILLINOIS A
    VENUE,B & O RAILROAD,ATLANTIC AVENUE,VENTNO
    R AVENUE,WATER WORKS,MARVIN GARDENS,GO TO J
    AIL,PACIFIC AVENUE
270 DATANORTH CAROLINA,COMMUNITY CHEST,PENNSYLVA
    NIA AVENUE,SHORT LINE,CHANCE,PARK PLACE,LUX
    URY TAX,BOARDWALK,GO
280 LPRINT"POSITION OF PLAYERS AFTER";I-1;"TURNS
    ":LPRINT""
290 FORR=0TO2+P
300    FORC=0TO63
310      X=PEEK(15360+(R*64)+C):IFX<32THENX=X+64
320      LPRINTCHR$(X);
330    NEXT
340    LPRINT""
350 NEXT
360 LPRINT"":ST=P*(I-1)
370 LPRINT"","","","PLAYER"
380 LPRINT"POSITION","    1","    2","    3","
     4","    5","TOTAL","PER CENT"
390 FORM=1TO40
400    LPRINTLEFT$(L$(M),8),
410    FORJ=1TOP:T(J)=0:NEXT:TT=0
420    FORJ=1TOI
430      FORK=1TOP
440        IFA(K,J)<>MTHEN460
450        T(K)=T(K)+1:TT=TT+1:CT(K)=CT(K)+1
460      NEXTK
470    NEXTJ
480    LPRINTT(1),T(2),T(3),T(4),T(5),TT,100*(TT/
    ST)
490 NEXT
500 LPRINT"TOTAL",CT(1),CT(2),CT(3),CT(4),CT(5),
    ST
510 LPRINT""
520 RETURN
```

RANDOM NUMBER GENERATION

Central to all of the foregoing programs in this chapter and to many simulations is the concept of a random number. We use random numbers to simulate the action of a game such as Monopoly, just as we use random numbers to help us know where in a neighborhood to conduct a survey. Random numbers are the key to modern cipher systems used to encrypt confidential commercial and classified military communications. This last concept leads us to the first characterization of random numbers.

We frequently refer to random numbers when we really are talking about *pseudo-random* numbers. Pseudo-random numbers, when viewed on a list, appear to have occurred in a random fashion. The truth is that the numbers actually appear in a very rational order. Usually, these numbers are generated by an algorithm, often keyed by the user with a *seed number*. One such algorithm is expressed in the equation:

$$R_{T+1} = (\pi + SN_T)^S - \text{integer part } (\pi + SN_T)^S$$

$$SN_{T+1} = R_{T+1}$$

So long as we use the same value for the first value of SN, we will always generate the same series of pseudo-random numbers. This is useful in simulations in which you want to repeat identical conditions for two or more test subjects, or in encrypted communications systems.

The other aspect of random numbers is the true (or apparently true) random number; that sequence of numbers that appear at random and cannot be forced into a repetition. We use these numbers in simulations where repeating the sequence would be meaningless. For example, we need a truly random sequence of numbers to effectively analyze the craps dice game and similar functions. In these applications we depend on the numbers being uniformly distributed throughout the allowable range. For example, in evaluating a dice routine, we want to be sure each of the faces appear in approximately equal frequencies. A bias for one number or another is most undesirable.

In queuing simulations, on the other hand, we want both the element of random events (customer arrival times), and a nonuniform distribution. Humans seldom behave uniformly. Rather, they tend to arrive at retail establishments not at discrete and even intervals, but in clumps and clusters as a function of some other factor. For example, the workload in fast food restaurants clusters around traditional meal hours. The bulk of the people arrive at peak periods. After each peak the number present gradually tapers off. The standard form of this distribution is known as the Poison Distribution, and is given by the following equation:

$$Y = \frac{\lambda^x e^{-\lambda}}{X!}$$

where λ is the mean of the distribution and e = 2.71828

The variance is equal to the mean and consequently, the standard deviation (although not commonly used in this distribution) is the square root of the variance (mean). As the mean grows larger, the distribution approaches the form of the normal distribution, which is the most common distribution. Applications of it are found throughout the whole of mathematics and industry and examples of it are shown in various other sections of this book.

It is useful to be able to compute random numbers that occur in nonuniform distributions. For example, in simulating the arrival of customers in a bank, we much prefer to use a Poisson Distribution over a uniform distribution. In other simulations, we prefer the normal distribution of random numbers over anything else.

EXERCISES:

1. Table 15-1 summarizes the results of one run of the Universal Game Machine for the odds of winning from 0.05 to 0.50 in increments of 0.05. At each level, there were 1000 iterations. Repeat the experiment, but use smaller and larger numbers of iterations. What effect does this figure have on the number of losses in a row at p = 0.05? At p = 0.45?

2. From the data obtained in exercise number

1, use a curve fitting routine to compute the coefficients of the exponential form: $Y = A\ 2.71828^{Bp}$.

3. Identify a commercial or governmentally-sponsored game such as the soda pop simulation, or a state-operated lottery, preferably a recently started game. Write a program to simulate the play of the game.

Contrast your findings with the advertised outcome.

SUGGESTED READING

McFadden, J. A., 1971. *Physical Concepts of Probability*. New York: Van Nostrand Reinhold Company.

Draper, N. R. and W. E. Lawrence, 1970. *Probability: An Introductory Course.*

Chapter 16

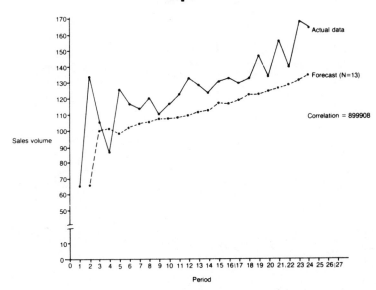

Miscellaneous Forecasting

In the course of our daily work and in researching materials for this book, we were able to organize the materials into the chapters you have read. There were, however, some materials that we desired to include in the book for which there was no obvious placement, other than in a chapter for miscellaneous routines. What follows are some of those routines.

FORECASTING PROJECT COMPLETION DATES USING PERT

Program evaluation and review technique (PERT) is a system designed to display and monitor the step-by-step progress of projects. While the comprehensive explanation of PERT is beyond the scope of this book, it is possible to use the microcomputer to aid in the evaluation of a project by someone who does understand PERT and uses the program outlined below.

There have been developed a number of approaches to illustrating a project in a PERT format over the last twenty to thirty years—each approach

suiting the particular purposes of the designer. Figure 16-1 illustrates one of these approaches.

Note that from the starting point, normally at the top or the left of the chart, the project growth is shown with related activities connected by a line. Along each path is a symbol indicating the duration of the first task. This value, D_i, is normally the mean time to complete such tasks. Where appropriate, we may compute and use the standard deviations of these durations and use them to compute the total time variations in our estimates. At each event point, the symbols used may vary in shape, but will convey at least three items of information: the event number, the earliest possible time the event can begin, and the last allowable time for completion. Within this context, three rules apply:

1. The first event in a project begins at time zero, $E_1 = 0$.
2. Each event is assumed to begin as soon as possible; that is, as soon as all preceding events are completed.
3. The "early finish" time (EF) of an event is

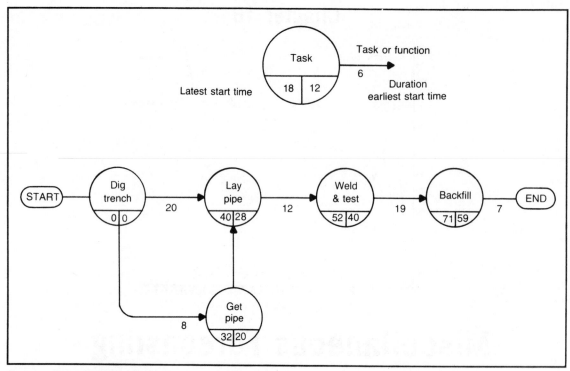

Fig. 16-1. Basic PERT event chart.

the sum of its "early start" (ES) time and the duration of the event: $EF_i = ES_i = D_i$.

Projects normally carry a specified completion date or time, T_s. Therefore, the latest allowable finish time for the very last event within the project is equal to the completion time; $LF_j = T_s$. The latest allowable start time for an event, LS_i, is the latest allowable finish time less the duration of the task: $LS_k = LF_k - D_k$. Finally, the latest allowable finishing time for any arbitrary event is the latest allowable starting time of the succeeding event: $LF_j = LS_{j+1}$. If two or more events follow and are dependent upon event j, LF_j is equal to the earliest of the LS_i values of the succeeding events.

With few exceptions, T_s must always be equal to or greater than E_t, the time required to complete each of the sequential tasks of the projects. For example, if it takes at least 18 hours for a fast drying concrete used in a highway to set up to a degree at which a vehicle can be supported, and a path of

concrete can be poured at the rate of 50 linear feet an hour (at a given width and depth), and the contract calls for the pouring of ten miles of highway, then the project completion date must be 44 days and 18 hours beyond the exact starting date and time of the project. (More precisely, the time is 44 days and 18 hours, less 10/speed limit, assuming a car were to start down the highway at such a time that it would reach the end at exactly 44 days and 18 hours.) It would be foolish for a small contractor, owning only enough equipment to handle one section of roadway at a time, to accept the contract if it called for completion time anything less than the 44.75 days. On the other hand, if the contract calls for completion within 60 days, a bid is clearly in order. The difference between the scheduled completion date and the minimum possible time, E_t, is called *slack*. In a similar fashion, the difference between the earliest and latest start or finish times for any given event is the slack for that interval, $S_i = LS_i - ES_i$ or $LF_i = EF_i$.

Critical Path Method (CPM)

The CPM of evaluating a project was developed independently of PERT, but it used so many similar features that it was soon absorbed by PERT technicians as a subset of the PERT technique. Given a diagram of a project with its various start and finish times, the critical path is that route through the project which permits the least slack. Figure 16-2 is the same as the preceding figure, except that the heavy line highlights the critical path. There may be two or more critical paths through a project where the total slack in each route is equal to that in the other. No task can be considered critical unless it lies along a critical path.

Event Matrix

The user of these routines may, of course, use any of the available conventions in diagramming the project, so long as each event is assigned a sequential event number. The forecasting program asks the user to specify whether there is a relationship between each of the event pairs and, if so, the duration of the task to completion of the sequence. For N events, there is a maximum of $(N(N - 1))/2$ possible positive combinations. For example, in a project consisting of ten events, there is a total of $(10(10 - 1))/2 = 90/2 = 45$ pair combinations to

be considered. Of these, there must be at least N − 1 pair combinations defined. In the example, there are a minimum of nine pair combinations defined. Since the program asks the user to respond either N (no relationship) or Y (positive relationship) and the duration is at least one integer value, the minimum number of keystrokes to enter the initial data is $2(N - 1)$. If M is the number of digits in the largest durations, including the stroke for a decimal point, the maximum number of keystrokes necessary to enter all of the data will be less than

$$(M + 1)\frac{N(N - 1)}{2}$$

Using $N = 10$ and $M = 4$, the number of keystrokes required to define each of the relationships will range from 18 to 225.

Our concern with keystrokes and data entry is based on the notion that many of the projects suitable for computer evaluation will consist of a number of tasks significantly greater than ten or so. If the number of related events is small, relative to the total possible, it may be better for the user to define which pairs are related by typing in the matrix coordinates and entering the duration directly, instead of answering Y/N to each of the possible combinations. The program asks the user to enter the total number of related events, K, and the length of the largest duration and computes

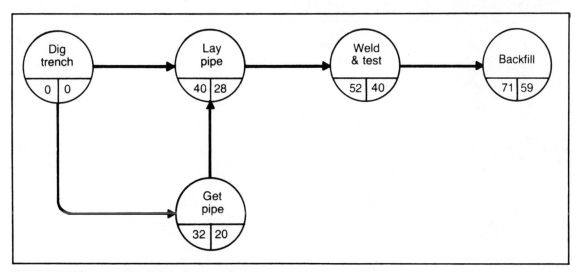

Fig. 16-2. PERT chart with critical path (heavy line).

343

whether it would be advantageous to use this entry scheme in lieu of examining the whole matrix.

Once the duration data are entered, the computer takes over the task of evaluating the earliest and latest start and finishing values for each task, identifying critical jobs in the process. Given a starting date and a decision as to whether or not work continues during weekends, the program gives an estimate of the estimated completion date: Completion = Start + E_t + Days Not Worked (weekends, etc.), and the total number of days involved. To be prudent, a bid on a project should not be made unless this completion date (or the total number of days) is earlier than (or less than) that called for in the contract. The difference between the completion date and the contract date is the amount of *free slack* in the project. It gives an indication of the total amount of time, the project may vary from the schedule without management actions required to complete the project on time.

The critical path is not computed, although the critical tasks are identified as part of the output. You can easily identify the critical path by connecting critical jobs with a heavy line or with color. (A routine to identify the critical path can be developed as a special case of a program to solve the traditional "Traveling Salesman" problem wherein the task is to specify the shortest route the salesman can take to reach a list of cities.) Listing 16-1 implements the foregoing discussion on PERT.

Listing 16-1. Forecasting with PERT

```
1   '*****************************************************
2   'FORECASTING WITH PERT                              *
3   'LISTING 16-1                                       *
4   '*****************************************************
5   '
10  CLS:CLEAR2000:PRINT"PERT EVALUATOR":PRINT:PRI
    NT
20  INPUT"WHAT IS THE NAME OF THE PROJECT";N$
30  PRINT:PRINT"HOW MANY EVENTS ARE REQUIRED TO C
    OMPLETE ";N$;:INPUTN
40  PC=(N*(N-1))/2:DIM E$(N),E(N,N),D(N),ES(N),EF
    (N),LS(N),LF(N),S(N)
50  PRINT:PRINT"THERE IS A TOTAL OF";PC;"POSSIBLE
        COMBINATIONS OF EVENTS.
    ";:INPUT"HOW MANY EVENT CONNECTIONS ARE THERE";K

60  PRINT:Z$="N":IFPC<(2*K)THEN100
70  PRINT:PRINT"YOU WILL SAVE TIME BY DEFINING AC
    TUAL RELATIONSHIPS.  IS THIS    OPTION DESIR
    ED?  (Y/N)";
80  Z$=""+INKEY$:IFZ$=""THEN80
90  PRINT:PRINT
100 FORI=1TON
110     PRINT"NAME OF EVENT #"I,:INPUTE$(I)
120 NEXTI
130 IFZ$="N"THEN150
140 GOSUB530  :GOTO230
150 FORI=1TON-1
160    FORJ=I+1TON
170      PRINT:PRINT"IS EVENT #";I;", ";E$(I);",
CONNECTED TO EVENT #";J;", ";E$(J),
180      Q$=""+INKEY$:IFQ$=""THEN180
190      PRINTQ$:IFQ$="Y"THENE(I,J)=1ELSEE(I,J)=-
    1
200    NEXTJ
210 NEXTI
```

```
220 ES(1)=0
230 FORI=1TON
240     PRINT"WHAT IS THE MEAN TIME TO COMPLETE
    ";E$(I);::INPUTMT:D(I)=MT/8:TD=TD+D(I)
250     EX=0:IFI=1THEN310
260     FORJ=1TOI-1
270       IFE(I,J)=-1THEN300
280       IFEF(J)<EXTHEN300
290       EX=EF(J)
300     NEXTJ
310     ES(I)=EX:EF(I)=ES(I)+D(I)
320 NEXTI
330 PRINT:INPUT"HOW MANY DAYS ARE ALLOWED TO COM
    PETE THE PROJECT";TS
340 LF(N)=TS:LS(N)=TS-D(N)
350 FORI=N-1TO1STEP-1
360     EX=N:LG=LS(N):IFI=NTHEN420
370     FORJ=I+1TON
380       IFE(I,J)=-1THEN410
390       IFLG<LS(J)THEN410
400       EX=J:LG=LS(J)
410     NEXTJ
420     LF(I)=LS(EX):LS(I)=LF(I)-D(I):S(I)=LS(I)-E
    S(I):TT=TT+S(I)
430 NEXTI
440 LPRINT"":LPRINT"PROJECT: ";N$:LPRINT""
450 LPRINT"","",""            EARLIEST
                LATEST"
460 LPRINT"EVENT NAME","DURATION","START","FINIS
    H","START","FINISH","SLACK"
470 FORI=1TON
480     LPRINTE$(I),D(I),ES(I),EF(I),LS(I),LF(I),S
    (I),
490     IFS(I)=0THENLPRINT"CRITICAL EVENT (?)"ELSE
    LPRINT""
500 NEXTI
510 LPRINT"":LPRINT"TOTAL SLACK = ";TS-TD
520 END
530 FORI=1TOK
540     INPUT"ENTER FIRST EVENT NUMBER";E1
550     INPUT"ENTER SECOND EVENT NUMBER";E2
560     PRINT:E(E1,E2)=1
570 NEXT
580 FORI=1TON-1
```

Influence of Statistical Variation

So far, we have assumed that each task in a project will take a certain length of time to complete. We have called this the duration of the task. In reality, this value is the mean time computed or deduced from prior experience in similar situations. This implies, however, some variation in the actual timing of the project. Computed from a simple mean duration, we may make an estimate of a completion date that is a day or two within the contract date, and yet, because of the implicit variation, we may not be able to complete the project on schedule. Expanding the preceding program to include consideration of these potential variations reduces the risk of such an error. In a project involving an automated production line, the variations may not

345

be very significant (depending on the mechanical reliability of the line), whereas projects involving creativity and human-intensive effort may call for considerably wider tolerances.

FORECASTING DELIVERY DATES

There are a number of businesses which involve the sale of products by telephone. as part of the transaction, the seller (in theory) informs the buyer when to expect receipt of the product. Federal law requires shipment of such items within a certain period of time unless the seller specifically cites a longer period. When asked when to expect an item, the seller will frequently just add three to six weeks to the current date. The program below is a simple routine that a more conscientious business can use to generate a rational and reasonable delivery date. We base the program on the assumed transaction flow in Fig. 16-3.

Order Received. The time to deliver a product begins with the completion of the sale or the receipt of the order. Ordinarily, the buyer understands that the product can not be shipped until sometime after the order is placed. In systems which use a recording device to take orders, an additional delay may be encountered.

Processing. Most businesses will require the generation of several documents to properly record the sale, arrange for payment, and affect the shipping of the package. The time before delivery is not necessarily the sum of these actions, but simply the sum of those actions that must be performed sequentially and that lead to the creation of an instruction to prepare the product for shipment.

Production. This phase begins when the actual fabrication of the product is triggered by receipt of an actual purchase order. The actual start of production may be held up pending approval from the accounting and credit division. If the production activity is physically removed from the shipping center, there may be additional packing and shipping process time involved, as well. On the other hand, if shipments are made from existing stock, production time should not be entered into the computation of delivery date.

Packaging. The time required to pack a product for shipment is included in the processing time only if packing takes place upon or after receipt of a shipping order. If packages are prewrapped, the only time involved in this step is that required to generate and apply a shipping label.

Accounting/Credit Approval. Upon receipt of cash or payment by an approved credit card, a COD agreement shipment of the product should begin promptly. Credit approval is an option, depending on whether or not the business accepts other forms of payment (personal checks) and delays shipment pending bank payment of the check, or otherwise delays shipment pending a credit evaluation and approval.

Shipping Authorization. Some businesses, especially those using the step just above, inject an authorization phase into the shipping process.

Providing the customer with an accurate estimated delivery date is frequently a courtesy extended by the seller in the interests of good customer relations. So long as the estimated delivery date is beyond the actual and normal delivery dates, however, no law exists requiring it be any more accurate.

Listing 16-2. Forecasting Shipping Dates

```
1  ´*******************************************
2  ´FORECASTING SHIPPING DATES            *
3  ´LISTING 16-2                          *
4  ´*******************************************
5  ´
10 CLS:CLEAR250:DIM P$(100),SA$(1000),PR(100),CL
   (1000),PT(100),PK(100)
20 ´IN THIS SECTION BUILD A DATA INPUT ROUTINE T
   O LOAD IN P$() (PART NAMES), CL() (CUSTOMER
     CREDIT LIMITS), SA$() (STATUS OF ACCOUNTS)
       PR() (PRODUCT PRICES), PT() (PRODUCTION T
```

```
          IME), PK() (SHIPPING TIME)
30 GOTO60
40 Q$=""+INKEY$:IFQ$=""THEN40
50 PRINTQ$:RETURN
60 PRINT:PRINT"TYPE '@' TO PLACE AN ORDER",
70 GOSUB40
80 IFQ$<>"@"THEN70
90 INPUT"NAME";N$
100 INPUT"ACCOUNT NUMBER";A
110 INPUT"STREET";S$
120 INPUT"CITY";C$
130 INPUT"STATE";ST$
140 INPUT"ZIP CODE";Z$
150 INPUT"TELEPHONE #";T$
160 INPUT"PRODUCT NUMBER";PN
170 INPUT"PRODUCT NAME";PN$
180 IFPN$=P$(PN)THEN200
190 PRINT"PRODUCT NAME DOES NOT MATCH NUMBER":GO
      TO160
200 INPUT"NUMBER OF UNITS DESIRED";N
210 BD=PR(PN):PRINT"WILL THIS BE A CASH/C.O.D. S
      ALE?  (Y/N)",:GOSUB40
220 IFQ$="Y"THEN330
230 IFAS$(A)="CURRENT"THEN280
240 IFAS$(A)="OPEN"THEN270
250 PRINT"ACCOUNT NOT ESTABLISHED.  ADVISE CUSTO
      MER CREDIT APPLICATION    WILL BE MAILED."
260 LPRINT"":LPRINT"ACCOUNT MEMO:":LPRINT"MAIL C
      REDIT APPLICATION TO:":LPRINT"",N$:LPRINT""
      ,S$:LPRINT"",C$;"  ";ST$,Z$:LPRINT"":GOTO210

270 PRINT"ACCOUNT IS OPEN, BUT NOT CURRENT":GOTO
      210
280 PR(PN)<=CL(A)THEN310
290 PRINT"CREDIT LIMIT LESS THAN PRICE BY $";PR(
      PN)-CL(A):PRINT"OPTIONS:     1 -- CHARGE
      TO LIMIT, PAY CASH ON BALANCE
                 2 --  PAY CASH
                 3 --  NO ACTION",:GOSUB40
300 ONVAL(Q$)GOTO320  ,330  ,310
310 RUN60
320 BD=PR(PN)-CL(A):CL(A)=0:GOTO330
330 PRINT"THE BALANCE DUE IS $";BD:PRINT"","1  --
      - CASH (CERTIFIED CHECK)
2  --  CHECK
3  --  C.O.D.",:GOSUB40
340 ONVAL(Q$)GOTO350  ,360  ,370
350 CT=7:PRINTP$(PN);" WILL BE SHIPPED UPON RECI
      EPT OF FUNDS.":GOTO370
360 CT=21:PRINT"PLEASE ALLOW 14 DAYS FOR CHECK P
      ROCESSING AND CLEARANCE.":GOTO370
370 SD=PT(PN)+CT+PK(PN)
380 PRINTPN$;" WILL BE SHIPPED IN ABOUT";SD;"DAY
      S.  ALLOW 7-10 DAYS FOR POSTAL HANDLING":
390 LPRINT"":LPRINT"TRANSACTION MEMO"
400 LPRINT"SHIP";N;P$(PN);", PART NUMBER";PN;"TO
      :":LPRINT""
```

Listing 16-2. Forecasting Shipping Dates (continued from page 347)

```
410 LPRINTN$:LPRINTS$:LPRINTC$;" ";ST$,Z$:LPRINT
    ""
420 RUN60
```

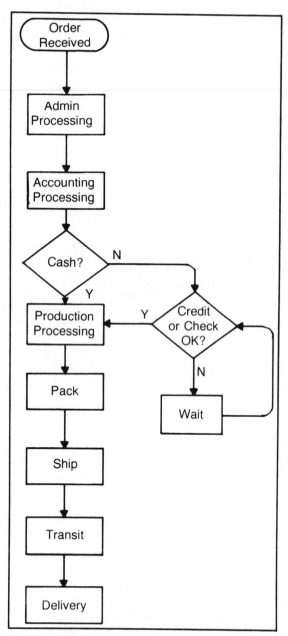

Fig. 16-3. Shipping date flowchart.

ESTIMATING VACATION COSTS

Every now and then the urge hits us to take some time off from work and take a vacation. The essential factors that influence the cost of the vacation include: how far you are going, how many people will be traveling, how many days will the vacation last, and what will the costs for fuel, repairs, lodging and food be.

The program in Listing 16-3 helps the would-be traveller forecast the costs likely to result from a specified trip.

EXERCISES

1. The PERT program in Listing 16-1 is a simple program based on the assumption that only one person would be available to perform the tasks of a given project. Write the program to allow for concurrent processing. That is, let the program account for sub-tasks which can be performed together, and not necessarily consecutively.
2. Modify the Delivery Date routine in Listing 16-2 so that the various outputs are directed to the appropriate devices. That is, enable the program to write shipping labels, invoices, credit memos, and so forth.
3. The program in Listing 16-3 is for a vacation using an automobile. Modify the program for travel by land, sea, or air modes.

SUGGESTED READING

Martino, R. L., 1964. *Project Management and Control, Volume I: Finding the Critical Path*. New York: American Management Association.

Stires, D. M. and R. P. Wenig, 1965. *Concept-Principles-Application: PERT/COST for the New DOD and NASA Requirements*. Boston: Industrial Education Institute.

Listing 16-3. Trip Costs

```
1  '*******************************************
2  'TRIP COSTS                                *
3  'LISTING 16-3                              *
4  '*******************************************
5  '
10 CLS:PRINT"VACATION COST PLANNING":PRINT:PRINT

20 INPUT"WHAT IS THE NAME OF YOUR DESTINATION";D
   $
30 PRINT"HOW MANY MILES FROM YOUR HOME IS ";D$;:
   INPUTMD
40 INPUT"WHAT IS YOUR AVERAGE HIGHWAY DRIVING SP
   EED";AS
50 INPUT"HOW MANY HOURS DO YOU DRIVE IN ONE DAY"
   ;HD
60 INPUT"HOW MANY PEOPLE WILL BE TRAVELING";NT
70 DT=(2*MD)/(HD*AS):PRINT"IT WILL TAKE APPROXIM
   ATELY";DT;"DAYS
TO TRAVEL TO ";D$;" AND RETURN":INPUT"HOW MANY D
   AYS DO YOU PLAN TO STAY THERE";DS
80 TD=DT+DS:INPUT"WHAT IS THE AVERAGE MOTEL COST
    YOU NORMALLY PAY";AM
90 IF(DT-1)<=0THEN110
100 NM=DT-1:PRINT"YOUR TRAVEL TIME INCLUDES AT L
    EAST";NM;"OVERNIGHT STOPS.
WILL YOU STAY IN MOTELS BOTH NIGHTS?  (Y/N)   "
110 Q$=""+INKEY$:IFQ$=""THEN110   ELSEIFQ$="Y"THE
    N130
120 INPUT"NUMBER OF NIGHTS IN MOTELS DURING TRIP
    ";NM
130 PRINT"HOW MANY NIGHTS WILL YOU SPEND IN A MO
    TEL AT ";D$,:INPUTX:NM=NM+X
140 MC=NM*AM:PRINT"MOTEL COST = $ ";MC:INPUT"WHA
    T DO YOU ESTIMATE TO BE THE AVERAGE
COST PER PERSON FOR FOOD";FC:TF=FC*NT*TD:PRINT"F
    OOD COST = $ ";TF
150 INPUT"WHAT WHAT IS THE MINIMUM NUMBER OF
MILES PER GALLON YOUR CAR GETS";MM
160 INPUT"WHAT IS THE BEST MILEAGE YOU CAN HOPE
    FOR";XM
170 INPUT"WHAT IS THE CHEAPEST PER GALLON PRICE
    FOR GAS";CP
180 INPUT"WHAT IS THE WORST PRICE FOR GAS";WP
190 G1=CP*((2*MD)/XM):G2=WP*((2*MD)/MM)
200 PRINT"YOUR FUEL COST WILL BE SOMEWHERE BETWE
    EN $";G1;"AND $";G2
210 PRINT:PRINT"THE TOTAL COST OF YOUR TRIP
WILL BE FROM $";G1+TF+MC;"TO $";G2+TF+MC
220 END
```

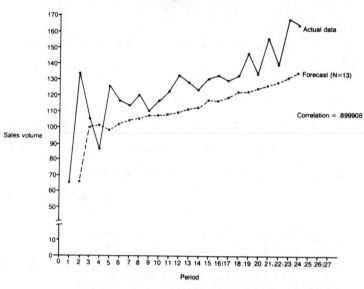

Chapter 17

Data Displays

The finest piece of forecasting is of little use if the results cannot be communicated to the user of the information. Whether the user is the forecaster, a supervisor, a work associate, or a paying customer, the relevant data must be displayed in a clear and persuasive manner. Ideally, the user should be able to come to the same conclusions that the forecaster has reached from an appropriate display of the data.

Data may be displayed in one of two formats: tabular and graphic. In tabular presentations, the data are placed into some sort of arrangement or table in their numeric form. In graphic representation, the data are converted into lines, curves, symbols, or divided into pie charts and so forth. Which form to be used is a function of the objective to be served by the display. The main function of tabular formats is to provide a source of precise and actual data for reference purposes and for the construction of special purpose tables and charts or graphics. On the other hand, graphic displays are generally used to convey a sense of relationships, relative quantities, or trends. There are some standard consid-

erations in the development of both tables and graphics.

TABLE CONSTRUCTION

There are both general and special-purpose tables. In general purpose tables, the data should be precisely stated. That is, to the extent that it is practical, the data should not be rounded off or converted to percentages. The data should be presented in such a way as to facilitate its use as a research device. In special purpose tables, the data may be manipulated and modified (converted to percentages or rounded off) so that specific relationships are highlighted.

In the construction of tables, certain conventions are generally observed. Among these are inclusion the title and source, the arrangement of data, the use of rows and columns, the presentation of totals and means, and the units of measurement.

Title. All tables should have a title or caption. The title should be as brief as possible, yet clearly tell what the table contains. It must indicate the nature of the data being displayed. If the data are time-dependent (e.g., 1980 Election Results), the title should include the time domain involved. If the data are from a particular geographic region, the title should include that as well; for example, 1980 New York City Mayoral Election Results.

Source. Except for originally generated data, the table should include a note concerning the source of the data. This serves to give the table authenticity, permits the reader to independently verify the data, and serves as a guide to additional data. In researching data, be careful to observe whether the actual data are copyrighted. Weather reports, for example, are frequently copyrighted by the newspaper in which they are published; yet the actual data are not copyrighted.

Arrangement of Data. There are a number of ways data may be displayed in a table. We may arrange data in alphabetic order, numerical order, chronological order, or according to geographic location, or some other convention. Again, the selection of the particular arrangement is a function of the purpose of the table.

Rows and Columns. Where there are two or more rows or columns, they should be identified by labels, numbers, or letters. Both columns and rows should have captions or labels identifying the nature of the data in the respective row or column.

Totals and Means. Column totals are normally shown at the bottom of the respective columns, while row totals are normally shown at the far right. If appropriate, the total may be divided by the number of items to compute and display the means. In those tables designed to contrast individual values with the table column or row totals, the total may be placed at the top of the column or, in an ordered listing at the point where the total relates to the components.

Units of Measurement. It is essential to include on the table the units in which the data will appear. The scale of the units should be appropriate to the display, using conventional units of measurement.

GRAPHICS CONSTRUCTION

To the extent they are appropriate, the rules given, particularly those concerning the title, source, and units of measurement, above also apply to graphics. In addition, line or bar graphs (those charts using X and Y axis formats) must indicate the relevant zero point. For example, in a chart showing the price of gold over the last one hundred years, the horizontal axis may begin with the first year of the data set without showing the year 0, but the vertical scale, the price of gold, must show the zero point. In those cases in which the actual data tend to cluster about a fairly high point above zero, it is allowable to break the vertical axis to indicate the truncation of the chart.

The second consideration in this type of chart is whether to use linear or logarithmic scale intervals. When the data range across several orders of magnitude (powers of ten) it may be convenient, if not absolutely necessary, to use a logarithmic scale. Logarithmic scales are also useful in displaying data that vary exponentially because lines that are normally curved on a linear scale tend to become straight lines on a logarithmic scale. The use of this phenomenon requires a sense of responsibility on the graphic designer, however, misuse of either the linear scale or the logarithmic can distort the true meaning or significance of the data.

Pie Chart

Another form frequently used is a pie chart or area chart in which the components of the total sum are illustrated as section of a geometric shape. The program in Listing 17-1 is a simple routine to build a pie chart from a set of data.

Listing 17-1. Pie Chart

```
1  '********************************************
2  'PIE CHART                                 *
3  'LISTING 17-1                              *
4  '********************************************
5  '
```

Listing 17-1. Pie Chart (continued from page 351)

```
10 CLS
20 PRINT"PIE CHART GENERATOR":PRINT:PRINT
30 INPUT"HOW MANY COMPONENTS ARE THERE TO THE CH
   ART (N <= 26)";N:IFN<27THEN50
40 PRINT"SORRY, N MUST BE <= 27":PRINT:GOTO30

50 DIM P(N)
60 FORI=1TON
70    PRINT"ENTER THE AMOUNT OF PORTION #";I,:INP
   UT P(I):T=T+P(I)
80 NEXT
90 CLS:PRINT"THANK YOU":PRINT
100 FORI=1TON:PRINTI;P(I),:NEXT:PRINT
110 PRINT"TOTAL = ";T,"",
120 PRINT"ARE THESE ALL CORRECT?   (Y/N)";
130 Q$=""+INKEY$:IFQ$=""THEN130
140 IFQ$="Y"THEN160
150 PRINT:PRINT:INPUT"ENTER ITEM NUMBER AND CORR
   ECT VALUE";X,Y:T=T-P(X):P(X)=Y:T=T+Y:GOTO090

160 CLS
170 FOR TH=0TO6.2832STEP.03
180    X=(45*COS(TH))+64:Y=((45*SIN(TH))*.4375)+2
   4
190    SET(X,Y)
200 NEXT
210 FORX=64TO109:SET(X,24):NEXT
220 A=0:L=65
230 FORI=1TON
240    TH=((P(I)/T)*6.283184)+A
250    X=(45*COS(TH))+64:Y=((45*SIN(TH))*.4375)+2
   4
260    S=(Y-24)/ABS(X-64):B=SGN(X-64)*1:X1=64:Y1=
   24
270    FORJ=1TOABS(X-64)
280      SET(X1,Y1):X1=X1+B:Y1=Y1+S
290    NEXTJ
300    F=(((P(I)/T)*6.283814)/2)+A
310    X=(22.5*COS(F))+64:Y=((22.5*SIN(F))*.4375)
   +24
320    LN=(INT(Y/3)*64)+(X/2):PRINT@LN,CHR$(L);:L
   =L+1
330    A=TH
340 NEXT
350 PRINT@0,"(P)RINTER     (N)EW DATA";
360 Q$=""+INKEY$:IFQ$=""THEN360
370 PRINTQ$;:IFQ$="P"THEN390
380 RUN
390 FORR=3TO44
400    FORC=0TO127
410      IFPOINT(C,R)THENLPRINT"*";ELSELPRINT" ";

420    NEXTC
430    LPRINT""
440 NEXTR
```

```
450 LPRINT"SEGMENT","VALUE","FRACTION OF WHOLE"
460 FORI=1TON
470   LPRINTCHR$(I+64),P(I),P(I)/T
480 NEXT
490 LPRINT""
500 RUN
```

EXERCISES

1. Review a copy of the *Statistical Abstract of the United States*. (If it is not in your library, it is for sale through the Government Printing Office, Washington, D.C.) Note the number of tables and charts that conform to the rules in this chapter. Note the number that don't. What reason would the chart designer have for deviating from the basic guides?

2. In the same book, note the tables on population estimates. One principle in table construction is that the intervals remain constant. What advantage or purpose does the table designer achieve by using several different intervals?

3. Using the data in the population forecasts of the *Abstract*, write a table showing the population forecast for the year 2000 in age group intervals of exactly five years each.

SUGGESTED READING

Enrick, N. L., 1972. *Effective Graphic Communication*. Princeton, NJ: Auerbach.

Hall, A. S., 1958. *The Construction of Graphs and Charts*. London: Pitman.

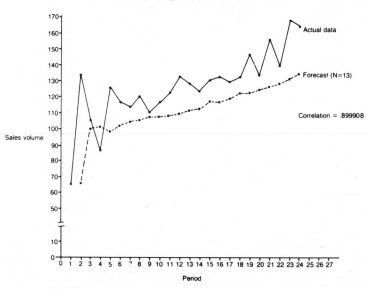

Chapter 18

Decision-Making Based on Forecasts

We've come full circle. We began this book on the premises that forecasting is as much an art as a science and that the reader was equipped with a microcomputer and ambition. We shared some of our philosophy concerning prognostication, and then led the reader through the underlying fundamentals of computer data base management and the essential mathematical procedures and relationships. Then, we wandered our way through eight chapters of specialized forecasting techniques. Now, nearly several hundred pages and ninety programs later, we've come to mankind's greatest question: What's it all about? Having developed the means to do forecasting, what do we do with the skill?

The first answer is that we share our forecasts with others. A lot of people make a nice living collecting data, chomping it up in a forecasting routine, and then selling the results to their customers. Many of these are doing market research or political surveys. The costs of running a political campaign being what they are, an interesting activ-

ity for many of you would be to approach a local politician and offer your research skills for the next campaign. Design a survey and collect the data. Process it and deliver the product to the client. You might want to offer your first effort gratis or for expenses. If you find the experience rewarding and successful, go ahead; do it again. The better and more confident you become, the more you should charge. But that's not decision-making. The decision-making is that done by your client.

Your client should know that all forecasts are characterized by two realities:

—No forecast is a mandate for the future.
—All forecasts contain a margin of error.

Because of these realities, good forecasts should make note of the margin of error to be expected and include encouragement to accept that margin as a reality. If the client is unable to accept the margin of error, the alternative is to make a decision based on some other criterion. Sometimes this is smart and necessary, sometimes it isn't. The political candidate whose conscientious researcher has, over the period of the campaign, selected reliable samples, performed an appropriate set of analysis routines, and come to the conclusion that the candidate will not pull in twenty percent of the vote, should be listened to. On the other hand, we can push the stock market data for a whole year through our computer and conclude that the market will hit a daily average of 1100 for the next week. Nonetheless, a seasoned market analysis, while agreeing with out mathematics, may conclude that the market will plunge to 800 or below next week. Such decisions are often based on a multitude of factors which affect the stock market that are very difficult to process in a computer. Even sophisticated stock market simulation routines frequently fail to include all of the relevant factors.

Well, what good are they, then? Forecasts provide data or estimates of data where the data are not otherwise available. They help us interpolate between the known and unknown. If we have some other, firm basis for "knowing" what the future will be, forecasting is an inappropriate use of time. If, for example, we are present when the Federal Reserve Board decides to drop (or raise) the interest rate five percent, we don't need a forecast based on open market data to know what the market will do after the Board decision is announced. Few of us, however, are blessed with such access.

This book was not written to provide answers to those whose personal or professional background and experiences better equip them to gauge future events than someone simply manipulating available data. Instead, it was written to aid the individual who has come to the point where intuition and professional judgment are leading to unsatisfactory conclusions—except for the conclusion that some other approach, such as microcomputer forecasting might provide better answers.

The balance of this chapter attempts to provide some techniques one can use to evaluate forecast data and use the microcomputer to reach rational decisions. We concern ourselves, first, with the measurement of error, and then turn our attention to four approaches to decision-making.

MEASUREMENT OF ERROR

Standard error is a useful technique in estimating the extent to which reality might deviate from our prediction. For example, during the 1982 elections, one of the national television broadcasting networks announced that their prediction indicated that 34 of the Democratic candidates for Congress would win seats in the House. In the same breath, they admitted that there was a standard estimate of error of plus or minus 9. As of the writing of this chapter, the actual result were 26 seats won by Democrats, an error of 8. Reasonably well within the computed standard error. Also keep in mind that the standard error, like the standard deviation, is not the whole spectrum but merely a fraction of it. The example above means that there is slightly better than a 68 percent chance that the outcome would be a certain value, plus or minus 9. It also means there is a 98 percent chance the outcome will be the mean value, plus or minus 18!

Some of the primary estimates of error include those for the sum, mean, median, standard deviation, and coefficient of correlation.

Standard Error of a Sum

The standard error for a sum is particularly useful for large sets of numbers that have been added by hand. If n quantities are selected at random from an infinite population and added up, we compute the sum and the standard deviation. From these statistics we can conclude that the sum (T) of any n items from the same data base will be equal to the computed sum plus or minus the standard error. The equation to compute this value is

$$s = \sigma \sqrt{n}$$

Standard Error of a Mean

In addition to computing a sum and the standard deviation of a set of numbers, we can also compute the mean of the set from $M = T / n$. The standard error of this mean can be computed from

$$s = \sigma / \sqrt{n}$$

Standard Error of a Median

We first encountered the median of a distribution in Chapter 2. In normal distributions, the mean and median are expected to be the same value. However, as the distributed becomes more and more skewed to one direction or another, the mean value will shift significantly away from the median. Nonetheless, the computation of the standard error of a median is quite simple: compute the standard error of the mean as shown above, and then multiply that value by 1.2533:

$$1.2533 \ (\sigma/\sqrt{n})$$

Standard Error of a Standard Deviation

More often than not, our statistical work involves sampling from a large population. We know that if we could interview or examine every member of a population we could, among other things, compute the standard deviation of a characteristic of that population. If we use, instead, a sampling from that population, we compute the standard deviation of the sample, and can estimate the true population standard deviation from

$$s = \sigma/\sqrt{2n}$$

It is not necessary to compute the standard error for every value we use in our work. We should compute it, however, for those concluding values upon which our decision-maker will rely for final judgment. In all fairness, that person must know the chances for failure as well as for success.

DECISION-MAKING TECHNIQUES

Deciding what to do with forecast data can often be as tedious and time consuming as the forecasting process itself. If the data are fairly straightforward and *univariate*, (having only one independent variable) the process is not so difficult. If the forecast is univariate and suggests that the price of a stock or a commodity will be such and such at a given point in time, the user has to decide on the reliability of the forecast, and then decide whether the reliability is sufficient to act on the information.

Multivariate data, on the other hand, don't always resolve themselves so neatly. We offer here two routines to use with multivariate forecast data. The first is known as the Multivariate Evaluator and

is based on a standard industrial procedure for the evaluation of several options against a number of criteria by several decision-makers. The second is simply called the Decision-Maker and is designed for use by one person and attempts to facilitate a rational decision-making process, eliminating as much personal bias as possible.

Multivariate Evaluator

This approach is most easily described by an example. Four neighbors, John, Sam, Joe, and Pete, decide to pool their money and purchase a car or van to share. After some research, each of the men nominates one or two vehicles for consideration. These include a Ford, a Chevrolet, a Chrysler, a Mercury, and a Lincoln. After some discussion, the five men decide on four characteristics of the cars to use for evaluation. These include price, economy of operation, styling, and maximum speed performance. As a final measure, the decision is made that the car will be used for five functions: shopping, hunting, camping, transportation to work, and recreational travel other than for hunting or camping.

The cars all range around $11,000. The case contributions from each man is:

John	$ 1,000
Sam	2,000
Joe	3,000
Pete	5,000

The men will decide to allocate votes among themselves according to the actual cash contribution.

On this basis, the men polled themselves on the relative importance of the different functions the vehicle is expected to perform. They used a rating scheme in which the most valuable function is rated an "8" and the least is rated "1." The votes for each of the functions are shown in Table 18-1.

The first step in the multivariate analysis process is to convert the voting strengths into weighted factors such that the total of the factors is 1.00. The easiest way to do this is to total the votes and then compute each man's vote as a percentage of the total. In a similar fashion, each of the ratings in the table matrix is converted into a percentage of the

Table 18-1. Initial Votes for Missions.

Owner	Votes	Missions Shopping	Hunting	Camping	Work	Travel
John	1	5	8	3	1	2
Sam	2	8	3	5	2	1
Joe	3	5	3	2	8	1
Pete	5	3	1	2	5	8

Table 18-2. Votes for Missions Computed for Weighting.

NAME	WEIGHT	* SHOPPI	SUB-FUNCTIONS HUNTIN	CAMPIN	WORK	TRAVEL
JOHN	0.0909	* 0.0239	0.0383	0.0144	0.0048	0.0096
SAM	0.1818	* 0.0766	0.0287	0.0478	0.0191	0.0096
JOE	0.2727	* 0.0718	0.0431	0.0287	0.1148	0.0144
PETE	0.4545	* 0.0718	0.0239	0.0478	0.1196	0.1914
TOTAL	1.0000	* 0.2440	0.1340	0.1388	0.2584	0.2249

Table 18-3. Votes for Criteria and Alternatives.

Criterion	Weight	Ford	Alternatives Chevrolet	Chrysler	Mercury	Lincoln
Speed	2	2	3	1	8	5
Style	4	1	2	3	5	8
Economy	6	8	5	3	2	1
Price	8	5	8	3	1	2

Table 18-4. Votes for Criteria and Alternatives Computed for Weighting.

CRIT.	WEIGHT	* FORD	ALTERNATIVES CHEVRO	CHRYSL	MERCUR	LINCOL
SPEED	0.1000	* 0.0105	0.0158	0.0053	0.0421	0.0263
STYLE	0.2000	* 0.0053	0.0105	0.0158	0.0263	0.0421
ECONOM	0.3000	* 0.0421	0.0263	0.0158	0.0105	0.0053
PRICE	0.4000	* 0.0263	0.0421	0.0158	0.0053	0.0105
TOTAL	1.0000	* 0.0842	0.0947	0.0526	0.0842	0.0842
ADJUST	1.0000	0.2105	0.2368	0.1316	0.2105	0.2105

Table 18-5. Final Analysis Results.

ALTER.	WEIGHT	*	SHOPPI	HUNTIN	CAMPIN	WORK	TRAVEL	SUM
				MISSIONS				
FORD	0.2105	*	0.0514	0.0578	0.0321	0.0514	0.0514	0.244
CHEVRO	0.2368	*	0.0282	0.0317	0.0176	0.0282	0.0282	0.134
CHRYSL	0.1316	*	0.0292	0.0329	0.0183	0.0292	0.0292	0.139
MERCUR	0.2105	*	0.0544	0.0612	0.0340	0.0544	0.0544	0.258
LINCOL	0.2105	*	0.0473	0.0533	0.0296	0.0473	0.0473	0.225
TOTAL	1.0000	*	0.2105	0.2368	0.1316	0.2105	0.2105	

row totals. The final step in this first stage is to multiply the voter's vote weight times the matrix percentage value. Table 18-2 gives the results of this operation. The column totals under each function give an estimate of the relative importance the owners attach to the function.

The second stage is to evaluate the alternatives against the stated criteria. This step is not nearly as subjective as the first. In this example, the comparisons can be readily made from published price and performance data. Table 18-3 shows the actual results of the first step in this stage. The only subjective factors are the weights assigned, by the owners, to the criterion factors. The remaining matrix values were computed from published data. Table 18-4 illustrates the results of the matrix multiplications of the weights converted to percentages. An adjustment is made so that the column totals for the alternatives total unity.

The data shown in Table 18-5 were computed by multiplying the column totals from Table 18-3 times the column totals in Table 18-4. A comparison of the row total leads us to a conclusion on the most desirable option. In this example, the Mercury ended up with a desirability factor of .258, higher than any of the others. If everything has been entered properly and the raters have been fair and objective, the Mercury should be the most satisfying purchase.

Although not included in this analysis, it is quite possible to include another evaluation routine in which the owners/raters allocate the criterion weights in the same fashion they determined the function weights.

Listing 18-1 implements the procedures just described. The particular layout of the data was

Listing 18-1. Multivariate Evaluator

```
1  '*******************************************
2  'MULTIVARIATE EVALUATOR                     *
3  'LISTING 18-1                               *
4  '*******************************************
5  '
10 CLEAR400
20 CLS:PRINT"MULTIVARIATE EVALUATOR":PRINT:PRINT

30 FORI=1TO4
40    PRINT"NAME OF DECISION-MAKER #";I,:INPUTN$:
      D$(I)=LEFT$(N$,6)
50    PRINT"VOTING STRENGTH OF ";D$(I),:INPUT V(I
      ):SV=SV+V(I)
60 NEXT
70 FORI=1TO4:WV(I)=V(I)/SV:NEXT
```

```
80 FORI=1TO5
90    PRINT"NAME OF MISSION #";I,:INPUT N$:M$(I)=
      LEFT$(N$,6)
100 NEXT
110 FORI=1TO4
120    PRINT"WHAT IS ";D$(I);"'S VOTE FOR:"
130    FORJ=1TO5
140      PRINT"       ";M$(J),:INPUT MV(I,J):TV=TV+
      MV(I,J)
150    NEXTJ
160    FORJ=1TO5:WM(I,J)=MV(I,J)/TV:NEXT:TV=0
170 NEXTI
180 CLS:PRINT"                          SUB-F
    UNCTIONS"
190 FORI=1TO4:FORJ=1TO5:M(I,J)=WV(I)*WM(I,J):CT(
    J)=CT(J)+M(I,J):NEXTJ:NEXTI
200 B$="%     %  %      %      % %         %%
      %%      % %      %"
210 PRINTUSINGB$;"NAME";"WEIGHT";M$(1);M$(2);M$(
    3);M$(4);M$(5)
220 FORX=0TO127:SET(X,7):NEXT
230 A$="%     %  #.####     #.####  #.####  #.####
        #.####  #.####"
240 PRINT@192,"";
250 FORI=1TO4
260    PRINTUSINGA$;D$(I);WV(I);M(I,1);M(I,2);M(I
    ,3);M(I,4);M(I,5)
270 NEXT
280 PRINT@512,"";
290 PRINTUSINGA$;"TOTAL";1;CT(1);CT(2);CT(3);CT(
    4);CT(5)
300 FORX=0TO127:SET(X,22):NEXT
310 FORY=0TO26:SET(32,Y):NEXT
320 GOSUB850
330 FORI=1TO5
340    PRINT"NAME OF ALTERNATIVE #";I,:INPUTN$:A$
    (I)=LEFT$(N$,6)
350 NEXT
360 FORI=1TO4
370    PRINT"NAME OF CRITERION #";I,:INPUTN$:C$(I
    )=LEFT$(N$,6)
380    PRINT"CRITERION WEIGHT OF ";C$(I),:INPUT C
    W(I):TC=TC+CW(I)
390 NEXT
400 FORI=1TO4:WC(I)=CW(I)/TC:NEXT
410 FORI=1TO4
420    PRINT"CONSIDERING ";C$(I);", WHAT IS THE V
    ALUE OF:"
430    FORJ=1TO5
440      PRINT"       ";A$(J),:INPUT CV(I,J):VC=VC+
    CV(I,J)
450    NEXTJ
460    FORJ=1TO5:AM(I,J)=CV(I,J)/VC:NEXTJ
470 NEXTI
480 CLS:PRINT"                          ALTE
    RNATIVES"
```

Listing 18-1. Multivariate Evaluator (continued from page 359)

```
490 FORI=1TO5:FORJ=1TO5:AM(I,J)=AM(I,J)*WC(I):CC
    (J)=CC(J)+AM(I,J):NEXTJ:NEXTI
500 PRINTUSINGB$;"CRIT.";"WEIGHT";A$(1);A$(2);A$
    (3);A$(4);A$(5)
510 FORX=0TO127:SET(X,7):NEXT
520 PRINT@192,"";
530 FORI=1TO4
540    PRINTUSINGA$;C$(I);WC(I);AM(I,1);AM(I,2);A
    M(I,3);AM(I,4);AM(I,5)
550 NEXT
560 PRINT@512,"";USINGA$;"TOTAL";1;CC(1);CC(2);C
    C(3);CC(4);CC(5)
570 FORI=1TO5:XX=XX+CC(I):NEXT
580 FORI=1TO5:CC(I)=CC(I)/XX:NEXT
590 PRINT@576,"";USINGA$;"ADJUST.";1;CC(1);CC(2)
    ;CC(3);CC(4);CC(5)
600 FORX=0TO127:SET(X,22):NEXT
610 FORY=0TO26:SET(32,Y):NEXT
620 GOSUB850
630 FORI=1TO5
640    FORJ=1TO5
650      M(I,J)=CT(I)*CC(J):TR(I)=TR(I)+M(I,J):TC
    (J)=TC(J)+M(I,
J)
660    NEXTJ
670 NEXTI
680 CLS:PRINT"                              MISSI
    ONS"
690 PRINTUSINGB$;"ALTER.";"WEIGHT";M$(1);M$(2);M
    $(3);M$(4);M$(5);:PRINT"SUM"
700 FORX=0TO127:SET(X,7):NEXT
710 PRINT@192,"";
720 FORI=1TO5
730    PRINTUSINGA$;A$(I);CC(I);M(I,1);M(I,2);M(I
    ,3);M(I,4);M(I,5);:PRINTUSING"   #.###";TR(
    I);
740 NEXT
750 PRINT@576,"";USINGA$;"TOTAL";1;TC(1);TC(2);T
    C(3);TC(4);TC(5);
760 FORX=0TO127:SET(X,25):NEXT
770 FORY=0TO29:SET(32,Y):NEXT
780 GOSUB850
790 FORI=1TO5
800    IFTR(I)<LGTHEN820
810    LG=TR(I):L=I
820 NEXTI
830 LPRINT"":LPRINT"BEST OPTION APPEARS TO BE ";
    A$(L):LPRINT""
840 END
850 FORI=15360TO15936STEP64
860    FORJ=ITOI+63
870      A=PEEK(J):IFA<32THEN910
880      IFA<58THEN900
890      IFA=32THENLLPRINT" ";ELSELPRINT"*";:GOTO
    920
```

```
900     LPRINTCHR$(A);:GOTO920
910     LPRINTCHR$(A+64);
920     NEXTJ
930     LPRINT""
940 NEXTI
950 LPRINT""
960 RETURN
```

selected solely for the purposes of illustrating the routine. There is no reason to limit your version of the program to this 4 × 5 matrix.

Decision-Maker

If you've ever been confronted with several options from which you have to make a choice and have been more or less overwhelmed by the alternatives and the related factors, this routine is for you. It won't make decisions for you, but it will provide a logical structure in which to evaluate each option; then let you know what the score is. The basic form of the program works like this. It begins by assuming that whatever your options are, you are applying some set of criteria against them. The first step of the program asks you to state what these criteria are. The next assumption is that among these criteria some are more important to you than others; therefore, the second step presents each of the criteria to you, paired with each of the other criteria. For each pair you are asked to identify which criterion of the pair you consider to be more significant. Once you've completed this phase, the program asks you to identify each of the options available.

The program now shows you three items at a time: a criterion measure and a pair of options. You are asked to choose which of the options is superior to the other in terms of the criterion shown. To the extent that the criterion is a quantifiable variable, this choice should be fairly easy. This process continues until all combinations of the options have been evaluated in terms of each of the criteria. At each step of this process the winning option is scored according to the relative weight of the criterion.

The last phase of the evaluation displays the options in order of their scores, the preferred choice first. If you don't like the result, you can always go back and start over.

The printed output of the program is based on a run where the objective was to pick a city to live in. The user had been able to narrow the choice of cities down to four. He knew that he could evaluate each of the options on at least six measures: tax rate, climate, cost of living, cultural opportunities (museums, operas, etc.) recreational facilities, and communications. On the first run of the program, the user felt a little dissatisfied with some of the combinations and factors. This was quickly solved by adding a seventh criterion, the "x-factor." Without further definition or any quantification, this allowed the user to score a subjective attitude toward the option pair. It was a way of saying, "all other things being equal, this is *my* vote . . . ."

Listing 18-2. Decision-Maker

```
1   '*********************************************
2   'DECISION-MAKER                             *
3   'LISTING 18-2                               *
4   '*********************************************
5   '
10 CLS:PRINTCHR$(210);"**** DECISION-MAKER ***
    *":PRINT:PRINT
20 PRINT"THIS ROUTINE ENABLES THE USER TO ENTER
        A SET OF CRITERIA AGAINSTWHICH A SET OF OPT
        IONS OR ALTERNATIVES MAY BE EVALUATED.
AT THIS POINT, PREPARE A LIST OF THE AVAILABLE A
        LTERNATIVES, A
```

Listing 18-2. Decision-Maker (continued from page 361)

```
LIST OF THE CRITERIA WHICH APPLY, AND THE RELATE
     D";
30 PRINT" DATA.

WHEN READY, TOUCH ANY KEY.";
40 Q$=""+INKEY$:IFQ$=""THEN40
50 CLS:CLEAR1000
60 INPUT"HOW MANY OPTIONS ARE THERE TO BE EVALUA
     TED";V:DIMV$(V),Q(V),QQ(V):PRINT:FORI=1TOV:
     PRINT"NAME OF OPTION #";I,:INPUTV$(I):NEXT
70 PRINT:INPUT"HOW MANY CRITERIA ARE THERE";F:A=
     (F*(F-1))/2:DIMF$(F),C(F,F),S(F):PRINT:FORI
     =1TOF:PRINT"ENTER CRITERION NAME #";I,:INPU
     TF$(I):NEXT
80 FORI=1TOF:S(I)=1:NEXT
90 FORI=1TOF-1
100    FORJ=I+1TOF
110       CLS:PRINT@384,"";:PRINTI,F$(I):PRINTJ,F$
     (J):PRINT:PRINT"ENTER NUMBER OF MORE IMPORT
     ANT CRITERION:";
120       N$=""+INKEY$:IFN$=""THEN120    ELSEN=VAL(N
     $)
130       IFN<>IANDN<>JTHEN120
140       C(I,J)=N:S(N)=S(N)+1
150    NEXTJ
160 NEXTI
170 CLS:PRINT"LIST OF PRIORITIES":PRINT:PRINT"CR
     ITERIA","","SCORE","WEIGHT":PRINT:LPRINT"CR
     ITERIA","","SCORE","WEIGHT":LPRINT""
180 FORI=F+1TO0STEP-1:FORJ=1TOF
190    IFS(J)<>ITHEN210
200    PRINTF$(J),"",I,I/(F+1):S(J)=I/(F+1):LPRINT
     F$(J),"",I,I/(F+1)
210 NEXT:NEXT
220 LPRINT"":PRINT:PRINT"ARE THESE CRITERIA IN P
     ROPER PRIORITY ORDER?   (Y/N)";
230 Q$=""+INKEY$:IFQ$=""THEN230    ELSEIFQ$="N"THE
     N80
240 FORI=1TOV-1:FORJ=I+1TOV:FORK=1TOF
250    CLS:PRINT@384,"";:PRINTF$(K):PRINT:PRINT:PR
     INT"A",V$(I):PRINT"B",V$(J):PRINT:PRINT"ENT
     ER THE LETTER OF THE OPTION WHICH IS SUPERI
     OR ON THIS SCALE",
260    Q$=""+INKEY$:IFQ$=""THEN260
270    IFQ$<>"A"ANDQ$<>"B"THEN260
280    IFQ$="A"THENN=IELSEN=J
290    Q(N)=Q(N)+S(K):IFQ(N)>LGTHENLG=Q(N)
300 NEXT:NEXT:NEXT
310 CLS:PRINT"TABLE OF RESULTS":PRINT"OPTION",""
     ,"SCORE":PRINT:LPRINT"":LPRINT"TABLE OF RES
     ULTS":LPRINT"OPTION","","SCORE":LPRINT""
320 FORI=LGTO0STEP-(1/F):FORJ=1TOV
330    IFQ(J)<ITHEN350
340    PRINTV$(J),"",Q(J):LPRINTV$(J),"",Q(J):Q(J)
     =-1
```

```
350 NEXT:NEXT
360 PRINT:PRINT"ARE THESE RESULTS ACCEPTABLE?  (
    Y/N)";
370 Q$=""+INKEY$:IFQ$=""THEN370   ELSEIFQ$="Y"THE
    N400
380 PRINT:PRINT"A  --  CRITERIA       B  --  OP
    TIONS":PRINT:PRINT"ENTER LETTER OF ELEMENT
    TO BE ADJUSTED";
390 Q$=""+INKEY$:IFQ$=""THEN390   ELSEIFQ$="A"THE
    N80   ELSE240
400 LPRINT"":LPRINT"REMEMBER!  THE VALUE OF THE
    RANKING OF THE OPTIONS IS A FUNCTION OF:
         A.   THE COMPREHENSIVENESS OF THE LIST OF
    OPTIONS.  BE SURE ALL RELEVANT OPTIONS ARE
    CONSIDERED, EVEN DISAGREEABLE ONES.
         B.   THE COMPRE";
410 LPRINT"HENSIVENESS OF LIST OF CRITERIA.
         C.   THE CANDOR WITH WHICH YOU RESPOND TO
    EACH OF THE SUBJECTIVE COMPARISONS.
         D.   THE ACCURACY OF THE OBJECTIVE DATA.

    IF YOU ARE DISPLEASED WITH THESE RESULTS, IT IS
    LIKELY THERE IS A";
420 LPRINT" PROBLEM WITH ONE OF THE FOUR ITEMS A
    BOVE."
430 LPRINTSTRING$(3,10):RUN:END
```

Criteria	Score	Weight
X-factor	7	.875
Cultural opportunities	6	.75
Communications	4	.5
Climate	3	.375
Cost of living	3	.375
Recreational facilities	3	.375
Tax rate	2	.25

Table of results

option	Score
New York	6.625
San Francisco	5.875
Chicago	4.375
Washington	4.125

Remember! The value of the ranking of the options is a function of:
   A. The comprehensiveness of the list of options. Be sure all relevant options are considered, even disagreeable ones.
   B. The comprehensiveness of list of criteria.
   C. The candor with which you respond to each of the subjective comparisons.
   D. The accuracy of the objective data.

If you are displeased with these results, it is likely there is a problem with one of the four items above.

Fig. 18-1. Results of Listing 18-2.

Exatron Stringy Floppy Guide

As indicated in the Introduction, the data base programs use the Exatron Stringy Floppy system for data storage. The Exatron Stringy Floppy (ESF) is a unique low-cost high speed, extremely-compact and reliable data storage system, which fits the gap between cassettes and disk drives. The system is based on a miniature endless-loop cartridge, called a wafer, a precision direct-driven transport mechanism, and associated electronic circuitry.

Each drive unit measures about 6¼" long by 4⅛" wide and 2½" high. Up to eight drive units can be connected in one operating system. Each wafer, smaller than most business cards, is only 2¾" long by 1-9/16" wide and 3/16" thick. The wafer contains an endless loop of magnetic tape (from 5 to 50 feet long), which is 1/16" wide. The amount of data that can be recorded on a wafer depends on the length of tape in it; typically, a 50-foot wafer can hold at least 40,000 bytes of data.

With only one moving part (the motor spindle), the transport mechanism is extremely reliable. The motor spindle is used as a direct drive on the tape, pulling it past the record/play head at a constant speed of 10 inches per second. With a 5-foot wafer a complete tape cycle takes less than 6 seconds.

The recording technique in the ESF system is called *bi-phase recording*, which is the same as that used in disk systems. This special electronic technique results in phenomenal reliability, even when the motor speed varies as much as ten percent. The entire system continues to function under extremely adverse conditions.

Solid state optical sensors are used to detect the physical presence and write-protection status of the wafer. A reflective splice in the tape loop, which acts as an end-of-tape/beginning-of-tape mark, is also detected optically.

Once connected to the computer system, the operating system is initialized and accessed through the SYSTEM command:

```
___SYSTEM
*?___12346              (which results in:)
EXATRON STRINGY FLOPPY VERSION 4.1
>___
```

The following chart outline the parameters and command functions available.

d — Drive number (0-7)
n — File number (1-99)
m — Number of I/O buffers (0-8)

Definitions

[ ] — Indicates optional parameters

All parameters are entered in decimal form.

Initialization Commands (after "SYSTEM")

Command	Syntax/Function	Example
/12340	Initialize firmware and load next file on wafer.	[same as @LOAD]
/12341	Initialize firmware and load File 1	[same as @LOAD1]
/12342-/12344	Initialize firmware and load Files 2, 3, or 4.	[same as @LOADn]
/12345	Initialize firmware and return to BASIC.	
/12346	Initialize firmware and return to BASIC without debounce routine— useful when your program has debounce included.	
/ESF	Model III ESF only—load BOOT and operating system.	

General Commands

@#d	@#d Select drive d and also change default drive to d. Default drive is 0 initially.	@#2
@NEW	@[#d]NEW[n] Certify wafer starting at file n to end of tape. Absence of n certifies whole tape.	@NEW2
@SAVE	@[#d]SAVEn Write BASIC program out to wafer at file n.	@#2SAVE1
@SAVE	@[#d]SAVEn start address,#bytes, [autostart address] Write a machine language program to wafer at file n. If the optional autostart address is omitted, the subsequent@LOAD will return to BASIC after the file is loaded.	@SAVE1,17152,5380,17512
@LOAD	@[#d]LOAD[n] Load file n from ESF. Absence of n causes next file to be loaded. The same command is used for BASIC and machine language programs.	@LOAD2

@CLEAR	CLEAR[m]	@CLEAR4

Abort all files that are open. If
m is specified, then m buffers are
reserved for I/O and all variables
are cleared. (Thus, this should
be used at the beginning of the
program only.) # of I/O buffers is
set to 1 when the Data I/O program
is loaded. @CLEAR will not change
the # of buffers nor clear variables
and can be used anywhere in the
program to abort all opened files.

@OPEN	@[#d]OPENn	@OPEN1

Open data file n. The next @INOUT
of @PRINT will dictate either the
read or write mode. To change modes,
@CLOSE the file and reopen first.
There may be only one open file per
ESF drive.

@INPUT	@[#d]INPUT list of variables	@#1INPUT A,B,C$

Read the list of variables from the
opened file.

@PRINT	@[#d]PRINT list of expressions	@PRINT A,D$,A+B

Write the values associated with
the list of expressions out to the
opened file.

@CLOSE	@[#d]CLOSE	@#2CLOSE

Close the file on the default
drive, unless drive is specified.

Glossary

absolute—Independent, not relative.

accuracy—The most common criterion for measuring the relative strength of alternative forecasting methods.

acre—A unit of area measure equal to 4,840 square yards.

adaptive response rate—The rate at which a forecasting technique responds to change in pattern.

algorithm—A standardized procedure for solving a given problem.

altitude (of a celestial object)—The spherical coordinate of the object measured in the plane of the circle passing through the object and crossing the horizon at right angles.

amortization—To pay off an expenditure or debt by prorating the cost plus interest over a fixed period.

annular eclipse—An eclipse of the sun in which the moon is surrounded by a ring of light.

anomalistic year—The time taken by the earth to travel in its orbit from the point where it is closest to the sun, perihelion, to the next such point. This is computed to be 365.25964 mean solar days, or 365 days, 6 hours, 13 minutes, and about 53 seconds. This value is about 25 minutes, 7 seconds greater than the tropical year.

aphelion—The point in the orbit of an object around the sun at which it is the farthest from the sun.

apogee—The point in the orbit of an object about the earth at which it is the farthest from the earth.

apparent solar noon—The moment when the center of the sun crosses the meridian of a location.

array—A display of data in rows and columns, as in tables or determinants.

assets—Things of value that may be used to pay off debts. For corporations, these may include cash, securities, buildings, machinery, land, inventory, etc.

astronomical unit (AU)—The mean distance from the center of the earth to the center of the sun. Taken to be about 92,897,000 miles.

autocorrelation—The correlation between items on one list lagged in time or sequence.

balance sheet—A report of the financial condition of a company as of a given date, usually the end of the firm's accounting year. Interim reports are often issued on a quarterly basis.

biannual—Twice a year.

biennial—Once every two years.

bimodal—A distribution of data with two distinct peaks.

bond—A legal document or expression of the fact money has been loaned to a corporation or governmental unit. The bond states that the issuer will pay interest at a specified rate until the debt is repaid at face value some time in the future.

book value—The net value of a corporation to common share-holders. Usually expressed on a per-share basis obtained by dividing the corporation's net worth by the number of common shares outstanding.

Boolean algebra—An mathematical interpretation of the rules of logic developed by Boole in the mid-1880's.

Boolean connectors—An expression of relationships in a data base. They are often found in a search of a data base for two or more pieces of information that satisfy the stated Boolean criteria.

break-even point—The price at which an investment instrument, if sold, would fully reimburse all costs connected with its acquisition and subsequent sale.

broker—Firm or individual holding a seat on the exchange of interest employed by an investor to execute securities transactions.

business cycle—Period of business profitability followed by periods of business lassitude or failure.

buy order—An order placed by an investor directing a broker to purchase a specified number of shares of stock, options, bonds, etc. Limits or conditions specifying price, time, or numerous factors may be imposed if desired.

calculus—A field of mathematics, developed independently in the 1700's by Leibniz and Newton, that deals with rates of changes, the lengths of curves, the area under curves, and the areas and volumes of various objects.

calendar—The division of time into arbitrary sections as years, months, days, generally based on the earth's revolution about the sun. The tropical year consists of 365.2422 days (each day consisting of 23 hours, 56 minutes, and 4.09 seconds).

call—The date before maturity on which all or part of a bond issue may be redeemed by the issuing company. Definite conditions are imposed for a bond to be called.

capital—Money or property needed by a person or corporation to carry out normal business activities.

catenary—The curve described by a rope or heavy cable hanging freely between two points of suspension.

causal model—Statistical or forecasting models in which there is presumed causal relationships between the input variables and the output.

central limit theorem—A theorem of statistics that states that the sampling distribution of means approaches a normal distribution when the sample size become sufficiently large; i.e., when s > 30.

classic decomposition—An approach used in forecasting which assumes a time-series data set consists of cyclic, seasonal, trend, and random error components. As each component is eliminated from the data, the remainder is assumed to contain the remaining components.

commission—The fee paid to a broker for executing a securities transaction, usually a percentage of the dollar amount involved and often subject to a minimum fee established by the brokerage firm.

commodity—Anything bought or sold. Investment usage refers to futures contacts bought or sold for delivery of specific quantities of corn, wheat, metals, or approximately 30 other tangible goods.

common stock—An ownership interest purchased in a corporation, entitling the holder to a share in any profits realized and to some influence in the management of the company.

computation—The process of determining a quantified result from numerical data using the mathematical tools of addition, multiplication, subtraction, division, and algebraic techniques.

computer—A mechanical or electronic device employed in the process of computation. Modern computers go beyond simple numerical manipulation and exploit the data switching and comparison capability to implement word processing, data handling and graphics tasks.

curve fitting—An approach in forecasting to fit the data to some form of standard or definable curve.

cyclic stocks—Stocks of corporations whose earnings are sensitive to business cycles and, most often, accentuate the peaks and valleys of the cycle. Prices of these stocks fluctuate widely over a complete business cycle.

data—The plural of the Latin word datum, which mean "that which is given." In a larger sense, data can include anything used in the process of a logical effort. In the sense often used in this book, data refer to those numerical values used in the different programs.

declination (of a clestial object)—The angular altitude of an object above the celestial horizon.

degrees of freedom—The number of variables in a data set less an adjustment for different statistical tests. In computing the mean of a set of n items, there are $n - 1$ degrees of freedom.

delphi method—A forecasting technique using the professional opinions of a panel of experts.

dependent variable—A quantity which is the function of one or more independent variables.

depreciation—An amount charged against earnings to write off the cost, less salvage, of an asset over its estimated useful life.

dividend—A portion of corporate profits received by shareholders. It may be paid in cash or shares.

diversification—Investing funds in several different industry groups in an attempt to hold securities that do not fluctuate in a similar fashion.

dollar cost averaging—A method of investing in which a set amount is invested in a selected stock at regular intervals. It is presumed that this amount of money will buy more shares when prices are low and fewer shares during periods of high prices. When averaging is used over a long enough period of time, the cost per share should be less than in strategies in which larger blocks of stock are purchased aperiodically.

economic indicator—An economic component which demonstrates an apparent correlation between itself and the national economy in general.

equity—The ownership interest of all classes of stockholders of a corporation. Also, the difference between the value of securities and the debit balance of a margin account.

exchange—An auction market for stocks, bonds, and other securities.

exponential data distribution—A pattern which exhibits the characteristics of an exponential curve.

file—A collection of data arranged in some pattern or order.

forecasting—The scientific art of predicting future conditions.

gain—An increase in the value of an investment relative to the purchase price.

gross national product (GNP)—The total amount of goods and services for a given economy over a period of time, normally a year.

growth stocks—Ideally, the stock of a corporation that gets bigger and better each year, causing the price of its stock to move up. In practice, the criteria used for defining a growth stock vary with an investors's ultimate objectives and perception of what is significant growth.

heteroscedasticity—A condition which exists when errors do not demonstrate constant variance across the whole range of the data values in a set.

heuristic—A system using trial and error to achieve an objective.

historic data—Data gleaned from a specific time period in the past. Generally they are used in an attempt to identify trend sequences likely to be repeated for some time in the future.

homoscedasticity—A condition that exists when errors demonstrate a constant variance across the whole data set.

income stock—A stock that yields generous current returns, often purchased by investors who have an immediate need for income combined with the assurance of capital preservation.

independent variable—Something whose value is determined outside of the system being examined.

index—An indicator constructed in such a fashion as to reflect the market performance of a specific group of securities or identify general market trends.

indicators—An index or economic group whose changes in basic trend or direction tend to signal changes in the economy as a whole. As their names imply, leading indicators reflect future market trends, lagging indicators trail behind and confirm market trends.

investment—Any financial instrument purchased in the anticipation of selling the same instrument at a later time for a significantly higher price.

Julian date—Normally, the day number of a date in a year with January 1 being Julian date 1, February 1 being Julian date 32, and so on. Alternatively, the Julian date is the number of days a given date is from a zero reference date far in the past.

Kuder-Richardson equations—A set of equations developed by the Kuder-Richardson team to aid in the validation and measurement of reliability of test instruments.

leverage—The degree to which a corporation or an individual uses borrowed funds as opposed to equity. If the anticipated return is significantly greater than the cost of borrowing money, leverage can increase gains. Maximum leverage, and risk, is obtained with the smallest use of equity. Margin buying, options, warrants, and rights are all ways for an individual investor to obtain leverage.

liabilities—Monies or debt obligation for which an individual or corporation is responsible. Usually defined in terms of current liabilities (due in less than one year) and long term debt. Liabilities may include money owed to suppliers, debt retirement, taxes due, dividends payable, and so forth.

liquidity—The ability to convert to cash or its equivalent any investment instrument. Stocks and bonds are regarded as having good liquidity because disposing of them in the open market is readily accomplished. Some other forms of investment holdings may show significantly less liquidity. Real estate or collectables, for instance, may take a long time to convert to cash.

margin—Buying on margin is using your securities as a collateral for a loan from your broker and is a way to increase an investor's leverage. Margin accounts are subject to strict limit for minimum equity as established by the Federal Reserve Board.

market—A broad term to encompass securities exchanges, although usually the "market" implies the New York Stock Exchange or the American Stock Exchange.

market value—The total amount investors would be willing to pay for all the common shares of a corporation.

mean—Normally taken as the arithmatic average of a set of data.

median—The middle number in a data set.

microcomputer—A colloquial term referring to a family of "small" computing systems distinguished, normally, by the amount of memory available in the basic system, generally 4 to 64 thousand bytes, with from one to four disk drives using floppy disk storage media. The precise boundary between micro and mini computing systems is not formally defined.

mode—The most frequently appearing number in a set of data.

model—A symbolic representation of an aspect of reality.

moving average—An average which moves with the unit of time considered. Primarily used as trend indicators, moving averages tend to smooth out short term fluctuations and react slowly, particularly to swift market changes.

mutual fund—A form of investment company that sells shares for the purpose of providing investor diversification, professional management and maximum liquidity of funds. All funds received for shares are comingled and invested in securities (or other forms of investment, depending on the purpose of the fund). The price of each share reflects the net value of its holdings at the time of purchase or redemptions.

n—The number of observations or the size of a sample.

N—The number of periods used in a moving average or the total size of a population.

net income—The amount remaining when all the expenses of doing business are subtracted from the total sales or revenue of a corporation.

net worth—A figure derived by subtracting all liabilities from the total assets.

noise—The random component of a set of data.

over-the-counter—Transactions in securities which do not take place on an exchange. There is no centralized place for trading, virtually any type of security may be listed; and brokers may act as principles or agents in the transaction.

par value—A dollar amount assigned to each share of stock or bond by a corporation. It is common practice to exclude assigning par value to common stock, but preferred stock and bonds usually carry a par value.

polynomial—An algebraic expression that carries two or more terms.

preferred stock—A security between common stocks and bonds which has fixed dividends and preference on all corporate income available after payment of bond interest and amortization.

price to earnings ratio (P/E)—A figure derived by dividing the price of a share of stock by the company's twelve month earnings per share.

quote—A term used to denote current price level, market volume, and other relevant data related to a security.

redemption price—The price at which a bond was redeemed before maturity by the issuing company, the price a corporation must pay to call in certain types of preferred stocks, or the amount received on liquidating mutual fund shares.

regression—A line or equation that expresses the average relationship between a dependent variable and one or more independent variables.

residual—The degree of error or deviation between a forecast and reality.

retained earnings—The amount of corporate earnings retained and reinvested in the business rather than being paid out as dividends to shareholders.

round lot—A standard unit of trading securities, usually one hundred shares of stock and $1000 par value for bonds.

sample—A limited number (relative to the total population) of observations or data values from the population.

S-curve—The normal curve of product innovation, dissemination and life.

Securities and Exchange Commission (SEC)—The agency responsible for administering federal laws regarding securities.

simulation—A model constructed to closely approximate the action of a large system with many interacting parts. Stock market simulations allow an investor to try different courses of action without actually risking capital.

standard deviation—The square root of the variance of a set of data. It is a statistical measure of dispersion of the data from the mean.

standard error—The distribution of statistical measures about a predicted value.

tender—An offer made by a corporation to buy back its own shares. Also, an offer by one corporation, interested in acquiring control, to buy the shares of another. Usually, tender offers are made at a price above that of the going market.

time-series—A set of data in which the independent variable is time.

trend—The general direction or movement of statistical data related to the stock market, populations, business activity, and other data that may change in magnitude as a function of time or changes in other independent variables.

undervalued stock—Shares of a corporation which are selling below book value, provided the company reports good profitability and growth.

variance—The amount of variation from the mean within a set of data.

volatility—The extent to which the price of stock rises or falls in comparison to others in its industry group or designated market index.

volume—The number of shares of stock, bonds, or options that changed hands during a particular period. It is usually stated in terms of daily volume.

warrants—An option to buy a specific number of shares of a security at a set price for a designated period of time.

weighting—A mathematical process in which statistical ratios are combined or in which sets of numbers are given coefficients establishing their relative importance.

x-axis—The first axis in the Cartesian system of coordinates.

y-axis—The second axis in the Cartesian system of coordinates.

year—The longest standard unit of time, measured by the earth's rotation about the sun. Between vernal equinoxes there are 365 days, 5 hours, and 48 minutes.

yield—The amount in dividends or interest paid by a company, expressed as a percentage of the current stock or bond price. Yield is one component of total return, capital gain being the other.

z-axis—The third axis in the Cartesian system of coordinates.

z-score—A statistical measure of a distribution computed by dividing the value of a given score less the mean, by the standard deviation.

zenith—The point on the celestial sphere directly above the observer.

Index

Forecasting on Your Microcomputer

If you are intrigued with the possibilities of the programs included in *Forecasting on Your Microcomputer* (TAB Book No. 1607), you should definitely consider having the ready-to-run disks or tapes containing the software applications. This software is guaranteed free of manufacturer's defects. (If you have any problems, return the disks or tapes within 30 days and we'll send you a new set.) Not only will you save the time and effort of typing the programs, the disks or tapes eliminate the possibility of errors that can prevent the programs from functioning. Interested?

Available on 2 disks for the TRS-80, Model III, 32K at $34.95 for each set of disks plus $1.00 each shipping and handling, and on 2 tapes for the TRS-80 Models I and III, 16K at $29.95 plus $1.00 each shipping and handling.

I'm interested. Send me:

_____ disks for *Forecasting on Your Microcomputer* (6045S) the TRS-80 Model III, 32K at $34.95 plus $1.00 each shipping and handling.

_____ tapes for *Forecasting on Your Microcomputer* (6044S) the TRS-80 Models I and III, 16K at $29.95 plus $1.00 each shipping and handling.

_____ Check/Money Order enclosed for $ _____

_____ VISA   _____ MasterCard

Acct. No. _____ Expires _____

City _____ State _____ Zip _____

Signature _____

Mail To: **TAB Books Inc.**
         Blue Ridge Summit, PA 17214

(Pa. add 6% sales tax. Orders outside U.S. must be prepaid with international money orders in U.S. dollars.)

TAB 1607